Maritime Communications
NP 289
Third Edition

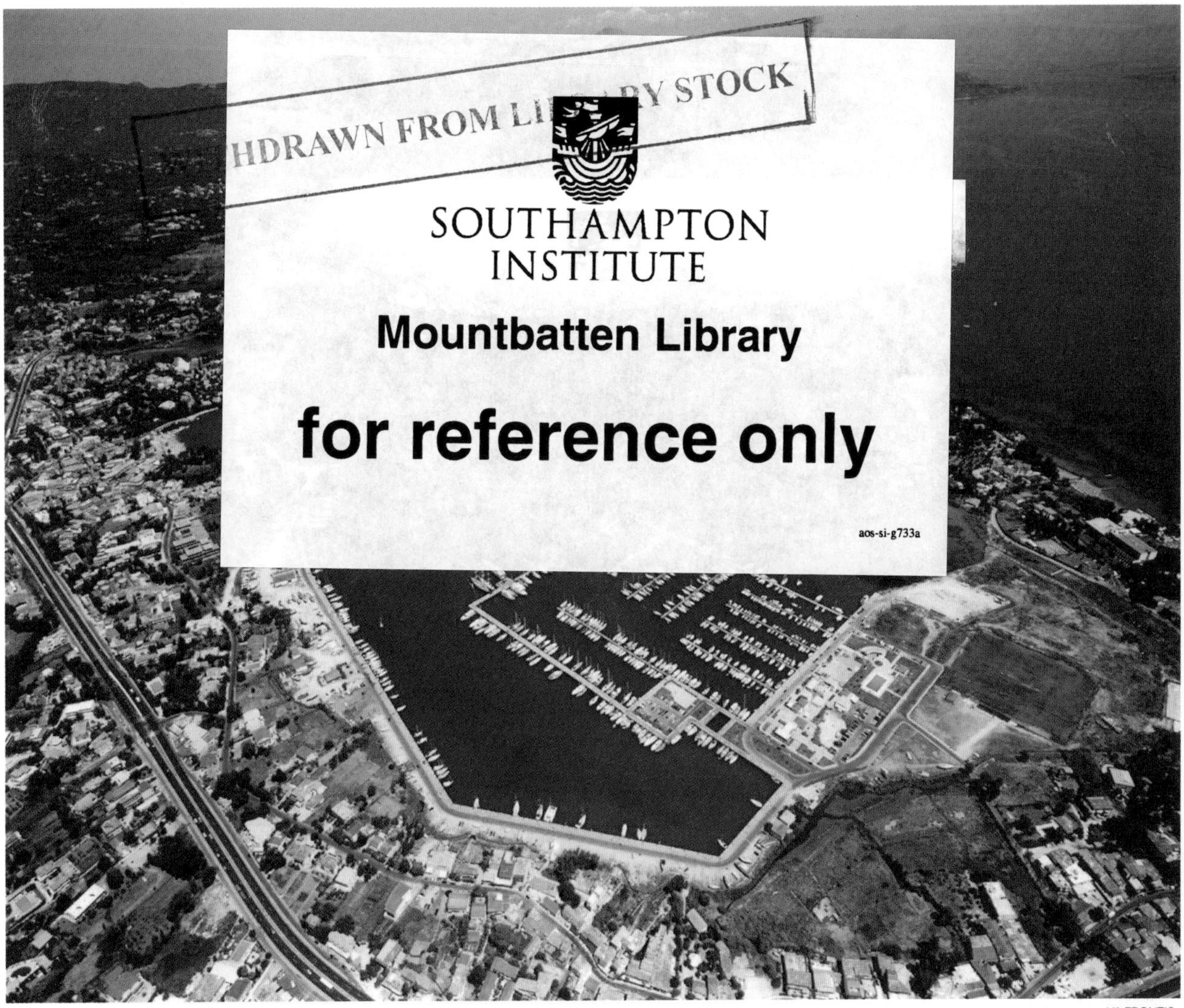

V9 FRONTIS

UK and the Mediterranean
Including the Azores

PUBLISHED BY THE UNITED KINGDOM HYDROGRAPHIC OFFICE

PREFACE

This series of publications now consists of three volumes covering different cruising areas and each new edition has received excellant reviews and bouquets. This third edition of NP289 has been edited by Brian Robertson and Des Thompson and includes improvements to presentation developed from the the other editions of NP290 and NP291. Each country is now listed in alphabetical order with all relevant information, on safety and weather now combined with marina communication information and vessel traffic broadcast services. Additional changes to presentation have been incorporated in this edition including a small alteration to the table format, which allows better use of the space available.

All colour diagrams have been updated and improved and this edition contains a number of new diagrams. A major change to the selection of marina and port aerial images have been introduced and the majority of photographs are new.

Monthly amendments can be be obtained from the new searchable Notice to Mariners website. Amended colour diagrams and text can be printed in colour, allowing the leisure mariner to maintain the accuracy of the information, in a prompt and easy operation. Navigational Charts and Publications Notice to Mariners can be found at www.nmwebsearch.com

Dr. D. W. WILLIAMS
United Kingdom National Hydrographer

DIRECTIONS FOR AMENDING THIS VOLUME

This edition contains information received up to Notices to Mariners No. 16/03, dated 17th April 2003 before going to press. Subsequent monthly amendments will be included in Section VI of the Weekly Edition of Admiralty Notices to Mariners. Laser label sheets (A4 size) can be used when downloading colour diagrams and new tables or extensively altered information from the website. When shorter amendments are made in manuscript, the date of the amendment should be included. The inclusion of amendments in NP289 can be recorded in the following table.

MONTHLY AMENDMENT RECORD

www.nmwebsearch.com　　www.ukho.gov.uk

2003		**2004**	
May		May	
June		June	
July		July	
August		August	
September		September	
October		October	
November		November	
December		December	
2004		**2005**	
January		January	
February		February	
March		March	
April		April	

TIMES quoted are in Co-ordinated Universal Time (UTC) unless otherwise stated, and are reckoned from 0000 (midnight) to 2400.

CONTENTS

PREFACE II
DIRECTIONS FOR AMENDING THIS VOLUME II
USEFUL CONTACTS WITHIN THE UNITED KINGDOM HYDROGRAPHIC OFFICE IV
ACKNOWLEDGEMENTS IV
GLOSSARY V
INTRODUCTION 1
GMDSS & DSC
- INTRODUCTION TO GMDSS 5
- DSC COMMUNICATIONS 16
- COMMUNICATIONS IN THE GLOBAL SYSTEM 22
- SEARCH AND RESCUE TRANSPONDER (SART) 32
- DISTRESS COMMUNICATIONS AND FALSE ALERTS 37
- FREQUENCIES FOR GMDSS 41

MANAGEMENT OF VHF 43
MARTIME SAFETY INFORMATION 49
SAFETYNET 51
NAVTEX 60
INMARSAT 67
RADIO FACSIMILE AND RADIO TELEX BROADCASTS 73
MARITIME SAFETY INFORMATION, MARINA AND PORT COMMUNICATIONS
- AZORES 82
- FRANCE, ATLANTIC COAST 84
- FRANCE, NORTH COAST 105
- GIBRALTAR 122
- IRELAND, REPUBLIC OF 125
- PORTUGAL 133
- SPAIN, ATLANTIC COAST 139
- SPAIN, NORTH COAST 148

UNITED KINGDOM 153
- UNITED KINGDOM, ENGLAND - EAST COAST 162
- UNITED KINGDOM, ENGLAND - SOUTH COAST 182
- UNITED KINGDOM, ENGLAND - WEST COAST 212
- UNITED KINGDOM, NORTHERN IRELAND 222
- UNITED KINGDOM, SCOTLAND 224
- UNITED KINGDOM, WALES 242

MEDITERRANEAN
- ALBANIA 252
- ALGERIA 258
- CROATIA 262
- CYPRUS 281
- EGYPT 283
- FRANCE, CORSE 284
- FRANCE, MEDITERRANEAN COAST 287
- GREECE 309
- ISRAEL 322
- ITALY, ADRIATIC COAST 324
- ITALY, SARDEGNA & SICILIA 339
- ITALY, WEST COAST 346
- LEBANON 357
- LIBYA 358
- MALTA 359
- MONACO 361
- MOROCCO 362
- SERBIA AND MONTENEGRO 364
- SLOVENIA 365
- SPAIN, MEDITERRANEAN COAST (INCLUDING ISLAS BALEARES) 367
- SYRIA 387
- TUNISIA 388
- TURKEY 390

DGPS BEACONS 398
APPENDICES:
- APPENDIX: BEAUFORT SCALE 402

INDEX 403

USEFUL CONTACTS WITHIN THE UNITED KINGDOM HYDROGRAPHIC OFFICE

Telephone Number: +44(0)1823 337900 Fax: +44(0)1823 284077 Telex: 46274

Admiralty List of Radio Signals — www.ukho.gov.uk

Senior Editorial Team	*E-Mail*	*Extension Numbers*
Head of ALRS	doug.huckle@ukho.gov.uk	3422 or +44(0)1823 723317 Direct
Senior Editor	dave.ridgway@ukho.gov.uk	3299

Admiralty Maritime Communications — www.admiraltyleisure.co.uk

Editorial Team (NP289, NP290 & NP291)	*E-Mail*	*Extension Numbers*
Editor	brian.robertson@ukho.gov.uk	4386
Editor	des.thompson@ukho.gov.uk	4224

Direct Fax: +44(0)1823 334752
ALRS Office E-Mail alrs@ukho.gov.uk

The editors would be grateful to receive any amendments, suggestions or additional information which customers may consider useful. The assistance of marina managers in providing aerial photographs or images showing the marina entrance would be appreciated.

ACKNOWLEDGEMENTS

ABP Ipswich
Adnan Çýplak
Agios Nikolaos Marina
Air Images
Ali E Bezirgin
Anne Hammick
Brian Robertson, ALRS
Camper & Nicholsons
Des Thompson, ALRS
Dimitrios Koutsodontis, Director Gouvia Marina
Dogus Tugutreis Marina, Turkey
Hasan Kaçmaz, Director Park Kemer Marina, Turkey
Inmarsat Ltd, London
Peter Kleinoth/Mare Team
Kos Marina
Marti Marina, Turkey
Marina del Cavallino (Mr Perocchio)
Marina Di Rimini (Leandro Gasperini)
Marina Dalmacija, (Studio Gobbo Photography)
Marina Developments Limited
Marina Punat, Croatia (Peter Zic)
Marina Veruda, (Studio Gobbo Photography)
Mylor Yacht Harbour
Portsmouth (Port Surveyor)
Porto San Rocco Marina, Italy (Roberto Sponza)
Premier Marinas Ltd
Royal Cruising Club Pilotage Foundation
Sovereign Harbour Marina
Service Hydrographique et Océanographique De la Marine, Brest
Studio Gobbo (sergio@intermedia-ips.si)
Tarquin Boat Company Limited (Emsworth)

GLOSSARY

AIS - Automatic Identification System

Alert data - Generic term for COSPAS-SARSAT 406 MHz and 121·5 MHz alert data derived from 406 MHz and 121·5 MHz distress beacon information. Alert data may contain beacon position and other beacon information such as beacon identification data and coded information.

ALRS - Admiralty List of Radio Signals.

AMVER - Automated Mutual-Assistance VEssel Rescue System.

AOR-E - Atlantic Ocean Region-East.

AOR-W - Atlantic Ocean Region - West.

approx - Approximate.

ASCII - American Standard Code for Information Interchange - a standard alpha-numeric character set based on 7-bit binary codes.

Associated Rescue Co-ordination Centre (ARCC) - A centre nominated by the national SAR agency to which an Inmarsat Coast Earth Station (CES) normally routes distress calls.

Aug - August.

Autolink RT - Any vessel fitted with Autolink RT equipment is able to make a radiotelephone call, using direct dialling on VHF, MF or HF frequencies, through any coast radio station operating an Autolink RT service.

Automatic DSC operation at a ship station - A mode of operation employing automatic tuneable transmitters, suitable for unattended operation which provide for automatic call acknowledgements upon reception of a DSC and automatic transfer to the appropriate working frequencies.

Baud - A measure of the rate of transfer of binary messages (1 bit/second = 1 baud for most purposes).

BBC - British Broadcasting Corporation.

BBS - Bulletin Board Service.

Bcst - Broadcast.

Bit - A single unit of binary data (see Kilobit).

bps - Bits per second (transmission rate).

brg - bearing.

Broadcasting service - A radiocommunication service in which the transmissions are intended for direct reception by the general public.

Byte - The collection of bits that make up a binary word.

°**C** - Degrees Celsius.

CCR - Coast Radio Station - Spain.

CG - Coastguard.

CES - Coast Earth Station, may also be called a LES (Land Earth Station).

Ch - Channel (As in VHF Ch).

CNIS - Channel Navigation Information Service.

Coast radio station - A land station in the maritime mobile service.

COSPAS - Space system for search and distress vessels.

COSPAS-SARSAT system - A satellite-aided search and rescue system based on low-altitude near-polar-orbiting satellites and designed to locate distress beacons transmitting on the frequencies 121·5 MHz and 406 MHz.

CROSS - Centres Régionaux Opérationnels de Surveillance et de Sauvetage (Regional centre of operations for surveillance and marine rescue MRCC).

CRS - Coast Radio Station.

dB - decibels.

Dec - December.

DF - Direction-finding.

DGPS - Differential Global Positioning System.

DGNSS - Differential Global Navigation Satellite Systems

Digital Selective Calling (DSC) system - A technique using digital codes which enables a radio station to establish contact with, and transfer information to, another station or group of stations, and complying with the relevant recommendations of the International Radio Consultative Committee (CCIR).

Distress Alerting - Rapid and successful reporting of a distress incident to a unit which can provide or co-ordinate assistance.

Distress Channel - An integrated channel between a ship in distress and a Rescue Co-ordination Centre. The channel consists of the ship's teletype or telephone set, Ship Earth Station, satellite channel, Coast Earth Station, land line and the end terminal at the Rescue Co-ordination Centre.

Distress Message - The definition of a distress message is as follows: The distress Signal MAYDAY; The name and/or callsign of the vessel in distress; The vessels position; The nature of distress; The type of assistance required; Any other information which may facilitate rescue. The contents of the message is defined by the Radio Regulations, RR3093, and may be formatted as defined by Inmarsat and IMO GMDSS for the Distress Message Generator (Inmarsat Ship Earth Station Technical Bulletin No 19, February, 1987 and Annex IV to COM 29/10).

Distress-Priority Request Message - A ship-to-shore request message containing priority indication 3, the highest priority of ship-to-shore calls. This is a signalling message to be processed within the Inmarsat-A access and control system in order to secure a proper assignment of the satellite (maritime distress) channel for ship and Coast Earth Stations.

DSC - Digital Selective Calling. See also: International DSC frequencies

DSC Distress Alert Distress Call - The Distress Call is simply: "consists of the spoken word MAYDAY, made 3 times followed by the name of the vessel 3 times". A part of the distress communication procedure, which includes a transmission of the distress-priority request message, and the reception of the Coast Earth Station answerback followed by the Rescue Co-ordination Centre answerback.

EGC - The Enhanced Group Call services provided in the Inmarsat-C system; these are the EGC SafetyNET service, the EGC FleetNET service, and the broadcasting of Inmarsat system messages.

EIRP - Effective Isotropic Radiated Power, value in dBW shown on satellite footprint contour maps.

Emergency Position-Indicating RadioBeacon (EPIRB) - A station in the mobile service, the emissions of which are intended to facilitate search and rescue operations.

ENID - EGC Network Identification Code used in the EGC FleetNET Service.

EPIRB - Emergency Position Indicating Radio Beacon.

EPIRB registration database - A register established and maintained for the purpose of:

(a) Establishing a readily accessible and up to date satellite EPIRB data register containing essential SAR information particular to individual EPIRBs for the use by SAR authorities; and

(b) providing readily accessible access to essential SAR data by recognized SAR authorities in the processing of distress situations.

ETA - Estimated Time of Arrival.

ETD - Estimated Time of Departure.

ext - Extension.

°F - Degrees Fahrenheit.

Fax - Facsimile.

Fcst - Forecast.

Feb - February.

Filtered alert data - The reduction of redundant alert data messages from the same beacon in the COSPAS-SARSAT system when two or more identical messages are received.

FleetNET - The EGC FleetNET Service.

FM - Frequency Modulation.

Fri - Friday.

FSK - Frequency Shift Keying.

FTP - File Transfer Protocol (INTERNET)

Geostationary-Satellite Orbit - The orbit of a geosynchronous satellite whose circular and direct orbit lies in the plane of the Earth's equator.

GEOSAR - COSPAS-SARSAT Geostationary Orbiting Search and Rescue satellite system.

GHz - Gigahertz.

GLONASS - GLObal NAvigation Satellite System

GMDSS - Global Maritime Distress and Safety System.

GMT - Greenwich Mean Time.

GNSS - Global Navigation Satellite System

GPS - Global Positioning System.

GRT - Gross Registered Tonnage.

h - Hours.

H+... - Commencing at...minutes past the hour.

H24 - Continuous.

HF - High Frequency (3-30 mHz).

HJ - Day service only.

HN - Night service only.

Hr - Harbour.

Hr Mr - Harbour Master.

HW - High Water.

HX - No specific hours or fixed intermittent hours.

Hz - Hertz.

IAMSAR - International Aeronautical and Maritime Search and Rescue Manual.

IHO - The International Hydrographic Organization.

IMN - Inmarsat Mobile Number.

IMO - The International Maritime Organization.

Inmarsat-A - The original Inmarsat communications system, operating since 1982, based on analog techniques and capable of global two-way voice-grade telephony (and voice-band data transfer), facsimile and telex communications.

Inmarsat-B - A digital communications system, capable of high quality two-way voice telephony, telex, distress alerting, fax and data services.

Inmarsat-C - A digital system, operating since 1991, based on low-cost SESs of low power-consumption, using an omni-directional antenna. This system provides the services of global two-way store-and-forward messaging, distress alerting, EGC SafetyNET and FleetNET, data reporting and polling.

Inmarsat-E - A distress alerting system based on EPIRBs.

Inmarsat-GAN - (Global Area Network) supporting high speed data, ISDN compatible service @ 64 kbit/s.

Inmarsat-M - Introduced in 1994, based on digital techniques, and capable of two-way voice telephony, distress alerting, fax and data services.

Inmarsat-mini M - Voice fax and low speed data.

Inop - Inoperative.

Int - International.

International Alphabet Number 5 - (Also known as ASCII) - a standard alpha-numeric character set based on 7-bit binary codes.

International DSC frequencies - Frequencies designated in the Radio Regulations for exclusive use for DSC on an international basis.

International NAVTEX Service - The co-ordinated broadcast and automatic reception on 518 kHz of Maritime Safety Information by means of narrow-band direct-printing using the English language. See also: NAVTEX.

IOR - Indian Ocean Region.

ISL - Interstation Signalling Links, used to pass information between CESs and the NCs in an Ocean Region.

ITU - International Telecommunication Union.

ITZ - Inshore Traffic Zone.

Jan - January.

JRCC - Joint Rescue Co-ordination Centre. A Rescue Co-ordination Centre responsible for both aeronautical and maritime search and rescue incidents.

kHz - Kilohertz.

Kilobit (Kbits) - 1 Kbit = 1024 bits = 128 characters (a character in ASCII (American Standard Code for Information Interchange) is a letter, digit or a special character, represented by a byte or a group of 8 bits). This code is used in computer-to-computer communication.

km - Kilometre(s).

kW - Kilowatt(s).

L.A.T. - Lowest Astronomical Tide.

L-band EPIRB system - A satellite EPIRB system operating in the 1·6 GHz frequency band through the INMARSAT geostationary satellite service.

Land Earth Station (LES) - See: Coast Earth Station (CES) and Mobile Earth Station (MES).

Ldg - Leading.

LEO - Low Earth Orbit.

LEOSAR - COSPAS_SARSAT Low Earth Orbit Search and Rescue polar orbiting satellite system.

LES — Land Earth Station. An earth station in the fixed-satellite service or, in the maritime mobile-satellite service, located at the specified fixed point on land to provide a feeder link for the maritime mobile-satellite service. The generic term LES applies to a station with services in both maritime and land-mobile communications.

LF - Low Frequency (30 kHz - 300 kHz).

LNB - Low-Noise Block, satellite antenna component

LOA - Length Over All.

Local user terminal (LUT) - A ground receiving station which receives alert data from COSPAS and SARSAT satellites, derives the position of the beacon, retrieves and checks coded information and forwards the resultant information.

LT - Local Time.

Lt - Light.

LW - Low Water.

m - Metre(s).

MAREP - Mariner Reporting System (Ship Movement Reporting System).

Maritime Distress Channel - An Inmarsat satellite channel between a ship in distress and a Coast Earth Station assigned in response to a distress-priority request message.

Maritime mobile-satellite service - A mobile-satellite service in which Mobile Earth Stations are located onboard ships; survival craft stations and emergency position-indicating radiobeacon stations may also participate in this service.

Maritime mobile service - A mobile service between coast stations and ship stations, or between ship stations, or between associated on-board communication stations; survival craft stations and Emergency Position-Indicating Radiobeacon (EPIRB) stations may also participate in this service.

Maritime Safety Information (MSI) - Navigational and meteorological warnings, meteorological forecasts, distress alerts and other urgent safety related information broadcast to ships.

Maritime SAR plan - A plan developed by coastal States following formal agreement between the parties concerned, based on SAR facilities previously declared, and including appropriate arrangements for providing SAR services in accordance with the 1979 SAR Convention.

MARPOL - International Convention for the Prevention of Pollution from Ships, 1973

mb - Millibar: unit of pressure previously used in meteorological work, superseded by the Hectopascal (1 hPa = 100 pascals = 1 mb).

MCC service area - The area for which an MCC accepts responsibility for the distribution of COSPAS-SARSAT alert data. The service area includes sub-areas serviced by SAR points of contact (SPOCs).

MCC (Mission Control Centre) - A COSPAS-SARSAT ground system element which receives alert data from its local user terminal(s) and distributes that information to affiliated SAR points of contact or forwards it to other MCCs. The MCC may also receive alert data from another MCC and receive and distribute COSPAS-SARSAT system information.

MEDILINK — MEDIcal LINK call.

MES - Mobile Earth Stations - For maritime use they are termed Ship Earth Stations (SES) and on land they are termed Land Earth Stations (LES) or Land Mobile Earth Stations (LMES).

METAREA - METeorological AREA: Short title of a meteorological service area, limits similar to NAVAREAs within the World-Wide Navigational Warning Service.

MF - Medium frequency (300-3000 kHz).

MHz - Megahertz.

MID - Maritime identification digits.

min - Minute(s).

MMSI - Maritime Mobile Service Identity code (as in accordance with GMDSS DSC).

Mon - Monday.

MRCC - Maritime Rescue Co-ordination Centre.

MRSC - Maritime Rescue co-ordination Sub-Centre.

ms - Millisecond(s).

MSI — Maritime Safety Information. Navigational and meteorological warnings, meteorological forecasts, distress alerts and other urgent safety related information broadcast to ships.

National DSC frequencies - Frequencies assigned to individual coast stations or groups of stations on which DSC calling is permitted (this may include working frequencies as well as calling frequencies). The use of these frequencies must be in accordance with Radio Regulations.

National Hydrographic Office - A National Organisation responsible for collecting and distributing navigational warnings.

National Meteorological Office - A National Organisation responsible for collecting and distributing meteorological warnings and forecasts.

NAVAREA - NAVigational AREA: Short title of an area in the world-wide navigational warning service.

NAVAREA/METAREA - One of the 16 areas of sea defined by the IMO, into which the world's oceans are divided for the dissemination of navigational and meteorological warnings and forecasts.

NAVAREA warning - Long-range warning broadcasts issued by an area co-ordinator of the world-wide navigational warning service for his area and broadcast by CRS(s) or CES(s) to cover the whole of the area, for which the area co-ordinator is responsible, and parts of an adjacent area.

Navigation safety communications - Intership VHF radiotelephone communications for the purpose of assisting the safe movement of ships.

NAVTEX - The International NAVTEX service is the medium frequency radio telex broadcasting system developed by the IMO for the purpose of broadcasting and automatic reception of MSI by means of direct-printing telegraphy.

NBDP - Narrow-Band Direct-Printing; automated telegraphy as used by the NAVTEX system and telex-over-radio.

NCS - Network Co-ordination Station, a CES which monitors and controls communication through the other CESs in an Ocean Region.

NM - Notice to Mariners.

n mile - International nautical mile.

Nov - November.

OCC - Operations Control Centre (for Inmarsat).

Ocean Region - The coverage area of an Inmarsat satellite, within which a suitably equipped SES can send and receive messages.

Oct - October.

On-scene communications - Communications between the ship in distress and assisting units.

OSC — On-scene co-ordinator. The commander of a rescue unit designated to co-ordinate surface search and rescue operations within a specified search area.

Paired frequencies - Frequencies which are associated in pairs; each pair consisting of one transmitting and one receiving frequency.

P.E - Port of Entry.

POB — Persons On Board — total number of.

Polar Orbiting Satellite Service - A service which is based on polar orbiting satellites which receive and relay distress alerts from satellite EPIRBs and which provides their position.

POR - Pacific Ocean Region.

Positioning - Establishing the geographical place of the unit in distress (normally expressed in degrees and minutes of latitude and longitude).

Pt - Point.

Public Correspondence - Any telecommunication which the offices and stations must, by reason of their being at the disposal of the public, accept for transmission.

PV - Pilot Vessel.

Radiolocation-Satellite Service - A radiodetermination satellite service used for the purpose of radiolocation.

Radio Regulations - Means the Radio Regulations annexed to, or regarded as being annexed to, the most recent International Telecommunication Convention which is in force at any time.

RCC - Rescue Co-ordination Centre.

Rescue Co-ordination Centre (RCC) - A unit responsible for promoting efficient organization of search and rescue (SAR) services and for co-ordinating the conduct of SAR operations within a SAR region.

Rescue unit - A unit composed of trained personnel and provided with equipment suitable for the expeditious conduct of SAR operations.

RT - Radio telephony.

Rx - Receiver.

s - Second(s)

SafetyNET - The International SafetyNET Service.

SAR - Search-and-Rescue

SAR co-ordinating communications - Communications necessary for the co-ordination of ships and aircraft participating in a SAR operation (resulting from a distress incident).

SARSAT - Search And Rescue Satellite Aided Tracking.

SART - Search And Rescue Transponder

Sat - Saturday.

Satellite EPIRB - An earth station in the mobile-satellite service, the emissions of which are intended to facilitate SAR operations.

Sea Area A1, A2, A3 and A4 - Under the GMDSS the (radio) equipment required to be carried by ships is determined in principle by the ship's area of operation; these areas are designated as 'Sea Area A1', 'Sea Area A2', 'Sea Area A3' or 'Sea Area A4'.

Search And Rescue (SAR) region - An area of defined dimensions within which search and rescue services are provided.

Sept - September.

SES - Ship Earth Station.

Ship Earth Station (SES) - A mobile earth station in the maritime mobile-satellite service located on board a vessel which is not permanently moored other than a survival craft station.

Ship Movement Service - A safety service in the maritime mobile service other than a port operations service between coast stations and ship stations or between ship stations, in which messages are restricted to those relating to the movements of ships. It does not include public correspondence.

Ship station - A mobile station in the maritime mobile service located on board a vessel which is not permanently moored, other than a survival craft station.

Sig - Signal.

Single frequency - The same frequency used for transmission and reception.

SOLAS - The International Convention on the Safety Of Life at Sea 1974 (SOLAS), as amended.

Sous-CROSS - Sous-Centres Régionaux Opérationells de Surveillance et de Sauvetage (Regional sub-centre of operations for surveillance and maritime rescue, MRSC).

SPOC - SAR points of contact. SPOCs, are established either through direct agreement between COSPAS-SARSAT participants, or through efforts of international institutions. IMO and ICAO have requested their member States to identify a single SAR point of contact which could serve as the national point to which Cospas-Sarsat alert data is delivered.

SRR - Search and Rescue Region.

SSB - Single SideBand.

Stn - Station.

Sun - Sunday.

SURNAV - Système français de comptes rendus de movements (French information and surveillance service for marine navigation).

Survival craft - A craft capable of sustaining the lives of persons in distress from the time of abandoning the ship.

Survival craft station - A mobile station in the maritime mobile service or in the aeronautical mobile service intended solely for survival purposes and located on any lifeboat, lifecraft or other survival equipment.

System information - In the COSPAS-SARSAT system tabulated data (ephemeris and time calibration) that affect the determination of distress beacon locations using the satellite sub-track; current status of all system elements; information related to interference.

TAI — International Atomic Time is determined by the comparison of the reading of very accurate (better than 1 microsecond a day) atomic clocks located at national observatories throughout the world. Unlike UT1, TAI does not change with variations in the rate of the Earth's rotation. TAI provides the most accurate and uniform unit of time interval for scientific purposes. The fundamental unit of TAI is the SI second, defined as "the duration of 9 192 631 770 periods of the radiation corresponding to the transition between two hyperfine levels of the ground state of the cesium 133 atom".

TCA (Time of closest approach) - The time that the satellite is closest to the beacon during a satellite pass.

Tel - Telephone.

Thurs - Thursday.

Time calibration - Data used to relate the SARSAT satellite time code in an alert message to the actual elapsed time from a known satellite time epoch. In association with the ephemeris data, the corrected satellite time information in each satellite processed beacon transmission is used to determine the location of the transmitting beacon.

TSS - Traffic Separation Scheme.

Tues - Tuesday.

Tx - Transmitter; Transmission.

ufn - Until further notice.

UHF - Ultra High Frequency (300-3000 MHz).

UK - United Kingdom.

UT - Universal Time.

UTC — Co-ordinated Universal Time: has been developed to meet the needs of scientific users for a precise scale of time interval and those of navigators, surveyors and others who require a time scale directly related to the Earth's rotation.
UTC corresponds exactly in rate with TAI but differs from it by an integral number of seconds. The UTC scale is adjusted by the insertion or deletion of seconds (positive or negative leap seconds) to ensure that departure of UTC from UT1 does not exceed ± 0·9 seconds.
Leap seconds are notified in advance as corrections, through Section VI of the Admiralty Weekly Notices to Mariners, to TABLE 1 within the RADIO TIME SIGNALS section of ALRS Volume 2 (NP 282).

VHF - Very High Frequency (30-300 MHz).

VLF - Very Low Frequency (3-30 kHz).

VTM - Vessel Traffic Management.

VTS - Vessel Traffic Service.

W - Watt.

WADGPS — Wide Area DGPS. A form of DGPS in which the user's GPS receiver receives corrections determined from a network of reference stations distributed over a wide geographical area. Separate corrections are usually determined for specific error sources — such as satellite clock, ionospheric propagation delay and ephemeris — and are applied in the user's receiver or attached computer in computing the receiver's co-ordinates. The corrections are typically supplied in real time by way of a geostationary communications satellite or through a network of ground-based transmitters. Corrections may also be provided at a later date for postprocessing collected data.

WARC - World Administrative Radio Conference.

Wed - Wednesday.

wef - With effect from.

WMO - The World Meteorological Organization.

World-Wide Navigational Warning Service (WWNWS) - A service established by the International Maritime Organization and International Hydrographic Organization for the purpose of co-ordinating the transmissions of radio navigational warnings in geographical areas.

WWW - World-Wide Web (INTERNET)

Wx - Weather.

INTRODUCTION

Countries are listed in alphabetical order and if necessary divided into two or more regions as shown in the following example:

- UNITED KINGDOM:
  - England East Coast: Berwick-upon-Tweed to Ramsgate
  - England South Coast: Ramsgate to S.Mary's including the Channel Islands
  - England West Coast: S. Ives to Maryport Marina
  - Northern Ireland: Londonderry to Warrenpoint
  - Scotland: Solway Yacht Club to Grangemouth
  - Wales: Newport to Conwy

Each section contains information on Maritime Safety Information (MSI), Safety and Weather Broadcast stations, Marinas and Ports. Details of Vessel Traffic Services (VTS) are also included although VTS compliance is not mandatory for leisure craft.

DIAGRAM AND TEXT COLOUR CODES

DISTRESS AND SAFETY BROADCASTS
RESCUE CO-ORDINATION CENTRES
NAVTEX 518 kHz TRANSMISSIONS IN ENGLISH

COAST RADIO STATIONS
MARINA AND PORT COMMUNICATIONS
NAVTEX 490 kHz TRANSMISSIONS

PORT CONTROL AND VESSEL TRAFFIC SERVICES
RADIO FACSIMILE BROADCASTS

Information on Vessel Traffic Services is included with the following caveat:

Vessel Traffic Services (VTS):
Details of VTS control centres and their broadcast frequencies have been included for information only - VTS compliance is **not** mandatory for leisure craft. Certain Ports with VTS areas request **all** vessels to monitor a certain VHF broadcast channel for navigational information and hazard warnings.

COMMERCIAL AND NATIONAL BROADCAST STATIONS

EXAMPLES AND DETAILED EXPLANATION

Maritime Safety Information including Weather Bulletins and Navigational Warnings are arranged in the following manner:

①

SPAIN

②

NAVTEX [E]

CORUÑA (CCR GROUP III)

RADIO TELEFÍS ÉIREANN — RADIO 1 (RTE — RADIO 1)

③

Ⓐ	Ⓑ	Ⓒ	Ⓓ	Ⓔ
A	1641	RT (MF)	Dubrovnik	42°39′N 18°07′E
B	Ch 07	VHF	Sv Mihovil	44°04′N 15°10′E
C	Ch 21	VHF	Labistica	43°35′N 16°13′E
DIAGRAM: page 126				

④ Ⓕ

Weather Bulletins	
A: On receipt	Storm and gale warnings for Areas 10–15 in English
A: 0735 1935	Weather bulletin for Eastern Mediterranean Sea. Route Eastern Tunis - Ródos
B–C: Every even H+35	Forecast and Storm and gale warnings for Areas 7–10 in English
Navigational Warnings	
A–C: On receipt	Urgent navigation warnings in English
B-C: Every odd H+50	Navigational warnings in English including firing practive warnings as necessary

EXPLANATION:

① SPAIN

Country: The name of the country in which a station is located appears in the centre of the page at the beginning of the section and at the head of subsequent pages.

② NAVTEX [E]
CORUÑA (CCR GROUP III)
RADIO TELEFÍS ÉIREANN — RADIO 1 (RTE — RADIO 1)

Station Name: The station name and/or a NAVTEX (518 kHz telex service) station identity letter in brackets. Alternative names by which a station is known may also be shown.

Red indicates a NAVTEX (518 kHz) transmitting station or a Marine Rescue Co-ordination Centre. Blue indicates any other Coast Radio Station or a NAVTEX (490 kHz) transmitting station. Green indicates a commercial broadcast station.

③ Ⓐ **A**
B

Letter designators are used to identify frequencies within the frequency table. Where a transmission is not qualified by a letter it takes place on all the quoted frequencies.

Ⓑ

Frequencies: MF and HF frequencies are expressed in kHz. VHF frequencies are expressed in MHz, in which case the units are quoted, or by the appropriate International Maritime VHF Channel (Ch) designator. In the case of single sideband emissions the carrier frequency is quoted; in the case of Telex Services frequencies shown are assigned (mid-point of the F1B emission), and care should be taken to ensure that the frequency of the suppressed carrier is set correctly, either 1700 or 1500 Hz below the assigned frequency, depending upon the equipment used. International channel numbers for RT (HF) and Telex paired frequencies are shown in brackets.

Ⓒ RT (MF)
RT (HF)
RADIO-TELEX
VHF

Mode of Transmission: RT (MF) amd RT (HF) indicates Radio Telephone SSB Upper Sideband, Medium Frequency and High Frequency respectively. VHF indicates Very High Frequency and RADIO-TELEX indicates Narrow Band Direct Printing.

Ⓓ Dubrovnik
Sv Mihovil
Labistica

Site Name: Where a station is known to employ a transmitting site remote from the main station, the site name is given against the appropriate frequency and the position may be given in column Ⓔ

Ⓔ 42°39′N 18°07′E
44°04′N 15°10′E

Position: The position of a transmitting site is explained above.

④ Ⓕ H+35
0735 - 1935

Hours of operation on the given frequency relate to UT (GMT) unless otherwise indicated. These are only given when the station transmits at non-scheduled times, e.g. on receipt. In many instances the hours may not be known and the absence of an entry should not be taken to imply that the service is continuous. If a frequency is used for only a part of the year the period of operation may be given.

Diagram Reference ④ DIAGRAMS: pages 181 and 190

Diagrams: The diagram is that on which the areas covered by the weather, navigational warnings and ice broadcasts are depicted. It should be noted that a broadcast may not relate to all the areas on a diagram.

The content of transmissions is set out under section headings as follows:

Ⓕ

Weather Bulletins	
A: On receipt	Storm and gale warnings for Areas 10–15 in English
A: 0735 1935	Weather bulletin for Eastern Mediterranean Sea. Route Eastern Tunis - Ródos
B–C: Every even H+35	Forecast and Storm and gale warnings for Areas 7–10 in English

Weather Warnings
These entries relate to storm warnings which are transmitted independently of other meteorological information. The wind force quoted is the minimum necessary for the issue of a warning.

Details are given of the frequencies employed (identified by the letter designators used in the frequency table above), the times of the transmissions, the language used and the sea area covered. Where a transmission is not qualified by a letter it takes place on all the quoted frequencies.

Weather Bulletins
These entries relate to routine weather bulletin transmissions.

Details are given of the frequencies employed, (identified by the letter designators used in the frequency table above), the times of the transmissions, the message content, the language used and the sea area covered. Dates are added if the service is limited to a period of the year. Where a transmission is not qualified by a letter it takes place on all the quoted frequencies.

Navigational Warnings	
A–C: On receipt	Urgent navigational warnings in English
B-C: Every odd H+50	Navigational warnings including firing practice warnings as necessary in English

The content of transmissions is set out under section headings. The general heading of Navigational Warnings includes specific types of warnings, e.g. Firing Practice, Ice Warnings, if they are broadcast together with Navigational Warnings. Where specific warnings are transmitted independently, an appropriate heading is used.

Details are given of the frequencies employed, the times of transmissions, the type of warning, the language used and the sea area covered. The frequency on which a service is transmitted is referred to by the letter designators used in the frequency table above. Where a transmission is not qualified by a letter it takes place on all the quoted frequencies.

Ice Reports
As shown in the above table under "Navigational Warnings"

Firing Practice and Exercise Areas
Firing and bombing practices, and defence exercises, take place in a number of coastal areas. These areas are only in force over limited periods, and information concerning them will normally be contained in navigational warnings.

FREQUENCY BAND INDICATORS:

FM	**NATIONAL AND COMMERCIAL BROADCAST STATIONS (VHF BAND 87.5 - 108 MHz)**
MF	**MARINE BAND - MEDIUM FREQUENCIES (1605 - 4200 kHz)**
MW	**BROADCAST BAND - MEDIUM WAVE SERVICE (530 - 1710 kHz)**
SSB	**MARINE HIGH FREQUENCY (HF) BANDS (4, 8, 12, 16 AND 22 MHz) LISTED IN KILOHERTZ AND WITH THE ITU CHANNEL NUMBER WHERE APPROPRIATE**
SW	**BROADCAST STATIONS - SHORT WAVE TRANSMISSION LISTED IN KILOHERTZ**
VHF	**MARINE VHF CHANNELS LISTED UNDER CHANNEL (Ch) NUMBER**

INTERNATIONAL DISTRESS, SAFETY AND CALLING - VHF CHANNEL 16:

Safety messages should be transmitted where practicable on a working frequency after making initial contact on Ch 16. Except for distress, safety and urgency purposes, communications on Ch 16 should be brief and not exceed one minute. Test calls should not normally be made on Ch 16. To make a radio transmit/receive check, call the local harbour office or marina on the appropriate frequency. Only if already at sea and radio serviceability *is in doubt* should a test call be made on Ch 16.
If there is no response, repeated calls should not be made; receiver failure should be assumed. Repeated transmissions could block distress traffic. Further information can be found in the **Management of VHF** section.

MARINA AND PORT INFORMATION

MYLOR MARINA

Marinas and Ports are listed alphabetically: Marinas and Ports with leisure facilities are coloured in blue and include all communication information available such as telephone and fax numbers, e-mail and website addresses. VHF radio channels monitored are listed together with further details on berths, access and hours open. Those Ports with either a full Vessel Traffic System (VTS) or navigation and radar control are coloured magenta and will include similar details to Marinas. Additional information will be listed as necessary to effect leisure craft compliance with local instructions at these Ports.

PORT WITH OPERATIONAL CONTROL:

DUNDEE	Port: CALL: Dundee Harbour Radio	56°28′N 2°57′W
☎ +44(0)1382 224121		Fax: Pilots & Port: +44(0)1382 200834 Port Control: +44(0)1382 459448
FREQUENCY: Port: Ch **12** 16		HOURS: H24
INFORMATION SERVICE: Local navigational warnings, weather forecasts, tidal information and visibility reports are available on request.		
NOTE: Dundee has an operational surveillance radar which allows Port Control to monitor shipping in the estuary.		

MARINA:

BRIGHTON MARINA	CALL: Brighton Control	50°48′·5N 0°06′·0W
☎ +44(0)1273 819919	Further marina information may also be included such as marina depth, number of berths and maximum LOA	Fax: +44(0)1273 675082
brighton@premiermarinas.com		www.premiermarinas.com
FREQUENCY: Ch 16 **M** 80		HOURS OPEN: H24 ACCESS: 0800-1800 LT through the lock

TELEPHONE NUMBERS: National Direct Dialling (NDD) prefixes are shown in brackets (0). This digit should only be dialled when calling from within that Country.

GLOBAL MARITIME DISTRESS AND SAFETY SYSTEM (GMDSS)

INTRODUCTION

GMDSS AND SOLAS CONVENTION

The International Convention for the Safety of Life at Sea (SOLAS) was established to complement the ITU regulations. The SOLAS Convention later became one of the main instruments of the International Maritime Organization (IMO) after its formation as the Inter-Governmental Maritime Consultative Organization in 1948 and coming into force in 1958.

The GMDSS requirements for radiocommunications are contained in Chapter IV of SOLAS adopted at the GMDSS Conference held in 1988. There was a transition period from the old Morse radiotelegraphy watchkeeping to the new system in order to allow the industry time to overcome any unforeseen problems in implementation of the new system. The transition period began on 1 February 1992 and continued until 1 February 1999.

The GMDSS provides a reliable ship-to-shore communications path in addition to ship-to-ship alerting communications. The new system is automated and uses ship-to-shore alerting by means of terrestrial radio and satellite radio paths for alerting and subsequent communications. The GMDSS applies to all cargo ships of 300 gross tons and above, and to all passenger ships, regardless of size, on international voyages.

The phased implementation of the GMDSS started with a general requirement for the carriage of NAVTEX receivers for the reception of Maritime Safety Information (MSI) and satellite Emergency Position Indicating Radio Beacons (EPIRBs) from 1 August 1993. During the transition period, ships operating under the GMDSS had to comply with the 1988 amendments to Chapter IV of SOLAS. Up to 1 February 1999, both systems required watchkeeping on 2182 kHz and VHF Channel 16.

In respect of VHF Channel 16, however, it was decided at the 69th Session of the IMO Maritime Safety Committee (May 1998) that an aural watch has to be maintained, as a mandatory requirement, until 1 February 2005. Governments have undertaken to ensure that the necessary shore installations will be in place in order to provide the required communication services.

LEISURE CRAFT AND THE GMDSS

Leisure vessels and cargo ships of less than 300 gross tonnage (gt) are as a general rule not covered by SOLAS requirements to fit GMDSS equipment. However, if such ships/vessels are going to install GMDSS radio equipment on a voluntary basis or mandatory basis according to national laws, the regulations contained within this volume will apply. A list of recommended radio equipment that should be fitted to leisure craft, dependant upon the prospective voyage can be found in the following table.

GMDSS REQUIREMENTS FOR LEISURE CRAFT

The following table shows the UK recommendations for fitting GMDSS equipment on non-SOLAS vessels. It is based on the distance normally sailed offshore and assumes full A1, A2 and A3 area coast radio station coverage of the area. This is merely a recommendation for non-compulsory fit vessels, although recent legislation has made it compulsory fit for fishing vessels over 12 metres in length.

Area of Operation from Coast (Nautical Miles)	Up to 5nm	Up to 30nm	Up to 60nm	Up to 150nm	Unrestricted
Hand held waterproofed VHF radio - also for use in liferaft	R	R	R	R	R
VHF fixed radio installation - fitted with DSC	O	R	R	R	R
406 MHz float-free EPIRB (with 121.5 MHz homer)	O	O	O	R	R
MF SSB radio installation - fitted with DSC	None	None	O	R	R
Inmarsat (1) Inmarsat M/mini-M for voice communications (2) Inmarsat C For MSI - information, Safety and Weather, text communications	None	None	O	O	R
NAVTEX Receiver - will receive up to 400 n miles from NAVTEX Transmitter	None	O	R	R	R
Search And Rescue radar Transponder (SART)	None	O	O	R	R

R = Recommended O = Optional

BASIC CONCEPT OF THE GMDSS

Prior to the introduction of the GMDSS, maritime distress and safety communications relied primarily on the capability of a vessel in distress to alert another vessel for assistance. The GMDSS emphasises the ability to alert Search And Rescue (SAR) authorities ashore as well as shipping in the vicinity in order to achieve a rapid co-ordinated response to distress situations. The shore-based rescue authorities now have the primary role of co-ordinating assistance and rescue operation following a distress alert **(see Figures: 1A, B, C, D)**. In the past, assistance was possible only if vessels capable of receiving the distress call were within radio range. The danger was that calls for assistance would go unheard in remote areas.

In the GMDSS, the initial acknowledgement of a distress alert should be by a shore-based station. Subsequent actions and communications should be controlled by the assigned Rescue Co-ordination Centre (RCC). In normal circumstances it should not be necessary for a vessel to relay a distress alert. In order to avoid confusion and delay, vessels must monitor the distress frequency to be certain that the original alert was not received before initiating a distress relay. Particular care is needed when a distress call is received on HF at a considerable distance from the incident to avoid making unnecessary or confusing transmissions in response. The method of distress alerting can depend on the sea area in which the vessel is sailing and on the equipment carried.

Figure 1 - Basic concept of the Global Maritime Distress and Safety System

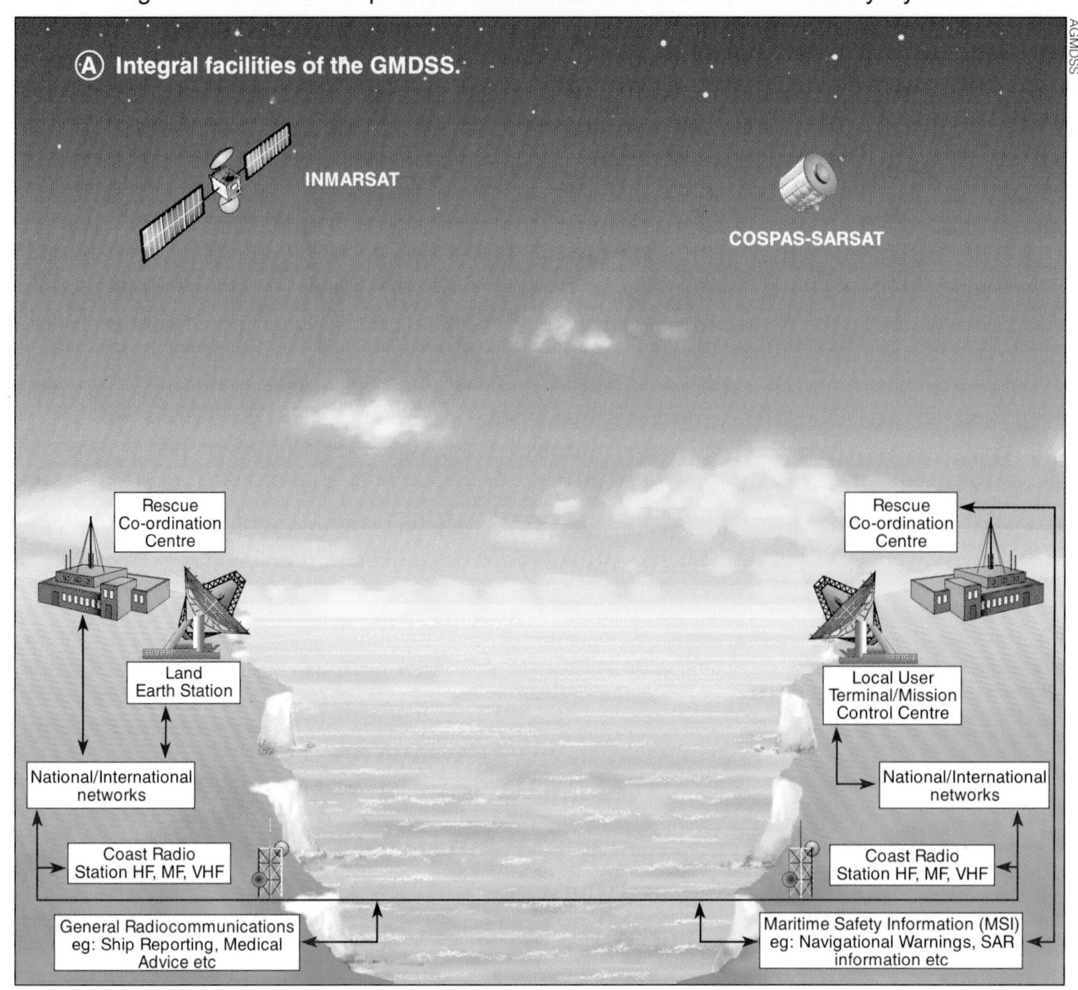

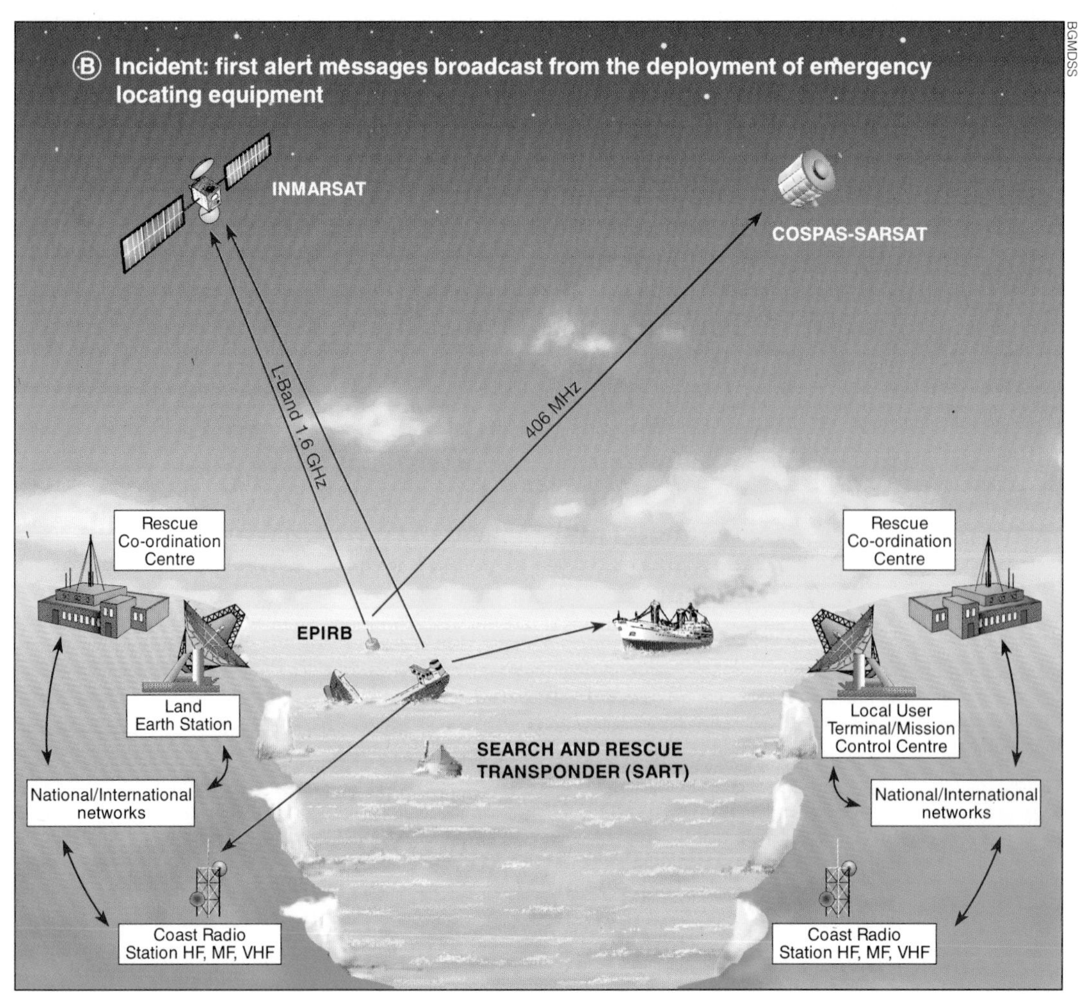

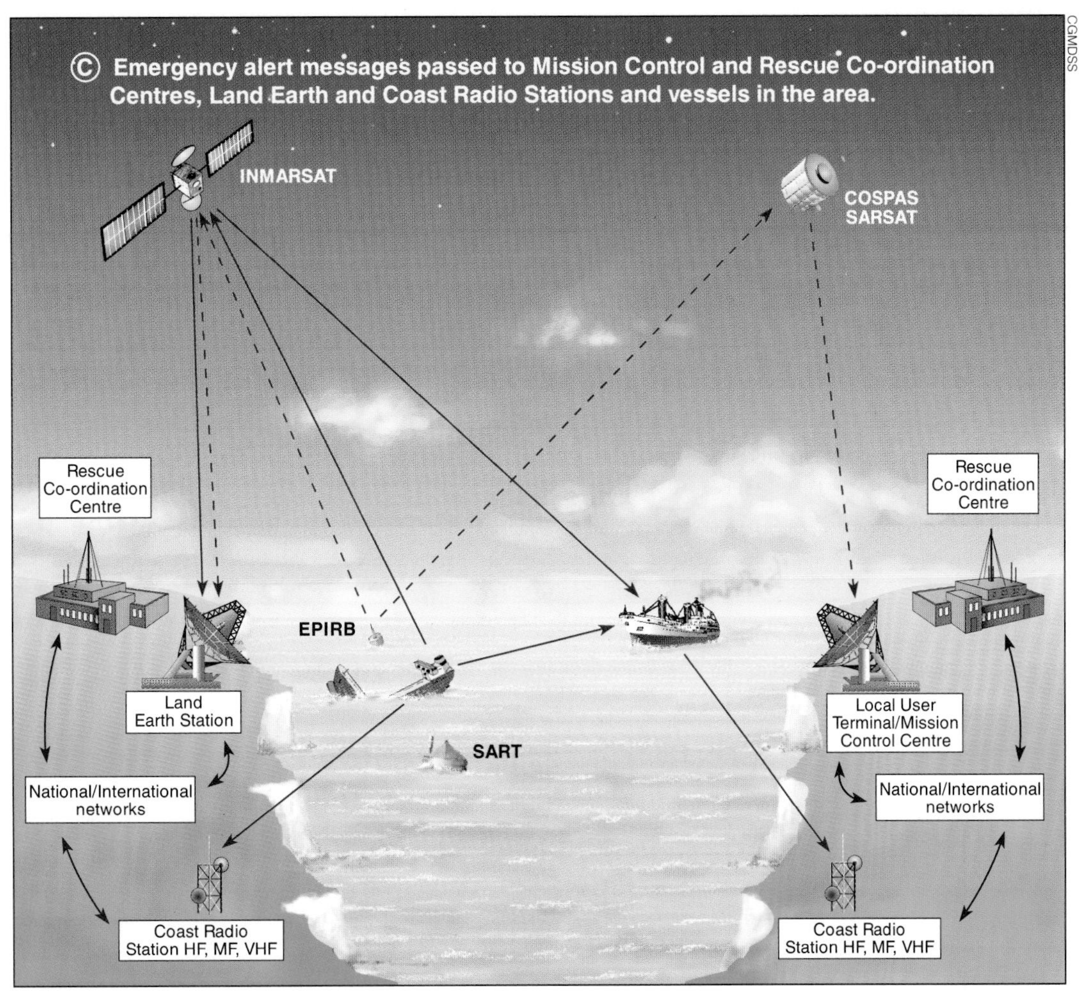
CGMDSS
Ⓒ Emergency alert messages passed to Mission Control and Rescue Co-ordination Centres, Land Earth and Coast Radio Stations and vessels in the area.
INMARSAT
COSPAS
SARSAT
Rescue
Co-ordination
Centre
Rescue
Co-ordination
Centre
EPIRB
Land
Earth Station
Local User
Terminal/Mission
Control Centre
SART
National/International
networks
National/International
networks
Coast Radio
Station HF, MF, VHF
Coast Radio
Station HF, MF, VHF

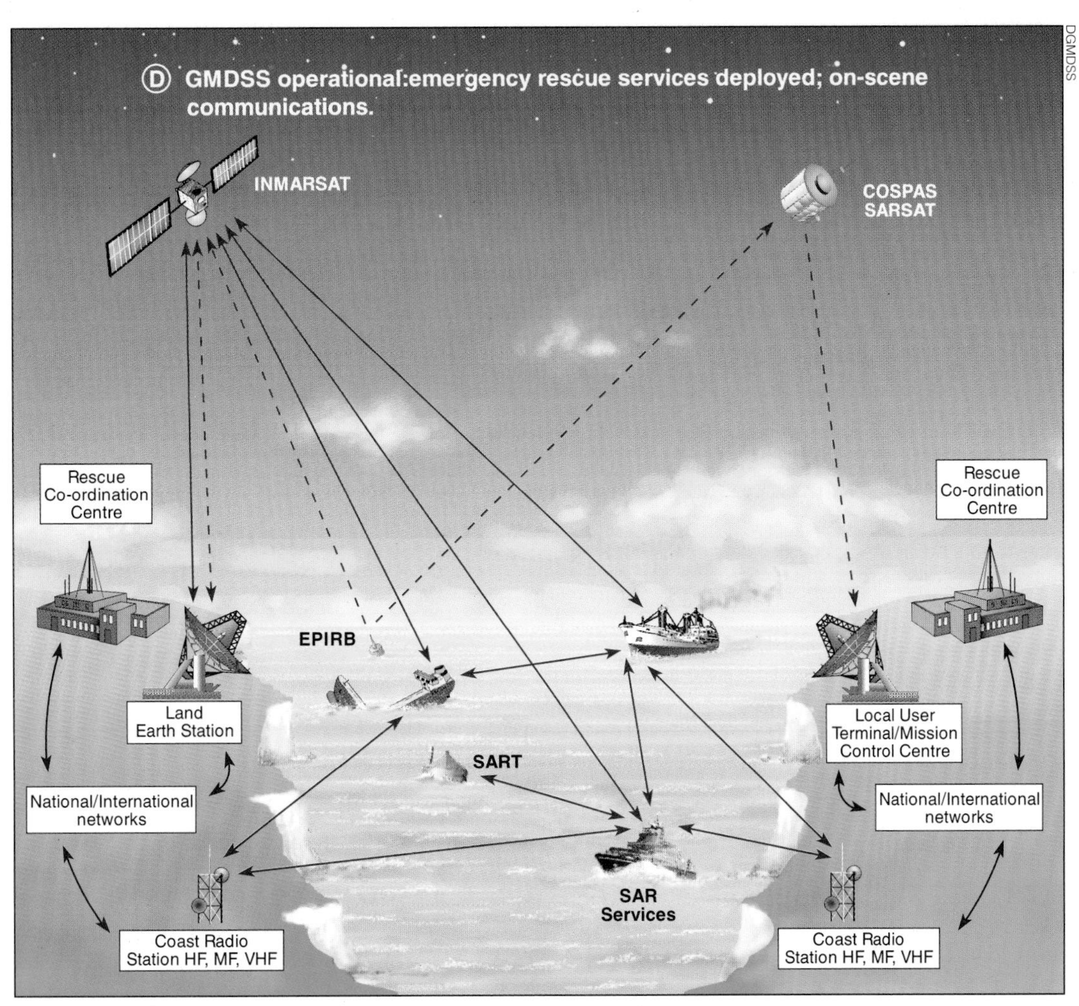
DGMDSS
Ⓓ GMDSS operational:emergency rescue services deployed; on-scene communications.
INMARSAT
COSPAS
SARSAT
Rescue
Co-ordination
Centre
Rescue
Co-ordination
Centre
EPIRB
Land
Earth Station
Local User
Terminal/Mission
Control Centre
SART
National/International
networks
National/International
networks
SAR
Services
Coast Radio
Station HF, MF, VHF
Coast Radio
Station HF, MF, VHF

NAVIGATIONAL SEA AREAS

The GMDSS is based on the concept of using four marine communication sea areas to determine the operational, maintenance and personnel requirements for maritime radiocommunications, viz:

Sea Area A1 Within the radiotelephone coverage of at least one VHF coast station in which continuous DSC alerting is available. Such an area could extend typically 20 - 50 nautical miles from the coast station.

Sea Area A2 An area, excluding sea area A1, within the radiotelephone coverage of at least one MF coast station in which continuous DSC alerting is available. For planning purposes this area typically extends to up to 150 nautical miles offshore, but would exclude any A1 designated areas. In practice, satisfactory coverage may often be achieved out to around 150 nautical miles offshore.

Sea Area A3 An area, excluding sea areas A1 and A2, within the coverage of an Inmarsat geostationary satellite in which continuous alerting is available. This area lies between about latitudes 70° North and South, but excludes A1 and/or A2 designated areas.

Sea Area A4 An area outside sea areas A1, A2 and A3. This is essentially the polar regions, north and south of about 70° of latitude, but excludes any other areas.

OPERATIONAL DETAILS

The worldwide communication coverage of the GMDSS is achieved by a combination of satellite and terrestrial systems. Based on the range limitations of each system the four sea areas have been defined according to the coverage of VHF, MF, HF Coast Radio Services and Inmarsat services. The type of radio equipment required to be carried by a vessel is therefore determined by its area of operations.

Area Description	Distance	Radio	Frequencies	EPIRBs	Survival Craft
A1 Within range of shore-based VHF stations	Depends on antenna height at shore-based VHF station, about 20-50 n miles	VHF	156·525 MHz (Ch 70) for DSC or 156·8 MHz (Ch 16) RT	Either L-Band (1·6 GHz) or 406 MHz COSPAS-SARSAT or VHF EPIRB (after February 1999)	9 GHz radar transponder (SART); VHF portable radio (Ch 16 and one other frequency)
A2 Within range of shore-based MF stations	about 50-150 n miles	MF VHF	as above, plus, 2187·5 kHz DSC, 2182 kHz RT, 2174·5 kHz NBDP, 518 kHz NAVTEX	L-Band (1·6 GHz) or 406 MHz COSPAS-SARSAT	as above
A3 Within geo-stationary satellite range (i.e. Inmarsat)	70°N-70°S	HF or Satellite MF VHF	as above, plus 1·5-1·6 GHz alerting or as A1 and A2 plus all HF frequencies	L-Band (1·6 GHz) or 406 MHz COSPAS-SARSAT	as above
A4 Other areas (i.e., beyond Inmarsat range)	North of 70°N or South of 70°S	HF MF VHF		406 MHz COSPAS-SARSAT	as above

SUB-SYSTEMS

An essential feature of the GMDSS is that radio watchkeeping is automatic, so that when the receiving equipment is activated, an operator is alerted. Subsequent distress and safety communications are, however carried out on radiotelephone or radiotelex.
On board the vessel, when communications are not in progress, radio operators (usually the bridge watchkeeping officers) are required to monitor just two essential conditions:-

a) that the equipment is in service and fully operational, and

b) that the equipment is correctly set up to perform all the mandatory GMDSS functions; this is done by carrying out regular tests according to the relevant regulations.

The GMDSS is actually composed of a number of "sub-systems" which are co-ordinated through shore-based authorities to provide all the required functions needed to ensure safety at sea.

The main sub-systems can be grouped as follows:

1) THE DIGITAL SELECTIVE CALLING (DSC) TERRESTRIAL CALLING SYSTEM

Terrestrial radio links can provide a quick reliable means of all purpose communications between vessels and the shore and between vessels. Vessel and shore stations can be addressed by general or individual calls, as necessary. Dedicated frequencies are available for maritime communication systems operating in the VHF, MF and HF bands, providing for short, medium and long range communications respectively.

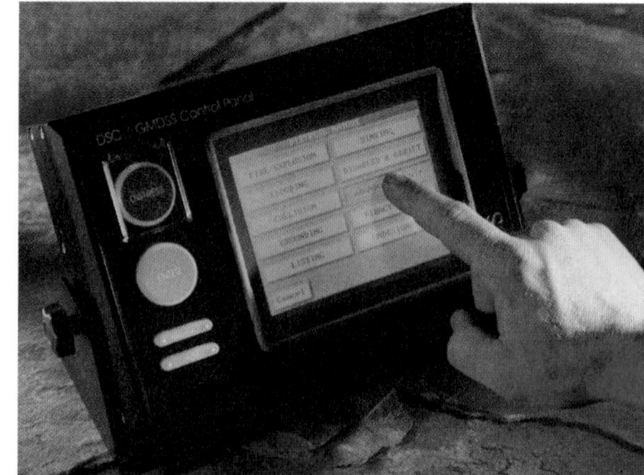

Modular GMDSS Communications System www.icselectronics.co.uk

GMDSS communications at VHF, MF and HF are based on DSC technology, which is a method of calling a station or groups of stations using digital modulation techniques. DSC provides automated access to coast stations and vessels for the transmission and reception of all types of messages from routine to distress category. The intention is that this automated calling system is used as the initial means of contact with other stations.

The DSC system is optimised for use in emergencies and allows for the name of the vessel in distress, the nature of the distress and the last recorded position to be displayed or printed out on receipt of a distress alert. DSC receivers sound an alarm whenever a distress call is received. Distress priority ship-to-shore DSC calls receive priority handling by coast stations and may be automatically routed to the nearest Rescue Co-ordination Centre (RCC).

2) THE SATELLITE COMMUNICATION SYSTEM

Satellite networks are capable of providing a full range of communication services encompassing all general communications requirements, as well as distress and safety functions, within the network coverage area. At present, Inmarsat (a fully commercial, non-government, company) is the only provider of comprehensive maritime communication services by satellite, but others may be in a position to provide such services later. These services are subject to intergovernmental oversight by IMSO.

3) THE MARITIME SAFETY INFORMATION (MSI) SYSTEM

MSI includes navigational and meteorological warnings, meteorological forecasts, and other urgent safety-related messages of vital importance to all vessels at sea and may also include electronic chart correction data. This is broadcast by MF telex (known as NAVTEX) for local MSI, and by satellite or HF telex for long-range MSI (i.e., Navarea warnings, etc.).

4) THE EPIRB (EMERGENCY POSITION INDICATING RADIO BEACON) SYSTEM

Extensive EPIRB alerting facilities are available through Inmarsat and COSPAS-SARSAT, a multi-national government-funded organisation. Full global coverage is provided by the polar-orbiting COSPAS-SARSAT system which allows the EPIRB position to be determined through the satellites using Doppler frequency shift measurement techniques. However, some 406 MHz EPIRBs have an interface to connect with the vessel's navigation systems and these can also transmit their position directly. A 121·5 MHz signalling facility is included on all current production COSPAS-SARSAT EPIRBs, which serves primarily to provide a homing signal for searching aircraft. Inmarsat EPIRBs operate at L-band (1·6 GHz) and will transmit their position directly using information obtained from the vessel's navigational system. Coverage through the Inmarsat geostationary satellites includes the Atlantic West, Atlantic East, Indian and Pacific Ocean Regions but excludes the polar regions above about 70° North or South.

5) THE SART (SEARCH AND RESCUE TRANSPONDER) SYSTEM

The SART is a portable radar transponder which is designed to provide a locating signal and, as such, is primarily intended to be deployed on survival craft. When interrogated by a 9 GHz (3cm) radar, the SART response paints a series of 12 dots, pointing to the distress location, on the radar screens of vessels and suitably equipped aircraft engaged in a search and rescue operation.

A full understanding of each of these sub-systems is essential to all operators and service technicians, whether ashore or afloat.

FUNCTIONAL REQUIREMENTS

The GMDSS is a largely, but not fully, automated system which requires vessels to have a range of equipment capable of performing the nine radiocommunication functions of the GMDSS, viz:

1. TRANSMISSION OF SHIP-TO-SHORE DISTRESS ALERTS BY AT LEAST TWO SEPARATE AND INDEPENDENT MEANS, EACH USING A DIFFERENT RADIOCOMMUNICATION SERVICE;

Details for each individual vessel are to be found on its Safety Radio Certificate. On a Sea Area A1 vessel, for example (which always remains within DSC range of a shore VHF station) the primary means would be the VHF DSC, and the secondary means could be an EPIRB. In the case of a Sea Area A4 ship, the primary means would have to be HF DSC and the secondary means a 406 MHz EPIRB.

2. RECEPTION OF SHORE-TO-SHIP DISTRESS ALERTS;

If, for example, a vessel sends a distress signal via an EPIRB or Inmarsat C satellite terminal, any vessels which might be in the vicinity will not become aware of the distress until the shore authorities relay the distress details by directing a DSC call and/or a satellite call to all vessels within a defined area.

3. TRANSMISSION AND RECEPTION OF SHIP-TO-SHIP DISTRESS ALERTS;

A vessel in distress can alert other vessels in the vicinity by sending a DSC distress alert on VHF and MF, simultaneously if desired, and follow it up with a distress (MAYDAY) voice message on Ch 16 or 2182 kHz. Note that HF DSC is for long-range work and is intended primarily for alerting the shore-based authorities, especially if there are no vessels in the vicinity.

4. TRANSMISSION AND RECEPTION OF SEARCH AND RESCUE CO-ORDINATING COMMUNICATIONS;

This means that vessels must be able to perform the functions described in the IAMSAR Manual (which has replaced the MERSAR Manual). For suitably equipped vessels, this might include the use of radiotelex (more properly called Narrow-Band Direct-Printing - NBDP) between the vessels involved in a search.

5. TRANSMISSION AND RECEPTION OF ON-SCENE COMMUNICATIONS;

"On-scene communications" are short to medium range communications carried out during the course of a search and rescue operation. For this purpose, vessels must be able to communicate with aircraft, as well as with other vessels and the shore, using the dedicated GMDSS frequencies for voice and NBDP distress communications.

The frequencies for radiotelephone use are:-

VHF (F3E)	Ch 16 (distress & safety communications) and Ch 6 (intership and ship-aircraft communications).
VHF (A3E)	121·5 & 123·1 MHz (ship-aircraft communications - compulsory for passenger vessels)
MF (J3E)	2182 kHz (distress & safety communications)
HF (J3E)	3023 kHz (ship-aircraft), 4125 kHz (ship-shore, ship-ship) and 5680 kHz (ship-aircraft).

6. TRANSMISSION AND RECEPTION OF SIGNALS FOR LOCATING

Locating and homing signals in the GMDSS are provided by radar beacons and EPIRBs. SART beacons are intended for use on-board survival craft and enable vessels and aircraft engaged in a search and rescue operation to locate survivors using 9 GHz (3cm) radar. Most EPIRBs in current manufacture also incorporate some form of locating function - a SART can be included in the Inmarsat E EPIRB, and the COSPAS-SARSAT 406 MHz EPIRBs now provide for an additional transmission on 121·5 MHz, which suitably equipped vessels and aircraft can use as a homing signal.

7. TRANSMISSION AND RECEPTION OF MARITIME SAFETY INFORMATION;

The GMDSS supports two independent systems for broadcasting MSI: the international NAVTEX and SafetyNET systems. Navigational and meteorological warnings, meteorological forecasts, and other urgent safety-related messages for a given area are generally broadcast over either NAVTEX or SafetyNET. Vessels equipped with both a NAVTEX receiver and SafetyNET receiver should select the appropriate receiver to receive MSI for the relevant area. Some long range information is also broadcast by HF radiotelex. NAVTEX is generally used for coastal warnings but where a coastal area is not covered by the International NAVTEX service MSI for that area will be broadcast on SafetyNET.

8. TRANSMISSION AND RECEPTION OF GENERAL RADIOCOMMUNICATIONS TO AND FROM SHORE-BASED RADIO SYSTEMS OR NETWORKS;

The GMDSS provides facilities for all types of commercial and personal communications. GMDSS radio operators need to know how to make telephone and telex calls to shipping agents, port authorities, the public telephone network etc. through commercial telecommunication networks.

9. TRANSMISSION AND RECEPTION OF BRIDGE-TO-BRIDGE COMMUNICATIONS;

This refers to the SOLAS requirement that access to VHF communication equipment must be available from the position at which the vessel is normally navigated and, furthermore, that this must include operation on Ch 13, the frequency reserved for intership communications relating to the Safety of Navigation.

A2/A3 GMDSS Communications System www.mcmurdo.co.uk

THE TERRESTRIAL COMMUNICATION SYSTEM

GMDSS terrestrial communications take place on VHF and on various frequencies in the 2, 4, 6, 8, 12 and 16 MHz bands. The 18, 22 and 25 MHz bands are also used for MSI broadcasts by radiotelex.

THE DIGITAL SELECTIVE CALLING (DSC) SUB-SYSTEM

The DSC system is a calling system that can be used for distress/safety and for general calling purposes. The DSC equipment is generally called a DSC controller that may operate with a receiver (DSC decoder) and a transmitter (DSC encoder). The system may be manual, semi-automatic or fully automatic.

The relevant information in a DSC message is displayed at the receiving equipment and may be printed out if a printer is connected. The DSC system may be used to remotely operate a transceiver on board a vessel if this equipment is designed for automated operation.

In the MF and HF bands, there are dedicated frequencies for distress and safety calls. It is important that business calls or routine calls are not allowed to be transmitted on these frequencies, but only on the DSC frequencies assigned for these categories of calls. In the VHF band, however, the same frequency (channel 70) is used for all categories of DSC calls.

In the MF band, the frequency 2177 kHz is assigned for ship-to-ship DSC calling. Technically, a vessel may call another ship on any routine DSC calling frequency in the MF/HF bands. However, ship-to-ship calls on HF is not widely used.

Before a DSC routine call is transmitted, it shall be verified that the frequency is free. On VHF this is done automatically by the equipment which prevents transmitting until the frequency is free for other calls than distress and safety.

One of the duties of the bridge watchkeeper is to ensure that the VHF DSC is keeping automatic watch on Ch 70, and that the MF/HF DSC is programmed to scan at least three of the six MF/HF distress and safety frequencies; that is in the 2 MHz, 8 MHz bands and one other frequency deemed to be suitable at the time.

Commercial frequencies and the Intership frequency may also be scanned but, normally this requires a separate DSC unit because the distress watch must be continuous, and this is usually achieved by using a dedicated DSC watch receiver.

If a Distress Alert is sent by DSC, subsequent communications are always carried out on the distress frequency in the same band. For example if a DSC Distress Alert is sent on 8 MHz, a subsequent voice MAYDAY message will be sent on the 8 MHz RT frequency (8291 kHz, which is more easily called up as Channel 833).

The DSC sub-system also provides for Urgency and Safety category calls. These announce that the transmission of an Urgency or Safety message will follow. An Urgency or Safety DSC call is always sent on the appropriate DSC Distress and Safety frequency. However, in contrast to a DSC Distress Alert, the DSC format for Urgency and Safety calls allows for the possibility of nominating a working frequency for the transmission of the actual message instead of the associated distress frequency. This may become necessary when the Urgency or Safety messages are of long duration and could therefore overload the associated distress frequency. In all cases, the DSC Urgency and Safety call must nominate the frequency to be used for subsequent communications whether it be the associated distress frequency or a working frequency. In practice, ship station operators will, in almost all cases, only need to nominate the associated distress frequency. However, coast stations will often have long Urgency or Safety messages to transmit and may therefore nominate one of their RT or NBDP working frequencies for the subsequent message. Ship station operators must take care to select the actual frequency nominated in the DSC Urgency and Safety call.

A Distress Alert is defined in the Radio Regulations as either a terrestrial DSC call using the unique Distress Format described below, or a satellite call which also has a special Distress Format to gain priority over the satellite link.

STRUCTURE AND CONTENT OF THE DSC CALL

DSC uses the same type of radio signals as telex, which means binary coding modulation system. Two audio frequencies are used representing "0" and "1" or "high" and "low" tone. In telex each character is represented by 7 bits but only the combinations which have 3 "low" and 4 "high" tones are used. This gives an error indicating effect and by using ARQ (Automatic Request for repetition), a reliable error correcting effect is obtained. In the DSC system, each character consists of 10 bits, where the first 7 are information bits and the last 3 are control bits. The control bits count the number of "0" in the information part and thereby gives an error indicating effect. The DSC calls, as well as telex in broadcasting mode, use time diversity (that is, each character is transmitted twice with a time delay) which gives an error correcting effect.

If the check-sum is incorrect, a distress/safety message should nevertheless be received, but automatic operation of the equipment should only take place when the character is received correctly.

Because the DSC signals are binary coded (digital), they are largely affected by static interference, but more resistant to atmospheric noise with slower fluctuations. Further, the DSC modulation system is more resistant to noise than amplitude modulated signals (such as J3E). Additionally, the band width of the transmitted DSC signal is substantially smaller than the voice signal (300 Hz to 3 kHz). Thus a successful DSC call does not indicate that subsequent RT signals on the same frequency band will be of intelligible quality. With this in mind, a DSC call can be acknowledged by a return DSC call. Such an acknowledgement can include a suggested change of frequency for subsequent communications.

COMPONENTS OF THE DSC CALL

A DSC call consists of nine sections, i.e.

1) Dot Pattern	to stop scanning receivers and perform bit synchronisation
2) Phasing signal	to perform character synchronisation
3) Format Specifier	to inform what kind of call it is
4) Address	the address of the receiving station (MMSI, group call or geographical call)
5) Category	informs the receiving operator how important the message is
6) Self-ID	the calling station's MMSI
7) Additional information	known as "messages" which are keyed in by the operator
8) End-of-sequence	a symbol which indicates whether an acknowledgement is required by a return DSC call
9) Error Check Symbol	is a parity check of the whole message.

The main features of each of these components is briefly described below. The entire call lasts for about 7 seconds on MF/HF, and about 0.6 seconds on VHF.

1) THE DOT PATTERN.

This is simply a series of alternating high and low tones, which will cause receiving equipment to stop scanning and "listen" to the forthcoming DSC call. The dot pattern is also used for bit synchronisation of the call. Whether or not they print or display the details of the call depends on the Address. On MF/HF the dot pattern lasts for 2 seconds, therefore watchkeeping receivers have to scan all six distress frequencies within 2 seconds.

2) THE PHASING SIGNAL

The signal arriving at a DSC receiver is nothing more than a stream of high and low tones, arriving at a steady and pre-determined rate (100 Baud on MF/HF, 1200 Baud on VHF DSC). The receivers have to break this up into groups of ten, starting at the correct point. Having found it, they continue to separate the incoming stream of highs and lows into groups of ten at exactly the right places.

3) THE FORMAT SPECIFIER

Can be any one of the following six alternatives:

i.	Distress	ii.	All Ships
iii.	Individual station	iv.	Groups of stations
v.	Stations in a Geographical Area	vi.	Automatic Phone Call.

Different types of call contain different numbers of symbols and in different sequences. In other words, each type of message has a different Format. The Format Specifier "tells" the receiver the exact order in which these symbols will be sent. For example the 27th symbol might be a part of the sending station's MMSI or it might be a Telecommand, or something else, depending on Format of the call.

A geographical call is a call to vessels within a defined rectangular geographical area. Note that when defining a Geographical Area, the northernmost latitude is entered first, and the southernmost latitude is defined by indicating how many degrees further south it is. Likewise, the westernmost longitude is entered first and the easternmost longitude is defined by indicating how many degrees further eastward it is.

4) THE ADDRESS

This is simply the MMSI of the receiving station (or group of stations). DSC receivers detecting a Format Specifier for Distress, All Ships or a position within a Geographical Area, will automatically display the received message. So, for these Formats, the transmission of Address symbols would be superfluous. Thus the sending operator is not prompted to enter the MMSI of the receiving station for these particular Formats.

5) THE CATEGORY

This indicates to the receiving operator how important the message is. There are five Categories - Distress, Urgency, Safety, Ship's Business and Routine. The receiver will display the Category as part of the message.

6) SELF-ID

The calling station's MMSI is automatically included in all DSC calls regardless of Format.

7) ADDITIONAL INFORMATION KEYED IN BY THE OPERATOR

A. DISTRESS FORMAT ONLY

contains four "messages" as follows:-

1. Nature of Distress: selected by the operator from a list of up to 12, including Piracy and Man Overboard. Note that "man overboard" has distress status for DSC purposes; however the subsequent RT procedure still uses the urgency signal PANPAN.
2. Position of vessel in distress. The position should be updated automatically, but may be put in manually for older equipment. If the position data is not known, or incorrect (e.g. too old), the character should consist of only digits "9" indicating that position data is not available.
3. UTC Time means the time that the position was valid. Note that this time is not the same as the equipment's internal date and time setting, which need not be displayed in UTC. If the UTC time is incorrect, rescue parties might start searching in the wrong position. If the internal clock is incorrect, the date and time displayed with incoming DSC calls will be incorrect, because DSC does not include a date and time group within the call itself; an incoming message is given a date and time by the receiving equipment.
4. Subsequent communications, selected as either RT (J3E) or NBDP (F1B-FEC).

If the operator does not enter any of the above information, the equipment will automatically send the following:

Nature of distress	"undesignated"
Position:	"9999999999"
Time:	"8888"
Ongoing traffic	J3E (which means RT)

Note the four 8s and ten 9s might be translated into a text phrase by some receivers.

NOTE: Operators should be aware that the DSC distress call is sent 5 times without a break. This is done to increase the possibility that it will be received at the first attempt and it is essentially this feature, together with its unique format, which makes it a "Distress Alert" and not just a "distress call". As a consequence of being repeated five times in a single burst, an MF/HF Distress Alert lasts for about 35 seconds instead of approximately 7 seconds for other calls (12 times faster on VHF, as mentioned above). Moreover, unless the transmission is manually terminated by the sender, this 35-second Distress Alert will be automatically and repeatedly re-transmitted with random intervals of 3.5 to 4.5 minutes between calls, until a DSC Distress Acknowledgement is received.

B. ALL OTHER FORMATS

contain three "messages" as follows:

1. Two Telecommands
2. Position or Working Frequency (or neither)
3. Country Code and telephone number (these are included only if the Format Specifier is for Autophone Format).

These "messages" are briefly described below.

TWO TELECOMMANDS

i. The **First Telecommand** is selected from a list of 26. It usually indicates the class of emission to be used in subsequent communications. It can also indicate that the call is a "distress acknowledgement" or a "distress relay". These are not "distress alerts" as defined above because they follow the Format for "other calls". **However they include the details of the vessel in distress and, as such, they must only be sent on the authority of the Master.**

ii. The **Second Telecommand** is selected from a different list of 26. For many DSC calls, only four of these are offered. The first two are for use in war zones. One indicates that the vessel is a neutral vessel according to Resolution 18 for Ships and Aircraft as printed in the ITU Manual. The other indicates that the vessel is a Hospital Ship as per "Medical Transports" covered by Radio Reg 33 in the ITU Manual. The third is used with the Auto Phone Format which remotely prepares the receiving equipment for automatic dialling. The fourth and most commonly used is "No information". Some of the remaining 22 Telecommands are used by coast stations when replying to a commercial DSC call from a vessel, e.g. "unable to comply", "busy", "cannot use channel" etc. Others relate to data transmissions.

POSITION OR WORKING FREQUENCY

If a working frequency is entered by the operator, equipment at the receiving station may automatically be set to the channel or frequencies nominated by the sender. Obviously this facility must be used with some care to avoid interfering with equipment on other vessels.

If a position is entered, the called station is obliged to reply by DSC and indicate a working frequency, or indicate inability and a reason for declining to communicate.

AUTOMATIC PHONE CALLS

If the Format Specifier indicates automatic or semi-automatic calls, the symbols appearing in this part of the message will be routed to the automatic dialling equipment.

Note that the operator does not necessarily have to key in every item of every DSC call. The DSC equipment is designed to insert essential components automatically. This reduces the number of entries to be keyed in or selected by the operator.

8) END-OF-SEQUENCE (EOS) SYMBOL

If the sender requires a DSC acknowledgement, the EOS symbol is signalled as "RQ". As mentioned above, this occurs automatically if a position was sent instead of a working frequency. A station receiving an "RQ" group is obliged to send a DSC acknowledgement, either automatically or manually. The EOS symbol in this mandatory acknowledgement is signalled as "BQ". Thus the original caller knows that the DSC call was received correctly. If the caller sent a position, then a working frequency must be included in the "BQ" acknowledgement.

9) ERROR CHECK SYMBOL

Sometimes known as an Error Check Character (ECC) this indicates if a parity-error has been detected in the received message. Call details will still be displayed but it might not be possible to determine which symbol or symbols were corrupted.

MMSI NUMBERS

Each ship station has its own unique 9-digit Maritime Mobile Service Identity (MMSI) which is included automatically in each call. Included in the MMSI number are the Maritime Identification Digits (MID) which identify the country licensing/controlling the station. Three types of MMSI numbers are in common use to identify individual vessels, groups of vessels and coast stations.

Examples, using the MID **232** (United Kingdom), are:

a) Ship Stations - **232**001021
b) Group of Ships - 0**232**01143 (1 leading zero)
c) Coast Station - 00**232**0018 (2 leading zeroes)

The MMSI number is used to form the international subscriber number for Inmarsat B, C & M Ship Earth Stations. Because of the way the MMSI is translated to a satellite terminal number, suitable MMSIs are limited to those with three trailing zeros for older Inmarsat terminals.

To avoid exhausting the supply of MID numbers too rapidly, MMSI numbers with three trailing zeroes should only be assigned to ships which expect to have automatic access to the public switched telephone network (PSTN) on a world-wide basis or which expect to use Inmarsat B, C or M.

In practice, most administrations assign MMSI numbers with three trailing zeroes only to vessels subject to the SOLAS Convention. Other vessels which require access to such networks on a national or regional level may be assigned MMSIs with only one or two trailing zeroes, for older Inmarsat terminals.

In all cases though, an appropriate MMSI number should be assigned before an Inmarsat B, C or M terminal is commissioned for use as a ship earth station.

TESTING OF DSC EQUIPMENT

MF/HF equipment is tested by selecting the Safety Category (in some equipment this might occur automatically) and transmitting a special "Test" format, on one of the DSC Distress and Safety frequencies, to a GMDSS coast station. It is necessary to firstly ascertain that the coast station keeps watch on the relevant frequency - not all GMDSS stations scan all 6 MF/HF frequencies. Also the frequency should be checked to ensure that the call is not initiated if other signals are in progress. A minute or so after receiving the call, the coast station will automatically send a DSC acknowledgement call back to the vessel, thereby indicating that the test was successful.

The only test which should be carried out on VHF DSC equipment is the daily internal test, without transmitting live signals. Live test calls on VHF Ch 70 should not be made. Regular use of DSC VHF Ch 70 on a routine basis to make contact with another vessel or a coast station will confirm the VHF DSC equipment is operating correctly.

Note especially that - except for VHF Ch 70 - the DSC and NBDP distress frequencies are reserved exclusively for Distress and Safety purposes. DSC or NBDP calls which are not related to Distress, Urgency or Safety matters must be initiated only on frequencies allocated for commercial or routine communications. Bona fide DSC test calls are included in the Safety Category.

WATCH KEEPING

Vessels, while at sea, shall maintain a continuous watch appropriate to the sea area in which the vessel is sailing using:

1) VHF DSC CH 70.
2) MF DSC distress and safety frequency 2187·5 kHz.
3) DSC distress and safety frequency 8414·5 kHz and at least one other HF DSC frequency appropriate to local time and vessel's position relative to the nearest DSC coast station.
4) SOLAS ships, where practical, should maintain a watch on VHF Ch 13 for communications related to the safety of navigation

A continuous watch for broadcasts of maritime safety information shall also be kept, for the area in which the vessel is sailing, by:

1) NAVTEX (518 kHz)
2) Inmarsat C or EGC SafetyNET Receiver
3) HF MSI

Weather and navigational warnings are also transmitted at fixed times throughout the day by coast stations on MF, HF and VHF (See ALRS Volume 3)

RADIOTELEPHONE PROCEDURES

For Distress purposes, communications are carried out on a single frequency so that all parties can hear both sides of any conversation. Radiotelephone transmissions are always J3E (upper side band). Operators are referred to the ITU Manual for full details of Distress, Urgency and Safety procedures, as well as those for commercial operations.

The RT distress frequencies are not, at present, used exclusively for Distress and Safety purposes. 2182 kHz is used for calling and reply, and some of the HF distress frequencies were originally used as part of a paired frequency channel for general use, and in some parts of the world they still are.

There is no international agreement on whether the HF RT distress frequencies should be used exclusively for Distress and Safety or whether they will continue to be used for other purposes. The issue is presently under discussion at the World Radio Conference and should be resolved in the near future. The silence period still applies for 3 minutes on the hour and half hour, over the frequency band 2173·5 to 2190·5 kHz. This band includes the DSC, RT and NBDP distress frequencies. It also includes 2177 kHz and 2189·5 kHz (DSC intership and commercial calling), but these frequencies have been specifically excluded from the requirement to remain silent. It is good practice to also observe silence on all of the other distress frequencies.

RADIOTELEX (NBDP) PROCEDURES

Like DSC, the radio signal uses two modulating tones. These are only 170 Hz apart, and thus occupy a narrow bandwidth, giving rise to the abbreviation NBDP for Narrow Band Direct Printing.

Operational Procedures are detailed in ITU–R M.492–6 (in the ITU Manual). Among other things, it describes the use of Mode A (ARQ) and Mode B (FEC) and how to set up a call with a coast station. The use of "free channel" signals is also described. Operators should be aware that vessel's telex terminals usually offer two types of ARQ call; one which makes the equipment wait for a "free channel" signal before transmitting the call, and one which transmits the call immediately, regardless of whether or not the called station has traffic in progress. Care should be taken to ensure that the correct type of call is made, depending on the circumstances.

M.492–6 also mentions that telex messages should be preceded by "carriage return" and "line feed" signals. This ensures that the receiving equipment starts printing at the beginning of a new line. The Radio Regulations S32 and S33 also require that the "letter shift" signal is sent, in case the receiving equipment has been left in "figure shift" and starts printing erroneous characters as a consequence. On computer keyboards, the "Enter" key performs all three functions in a single keystroke.

Figure 2a - Actions by ships upon reception of **VHF** / **MF** DSC Distress alert

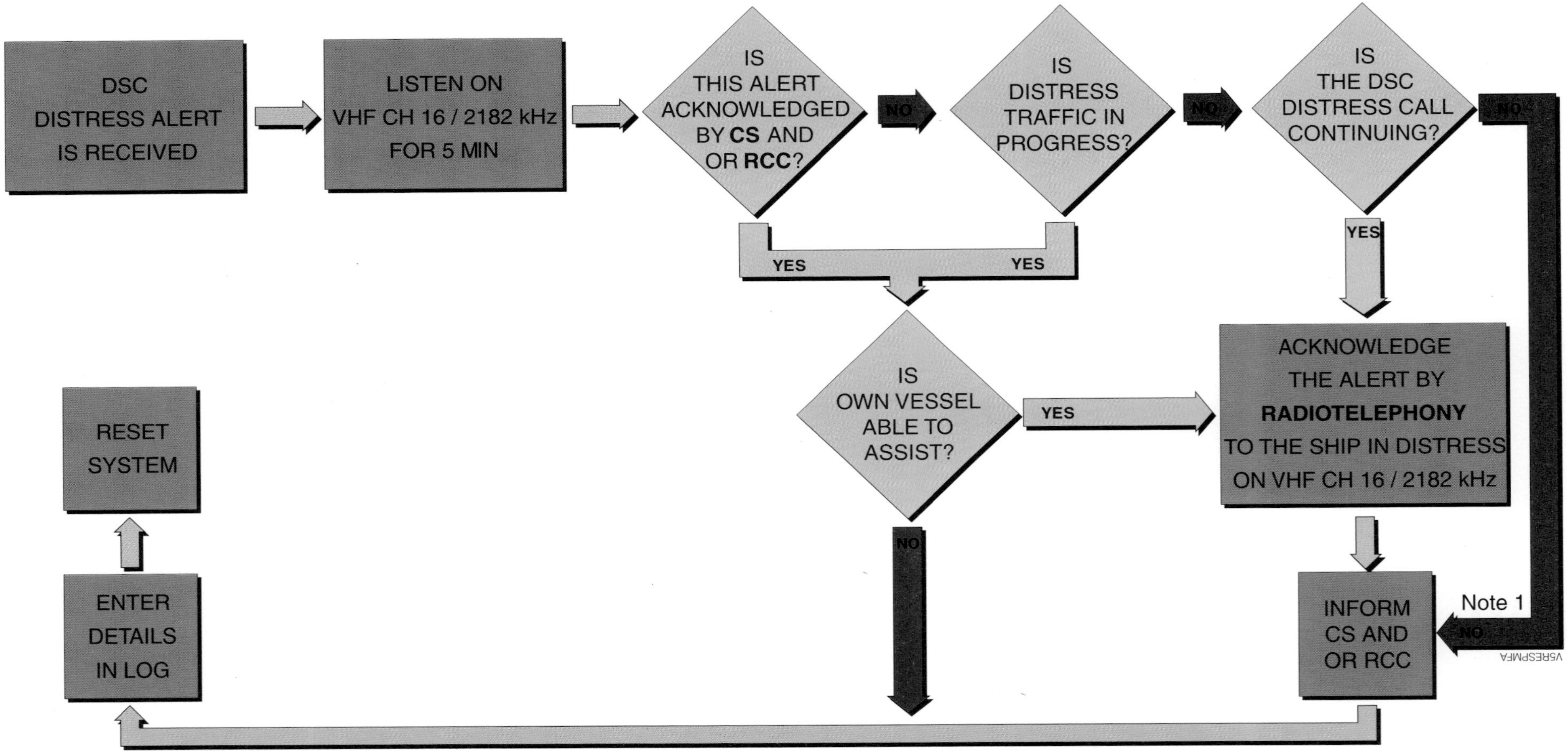

REMARKS:

Note 1: Appropriate or relevant RCC and/or Coast Station shall be informed accordingly. If further DSC alerts are received from the same source and the ship in distress is beyond doubt in the vicinity, a DSC acknowledgement may, after consultation with an RCC or Coast Station, be sent to terminate the call.

Note 2: In no case is a ship permitted to transmit a DSC distress relay call on receipt of a DSC distress alert on either VHF Channel 70 or MF Channel 2187·5 kHz

CS = Coast Station RCC = Rescue Co-ordination Centre

Figure 2b - Actions by ships upon reception of **HF** DSC Distress alert

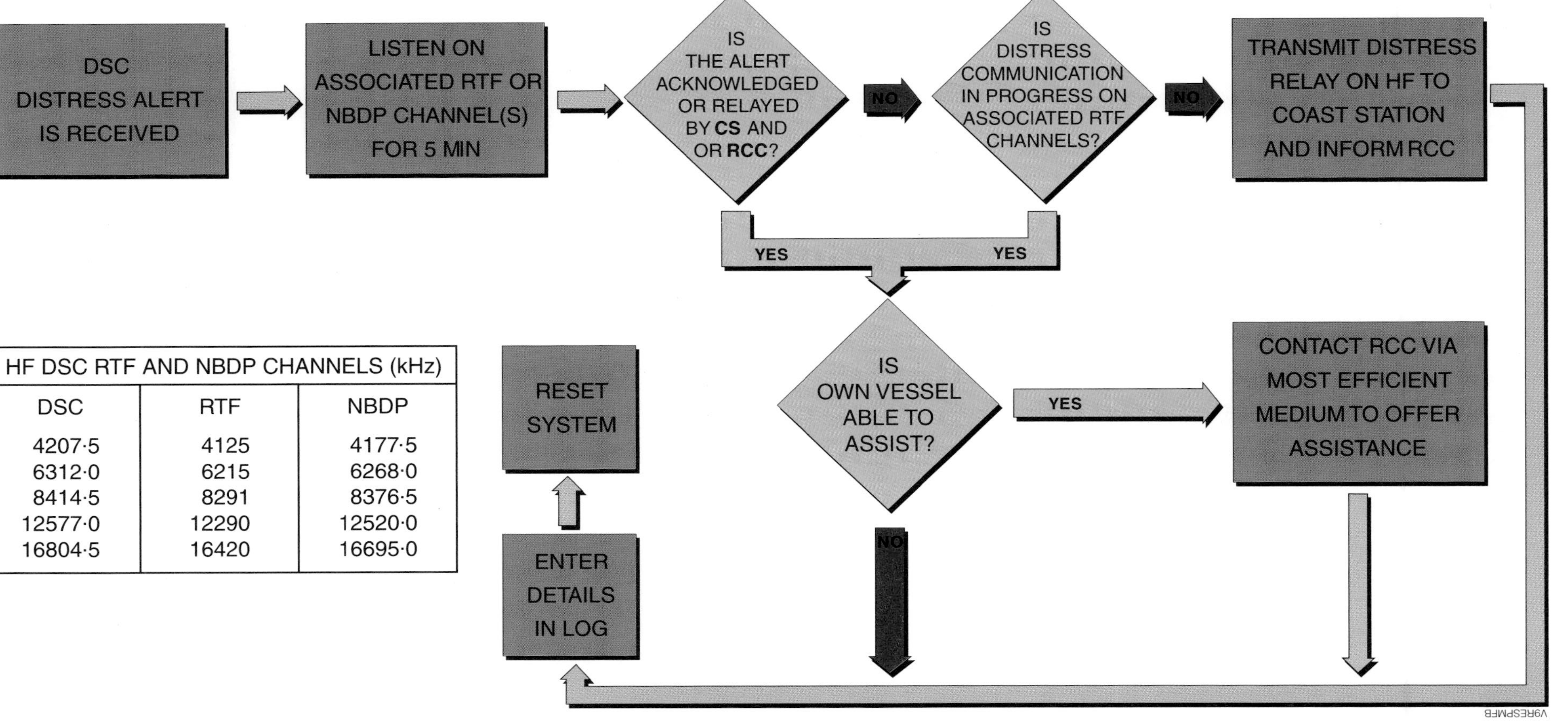

HF DSC RTF AND NBDP CHANNELS (kHz)		
DSC	RTF	NBDP
4207·5	4125	4177·5
6312·0	6215	6268·0
8414·5	8291	8376·5
12577·0	12290	12520·0
16804·5	16420	16695·0

Note 1: If it is clear the ship or person in distress are not in the vicinity and/or other craft are better placed to assist, superfluous communications which could interfere with search and rescue activities are to be avoided. Details should be recorded in the appropriate logbook.

Note 2: The ship should establish communications with the station controlling the distress as directed and render such assistance as required and appropriate.

Note 3: Distress relay calls should be initiated manually

CS = Coast Station RCC = Rescue Co-ordination Centre

M.492–6 refers to two other Recommendations, i.e. M.476 and M.625. M.476 also describes the radiotelex system, specifying that vessels should be issued with a 5–digit Selcall number for automatic reception of incoming calls. M.625 came later and introduced some new features, including the use of the vessel's 9–digit MMSI number instead of the Selcall number. It also specified that the ARQ mode will allow 32 cycles of repetition of each group of three characters, before breaking off radio contact, a change from the M.476 terminology which simply said "after a predetermined time of continuous repetition". At present, both M.476 and M.625 remain valid.

GENERAL BUSINESS AND COMMERCIAL COMMUNICATIONS

General communications are one of the nine functions of the GMDSS. The emphasis of general communications in the GMDSS has shifted to Narrow-Band Direct-Printing (NBDP) techniques, otherwise known as telex, in preference to voice communications.
It is possible to make telex calls to any subscriber to the International Telex Network by using the MF/HF or satellite communications equipment forming part of the GMDSS installation.

DSC COMMUNICATIONS (EXTACTS FROM ITU):

OPERATIONAL PROCEDURES FOR SHIPS FOR DSC COMMUNICATIONS ON MF, HF AND VHF

INTRODUCTION

Procedures for DSC communications on MF and VHF are described in the sections 1 to 5 below.

The procedures for DSC communications on HF are in general the same as for MF and VHF. Special conditions to be taken into account when making DSC communications on HF are described in section 6 below.

1. DISTRESS

1.1 TRANSMISSION OF DSC DISTRESS ALERT

A distress alert should be transmitted if, in the opinion of the Master, the ship or a person or persons on it is in distress and requires immediate assistance.

A DSC distress alert should as far as possible include the ship's last known position and the time (in UTC) when it was valid. The position and the time may be included automatically by the ship's navigational equipment or may be inserted manually.

The DSC distress alert is transmitted as follows:

* Tune the transmitter to the DSC distress channel (2187·5 kHz on MF, Channel 70 on VHF) [1]
* If time permits, key in or select on the DSC equipment keyboard:
  - the nature of distress;
  - the ship's last known position (latitude and longitude);
  - the time (in UTC) the position was valid;
  - type of subsequent distress communication (telephony);

in accordance with the DSC equipment manufacturer's instructions.

* Transmit the DSC distress alert [2].
* Prepare for the subsequent distress traffic by tuning the transmitter and the radiotelephony receiver to the distress traffic channel in the same band, ie. 2182 kHz on MF, Channel 16 on VHF, while waiting for the DSC distress acknowledgement.

1 Some maritime MF radiotelephony transmitters shall be tuned to a frequency 1700 Hz lower than 2187·5 kHz, ie 2185·8 kHz, in order to transmit the DSC alert on 2187·5 kHz.
2 Add to the DSC distress alert, whenever practicable and at the discretion of the person responsible for the ship in distress, the optional expansion in accordance with Recommendation ITU-R M.821, with additional information as appropriate, in accordance with the DSC equipment manufacturer's instructions.

1.2 ACTIONS ON RECEIPT OF A DISTRESS ALERT [1]

Ships receiving a DSC distress alert from another ship should normally not acknowledge the alert by DSC since acknowledgement of a DSC distress alert by use of DSC is normally made by coast stations only.

Only if no other station seems to have received the DSC distress alert, and the transmission of the DSC distress alert continues, the ship should acknowledge the DSC distress alert by use of DSC to terminate the call. The ship should then, in addition, inform a coast station or a Land Earth Station by any practicable means **(see Figures 2A and 2B)**.

Ships receiving a DSC distress alert from another ship should also defer the acknowledgement of the distress alert by radiotelephony for a short interval, if the ship is within an area covered by one or more coast stations, in order to give the coast station time to acknowledge the DSC distress alert first.

A ship receiving a DSC distress alert from another ship shall:

* Watch for the reception of a distress acknowledgement on the distress channel (2187·5 kHz on MF, Channel 70 on VHF);
* Prepare for receiving the subsequent distress communication by tuning the radiotelephony receiver to the distress traffic frequency in the same band in which the DSC distress alert was received, ie. 2182 kHz on MF, channel 16 on VHF;
* Acknowledge the receipt of the distress alert by transmitting the following by radiotelephony on the distress traffic frequency in the same band in which the DSC distress alert was received, ie. 2182 kHz on MF, Channel 16 on VHF:
  - "MAYDAY";
  - the 9-digit identity of the ship in distress, repeated 3 times;
  - "this is";
  - the 9-digit identity or the call sign or other identification of own ship, repeated 3 times;
  - "RECEIVED MAYDAY".

1 Vessels out of range of a distress event or not able to assist should only acknowledge if no other station appears to acknowledge the receipt of the DSC distress alert.

1.3 DISTRESS TRAFFIC

On receipt of a DSC distress acknowledgement the ship in distress should commence the distress traffic by radiotelephony on the distress traffic frequency (2182 kHz on MF, Channel 16 on VHF) as follows:

- "MAYDAY";
- "this is";
- the 9-digit identity and the call sign or other identification of the ship;
- the ship's position in latitude and longitude or other reference to a known geographical location;
- the nature of distress and assistance wanted;
- any other information which might facilitate the rescue.

1.4 TRANSMISSION OF A DSC DISTRESS RELAY ALERT

A ship knowing that another ship is in distress shall transmit a DSC distress relay alert if:

- the ship in distress is not itself able to transmit the distress alert;
- the master of the ship considers that further help is necessary.

The DSC distress relay alert is transmitted as follows:

* Tune the transmitter to the DSC distress channel (2187·5 kHz on MF, Channel 70 on VHF);
* Select the distress relay call format on the DSC equipment;
* Key in or select on the DSC equipment keyboard:
  - All Ships Call or the 9-digit identity of the appropriate coast station;
  - the 9-digit identity, of the ship in distress, if known;
  - the nature of distress;
  - the latest position of the ship in distress, if known;
  - the time (in UTC) the position was valid (if known);
  - type of subsequent distress communication (telephony).
  - transmit the DSC distress relay call;
  - prepare for the subsequent distress traffic by tuning the transmitter and the radiotelephony receiver to the distress traffic channel in the same band, i.e. 2182 kHz on MF and Channel 16 on VHF, while waiting for the DSC distress acknowledgement.

1.5 ACKNOWLEDGEMENT OF A DSC DISTRESS RELAY ALERT RECEIVED FROM A COAST STATION (SEE FOOTNOTE 1 OF SECTION 1.2)

Coast stations, after having received and acknowledged a DSC distress alert, may if necessary, re-transmit the information received as a DSC distress relay call, addressed to all ships, all ships in a specific geographical area, a group of ships or a specific ship.

Ships receiving a distress relay call transmitted by a coast station shall not use DSC to acknowledge the call, but should acknowledge the receipt of the call by radiotelephony on the distress traffic channel in the same band in which the relay call was received, ie. 2182 kHz on MF, Channel 16 on VHF.

Acknowledge the receipt of the distress alert by transmitting the following by radiotelephony on the distress traffic frequency in the same band in which the DSC distress relay alert was received:

- "MAYDAY";
- the 9-digit identity or the call sign or other identification of the calling coast station;
- "this is";
- the 9-digit identity or call sign or other identification of own ship;
- "RECEIVED MAYDAY".

1.6 ACKNOWLEDGEMENT OF A DSC DISTRESS RELAY ALERT RECEIVED FROM ANOTHER SHIP

Ships receiving a distress relay alert from another ship shall follow the same procedure as for acknowledgement of a distress alert, ie. the procedure given in section 1.2 above.

1.7 CANCELLATION OF AN INADVERTENT DISTRESS ALERT (DISTRESS CALL)

A station transmitting an inadvertent distress alert shall cancel the distress alert using the following procedure:

1.7.1 Immediately transmit a DSC "distress cancellation" if provided in accordance with Recommendation ITU-R M.493, section 8.3.2 [1] e.g. with own ship's MMSI inserted as identification of ship in distress. In addition cancel the distress alert aurally over the telephony distress traffic channel associated with each DSC channel on which the "distress call" was transmitted [2].

1.7.2 Monitor the telephony distress traffic channel associated with the DSC channel on which the distress was transmitted, and respond to any communications concerning that distress alert as appropriate.

1 To cancel an inadvertent transmitted "distress" call, a "distress cancellation" call may be transmitted with the ship's own MMSI inserted as identification of ship in distress. This cancellation should be followed immediately by a voice cancellation procedure.

2 *A ship could cancel its false DSC distress alert by following it with a DSC acknowledgement using its own MMSI number. Sending an acknowledgement to one's own distress alert would be a clear indication to receiving operators that the alert may be ignored. Stations receiving the original alert may not be able to hear the subsequent voice cancellation (which must still be sent, as well as notification to a suitable RCC). But if they received the DSC alert, they would very likely receive the DSC acknowledgement as well.*

2. URGENCY

2.1 TRANSMISSION OF URGENCY MESSAGES

Transmission of urgency messages shall be carried out in two steps:

* Announcement of the urgency message,
* Transmission of the urgency message.

The announcement is carried out by transmission of a DSC urgency call on the DSC distress calling channel (2187·5 kHz on MF, Channel 70 on VHF).

The urgency message is transmitted on the distress traffic channel (2182 kHz on MF, Channel 16 on VHF).

The DSC urgency call may be addressed to all stations or to a specific station. The frequency on which the urgency message will be transmitted shall be included in the DSC urgency call.

The transmission of an urgency message is thus carried out as follows:

Announcement:

* Tune the transmitter to the DSC distress calling channel (2187·5 kHz on MF, Channel 70 on VHF);
* Key in or select on the DSC equipment keyboard:
  - All Ships Call or the 9-digit identity of the specific station;
  - the category of the call (urgency);
  - the frequency or channel on which the urgency message will be transmitted;
  - the type of communication in which the urgency message will be given (radiotelephony);

in accordance with the DSC equipment manufacturer's instructions.

* Transmit the DSC urgency call.

Transmission of the urgency message:

* Tune the transmitter to the frequency or channel indicated in the DSC urgency call;
* Transmit the urgent message as follows:
  - "PAN PAN", repeated 3 times;
  - "ALL STATIONS" or called station, repeated 3 times;
  - "this is";
  - the 9-digit identity *and* the call sign or other identification of own ship;
  - the text of the urgency message.

2.2 RECEPTION OF AN URGENCY MESSAGE

Ships receiving a DSC urgency call announcing an urgency message addressed to all ships shall NOT acknowledge the receipt of the DSC call, but should tune the radiotelephony receiver to the frequency indicated in the call and listen to the urgency message.

3. SAFETY

3.1 TRANSMISSION OF SAFETY MESSAGES

Transmission of safety messages shall be carried out in two steps:

* Announcement of the safety message,
* Transmission of the safety message.

The announcement is carried out by transmission of a DSC safety call on the DSC distress calling channel (2187·5 kHz on MF, Channel 70 on VHF).

The safety message is normally transmitted on the distress and safety traffic channel in the same band in which the DSC call was sent, ie. 2182 kHz on MF, channel 16 on VHF.

The DSC safety call may be addressed to all ships, all ships in a specific geographical area or to a specific station.

The frequency on which the safety message will be transmitted shall be included in the DSC call.

The transmission of a safety message is thus carried out as follows:

Announcement:

* Tune the transmitter to the DSC distress calling channel (2187·5 kHz on MF, Channel 70 on VHF);
* Select the appropriate calling format on the DSC equipment (all ships, area call or individual call);
* Key in or select on the DSC equipment keyboard:
  - specific area or 9-digit identity of specific station, if appropriate;
  - the category of the call (safety);
  - the frequency or channel on which the safety message will be transmitted;
  - the type of communication in which the safety message will be given (radiotelephony);

in accordance with the DSC equipment manufacturer's instructions.

* Transmit the DSC safety call.

Transmission of the safety message:

* Tune the transmitter to the frequency or channel indicated in the DSC safety call.
* Transmit the safety message as follows:
  - "SECURITÉ", repeated 3 times;
  - "ALL STATIONS" or called station, repeated 3 times;
  - "this is";
  - the 9-digit identity *and* the call sign or other identification of own ship;
  - the text of the safety message.

3.2 RECEPTION OF A SAFETY MESSAGE

Ships receiving a DSC safety call announcing a safety message addressed to all ships shall NOT acknowledge the receipt of the DSC safety call, but should tune the radiotelephony receiver to the frequency indicated in the call and listen to the safety message.

4. PUBLIC CORRESPONDENCE

4.1 DSC CHANNELS FOR PUBLIC CORRESPONDENCE

4.1.1 VHF

The VHF DSC Channel 70 is used for DSC for distress and safety purposes as well as for DSC for public correspondence.

4.1.2 MF

International and national DSC channels separate from the DSC distress and safety calling channel 2187·5 kHz are used for digital selective calling on MF for public correspondence.

Ships calling a coast station by DSC on MF for public correspondence should preferably use the coast station's national DSC channel.

The international DSC channel for public correspondence may as a general rule be used between ships and coast stations of different nationality. The ships transmitting frequency is 2189·5 kHz, and the receiving frequency is 2177 kHz.

The frequency 2177 kHz is also used for digital selective calling between ships for general communication.

4.2 TRANSMISSION OF A DSC CALL FOR PUBLIC CORRESPONDENCE TO A COAST STATION OR ANOTHER SHIP

A DSC call for public correspondence to a coast station or another ship is transmitted as follows:

* Tune the transmitter to the relevant DSC channel;
* Select the format for calling a specific station on the DSC equipment;
* Key in or select on the DSC equipment keyboard:
  - the 9-digit identity of the station to be called;
  - the category of the call (routine);
  - the type of the subsequent communication (normally radiotelephony);
  - a proposed working channel if calling another ship. Proposal for working channel should NOT be included in calls to a coast station; the coast station will in its DSC acknowledgement indicate a vacant working channel;

in accordance with the DSC equipment manufacturer's instructions.

* Transmit the DSC call.

4.3 REPEATING A CALL

A DSC Call for public correspondence may be repeated on the same or another DSC channel, if no acknowledgement is received within 5 minutes.

Further call attempts should be delayed at least 15 minutes, if acknowledgement is still not received.

4.4 ACKNOWLEDGEMENT OF A RECEIVED CALL AND PREPARATION FOR RECEPTION OF THE TRAFFIC

On receipt of a DSC call from a coast station or another ship, a DSC acknowledgement is transmitted as follows:

* Tune the transmitter to the transmit frequency of the DSC channel on which the call was received;
* Select the acknowledgement format on the DSC equipment;
* Transmit an acknowledgement indicating whether the ship is able to communicate as proposed in the call (type of communication and working frequency).
* If able to communicate as indicated, now tune the transmitter and the radiotelephony receiver to the indicated working channel and prepare for receiving the traffic.

4.5 RECEPTION OF ACKNOWLEDGEMENT AND FURTHER ACTIONS

When receiving an acknowledgement indicating that the called station is able to receive the traffic, prepare for transmitting the traffic as follows:

* Tune the transmitter and receiver to the indicated working channel;
* Commence the communication on the working channel by:
  - the 9-digit identity or call sign or other identification of the called station;
  - "this is";
  - the 9-digit identity or call sign or other identification of own ship.

It will normally rest with the ship to call again a little later in case the acknowledgement from the coast station indicates that the coast station is not able to receive the traffic immediately.

In case the ship in response to a call to another ship receives an acknowledgement indicating that the other ship is not able to receive the traffic immediately, it will normally rest with the called ship to transmit a call to the calling ship when ready to receive the traffic.

5. TESTING THE EQUIPMENT USED FOR DISTRESS AND SAFETY CALLS

Testing on the exclusive DSC distress and safety calling frequency 2187·5 kHz should be avoided as far as possible by using other methods.

No test transmissions should be made on VHF DSC calling Channel 70.

Test calls should be transmitted by the ship station and acknowledged by the called coast station. Normally there would be no further communication between the two stations involved.

A test call to a coast station is transmitted as follows:

* Tune the transmitter to the DSC distress and safety calling frequency 2187·5 kHz;
* Key in or select the format for the test call on the DSC equipment in accordance with the DSC equipment manufacturer's instructions;
* Key in the 9-digit identity of the coast station to be called;
* Transmit the DSC call after checking as far as possible that no calls are in progress on the frequency;
* Wait for acknowledgement.

6. SPECIAL CONDITIONS AND PROCEDURES FOR DSC COMMUNICATION ON HF

General

The procedures for DSC communication on HF are - with some additions described in section 6.1 to 6.5 below - equal to the corresponding procedures for DSC communications on MF/VHF

Due regard to the special conditions described in section 6.1 to 6.5 should be given when making DSC communications on HF.

6.1. DISTRESS

6.1.1 TRANSMISSION OF DSC DISTRESS ALERT

DSC distress alert should be sent to coast stations - eg. in A3 and A4 sea areas on HF - and on MF and/or VHF to other ships in the vicinity.

The DSC distress alert should as far as possible include the ship's last known position and the time (in UTC) it was valid. If the position and time is not inserted automatically from the ship's navigational equipment, it should be inserted manually.

Ship-to-shore Distress Alert

Choice of HF band

Propagation characteristics of HF radio waves for the actual season and time of the day should be taken into account when choosing HF bands for transmission of DSC distress alert.

As a general rule the DSC distress channel in the 8 MHz maritime band (8414·5 kHz) may in many cases be an appropriate first choice.

Transmission of the DSC distress alert in more than one HF band will normally increase the probability of successful reception of the alert by coast stations.

DSC distress alert may be sent on a number of HF bands in two different ways:

a) either by transmitting the DSC distress alert on one HF band, and waiting a few minutes for receiving acknowledgement by a coast station;

   if no acknowledgement is received within 3 minutes, the process is repeated by transmitting the DSC distress alert on another appropriate HF band etc;

b) or by transmitting the DSC distress alert at a number of HF bands with no or only very short pauses between the calls, without waiting for acknowledgement between the calls.

It is recommended to follow procedure a) in all cases, where time permits to do so; this will make it easier to choose the appropriate HF band for commencement of the subsequent communication with the coast station on the corresponding distress traffic channel.

Transmitting the DSC alert [1]

* Tune the transmitter to the chosen HF DSC distress channel (4207·5, 6312, 8414·5, 12577, 16804·5 kHz) [2]
* Follow the instructions for keying in or selection of relevant information on the DSC equipment keyboard as described in Section 1.1.
* Transmit the DSC distress alert.

In special cases, for example in tropical zones, transmission of DSC distress alert on HF may, in addition to ship-to-shore alerting, also be useful for ship-to-ship alerting.

1 Ship-to-ship distress alert should normally be made on MF and/or VHF, using the procedures for transmission of DSC distress alert on MF/VHF described in section 1.1.
2 Some maritime HF transmitters shall be tuned to a frequency 1700 Hz lower than the DSC frequencies given above in order to transmit the DSC alert on the correct frequency.

6.1.2 PREPARATION FOR THE SUBSEQUENT DISTRESS TRAFFIC

After having transmitted the DSC distress alert on appropriate DSC distress channels (HF, MF and/or VHF), prepare for the subsequent distress traffic by tuning the radiocommunication set(s) (HF, MF and/or VHF as appropriate) to the corresponding distress traffic channel(s).

If method b) described in section 6.1.1 above has been used for transmission of DSC distress alert on a number of HF bands:

- take into account in which HF band(s) acknowledgement has been successfully received from a coast station;
- if acknowledgements have been received on more than one HF band, commence the transmission of distress traffic on one of these bands, but if no response is received from a coast station then the other bands should be used in turn.

The distress traffic frequencies are:

HF:					
Telephony	4125 kHz	6215 kHz	8291 kHz	12290 kHz	16420 kHz
Telex	4177·5 kHz	6268 kHz	8376·5 kHz	12520 kHz	16695 kHz
MF:					
Telephony	2182 kHz				
Telex	2174·5 kHz				
VHF:	Channel 16 (156·800 MHz)				

6.1.3 DISTRESS TRAFFIC

The procedures described in section 1.3 are used when the distress traffic on MF/HF is carried out by *radiotelephony*.

The following procedures shall be used in cases where the distress traffic on MF/HF is carried out by *radiotelex*:

* The Forward Error Correcting (FEC) mode shall be used unless specifically requested to do otherwise.
* All messages shall be preceded by
  - at least one carriage return
  - line feed
  - one letter shift
  - the distress signal "MAYDAY".
* The ship in distress should commence the distress telex traffic on the appropriate distress telex traffic channel as follows:
  - carriage return, line feed, letter shift;
  - the distress signal "MAYDAY";
  - the words "this is";
  - the 9-digit identity and call sign or other identification of the ship;
  - the ship's position if not included in the DSC distress alert;
  - the nature of distress;
  - any other information which might facilitate the rescue.

6.1.4 ACTIONS ON RECEPTION OF A DSC DISTRESS ALERT ON HF FROM ANOTHER SHIP

Ships receiving a DSC distress alert on HF from another ship shall *not* acknowledge the alert, but should:

* Watch for reception of a DSC distress acknowledgement from a coast station.
* While waiting for reception of a DSC distress acknowledgement from a coast station:

Prepare for reception of the subsequent distress communication by tuning the HF radiocommunication set (transmitter and receiver) to the relevant distress traffic channel in the same HF band in which the DSC distress alert was received, observing the following conditions:

  - If radiotelephony mode was indicated in the DSC alert, the HF radiocommunication set should be tuned to the radiotelephony distress traffic channel in the HF band concerned;
  - If telex mode was indicated in the DSC alert, the HF radiocommunication set should be tuned to the radiotelex distress traffic channel in the HF band concerned. Ships able to do so should additionally watch the corresponding radiotelephony distress channel;
  - If the DSC distress alert was received on more than one HF band, the radiocommunication set should be tuned to the relevant distress traffic channel in the HF band considered to be the best one in the actual case. If the DSC distress alert was received successfully on the 8 MHz band, this band may in many cases be an appropriate first choice.

* If no distress traffic is received on the HF channel within 1 to 2 minutes, tune the HF radiocommunication set to the relevant distress traffic channel in another HF band deemed appropriate in the actual case.
* If no DSC distress acknowledgement is received from a coast station within 3 minutes, and no distress communication is observed going on between a coast station and the ship in distress:
  - Transmit a DSC distress relay alert;
  - Inform a Rescue Co-ordination Centre via appropriate radiocommunications means.

6.1.5 TRANSMISSION OF DSC DISTRESS RELAY ALERT

In case it is considered appropriate to transmit a DSC distress relay alert:

* Considering the actual situation, decide in which frequency bands (MF, VHF, HF) DSC distress relay alert(s) should be transmitted, taking into account ship-to-ship alerting (MF, VHF) and ship-to-shore alerting;
* Tune the transmitter(s) to the relevant DSC distress channel, following the procedures described in section 6.1.1 above;
* Follow the instructions for keying in or selection of call format and relevant information on the DSC equipment keyboard as described in section 1.4.
* Transmit the DSC distress relay alert.

6.1.6 ACKNOWLEDGEMENT OF A HF DSC DISTRESS RELAY ALERT RECEIVED FROM A COAST STATION

Ships receiving a DSC distress relay alert from a coast station on HF, addressed to all ships within a specified area, should NOT acknowledge the receipt of the relay alert by DSC, but by *radiotelephony* on the telephony distress traffic channel in the same band(s) in which the DSC distress relay alert was received.

6.2 URGENCY

Transmission of urgency messages on HF should normally be addressed

- either to all ships within a specified geographical area
- or to a specific coast station.

Announcement of the urgency message is carried out by transmission of a DSC call with category urgency, on the appropriate DSC distress channel.

The transmission of the urgency message itself on HF is carried out by radiotelephony or radiotelex on the appropriate distress traffic channel in the same band in which the DSC announcement was transmitted.

6.2.1 TRANSMISSION OF DSC ANNOUNCEMENT OF AN URGENCY MESSAGE ON HF

* Choose the HF band considered to be the most appropriate, taking into account propagation characteristics for HF radio waves at the actual season and time of the day; the 8 MHz band may in many cases be an appropriate first choice;
* Tune the HF transmitter to the DSC distress channel in the chosen HF band;
* Key in or select call format for either geographical area call or individual call on the DSC equipment, as appropriate;
* In case of area call, key in specification of the relevant geographical area;
* Follow the instructions for keying in or selection of relevant information on the DSC equipment keyboard as described in section 2.1, including type of communication in which the urgency message will be transmitted (radiotelephony or radiotelex);
* Transmit the DSC call;
* If the DSC call is addressed to a specific coast station, wait for DSC acknowledgement from the coast station. If acknowledgement is not received within a few minutes, repeat the DSC call on another HF frequency deemed appropriate.

6.2.2 TRANSMISSION OF THE URGENCY MESSAGE AND SUBSEQUENT ACTION

* Tune the HF transmitter to the distress traffic channel (telephony or telex) indicated in the DSC announcement;
* If the urgency message is to be transmitted using *radiotelephony*, follow the procedure described in section 2.1;
* If the urgency message is to be transmitted by *radiotelex*, the following procedure shall be used:
  - Use the Forward Error Correcting (FEC) mode unless the message is addressed to a single station whose radiotelex identity number is known;
  - commence the telex message by:
    * at least one carriage return, line feed, one letter shift
    * the urgency signal "PAN PAN"
    * "this is";
    * the 9-digit identity of the ship *and* the call sign or other identification of the ship
    * the text of the urgency message.

Announcement and transmission of urgency messages addressed to all HF equipped ships within a specified area may be repeated on a number of HF bands as deemed appropriate in the actual situation.

6.2.3 RECEPTION OF AN URGENCY MESSAGE

Ships receiving a DSC urgency call announcing an urgency message shall NOT acknowledge the receipt of the DSC call, but should tune the radiocommunication receiver to the frequency and communication mode indicated in the DSC call for receiving the message.

6.3 SAFETY

The procedures for transmission of DSC safety announcement and for transmission of the safety message are the same as for frequency messages, described in section 6.2, *except* that:

- in the DSC announcement, the category SAFETY shall be used
- in the safety message, the safety signal "SECURITÉ" shall be used instead of the urgency signal "PAN PAN".

6.4 PUBLIC CORRESPONDENCE ON HF

The procedures for DSC communication for public correspondence on HF are the same as for MF.

Propagation characteristics should be taken into account when making DSC communication on HF.

International and national HF DSC channels different from those used for DSC for distress and safety purposes are used for DSC for public correspondence.

Ships calling a HF coast station by DSC for public correspondence should preferably use the coast station's national DSC calling channel.

COMMUNICATIONS IN THE GLOBAL SYSTEM

TERRESTRIAL COMMUNICATIONS

LONG-RANGE SERVICE

Use of HF provides a long-range service in both the ship-to-shore and shore-to-ship directions. In areas covered by Inmarsat it can be used as an alternative to satellite communications and outside these areas it provides the only long-range communication capability. Frequencies have been designated in the 4, 6, 8, 12 and 16 MHz bands for this service.

Digital selective calling (DSC) forms the basis of distress alerting and safety communications. Distress and safety communications following a DSC call can be performed by radiotelephony or NBDP.

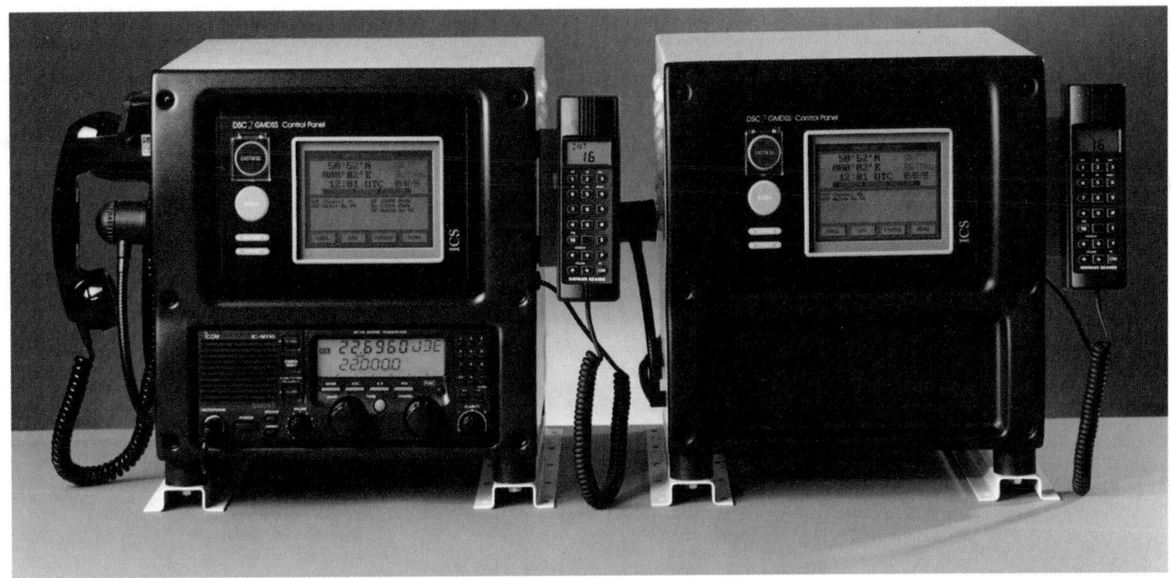
A3 GMDSS Communications System www.mcmurdo.co.uk

MEDIUM-RANGE SERVICE

A medium-range service is provided on frequencies in the 2 MHz band. In the ship-to-shore, ship-to-ship and shore-to-ship directions 2187·5 kHz will be used for distress alerts and safety calls using DSC, and 2182 kHz will be used for distress and safety traffic by radiotelephony, including SAR co-ordinating and on-scene communications. 2174·5 kHz will be used for radiotelex (NBDP) distress and safety traffic.

SHORT-RANGE SERVICE

VHF provides short-range service on the frequencies:

a. 156·525 MHz (Channel 70) for distress alerts and safety calls using DSC, and
b. 156·8 MHz (Channel 16) for distress and safety traffic by radiotelephony, including SAR co-ordinating and on-scene communications.

A2/A3 GMDSS Communications System www.mcmurdo.co.uk

SATELLITE COMMUNICATIONS

INTRODUCTION

Satellite communications are particularly important elements of the GMDSS.

The Inmarsat system, which employs geostationary satellites and operates in the 1·5 and 1·6 GHz bands, provides vessels fitted with suitable Inmarsat Mobile Earth Stations (MES) a means of alerting and a capability for two-way communications using radiotelex and radiotelephone. L-band satellite EPIRBs are also used for alerting. The Inmarsat SafetyNET system is used for broadcasts of MSI to areas not covered by the NAVTEX system.

A polar-orbiting satellite system (COSPAS-SARSAT system), operating in the 406 - 406·1 MHz band, and the use of 406 MHz satellite EPIRBs provides one of the main means of distress alerting and determining the position of the distress call in the GMDSS.

INMARSAT SYSTEM

INTRODUCTION

Inmarsat grew out of an idea that originated within IMO in 1966. Following extensive study by IMO experts a series of international conferences were convened which, in September 1976, resulted in the unanimous adoption of the Convention and Operating Agreement of the International Maritime Satellite Organisation (Inmarsat). According to its Convention, the purpose of Inmarsat was to make provision for the space segment necessary for improved maritime communications and, in particular, for improved safety of life at sea communications and the Global Maritime Distress and Safety System (GMDSS). This purpose was later extended through amendments to the Convention and Operating Agreement to provide the space segment for land mobile and aeronautical communications, and the name of the organisation was changed to the International Mobile Satellite Organisation to reflect the amended purposes.

After twenty years of successful operation, Member States and Signatories of the intergovernmental organisation (IGO) Inmarsat decided to challenge rapidly growing competition from private providers of satellite communications services and pioneered the first ever privatisation of all the assets and business carried on by an intergovernmental organisation. Thus, in April 1998, the Inmarsat Assembly adopted amendments to the Inmarsat Convention and Operating Agreement which were intended to transform the Organisation's business into a privatised corporate structure, while retaining intergovernmental oversight of certain public service obligations and, in particular, the GMDSS. The Assembly and Council of Inmarsat subsequently decided to implement the amendments as from 15 April 1999.

The restructuring of Inmarsat involved the incorporation of holding and operating companies, located in the UK and registered under British law. The Inmarsat satellites and all other assets of the former IGO were transferred to the privatised operating company which continues to manage the global satellite communications system for the future.

Figure 3 - Inmarsat System

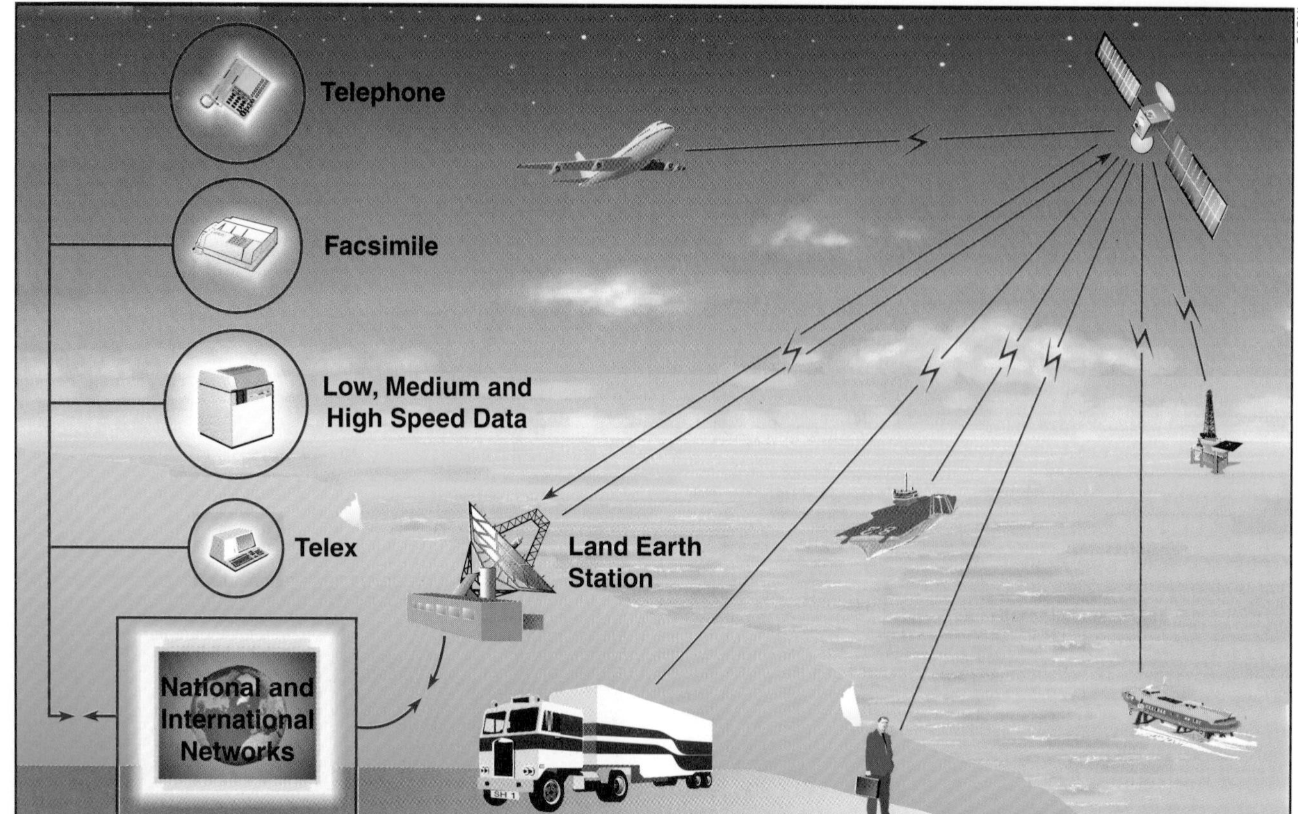

The intergovernmental organisation (IMSO) continues with 8 member states. Under the relevant provisions of the Convention, as amended, a Public Services Agreement between IMSO and the company, and the Articles of Association of the company, IMSO is charged with overseeing, and under some circumstances may enforce fulfilment of some of the company's public service obligations and, in particular, GMDSS services.

The maritime satellite system has three major components; the space segment provided by Inmarsat, the Land Earth Stations (LES) provided by Inmarsat signatories and Mobile Earth Stations (MESs).

The Inmarsat system provides vessels at sea with the same types and quality of modern communications as are available ashore. The capability for direct-dial, automatic connection without delay using high-quality multi-mode communications is provided by MESs. Teleprinters, visual display units (VDUs) and telephone sets, as well as facsimile machines and data equipment, can serve as peripheral equipment to MESs.

The nerve centre of the system is the Network Operations Centre (NOC) located at Inmarsat's headquarters in the United Kingdom. Operating 24 hours a day, it co-ordinates a wide range of activities. The NOC, together with the Electronic Service Activation System (ESAS) also arranges the commissioning of MESs upon application by the terminal owner.

SPACE SEGMENT

The Space Segment is provided by Inmarsat, and consists of four primary communications satellites, with five backup satellites in orbit, ready to be used if necessary.

Each satellite is in a geostationary orbit in space. In this orbit, each satellite moves at exactly the same rate as the rotation of the earth, and so remains in the same relative position to the earth, above the earth's equator. In this position, antennae on the earth can easily maintain communications with the satellite. The satellite's solar panels provide it with electrical power to perform its functions.
The Inmarsat satellites are controlled from the Satellite Control Centre (SCC) based in the Inmarsat Headquarters in London, UK.

Each satellite has a coverage area (also known as its footprint), which is defined as the area on the earth's surface (sea and / or land) within which a mobile or fixed antenna can obtain line-of-sight communications with the satellite. **Figure 4** shows the four satellites in space, and their coverage areas, corresponding to the four Ocean Regions:

- Atlantic Ocean Region-East (AOR-East).
- Atlantic Ocean Region-West (AOR-West).
- Indian Ocean Region (IOR).
- Pacific Ocean Region (POR).

GROUND SEGMENT

The Ground Segment comprises a global network of Land Earth Stations (LESs), Network Co-ordination Stations (NCSs), and a Network Operations Centre (NOC).

Each LES provides a link between the satellites and the national/international telecommunications networks. The large antennae used by the LESs to communicate with the satellite for its Ocean Region are capable of handling many calls simultaneously to and from the MESs.

A LES Operator is typically a large telecommunications company, which can provide a wide range of communications services to the MESs communicating through the LES.

Each of the Inmarsat communications systems (Inmarsat A, B & C etc.) has its own network of LESs.

For each Inmarsat system a prime and back-up Network Co-ordination Station (NCS) is located within each Ocean Region, to monitor and control the communications traffic within its Ocean Region. Each NCS communicates with the LESs in its Ocean Region, and with the other NCSs, as well as with the Network Operations Centre (NOC) located in the Inmarsat Headquarters, making possible the transfer of information throughout the system.

The LESs provide the link between the satellites and terrestrial telecommunications networks. A typical LES consists of a parabolic antenna about 11-14 m in diameter, which is used for transmission of signals to the satellite at 6 GHz and for reception from the satellite at 4 GHz. The same antenna or another dedicated antenna is used for L-band transmission (at 1·6 GHz) and reception (at 1·5 GHz) of network control signals. Each LES provides, as a minimum, telex and telephone services. Three LES, at Southbury (USA), Yamaguchi and Ibaraki (Japan), serve as Network Co-ordination Stations (NCS).

Figure 4 - Inmarsat Geostationary Satellite Coverage

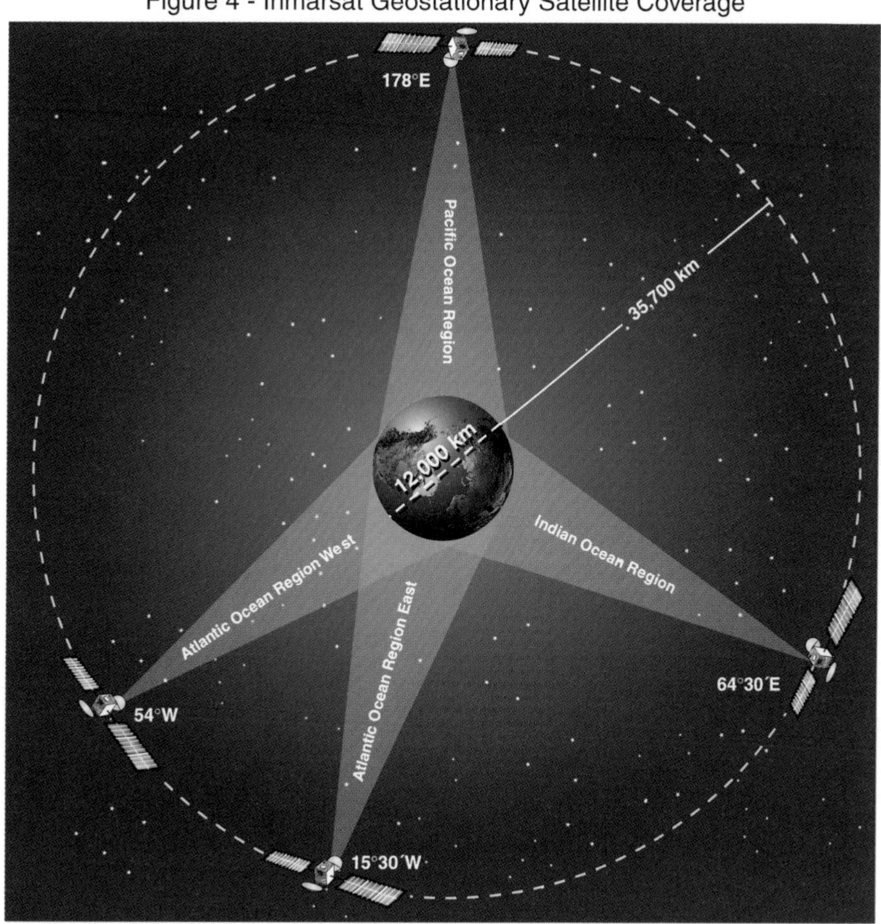

MOBILE EARTH STATIONS

The satellite communication requirements of chapter IV of the 1974 SOLAS Convention can be met, either wholly or in part, by Inmarsat MESs capable of two-way communications, such as Inmarsat A or Inmarsat B and Inmarsat C.

a. Inmarsat A MES[1]

Inmarsat A MES consists of two parts, above-deck equipment and below-deck equipment. The above-deck equipment includes a parabolic antenna, about 0.85 to 1.2 m in diameter, mounted on a platform and stabilized, so that the antenna remains pointed at the satellite regardless of ship motion. It can also include a solid state L-band power amplifier, an L-band low-noise amplifier, a diplexer and a low-loss protective radome. The below-deck equipment consists of an antenna control unit; communications electronics used for transmission, reception, access control and signaling; and telephone, telex and other peripheral equipment.

Above-deck equipment is now available weighing less than 50 kilograms, making it suitable for installation on most types and sizes of vessels and yachts. Many of the current systems are modular in design and allow the addition of optional equipment for e.g. facsimile, data and slow-scan television. Most below-deck units have a microcomputer with a VDU, alphanumeric keyboard, hard copy printer and a modem. The computer can be used to prepare telex messages with the ease of modern word-processing equipment. Messages can be composed, edited and transmitted directly from the screen or stored for later transmission.

With additional facilities users have modified their terminals to allow automated vessel reporting. Those involved in vessel management on shore can dial the ship at any time of the day or night and automatically receive information as to its position, heading etc, as well as data on its cargo and operation all without disturbing or distracting the crew. A distress message generator is normally built into a terminal for storage of basic essential vessel information and automatic transmission of a distress alert.

1 Inmarsat has formally advised the IMO that they intend to switch off Inmarsat A on 31st December 2007. Inmarsat has also confirmed that Inmarsat A services will be fully available until that date. No other Inmarsat services are affected.

b. Inmarsat B MES

Inmarsat B MESs provides high quality, reliable mainstream communications services, aimed primarily at the maritime community, for telephony, telex, facsimile and data in a cost effective manner, using digital technology in order to achieve substantial economies in satellite power and bandwidth utilisation. The system design is compatible with future developments in the space segment and in the terrestrial networks, and is capable of future enhancements in order to accommodate additional customer service requirements as they develop. The Inmarsat B system design has drawn extensively on experience gained from Inmarsat A operation and from the designs developed for the Inmarsat C and Aeronautical systems.

Inmarsat B coverage requirements, performance availability and MES environmental conditions are identical to Inmarsat A and thus are compatible with IMO/GMDSS requirements.

The Inmarsat B system comprises four primary, independent communications networks (satellite Ocean Regions), each containing an operational satellite, a Network Co-ordination Station (NCS) and Land Earth Stations (LES); the latter provides access to the international terrestrial communications networks. The NCS provides overall network management functions including assignments for telephone and data communications services, and ensures all distress calls are handled by LESs. LESs perform channel assignments for all Inmarsat B telex calls.

c. Inmarsat C MES

Inmarsat C MESs are small, light weight terminals designed for two-way message communication. Inmarsat C MESs cannot be used for radiotelephone communications. They operate at 600 bit/s and provide access to the international telex/telex networks, electronic mail services and computer data bases. This low powered terminal with its omni-directional antenna and light weight is a practical solution for installation on the smallest of vessels, thereby bringing benefits of satellite communications within the reach of all mariners. Inmarsat C is mandatory for most vessels equipping themselves to sail in Sea Area A3.

Additionally, Inmarsat C MESs can serve as a back-up for an Inmarsat A MES on large ships and also fulfill a potentially vital role as a fixed or portable transmitter/receiver for use on board ship or in survival craft. The omni-directional antenna characteristics are particularly valuable for a vessel in distress as the MES continues to operate even when the vessel is listing severely. As with the Inmarsat A MES, a distress message generator is included in the terminal software for storage of basic essential vessel information and automatic transmission of a distress alert. All modern Inmarsat C equipment nowadays features built-in GPS.

d. Inmarsat Fleet F77 MES

Inmarsat Fleet F77 brings a new dimension to Inmarsat's provision of GMDSS services, by offering call prioritisation to 4 levels and real-time, hierarchical call pre-emption in both directions.

Inmarsat Fleet F77 is the first and only satellite communications product to enter the GMDSS since 1 February 1999 that is capable of meeting the criteria of four levels of priority:

- Distress; *Inmarsat Priority 43 (P3)*
- Urgency; *Inmarsat Priority 42 (P2)*
- Safety; and *Inmarsat Priority 41 (P1)*
- Other (general/routine) communications. *Inmarsat Priority 40 (P0)*

and give appropriate access for communications in both ship-to-shore direction and shore-to-ship directions for distress, urgency and safety traffic originated by RCCs or other search and rescue authorities, stipulated by the IMO for new systems. Pre-emption and prioritisation comes as standard on Inmarsat Fleet F77, together with high system availability.

Inmarsat Fleet F77 also meets all the commercial needs of; voice, fax, e-mail, data (both packet and circuit-switched) and uses the same system that provides the stringent requirements for the GMDSS.

With Inmarsat Fleet F77, the rescue authorities will always get a call through to a vessel, even if the voice data channel is being used continuously. Not only will pre-emption work seamlessly, it will also work in a clearly hierarchical way:

- A distress (P3) call will pre-empt **all** other communications;
- An urgency (P2) call will pre-empt both safety (P1) and routine (P0) calls; and
- A safety (P1) call will pre-empt a routine (P0) call.

INMARSAT NUMBERS (IMN)

Each system uses a distinctive Inmarsat Number series which allows the functionality to be recognised from the number allocated to a specific terminal:

Inmarsat A Seven (7) digits beginning with **1**

Inmarsat B Nine (9) digits beginning with **3**

Inmarsat C Nine (9) digits beginning with **4**

Inmarsat M Nine (9) digits beginning with **6**

Inmarsat mini-M Nine (9) digits beginning with **76**

INMARSAT SERVICES

SHIP-TO-SHORE DISTRESS ALERTING

The Inmarsat system provides priority access to satellite communications channels in emergency situations. Each MES is capable of initiating a request message with distress priority. Any request message with a distress priority indication is automatically recognized at the LES and a satellite channel is instantly assigned. If all satellite channels happen to be busy, one of them will be pre-empted and allocated to the MES which initiated the distress priority call. The processing of such calls is completely automatic and does not involve any human intervention. The LES personnel, however, are notified of the reception and passing through of a distress priority message by audio/visual alarms.

To ensure the correct treatment of distress priority request the NCS in each ocean region automatically monitors the processing of such calls by all other LESs in that region. In the event that any anomalies in processing are detected, the NCS will take appropriate action for the establishment of the end-to-end connections. In addition, the monitoring NCS also checks the LES identity contained in the distress priority message and automatically accepts the call if an identity of a non-operational LES has been detected (which may happen due to operator error aboard the vessel in distress).

The distress priority applies not only with respect to satellite channels but also to the automatic routeing of the call to the appropriate rescue authority. Each LES in the system is required to provide reliable telephone and telex interconnection with a rescue co-ordination centre (RCC). These national rescue centres are usually known as associated RCCs. The means of LES-RCC interconnection may vary from country to country and may include use of dedicated lines or public switched networks. Thus, any distress priority request message received at the LES is automatically processed and passed to the associated RCC. Some LESs, due to national considerations, pass distress priority messages to special operators, who are responsible for the subsequent routeing of the call to the appropriate RCC or provide an option which allows the shipboard operator to contact any RCC when a satellite channel has been assigned on the distress priority basis.

The initiation of a distress priority message in most MESs is made simple for vessel crew members by provision of a distress button or code in the MES. On activation of this button, the equipment instantaneously transmits a distress priority alert. This single operation, a push of the distress button provides automatic, direct and assured connection to a competent rescue authority. This avoids the need for the MES operator to select or key the telex or telephone number of the RCC thereby eliminating possible human error. The establishment of this end-to-end connection, being completely automatic and on a priority basis, takes only a few seconds.

The procedure described above is the primary means of ship-to-shore distress alerting in the Inmarsat system. It should be noted, however, that Inmarsat-equipped ships can also contact any RCC of their choice by following the calling procedure for routine calls. In this case, the complete international telephone/telex number has to be selected.

A major benefit of the Inmarsat satellite system is that it eliminates the need for dedicated frequencies to provide for distress and safety communications. Distress messages made through the Inmarsat system use the existing services on a priority basis to ensure an immediate connection.

SHORE-TO-SHIP DISTRESS ALERTING THROUGH THE INMARSAT SafetyNET SYSTEM

The EGC receiver is an integral part of an Inmarsat C MES. This receiver will be dedicated to the enhanced group call (EGC) function which ensures a very high probability of receipt of shore-to-ship distress alert messages. When a distress priority message is received, an audible alarm will sound which can only be reset manually.

Accessing the EGC SafetyNET service by RCCs requires arrangements similar to those needed for shore-to-ship distress alerting to a standard MES. Those RCCs who may be unable to obtain a reliable terrestrial connection to a Land Earth Station can install an Inmarsat MES at the RCC. The RCC could then transmit the distress alert through the MES to a LES where it would be relayed by means of a broadcast over the Inmarsat SafetyNET system.

SEARCH AND RESCUE (SAR) CO-ORDINATING COMMUNICATIONS

For the co-ordination and control of SAR operations, RCCs require communications with the ship in distress as well as with units participating in the operation. The methods and modes of communication (terrestrial, satellite, telephone, telex) used will be governed by the capabilities available onboard the vessel in distress as well as those onboard assisting units. Where some or all are equipped with satellite terminals the advantage of the Inmarsat system for rapid, reliable communications including receipt of Maritime Safety Information (MSI) can be achieved.

A reliable interlinking of RCCs is important for the GMDSS in which a distress message may be received by an RCC thousands of miles away from where the assistance is needed and may not be the RCC best suited to provide the necessary assistance. In these cases prompt relay of the distress message to the appropriate RCC is essential and any communications means, whether landlines, terrestrial radio networks or satellite links, must be used in such circumstances.

To increase the speed and reliability of RCC-to-RCC communications, some RCCs have installed MES providing them with the capability of communicating through the Inmarsat system. This is known as SARNET and these facilities are useful for rapid long-distance interconnection of SAR organisations, especially when dedicated lines or public switched networks are unavailable or unreliable.

ON-SCENE SAR COMMUNICATIONS

On-scene communications are those between the vessel in distress and assisting vessels, and between SAR vessels and the on-scene commander or the co-ordinator of the surface search. These communications are normally short-range communications which will be made on the VHF or MF distress and safety frequencies in the GMDSS. However, vessels fitted with Inmarsat MES could, if necessary, use satellite communications as a supplement to their VHF and MF facilities.

L-BAND SATELLITE EPIRBs

The Inmarsat E system provides global maritime distress alerting services via Inmarsat satellites. Distress alerts transmitted from Inmarsat E Emergency Position Indicating Radio Beacons (EPIRBs) are relayed through Inmarsat satellites to dedicated receiving equipment located at four Land Earth Stations (LESs). These LESs, operating with the Inmarsat E system, are Goonhilly (United Kingdom) which covers the Atlantic Ocean East and West regions satellites; Aussaguel (Germany), which covers the Atlantic Ocean East and Indian Ocean region satellites; Perth (Australia) which covers the Indian Ocean and Pacific Ocean satellites; and Niles Santa Paula and Southbury (USA) covering the Pacific and Atlantic Ocean West.

Each LES is connected to its national rescue authority via a dedicated link. In United Kingdom this is MRCC Falmouth; In Germany it is RCC Bremen; in Australia it is RCC Canberra and in the USA it is the US Coast Guard network. These authorities deal with the emergency themselves or pass the information on to an appropriate RCC, usually the one nearest the source of the distress alert and therefore in the best position to co-ordinate rescue efforts.

Inmarsat E combines the position determination of the Global Positioning System (GPS) with the geostationary satellite technology of the Inmarsat communications system. The use of geostationary satellites greatly increases the speed at which a distress alert can be delivered, as no time is lost waiting for a satellite to appear over the horizon.

Inmarsat transmitters use the L-band range of frequencies specifically allocated for search and rescue maritime communications because they are virtually unaffected by adverse meteorological conditions and interference from other L-band spectrum users.

A distress signal can be triggered manually or automatically when a float-free terminal is submerged. As a minimum, the message contains the identity of the terminal and its position at the time of the alert.

The distress alert transmitted by an EPIRB is received by two Land Earth Stations in each ocean region giving 100 percent duplication for each ocean region in case of outages that may be associated with any of the LESs.

Following reception of the distress alert, it is immediately forwarded automatically to a Maritime Rescue Co-ordination Centre (MRCC), via a direct connection, so that appropriate action can be taken.

The time taken from the transmission of an Inmarsat E EPIRB distress alert to reception at the MRCC is within five minutes and typically under two minutes.

The following features are incorporated into the Inmarsat E Float Free EPIRB system:

- Global Positioning System (GPS) position which is accurate to within 200 metres;
- automatic activation when the EPIRB is released by "Floating Free";
- remote activation and information input from vessels bridge or other manned situation;
- optional Search and Rescue Radar Transponder (SART);
- optional 121·5 MHz locator beacon;
- high intensity, low duty cycle flashing light.

The contents of the distress message are as follows;

- System code (Unique Beacon Identity)
- Position (Latitude, Longitude)
- Time of position up-date
- Nature of distress (either entered manually from a remote control unit (RCU) or as "Sinking" if the EPIRB floats free and is activated automatically
- Course
- Speed
- Time of activation

The size of the Inmarsat E EPIRB is between 220mm and 330mm high (depending on manufacturer and model). The EPIRBs may also be hand held, and thus carried into a survival craft.

Vessels may carry a remote control unit (RCU) on-bridge display showing the status and position reading from the EPIRB. In an emergency, crew members have the option of triggering an alert message and including, via a short code keyboard, additional information on the nature of the emergency. Users of hand-held terminals can input similar information.

Once triggered, terminals will continue transmitting for a minimum of 48 hours unless de-activated manually. Some models also feature a Search And Rescue radar Transponder (SART) beacon to enable rescuers to home in using 3cm (or X-Band) radar once they reach the area of the transmitted position.

In December 2001, Inmarsat introduced an improved version of its Inmarsat E, known as Inmarsat E+. The new Inmarsat E+ EPIRB assures the seafarer that the distress signal sent from the Inmarsat E+ fitted to his vessel has been received at a number of MRCCs, thereby increasing the possibility of a quick rescue and enhancing the will to live.

COSPAS-SARSAT SYSTEM

The COSPAS-SARSAT (COSPAS: Space System for the Search of Vessels in Distress; SARSAT: Search and Rescue Satellite-Aided Tracking) System provides distress alert and location information to search and rescue (SAR) services for aviation, maritime, and land users in distress, with no discrimination and free of charge for the persons in distress. This objective is accomplished through the use of satellite systems which relay or process the transmissions of distress radiobeacons operating on 121·5 MHz[1] or 406 MHz.

COSPAS-SARSAT is a joint international satellite-aided SAR system, established by organizations in Canada, France, Russia, and the United States, which now has over 30 countries and organizations contributing to the operation and management of the system.

Unless, as an alternative, a vessel is provided with a L-band satellite EPIRB operating in sea areas A1, A2 and A3 only, the carriage of a float-free satellite EPIRB operating on the 406 MHz in the Cospas-Sarsat system is required on all SOLAS ships.

1 Some beacons also transmit on 243 MHz, the second harmonic of 121·5 MHz. Since the 243 MHz system operates in the same manner as the 121·5 MHz system, and because not all satellites and ground segment components relay or process the 243 MHz transmissions, future references will only be made to the 243 MHz system as necessary to highlight a difference from the 121·5 MHz system.

BASIC CONCEPT OF THE SYSTEM

The basic COSPAS-SARSAT System concept is given in **Figure 6**. There are at present three types of distress beacons, namely Emergency Locator Transmitters (ELTs) (aviation), EPIRBs (maritime) and Personal Locator Beacons (PLBs) (land). These beacons transmit signals that are detected by COSPAS-SARSAT polar-orbiting and geostationary satellites equipped with suitable receivers/processors. The signals are then relayed to a ground receiving station, termed a Local User Terminal (LUT), which processes the signals. An alert is then relayed, together with location data and other information as available, through a Mission Control Centre (MCC), either to a national RCC, another MCC or to the appropriate SAR authority to initiate SAR activities.

DISTRESS BEACONS

121·5 MHz BEACONS

There are about 600,000 121·5 MHz beacons in use world-wide. These simple inexpensive devices emit a low power continuous analogue signal which includes a sweeping audible tone. The original concept of operation for their use was for all aircraft to routinely monitor the distress frequency bands and report to search and rescue services instances when they heard the distinct audible tone transmitted by distress beacons. The beacon signals would then provide for homing by SAR services and overflight monitoring by aircraft.

These beacons were never designed for detection by satellite and they do not transmit information that can be used by COSPAS-SARSAT to uniquely identify a specific beacon. In fact the COSPAS-SARSAT System finds it difficult, if not impossible, to automatically distinguish between 121·5 MHz distress beacons and other types of transmitters that also operate in the frequency band.

Figure 5a - Basic concept of the L - band satellite EPIRB system

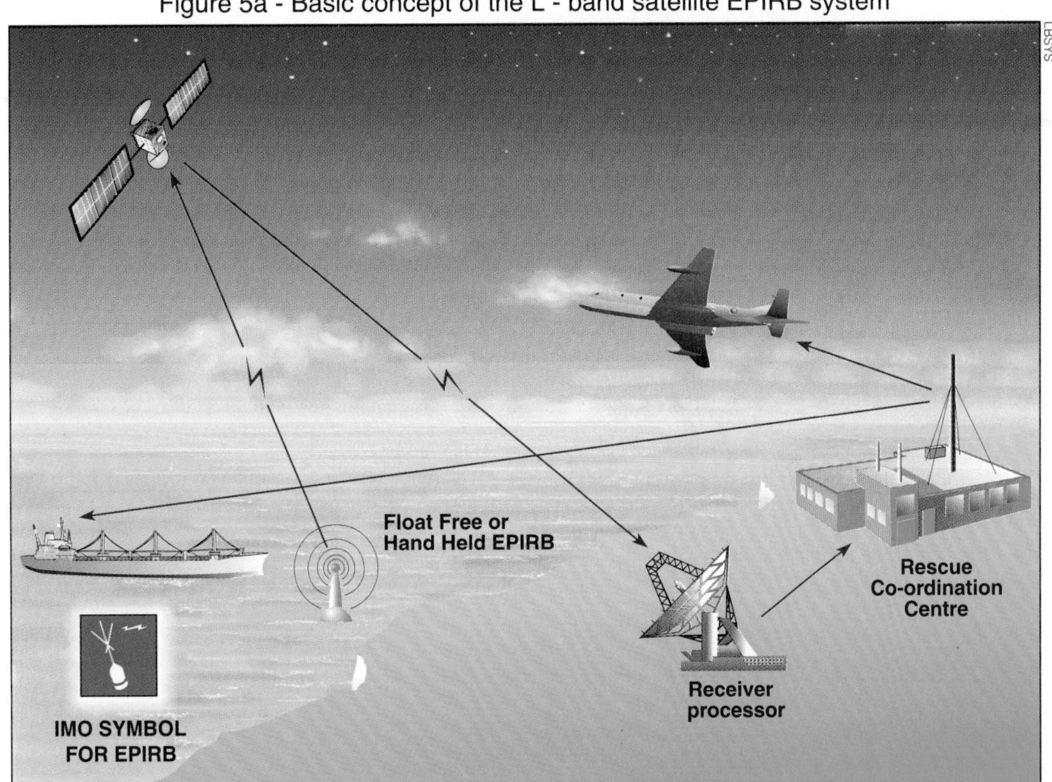

Figure 5b - Inmarsat E L-Band satellite relay stations

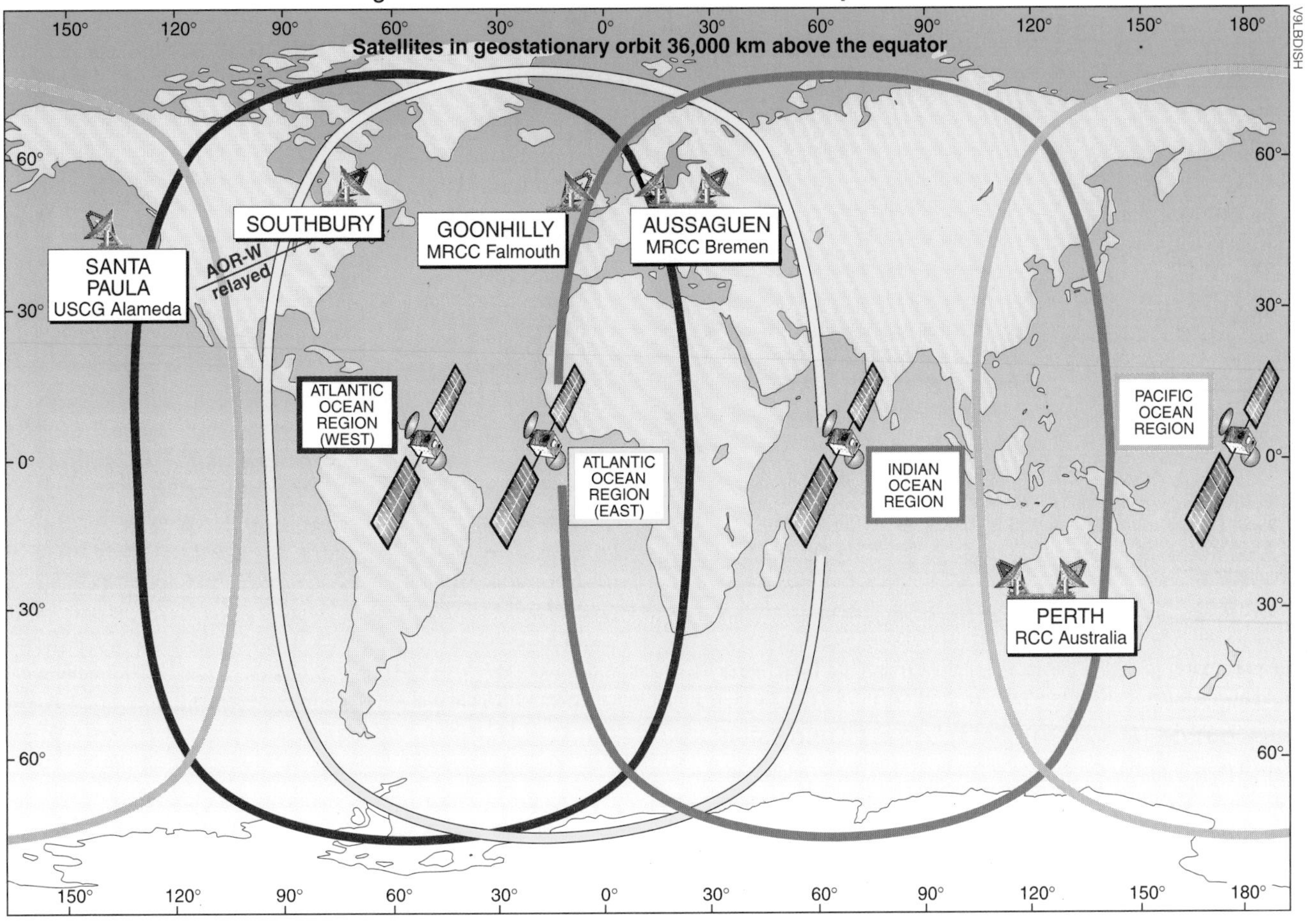

Figure 6 - Basic concept of COSPAS-SARSAT system

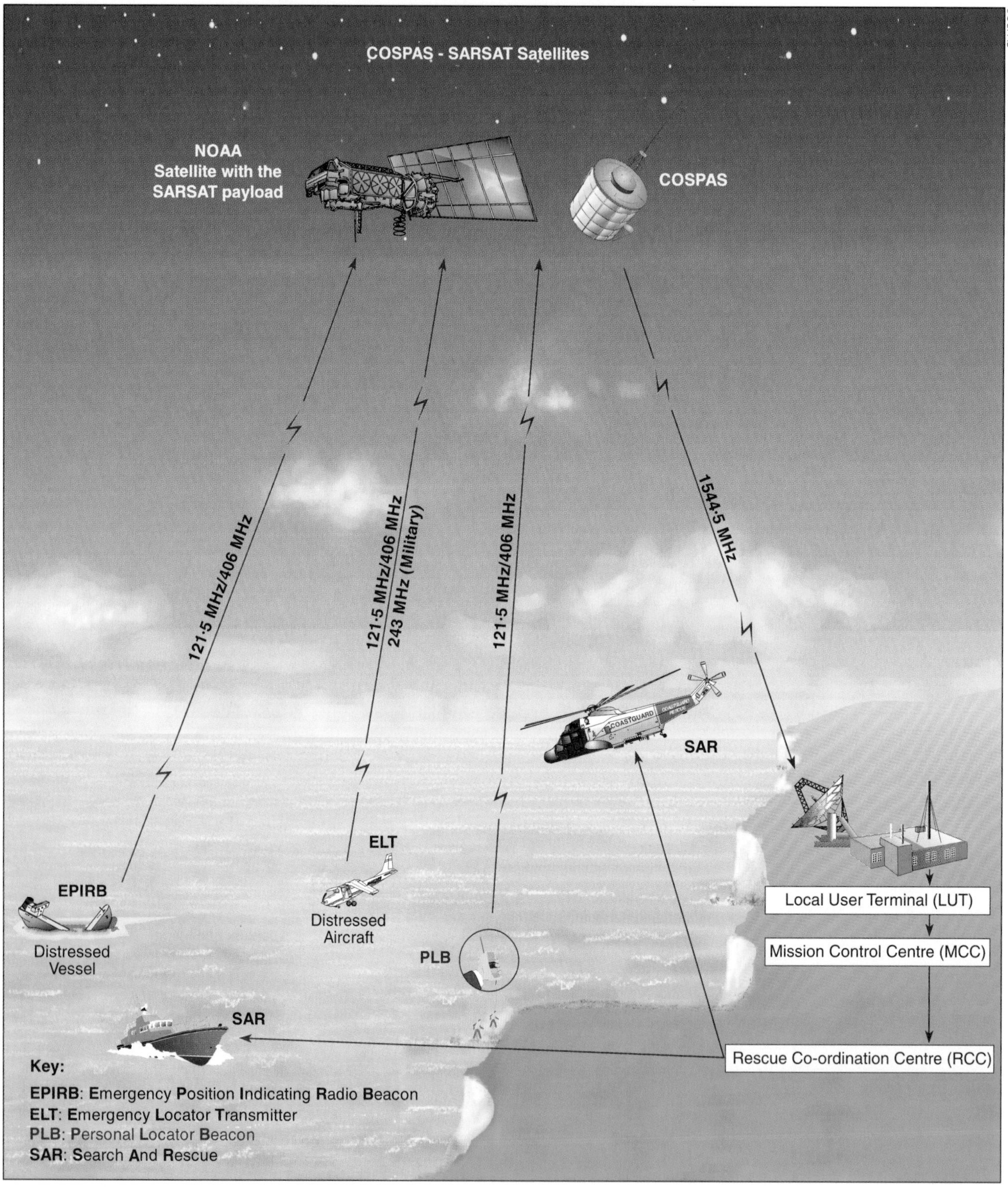

Key:
EPIRB: **E**mergency **P**osition **I**ndicating **R**adio **B**eacon
ELT: **E**mergency **L**ocator **T**ransmitter
PLB: **P**ersonal **L**ocator **B**eacon
SAR: **S**earch **A**nd **R**escue

Most 121·5 MHz beacons are used on aircraft and are required to meet national specifications based upon standards issued by international organisations such as ICAO or the ITU. COSPAS-SARSAT does not maintain its own specifications for 121·5 MHz beacons.

PHASE-OUT OF 121.5/243 MHz SATELLITE ALERTING SERVICES

121·5 MHz beacons are available at low cost, but this outdated technology has serious limitations and cannot be improved. It is the source of a very large number of false alerts and the absence of an automatic capability for identification significantly increases the workload of Rescue Co-ordination Centres (RCCs). This situation has impacted on the efficiency of SAR operations and led to a request by the International Maritime Organization (IMO) for a termination of the satellite processing of 121·5 MHz signals.

In 1999, the Council of the International Civil Aviation Organization (ICAO) adopted amendments to the annexes of the Convention on International Civil Aviation requiring all new aircraft from 2002, and all aircraft from 2005, under the jurisdiction of the ICAO Convention, to carry an Emergency Locator Transmitter (ELT) operating on 406 MHz, and on 121·5 MHz for homing purpose. The ICAO Council also agreed that COSPAS-SARSAT processing of 121·5 MHz ELTs could be discontinued from 2008.

In response to the request of IMO and the decisions of ICAO, COSPAS-SARSAT decided in October 2000 to plan and prepare for the termination of 121·5 MHz satellite alerting services on 1 February 2009. COSPAS-SARSAT has also invited administrations and international organisations to note the planned phase-out date and the recommendations listed in the COSPAS-SARSAT Phase-Out Plan for 121·5/243 MHz Satellite Alerting Services (C/S R.010) with a view to preparing for the termination of these alerting services. (Note: the document C/S R.010 is available for downloading from the COSPAS-SARSAT web site at www.cospas-sarsat.org.)

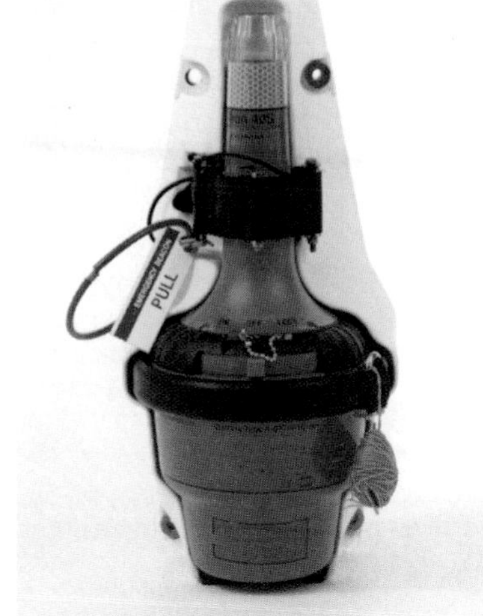

406 MHz EPIRB – www.jotron.com

406 MHz Beacons

In contrast to 121·5 MHz beacons, 406 MHz beacons were specifically designed to be processed by COSPAS-SARSAT satellites. 406 MHz devices transmit a significantly more powerful signal than 121·5 MHz beacons and exhibit extremely stable transmit frequency performance. These two characteristics directly impact upon the system's ability to detect and accurately locate transmitting beacons. The improved performance of 406 MHz satellite EPIRBs is the reason these devices were selected for the GMDSS and included in the 1988 amendments to the 1974 SOLAS Convention. At the end of 2000, there were over 250,000 406 MHz beacons in use world-wide.

406 MHz beacons transmit a 0·5 second burst every 50 seconds. Included in this burst is a digital message which uniquely identifies each beacon thereby enabling the COSPAS-SARSAT System to:

- categorically distinguish between beacon signals and other transmissions (e.g. interference);
- obtain information about the operator of the beacon that might be critical to any rescue mission; and
- uniquely identify and track specific distress events in the presence of several events active simultaneously.

Finally, unlike 121·5 MHz beacons, COSPAS-SARSAT has developed and maintains its own 406 MHz beacon specification which it makes available free of charge to administrations, international organisations, and individuals to use as appropriate. In addition, COSPAS-SARSAT implements a beacon type approval process, in which 406 MHz beacon models are tested at approved test facilities to confirm their conformance to the specifications. Upon successfully completing all these tests, COSPAS-SARSAT awards the beacon model a type approval certificate. It is this certificate that assures the public and administrations that the beacon design/type has been proven to work with the system.

406 MHz BEACON REGISTRATION (Refer to UK Section on page 153)

Because a beacon may be transmitting from anywhere in the world each beacon should be registered whereby the serial number of the beacon, together with any other relevant information, is included in a suitable registration database. Information encoded in the 406 MHz beacon message includes information on the specific databases location. It is vitally important that the registration authorities are informed promptly of any changes affecting the information given on the registration cards, e.g., change of vessel, change of ownership, loss, theft etc.

COSPAS-SARSAT SPACE SEGMENT

COSPAS-SARSAT uses search and rescue (SAR) instruments on satellites in Low-altitude Earth Orbit (LEO) and Geostationary Earth Orbit (GEO). These space segments are known respectively as LEOSAR and GEOSAR. Satellites in the LEOSAR system relay 121·5 MHz signals for ground processing. The 406 MHz beacon messages are partially processed on board the LEOSAR satellites, then the data are directly transmitted on the satellite downlink as well as being stored on board for re-transmission in the global mode[1]. Satellites in the GEOSAR system only relay 406 MHz transmissions for ground processing.

1 SARSAT satellites are also equipped with a 406 MHz repeater instrument which relays beacon signals directly for ground processing in same manner as for 121·5 MHz.

LEOSAR SPACE SEGMENT

The nominal LEOSAR system configuration comprises four satellites, two COSPAS and two SARSAT. Russia supplies two COSPAS satellites placed in near-polar orbits from 700 to 1,000 km altitude and equipped with SAR instrumentation at 121·5 MHz and 406 MHz. The USA supplies two NOAA meteorological satellites of the SARSAT system placed in sun-synchronous, near-polar orbits at about 850 km altitude, and equipped with SAR instrumentation at 121·5 MHz and 406 MHz supplied by Canada and France.

Each satellite makes a complete orbit of the earth around the poles in about 100 minutes, travelling at a velocity of 7 km per second. The satellite views a "swath" of the earth over 6,000 km wide as it circles the globe, giving an instantaneous "field of view" about the size of a continent. When viewed from the earth, the satellite crosses the sky in about 15 minutes, depending on the maximum elevation angle of the particular pass. The satellites' low-altitude results in a low uplink power requirement, a pronounced Doppler shift, and short intervals between successive passes. The near-polar orbit results in complete world coverage over a period of time.

The satellites of the LEOSAR space segment consist of:

- a 121·5 MHz repeater unit (SARR) on COSPAS satellites and a 121·5, 243 and 406 MHz repeater unit on SARSAT satellites designed for re-transmission of distress signals to a ground receiving station located within its current footprint; and
- a receiver-processor and memory unit (SARP) on COSPAS and SARSAT satellites designed to receive, process and store signals received on 406 MHz for re-transmission directly to a ground station in its footprint, or to any other station located around the world.

GEOSAR SPACE SEGMENT

The GEOSAR space segment is composed of geostationary satellites with the capability to relay the transmissions of COSPAS-SARSAT 406 MHz beacons. Geostationary satellites orbit at an altitude of 36,000 km, with an orbit period of 24 hours, thus appearing fixed relative to the Earth, at approximately 0 degrees latitude (i.e., over the Equator).

GEOSAR payloads are available on board geostationary satellites provided by the USA and India. EUMETSAT (Eur.met.org) satellite MSG-1 was launched in August 2002 and is under post-launch test. Russia and EUMETSAT (European Meteorological Satellite Organization) also have plans for equipping geostationary satellites with 406 MHz SAR payloads in the future.

The 406 MHz GEOSAR system currently comprises:

- 406 MHz repeaters onboard three geostationary satellites, plus three spare; and
- Nine ground receiving stations (GEOLUTs) in eight countries, linked to the COSPAS-SARSAT MCC network for the distribution of GEOSAR alert data.

A single geostationary satellite provides GEOSAR uplink coverage of about one third of the globe, except for polar regions. Therefore, three geostationary satellites equally spaced in longitude can provide continuous coverage of all areas of the globe between approximately 70° North and 70° South. The coverage area of the COSPAS-SARSAT GEOSAR satellites and the location of the GEOLUTs are shown at **Figure 7**.

Combined 406 MHz LEOSAR-GEOSAR System Concept

The major advantage of the 406 MHz system is the provision of global Earth coverage using a limited number of polar-orbiting satellites in low-altitude Earth orbit. However, the use of satellites in low-altitude Earth orbit does not permit, as noted above, continuous coverage. This results in possible delays in the reception of the alert. By the nature of the polar orbits, the waiting time for detection by the LEOSAR system is greater in equatorial regions than at higher latitudes. In contrast, geostationary satellites provide continuous coverage of a large area centered on the equator with a near-immediate alerting capability.

Access to the geostationary satellite can be masked due to ground relief or obstructions, particularly on land, at high latitudes, and GEOSAR satellites do not provide coverage of the polar regions. On the other hand, LEOSAR satellites will eventually come into visibility of any beacon at the surface of the Earth, whatever the terrain and the obstructions which may mask the distress transmission. Therefore, in terms of coverage, the specific characteristics of LEOSAR and GEOSAR systems are clearly complementary. See **Figure 8** for a depiction of the LEOSAR-GEOSAR satellite systems.

LOCAL USER TERMINALS (LUTs) AND MISSION CONTROL CENTRES (MCCs)

LEOSAR Local User Terminals (LEOLUTs)

The configuration and capabilities of each LEOLUT vary to meet the specific requirements of countries, but the COSPAS and SARSAT satellite downlink signal formats ensure inter-operability between the various satellites and all LUTs meeting COSPAS-SARSAT specifications. All COSPAS-SARSAT LEOLUTs must, as a minimum, process the output of the 406 MHz receiver-processor system (SARP) which provides the 406 MHz global coverage.

For the 121·5 MHz signal, each transmission is detected and the Doppler shift information calculated. The Doppler shift (using the relative motion between the satellite and the beacon) is used to locate beacons in the LEOSAR system. The carrier frequency transmitted by the beacon is reasonably stable during the period of mutual beacon-satellite visibility, and the low-altitude near-polar orbit of the LEOSAR satellites optimize the Doppler location process. A similar type of processing is also applied to the 406 MHz signals in the 406 MHz repeater band (SARR) which can be processed by LEOLUTs either separately or combined with the 406 MHz SARP data.

Processing of 406 MHz SARP data is relatively straightforward since the Doppler shifted frequency is measured and time-tagged on-board the spacecraft. All 406 MHz data received from the satellite memory on each pass can be processed within a few minutes of pass completion.

GEOSAR Local User Terminals (GEOLUTs)

GEOLUTs receive and process distress alerts from 406 MHz beacons relayed by the geostationary satellites of the GEOSAR system and provide permanent monitoring of the frequency band.

Almost as soon as a beacon is activated in the monitored GEOSAR satellite coverage area, it can be detected by the LUT. As there is no relative movement between a transmitting beacon and the satellite, it is not possible to use the Doppler effect to calculate the beacon position. However, when location information provided by external or internal navigation devices is included in the digital message of a 406 MHz beacon, this position data can be sent with the alert message to the MCC for re-transmission to the appropriate search and rescue point of contact (SPOC).

Mission Control Centres (MCCs)

MCCs have been set up in most of those countries or organizations operating at least one LUT. Their main functions are to:

- collect, store and sort the data from LUTs and other MCCs;
- provide data exchange within the COSPAS-SARSAT system; and
- distribute alert and location data to associated RCCs or SPOCs.

MCCs in the system are interconnected through appropriate networks for the distribution of system information and alert data.

SEARCH AND RESCUE RADAR TRANSPONDER (SART)

SART – www.jotron.com

INTRODUCTION

A Search And Rescue radar Transponder (SART) is the main means in the GMDSS for locating ships in distress or their survival craft. The SART operates in the 9 GHz frequency band and generates a series of response signals on being interrogated by any ordinary 9 GHz shipborne radar or suitable airborne radar. No modification is required to vessels' radar equipment. SARTs can be either portable for use onboard vessel or carrying to survival craft, permanently installed on the vessel and in the survival craft or operate in a float-free position. They may also be incorporated into a float-free satellite EPIRB.

OPERATIONAL AND TECHNICAL CHARACTERISTICS

The SART can be activated manually or automatically when placed into the water so that it will thereafter respond when interrogated.

When activated in a distress situation, a SART responds to radar interrogation by transmitting a swept frequency signal which generates as a line of 12 blip code on a radar screen outward from the SART's position along its line of bearing. Displayed on the Plan Position Indicator (PPI), the spacing between each pair of dots will be 0·6 nautical miles. In order to distinguish the SART from other responses it is preferable to use a radar scale between 6 and 12 n miles, this will assist in differentiating between the SART and other responses. As the

Figure 7 - 406 MHz GEOSAR Satellite Coverage and GEOLUTs

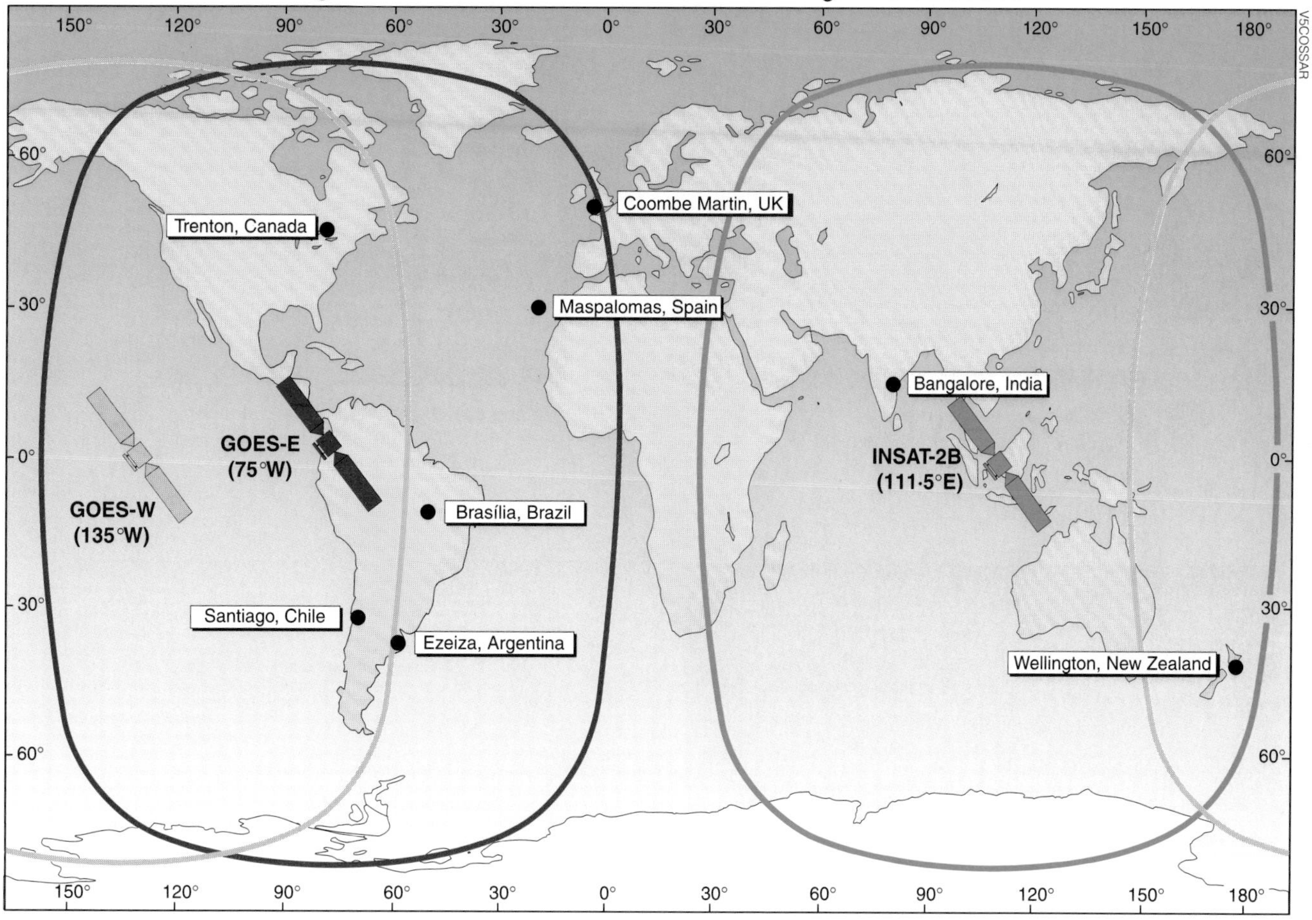

V5COSSAR
Trenton, Canada
Coombe Martin, UK
Maspalomas, Spain
Bangalore, India
Brasília, Brazil
Santiago, Chile
Ezeiza, Argentina
Wellington, New Zealand
GOES-W
(135°W)
GOES-E
(75°W)
INSAT-2B
(111·5°E)

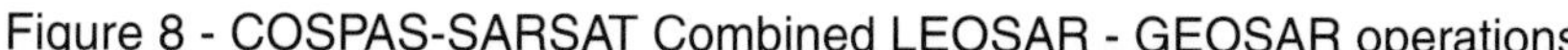

Figure 8 - COSPAS-SARSAT Combined LEOSAR - GEOSAR operations

POLAR
SARSAT
COSPAS
GOES-E
INSAT-2B
GOES-W
COSPAS
SARSAT

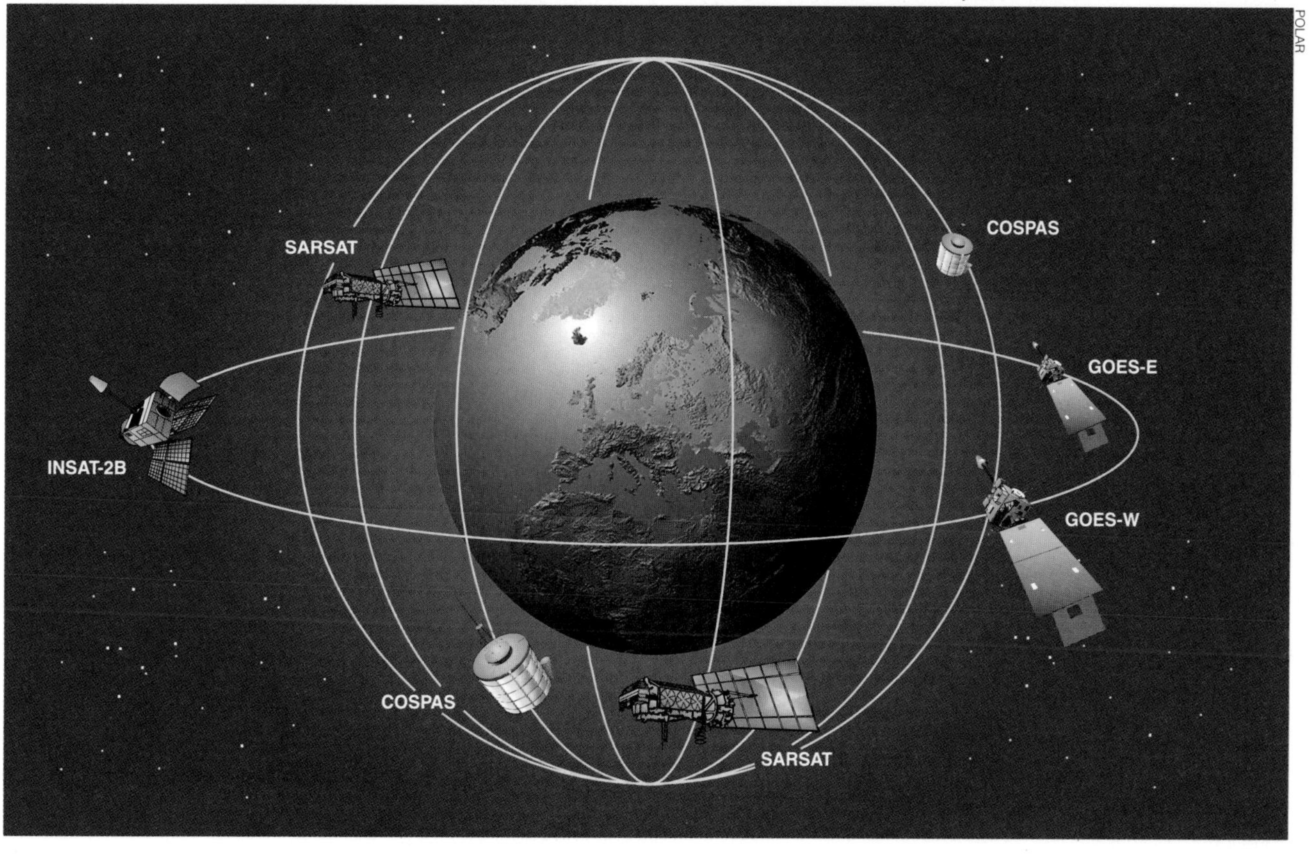

Figure 9 - Basic concept of the Search and Rescue Radar Transponder (SART)

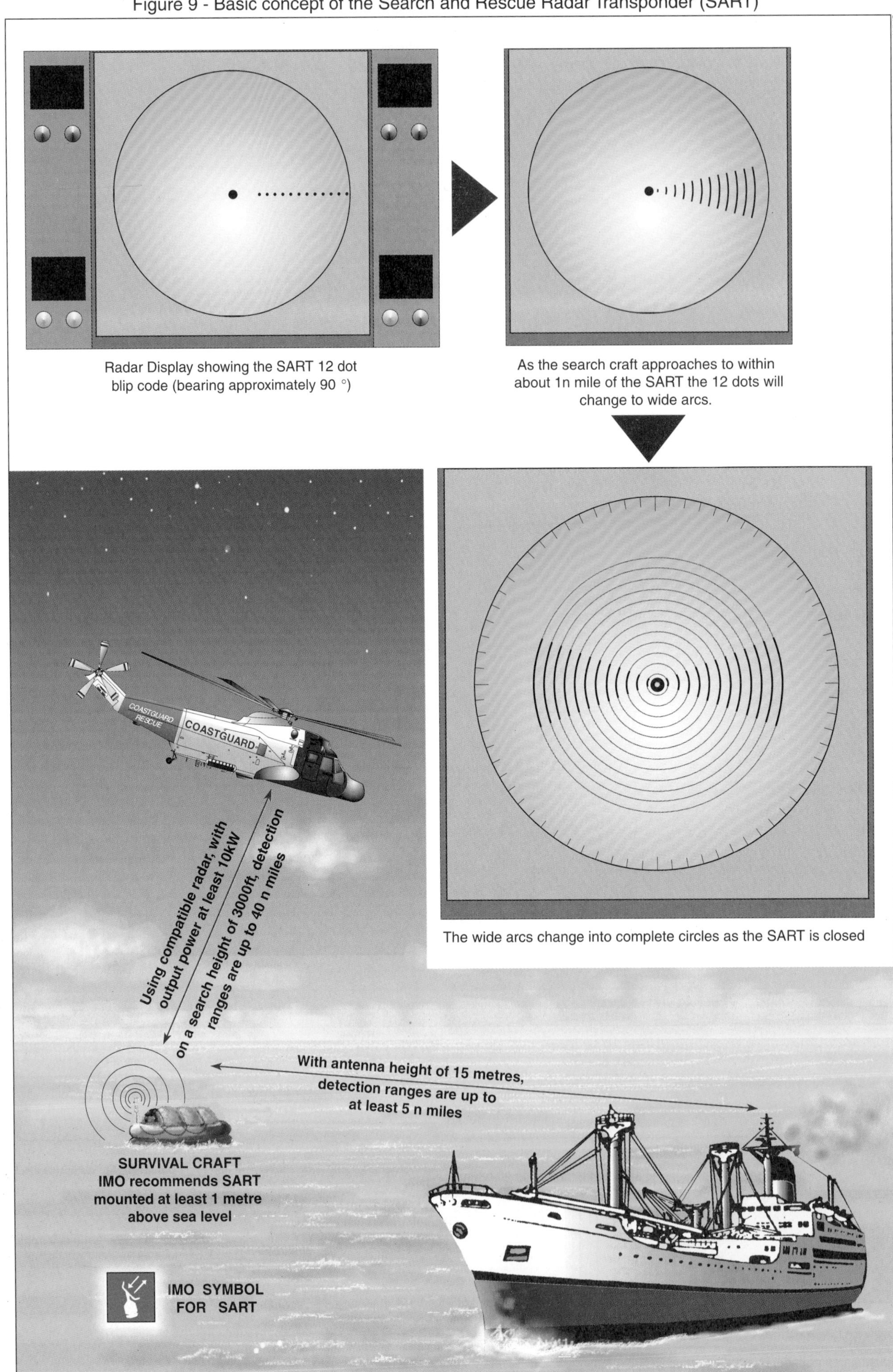

search craft approaches to within about 1 n mile of the SART, the blip dots will change into wide arcs, and even become complete circles as the SART is closed and becomes continually triggered. This is a useful warning to the search craft to slow down! This distinctive and unique radar signal is easily recognized and is therefore much easier to spot than a single echo such as from a radar reflector. Moreover, the fact that the SART is actually a transmitter means that the return pulses can be as strong as echoes received from much larger objects. Any radar bandwidth of less than 5 MHz will attenuate the SART signal slightly, so it is preferable to use a medium bandwidth to ensure optimum detection of the SART. The specific Radar Operating Manual should be consulted about the particular radar parameters and bandwidth selection.

The SART also provides a visual or audible indication of its correct operation and will also inform survivors when it is interrogated by a radar.

The SART should have sufficient battery capacity to operate in the stand-by condition for 96 hours followed by a minimum 8 hours of transmission while being interrogated by a radar. It should also be able to operate under ambient temperatures of -20°C to + 55°C.

A SART built to the latest specifications will have excellent receiver sensitivity, and will detect the high power pulses from a search radar at a much greater range than it's relatively weak return pulses will be detected by the radar. The limiting range is therefore determined by the return path.

Three main factors will affect the range at which a SART will be detected on a ship's radar screen:

1. THE TYPE OF RADAR USED, AND HOW IT IS OPERATED

   Clearly, some radars are better than others. Larger vessels will have higher gain antennae, set higher above sea level. The radar receiver performance is also very important and should be optimised by following the procedures described in paragraphs 5 and 6 in the **Safety of Navigation Circular 197** reproduced below.

2. THE WEATHER CONDITIONS

   A flat calm will affect performance due to 'multi-path' propagation - radar pulses being reflected from the surface of the sea.

   High waves may result in reception at greater distances, due to occasional elevation of both radar and SART; however, detection will be sporadic, due to masking of the signal in the troughs.

   Elimination of sea and rain clutter will depend on the radar used, and the skill of the operator, as for normal radar operations.

3. THE MOUNTING OF THE SART ON THE SURVIVAL CRAFT

   The mounting of the SART is the one factor over which the SART user has some control. For maximum range an unobstructed mounting as high as possible is required.

   The IMO Recommended Performance Standard for the SART calls for a range of "up to at least 5 nautical miles", for a SART mounted 1m above sea level. This assumes a search radar complying with IMO requirements, with its antenna 15m above sea level. Tests have shown the importance of maintaining the SART antenna height of at least 1m above sea level; the following results which give some indication on the degrading of the detection range, were obtained with a SART in a survival craft:

   a. SART lying flat on the floor — range 1·8 n miles
   b. SART standing upright on the floor — range 2·5 n miles
   c. SART floating in the water — range 2·0 n miles

   Survivors are advised not to deploy a SART and a radar reflector on the same survival craft because the reflector may obscure the SART.

   A well mounted SART in moderate weather conditions is capable of giving a detection range of over 10 n miles to a large vessel radar. A poorly mounted SART, perhaps operated inside a liferaft or floating in the sea, may provide little better than visual search range to a small fishing boat radar.

   Line-of-sight problems are much less of a problem for airborne detection of SARTs. With the increased sensitivity of the latest SARTs, compatible radars should have no problem in picking up SARTs at ranges up to 40 n miles, given an initial search height of 3000 ft.

Safety of Navigation Circular 197

OPERATION OF MARINE RADAR FOR SART DETECTION

WARNING: A SART WILL ONLY RESPOND TO AN X-BAND (3 CM) RADAR. IT WILL NOT BE SEEN ON AN S-BAND (10 CM) RADAR.

INTRODUCTION

1. A Search and Rescue Transponder (SART) may be triggered by any X-Band (3 cm) radar within a range of approximately 8 n miles. Each radar pulse received causes it to transmit a response which is swept repetitively across the complete radar frequency band. When interrogated, it first sweeps rapidly (0·4 µsec) through the band before beginning a relatively slow sweep (7·5 µsec) through the band back to the starting frequency. This process is repeated for a total of twelve complete cycles. At some point in each sweep, the SART frequency will match that of the interrogating radar and be within the pass band of the radar receiver. If the SART is within range, the frequency match during each of the 12 slow sweeps will produce a response on the radar display, thus a line of 12 dots equally spaced by about 0·64 n miles will be shown.

2. When the range to the SART is reduced to about 1 n mile, the radar display may show also the 12 responses generated during the fast sweeps. These additional dot responses, which also are equally spaced by 0·64 n miles, will be interspersed with the original line of 12 dots. They will appear slightly weaker and smaller than the original dots.

RADAR RANGE SCALE

3. When looking for a SART it is preferable to use either the 6 or 12 n mile range scale. This is because the total displayed length of the SART response of 12 (or 24) dots may extend approximately 9·5 n miles beyond the position of the SART and it is necessary to see a number of response dots to distinguish the SART from other responses.

SART RANGE ERRORS

4. When responses from only the 12 low frequency sweeps are visible (when the SART is at a range greater than about 1 n mile), the position at which the first dot is displayed may be as much as 0·64 n miles beyond the true position of the SART. When the range closes so that the fast sweep responses are seen also, the first of these will be no more than 150 metres beyond the true position.

RADAR BANDWIDTH

5. This is normally matched to the radar pulse length and is usually switched with the range scale and the associated pulse length. Narrow bandwidths of 3-5 MHz are used with long pulses on long range scales and wide bandwidths of 10–25 MHz with short pulses on short ranges.

6. A radar bandwidth of less than 5 MHz will attenuate the SART signal slightly, so it is preferable to use a medium bandwidth to ensure optimum detection of the SART. The Radar Operating Manual should be consulted about the particular radar parameters and bandwidth selection.

RADAR SIDE LOBES

7. As the SART is approached, side lobes from the radar antenna may show the SART responses as a series of arcs or concentric rings. These can be removed by the use of the anti-clutter sea control although it may be operationally useful to observe the side lobes as they may be easier to detect in clutter conditions and also they will confirm that the SART is near to own ship.

DETUNING THE RADAR

8. To increase the visibility of the SART in clutter conditions, the radar may be detuned to reduce the clutter without reducing the SART response. Radars with automatic frequency control may not permit manual detune of the equipment. Care should be taken in operating the radar in the detuned condition as other wanted navigational and anti-collision information may be removed. The tuning should be returned to normal operation as soon as possible.

GAIN

9. For maximum range SART detection the normal gain setting for long range detection should be used i.e., with a light background noise speckle visible.

ANTI-CLUTTER SEA CONTROL

10. For optimum range SART detection this control should be set to the minimum. Care should be exercised as wanted targets in sea clutter may be obscured. Note also that in clutter conditions the first few dots of the SART response may not be detectable, irrespective of the setting of the anti-clutter sea control. In this case, the position of the SART may be estimated by measuring 9·5 n miles from the furthest dot back towards own ship.

11. Some sets have automatic/manual anti-clutter sea control facilities. Because the way in which the automatic sea control functions may vary from one radar manufacturer to another, the operator is advised to use manual control initially until the SART has been detected. The effect of auto sea control on the SART response can then be compared with manual control.

ANTI-CLUTTER RAIN CONTROL

12. This should be used normally (i.e. to break up areas of rain) when trying to detect a SART response which, being a series of dots, is not affected by the action of the anti-clutter rain circuitry. Note that Racon responses, which are often in the form of a long flash, will be affected by the use of this control.

13. Some sets have automatic/manual anti-clutter rain control facilities. Because the way in which the automatic rain control functions may vary from one radar manufacturer to another, the operator is advised to use manual initially until the SART has been detected. The effect of the auto rain control on the SART response can then be compared with manual control.

NOTE:

The automatic rain and sea clutter controls may be combined in a single “auto-clutter” control, in which case the operator is advised to use the manual controls initially until the SART has been detected, before assessing the effect of auto.

DISTRESS COMMUNICATIONS & FALSE ALERTS

PART A - DISTRESS COMMUNICATIONS

After any GMDSS equipment has been installed, the necessary operating instructions should be given to the appropriate personnel, specifically pointing out operating procedures for the equipment in question. It is important that operating instructions should be as clear and precise as possible in order that they are easy to understand.

Radio equipment used for transmitting distress alerts should be so designed that it should not be possible to transmit a distress alert unless the distress button is deliberately depressed. It is strongly recommended that personnel have full knowledge of the GMDSS and the consequences of transmitting a false alert. To reduce the chance of false alerts, routine testing of GMDSS equipment should only be undertaken under the direct supervision of the person responsible for communications.

To take maximum advantage of GMDSS masters should ensure that all crew members who may be required to send a distress alert are instructed and knowledgable in the operation of all relevant radio equipment on the vessel. Such instructions should also be given periodically onboard the vessel to all relevant crew members by the person responsible for communications.

The following diagram could form the basis for the standard procedures for distress message routeing procedures, this may be displayed or be readily available at the control position for the radio installations.

Figure 10 - GMDSS operating guidance for small craft in distress situations

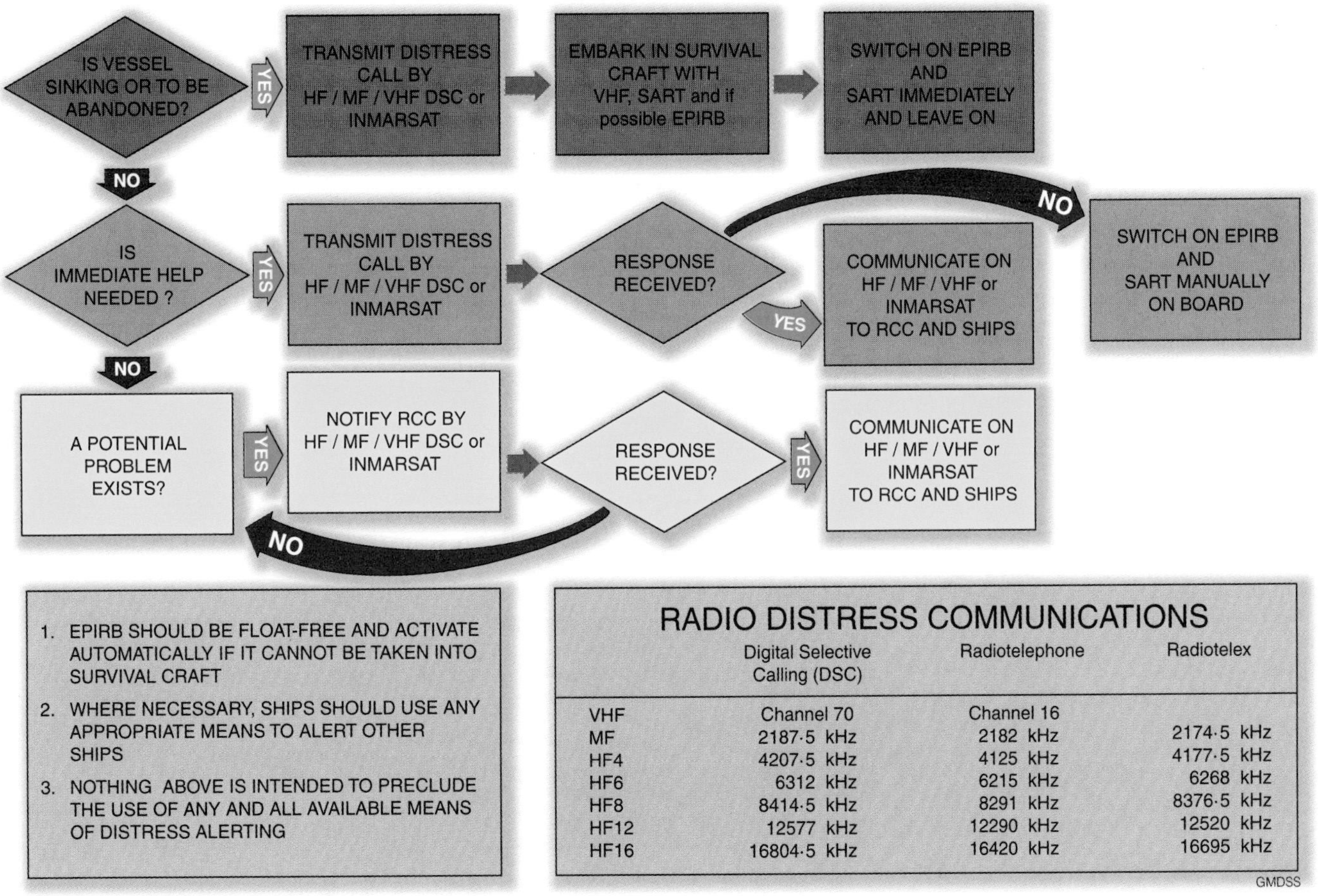

IS VESSEL SINKING OR TO BE ABANDONED?
YES
TRANSMIT DISTRESS CALL BY HF / MF / VHF DSC or INMARSAT
EMBARK IN SURVIVAL CRAFT WITH VHF, SART and if possible EPIRB
SWITCH ON EPIRB AND SART IMMEDIATELY AND LEAVE ON
NO
IS IMMEDIATE HELP NEEDED ?
YES
TRANSMIT DISTRESS CALL BY HF / MF / VHF DSC or INMARSAT
RESPONSE RECEIVED?
NO
SWITCH ON EPIRB AND SART MANUALLY ON BOARD
YES
COMMUNICATE ON HF / MF / VHF or INMARSAT TO RCC AND SHIPS
NO
A POTENTIAL PROBLEM EXISTS?
YES
NOTIFY RCC BY HF / MF / VHF DSC or INMARSAT
RESPONSE RECEIVED?
YES
COMMUNICATE ON HF / MF / VHF or INMARSAT TO RCC AND SHIPS
NO

1. EPIRB SHOULD BE FLOAT-FREE AND ACTIVATE AUTOMATICALLY IF IT CANNOT BE TAKEN INTO SURVIVAL CRAFT
2. WHERE NECESSARY, SHIPS SHOULD USE ANY APPROPRIATE MEANS TO ALERT OTHER SHIPS
3. NOTHING ABOVE IS INTENDED TO PRECLUDE THE USE OF ANY AND ALL AVAILABLE MEANS OF DISTRESS ALERTING

RADIO DISTRESS COMMUNICATIONS

	Digital Selective Calling (DSC)	Radiotelephone	Radiotelex
VHF	Channel 70	Channel 16	
MF	2187·5 kHz	2182 kHz	2174·5 kHz
HF4	4207·5 kHz	4125 kHz	4177·5 kHz
HF6	6312 kHz	6215 kHz	6268 kHz
HF8	8414·5 kHz	8291 kHz	8376·5 kHz
HF12	12577 kHz	12290 kHz	12520 kHz
HF16	16804·5 kHz	16420 kHz	16695 kHz

GMDSS

These procedures are intended for guidance only and may be amended to suit the specific equipment available, the diagram should be continuously updated in line with the latest GMDSS recommendations. Particular attention should be given to Note 3 in the above example.

Distress Relays and Acknowledgements have the same priority as the original Alert and must only be sent on the Master's authority.

Ships must not send DSC Relays for DSC Alerts received on MF and VHF.

Relays of HF Alerts by DSC must be initiated manually, and must be sent only to coast stations, after a minimum delay of 5 minutes.

EXTRACT FROM IMO COMSAR/CIRC.17

Use of GMDSS equipment for transmission of general radiocommunications is one of the functional requirements in SOLAS chapter IV, regulation 4. Regular use of GMDSS equipment helps to develop operator competency and ensure equipment availability. If ships use other radiocommunication systems for the bulk of their business communications, they should adopt a regular programme of sending selected traffic or test messages via GMDSS equipment to ensure operator competency and equipment availability and to help reduce the incidence of false alerts. This policy extends to all GMDSS equipment suites including Digital Selective Calling on VHF, MF and HF, to the Inmarsat A, B and C systems, and to any duplicated VHF and long-range communications facilities.

PART B - FALSE ALERTS

False alerts caused by the inadvertent or incorrect operation of GMDSS equipment can put a significant burden on Search and Rescue Centres. The chances of false alerts coinciding with an actual distress situation are very real and as a consequence, search and rescue resources could be delayed in responding to a real distress.

Most false alerts are caused as a result of human error; the flow chart below is intended as guidance for use in the event of either a known or suspected false alert having been transmitted.

As well as the problems caused by the inadvertent transmission of an alert on DSC, Inmarsat C and by 406 MHz EPIRBs, the acknowledgement of a DSC distress alert on 2187·5 kHz can lead to the broadcast of a large number of unnecessary DSC calls. The following procedures should therefore be followed.

MF

a. A vessel operating in an A2 Sea Area which receives a MF DSC distress alert on 2187·5 kHz should not transmit a DSC acknowledgement, notwithstanding any prompt on the DSC equipment; it can be assumed the alert will have been heard and acknowledged by a coast station (this might not be obvious to the receiving vessel if it is beyond the reception range of the coast station).

Figure 11 – Procedures False Alert cancellations

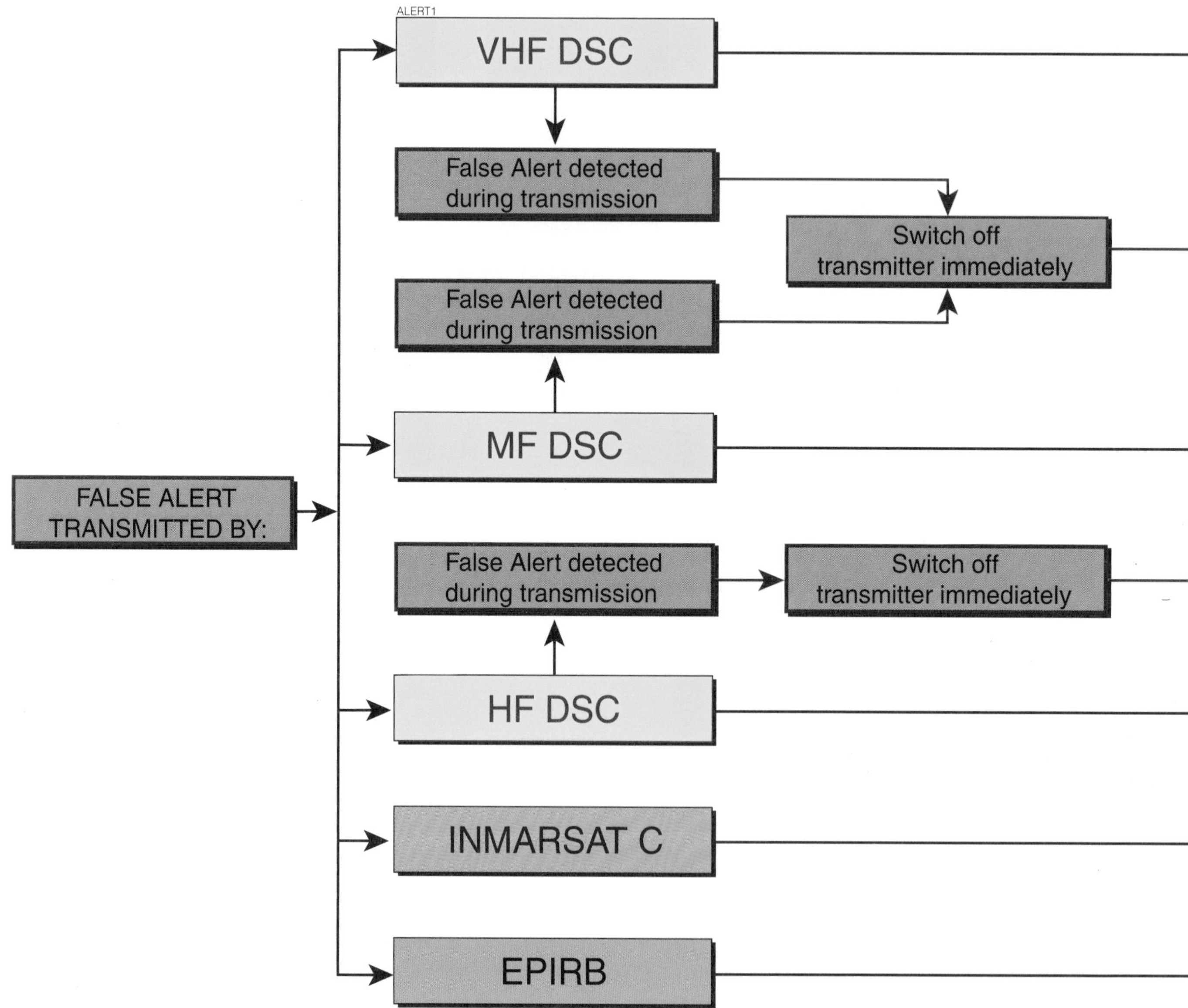

NOTE: Any vessel may use any frequency in any system to inform the appropriate authorities that a false alert has been transmitted and should be cancelled.

Therefore, following receipt of a DSC distress alert or distress relay, radio operators should listen on 2182 kHz for further distress traffic and (subject to the master's instructions) acknowledge using RT. Assistance should then be rendered as required and appropriate.

b. A ship operating outside of an A2 Sea Area which receives a distress alert which is, beyond doubt, in its vicinity, should send an acknowledgement as soon as possible using RT on 2182 kHz. If further DSC distress alerts are heard from the same source, a DSC acknowledgement may be sent. RCCs should be informed through a coast radio station or CES and assistance rendered as required and appropriate.

HF

a. On receipt of an HF DSC distress alert a vessel should not transmit an acknowledgement. Radio operators must listen out on the RT and NBDP distress and safety traffic frequencies associated with the distress and safety calling frequencies on which the alert was received.

b. If subsequent DSC distress alerts are received, or it is clear there has been no acknowledgement by a coast radio station, the vessel must relay the distress alert to the appropriate coast radio station or RCC, **NOT TO ALL STATIONS**.

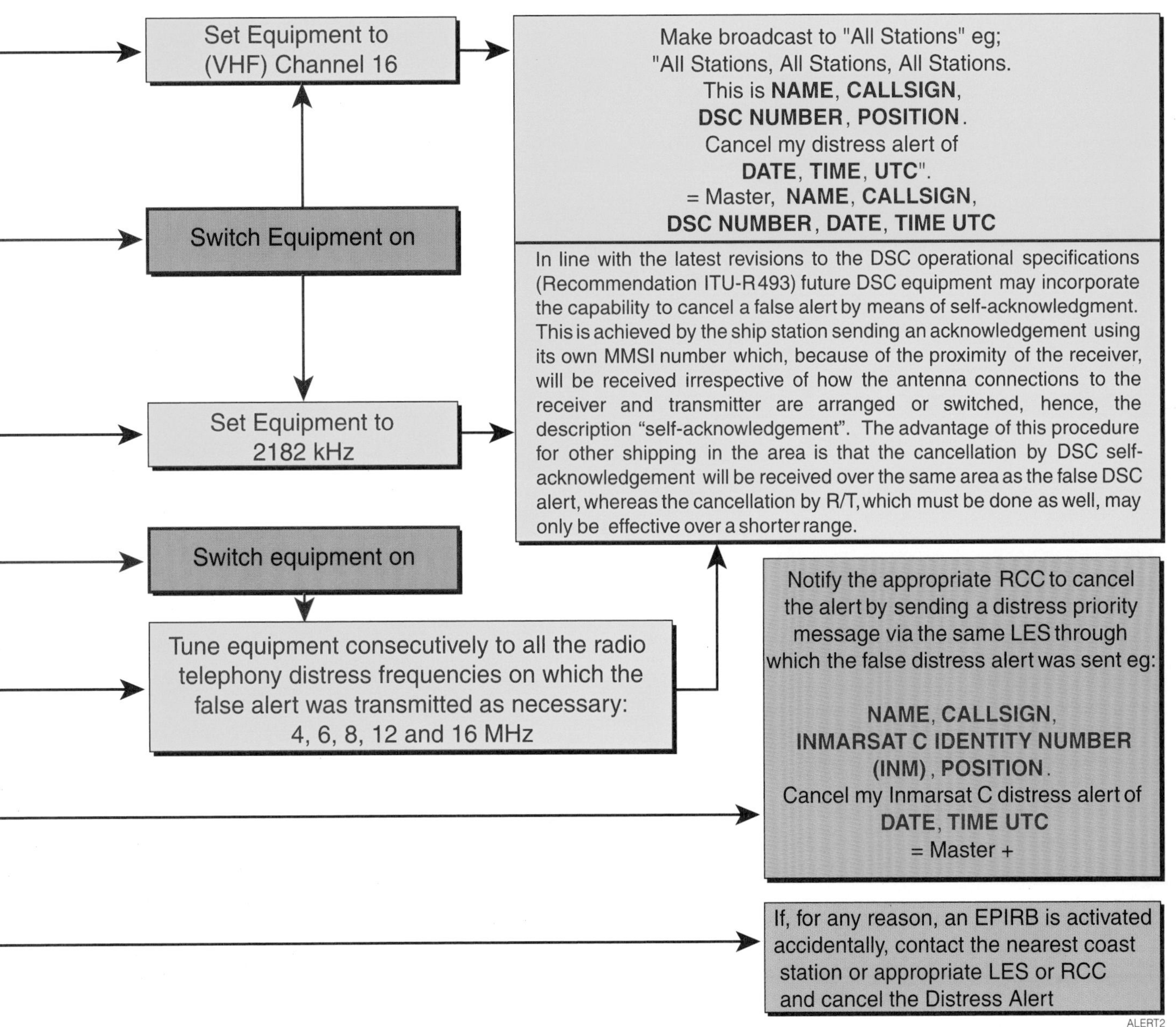

No action will normally be taken against any vessel or mariner for reporting and cancelling a false distress alert. However, in view of the serious consequences of false alerts, and the strict ban on their transmission, Governments may prosecute in cases of repeated violations.

EXTRACTS FROM IMO GUIDELINES FOR AVOIDING FALSE DISTRESS ALERTS

COMPANIES, MASTERS AND SEAFARERS SHOULD, AS APPROPRIATE:

1. ensure that all GMDSS certificated personnel responsible for sending a distress alert have been instructed about, and are competent to operate, the particular radio equipment on the ship;
2. ensure that the person or persons responsible for communications during distress incidents give the necessary instructions and information to all crew members on how to use GMDSS equipment to send a distress alert;
3. ensure that as part of each "abandon ship" drill, instruction is given on how emergency equipment should be used to provide GMDSS functions;
4. ensure that GMDSS equipment testing is only undertaken under the supervision of the person responsible for communications during distress incidents;
5. ensure that GMDSS equipment testing or drills are never allowed to cause false distress alerts;
6. ensure that encoded identities of satellite EPIRBs, which are used by SAR personnel responding to emergencies, are properly registered in a database accessible 24h a day or automatically provided to SAR authorities (masters should confirm that their EPIRBs have been registered with such a database, to help SAR services identify the ship in the event of distress and rapidly obtain other information which will enable them to respond appropriately);
7. ensure that EPIRB, Inmarsat and DSC registration data is immediately updated if there is any change in information relating to the ship such as owner, name or flag, and that the necessary action is taken to reprogram the ship's new data in the GMDSS equipment concerned;
8. ensure that, for new ships, positions for installing EPIRBs are considered at the earliest stage of ship design and construction;
9. ensure that satellite EPIRBs are carefully installed in accordance with manufacturers' instructions and using qualified personnel (sometimes satellite EPIRBs are damaged or broken due to improper handling or installation. They must be installed in a location that will enable them to float free and automatically activate if the ship sinks. Care must be taken to ensure that they are not tampered with or accidentally activated. If the coding has to be changed or the batteries serviced, manufacturers requirements must be strictly followed. There have been cases where EPIRB lanyards were attached to the ship so that the EPIRB could not float free; lanyards are only to be used by survivors for securing the EPIRB to a survival craft or person in water);
10. ensure that EPIRBs are not activated if assistance is already immediately available (EPIRBs are intended to call for assistance if the ship is unable to obtain help by other means, and to provide position information and homing signals for SAR units);
11. ensure that, if a distress alert has been accidentally transmitted, the ship makes every reasonable attempt to communicate with the RCC by any means to cancel the false distress alert;
12. ensure that, if possible, after emergency use, the EPIRB is retrieved and deactivated; and
13. ensure that when an EPIRB is damaged and needs to be disposed of, if a ship is sold for scrap, or if for any other reason a satellite EPIRB will no longer be used, the satellite EPIRB is made inoperable, either by removing its battery and, if possible, returning it to the manufacturer, or by demolishing it.

Note: If the EPIRB is returned to the manufacturer, it should be wrapped in tin foil to prevent transmission of signals during shipment.

EXTRACTS FROM COMSAR/CIRC.25

PROCEDURE FOR RESPONDING TO DSC DISTRESS ALERTS BY SHIPS

The Sub-Committee on Radiocommunications and Search and Rescue (COMSAR), at its fourth session (12 to 16 July 1999), decided that digital selective calling (DSC) relays of distress alerts on all shipborne DSC equipment should be reduced and prepared a procedure for responding to VHF/MF and HF distress alerts, given in flow diagrams 1 and 2, recommending that it be displayed on the ship's bridge as A4 size posters. It also prepared the following guidance.

DISTRESS RELAYS

Radio personnel serving on ships should be made aware of the consequences of transmitting a distress relay call and of routeing a DSC distress relay alert to other than coast stations.

The number of unintended activations of DSC distress alerts and DSC distress relay alerts creates extra work load and confusion to MRCCs and also causing delay in the response-time. The original distress alert from a ship in distress should not be disrupted by other ships, by transmitting a DSC distress relay alert.

Recommendation ITU-R M.541-8 on Operational procedures for the use of DSC equipment in the Maritime Mobile Service identifies only two situations in which a ship would transmit a distress relay call (distress relay alert):

1. on receiving a distress alert on a HF channel, which is not acknowledged by a coast station within 5 minutes. The distress relay call should be addressed to the appropriate coast station; and
2. on knowing that another ship in distress is not itself able to transmit the distress alert and the Master of the ship considers that further help is necessary. The distress relay call should be addressed to "all ships" or to the appropriate coast station (Annex 3, paragraph 1.4).

In no case is a ship permitted to transmit a DSC distress relay call on receipt of a DSC distress alert on either VHF or MF channels.

Distress relay calls on HF channels should be initiated manually.

Compliance with operational and technical provisions above would prevent transmission of inappropriate distress relay calls.

FREQUENCIES FOR THE GMDSS

The frequencies to be used for the transmission of distress and safety information under the GMDSS are shown in the following tables.

FREQUENCIES BELOW 30 MHz

Frequency (kHz)	Description of usage	Notes
490	MSI	490 kHz is used exclusively for MSI in a national language through the international NAVTEX system.
518	MSI	518 kHz is used exclusively for MSI by the international NAVTEX system.
*2174·5 4177·5 6268 8376·5 12520 16695	NBDP	Frequencies 2174·5, 4177·5, 6268, 8376·5, 12520, and 16695 kHz are used exclusively for distress and safety communications (traffic) using NBDP.
*2182	RT	2182 kHz is a carrier frequency used for distress and safety communications (traffic) by RT. 2182 kHz uses class of emission J3E.
*2187·5 4207·5 6312 8414·5 12577 16804·5	DSC	Frequencies 2187·5, 4207·5, 6312, 8414·5, 12577 and 16804·5 kHz are used exclusively for distress and safety calls using digital selective calling in accordance with the Radio Regulations.
*4125	RT	4125 kHz is a ship station carrier frequency for calling on RT. 4125 kHz is authorised for common use by ship and coast stations for distress and safety. Aircraft stations may also use this frequency to communicate with stations of the maritime mobile service for SAR purposes. 4125 kHz is authorised for common use by coast and ship stations for SSB RT on a simplex basis for call and reply purpose provided that the peak power does not exceed 1 kW. The use of this frequency for working purposes is not permitted. In the United States, 4125 kHz is also authorised for common use by coast and ship stations for SSB RT on a simplex basis, provided that the peak power does not exceed 1 kW.
4209·5	MSI	The frequency 4209·5 kHz is exclusively used for NAVTEX-type transmissions.
4210 6314 8416·5 12579 16806·5 19680·5 22376 26100·5	MSI-HF	Frequencies 4210, 6314, 8416·5, 12579, 16806·5, 19680·5, 22376 and 26100·5 kHz are used in the maritime mobile service, exclusively for the transmission of high seas MSI by coast stations to vessels by means of narrow-band direct-printing.
*6215	RT	6215 kHz is a ship station carrier frequency for calling in RT. 6215 kHz is authorised for common use by ship and coast stations for distress and safety. Aircraft stations may also use this frequency to communicate with stations of the maritime mobile service for SAR purposes. 6215 kHz is authorised for common use by coast and ship stations for SSB RT on a simplex basis for call and reply purpose provided that the peak power does not exceed 1 kW. The use of this frequency for working purposes is not permitted.
*8291 12290 16420	RT	The carrier frequencies 8291, 12290 and 16420 kHz are used exclusively for distress and safety communications (traffic) on RT.

FREQUENCIES ABOVE 30 MHz (VHF/UHF)

Frequency (mHz)	Description of usage	Notes
*121·5	AERO-SAR	The aeronautical emergency frequency 121·5 MHz is used for the purposes of distress and urgency for RT by stations of the aeronautical mobile service using frequencies in the band between 117·975 MHz and 137 MHz. This frequency may also be used for these purposes by survival craft stations. Some EPIRBs also use the frequency 121·5 MHz as indicated in The Radio Regulations. Mobile stations of the maritime mobile service may communicate with stations of the aeronautical mobile service on the aeronautical emergency frequency 121·5 MHz for the purposes of distress and urgency only, and on the aeronautical auxiliary frequency 123·1 MHz for co-ordinated search and rescue operations, using class A3E emissions for both frequencies. They shall then comply with any special arrangement between governments concerned by which the aeronautical mobile service is regulated.
123·1	AERO-SAR	The aeronautical auxiliary, frequency 123·1 MHz, which is auxiliary to the aeronautical emergency frequency 121·5 MHz, is for use by stations of the aeronautical mobile service and by other mobile and land stations engaged in co-ordinated search and rescue operations. Mobile stations of the maritime mobile service may communicate with stations of the aeronautical mobile service on the aeronautical emergency frequency 121·5 MHz for the purposes of distress and urgency only, and on the aeronautical auxiliary frequency 123·1 MHz for co-ordinated search and rescue operations, using class A3E emissions for both frequencies. They shall then comply with any special arrangement between governments concerned by which the aeronautical mobile service is regulated.
156·3	VHF Ch 06	The frequency 156·3 MHz may be used for communication between ship stations and aircraft stations engaged in co-ordinated search and rescue operations. It may also be used by aircraft stations to communicate with ship stations for other safety purposes. Vessels shall avoid harmful interference to such communications on Ch 06 as well as to communications between aircraft stations, ice-breakers and assisted vessels during ice seasons.
*156·525	VHF Ch 70	The frequency 156·525 MHz is used in the maritime mobile service for distress and safety calls using digital selective calling.
156·650	VHF Ch 13	The frequency 156·650 MHz is used for ship-to-ship communications. Channel 13 is designated for use on a worldwide basis as a navigation safety communication channel, primarily for intership navigation safety communications. It may also be used for the vessel movement and port operations service subject to the national regulations of the administrations concerned.
156·8	VHF Ch 16	The frequency 156·8 MHz is used for distress and safety communications by RT. Additionally, the frequency 156·8 MHz may be used by aircraft stations for safety purposes only.
*406-406·1	406-EPIRB	This frequency band is used exclusively by satellite EPIRBs in the Earth-to-space direction.
9200-9500	SARTs	This frequency band is used by radar transponders to facilitate search and rescue.

Except as provided in these Regulations, any emission capable of causing harmful interference to distress, alarm, urgency or safety communications on the frequencies denoted by an asterisk (*) is prohibited.

The number and duration of test transmissions shall be kept to a minimum on the frequencies identified above; they should be co-ordinated with a competent authority, as necessary, and, wherever practicable, be carried out on artificial antennæ or with reduced power. However, testing on the distress and safety calling frequencies should be avoided, but where this is unavoidable, it should be indicated that these are test transmissions.

Before transmitting for other than distress purposes on any of the frequencies identified above for distress and safety, a station shall, where practicable, listen on the frequency concerned to make sure that no distress transmission is being sent.

SURVIVAL CRAFT STATIONS

Equipment for radiotelephony use in survival craft stations shall, if capable of operating on any frequency in the bands between 156 MHz and 174 MHz, be able to transmit and receive on 156·8 MHz and at least one other frequency in these bands.

Equipment for transmitting locating signals from survival craft stations shall be capable of operating in the 9200–9500 MHz band.

Equipment with DSC facilities for use in survival craft shall, if capable of operating:

a) in the bands between 1605 kHz and 2850 kHz, be able to transmit on 2187·5 kHz;

b) in the bands between 4000 kHz and 27500 kHz, be able to transmit on 8414·5 kHz;

c) in the bands between 156 MHz and 174 MHz, be able to transmit on 156·525 MHz.

THE MANAGEMENT OF VHF

The widespread misuse of VHF channels at sea, especially the distress, safety and calling Channel 16 (156·8 MHz) and channels used for port operations, ship movement services and reporting systems, is giving concern.

Often the misuse of VHF channels causes serious interference to essential communications and becomes a potential danger to safety at sea.

The proper use of VHF channels at sea makes an important contribution to navigational safety. In accordance with the ITU Radio Regulations:

a. Channel 16 may only be used for distress, urgency and very brief safety communications and for calling to establish other communications which should then be conducted on a suitable working channel.

b. On VHF channels allocated to the port operations service the only messages permitted are restricted to those relating to the operational handling, the movement and safety of ships and, in emergency, to the safety of persons; as the use of these channels for ship-to-ship communications may cause serious interference to communications related to the movement and safety of shipping in congested port areas.

VHF equipment is frequently operated by persons not trained in its proper use though the ITU Radio Regulations require that the service of every ship radio-telephone station shall be controlled by an operator holding a certificate issued or recognized by, the Government concerned.

The following guidelines have been prepared and, if followed, should ensure that VHF channels are used correctly.

Proper Use of VHF Channels at Sea
(An extract from the IMO Resolution A.474 (XII))

GUIDELINES ON THE USE OF VHF AT SEA

1 VHF COMMUNICATION TECHNIQUE

1.1 Preparation

Before transmitting, think about the subjects which have to be communicated and, if necessary, prepare written notes to avoid unnecessary interruptions and ensure that no valuable time is wasted on a busy channel.

1.2 Listening

Listen before commencing to transmit to make certain that the channel is not already in use. This will avoid unnecessary and irritating interference.

1.3 Discipline

VHF equipment should be used correctly and in accordance with the Radio Regulations. The following in particular should be avoided:

1.3.1 calling on Channel 16 for purposes other than distress, urgency and very brief safety communications when another calling channel is available;

1.3.2 communications not related to safety and navigation on port operation channels;

1.3.3 non-essential transmissions, e.g. needless and superfluous signals and correspondence;

1.3.4 transmitting without correct identification;

1.3.5 occupation of one particular channel under poor conditions;

1.3.6 use of offensive language.

1.4 Repetition

Repetition of words and phrases should be avoided unless specifically requested by the receiving station.

1.5 Power Reduction

When possible, the lowest transmitter power necessary for satisfactory communication should be used.

1.6 Automatic Identification systems (AIS)

AIS is used for the exchange of data in ship-to-ship communications and also in communication with shore-based facilities. The purpose of AIS is to help identify vessels; assist in target tracking; simplify information exchange (e.g. reduce verbal reporting); and provide additional information to assist situation awareness. AIS may be used together with VHF voice communications. AIS should be operated in accordance with resolution A.917(22) - Guidelines for the onboard operational use of shipborne automatic identification systems (AIS).

1.7 Communications with shore stations

1.7.1 On VHF channels allocated to port operations service, the only messages permitted are restricted to those relating to the operational handling, the movement and the safety of ships and, in emergency, to the safety of persons; as the use of these channels for ship-to-ship communications may cause serious interference to communications related to the movement and safety of shipping in port areas.

1.7.2 Instructions given on communication matters by shore stations should be obeyed.

1.7.3 Communications should be carried out on the channel indicated by the shore station. When a change of channel is requested, this should be acknowledged by the ship.

1.7.4 On receiving instructions from a shore station to stop transmitting, no further communications should be made until otherwise notified (the shore station may be receiving distress or safety messages and any other transmissions could cause interference).

1.8 Communications with other ships

1.8.1 VHF Channel 13 is designated by the Radio Regulations for bridge-to-bridge communications. The ship called may indicate another working channel on which further transmissions should take place. The calling ship should acknowledge acceptance before changing channels.

1.8.2 The listening procedure outlined in paragraph 1.2 should be followed before communications are commenced on the chosen channel.

1.9 Distress communications

1.9.1 Distress calls/messages have absolute priority over all other communications. When hearing them all other transmissions should cease and a listening watch should be kept.

1.9.2 Any distress call/message should be recorded in the ship's log and passed to the master.

1.9.3 On receipt of a distress message, if in the vicinity, immediately acknowledge receipt. If not in the vicinity, allow a short interval of time to elapse before acknowledging receipt of the message in order to permit ships nearer to the distress to do so.

1.10 Calling

1.10.1 In accordance with the Radio Regulations Channel 16 may only be used for distress, urgency and very brief safety communications and for calling to establish other communications which should then be conducted on a suitable working channel.

1.10.2 Whenever possible, a working frequency should be used for calling.

If a working frequency is not available, VHF Channel 16 may be used for calling, provided it is not occupied by a distress call/message.

1.10.3 In case of difficulty to establish contact with a ship or shore station, allow adequate time before repeating the call. Do not occupy the channel unnecessarily and try another channel.

1.11 Changing channels

If communications on a channel are unsatisfactory, indicate change of channel and await confirmation.

1.12 Spelling

If spelling becomes necessary (e.g. descriptive names, call signs, words which could be misunderstood) use the spelling table contained in the International Code of Signals and the Radio Regulations.

1.13 Addressing

The words "I" and "You" should be used prudently. Indicate to whom they refer.

Example:

Seaship, this is Port Radar, do you have a Pilot?
Port Radar, this is Seaship, yes I do have a Pilot.

1.14 Watchkeeping

Every ship, while at sea, is required to maintain watches (Regulation on Watches in Chapter IV of SOLAS, 1974, as amended). Continuous watchkeeping is required on VHF DSC Channel 70 and also when practicable, a continuous listening watch on VHF Channel 16.

2 VHF COMMUNICATION PROCEDURE

2.1 Calling

When calling a shore station or another ship, say the name of that shore station once (twice if considered necessary in heavy radio traffic conditions) followed by the phrase THIS IS and the ship's name twice, indicating the channel in use.

Example:

Port City, this is Seastar, Seastar, on Channel 14.

2.2 Exchange of messages

2.2.1 When communicating with a ship whose name is unknown but whose position is known, that position may be used. In this case the call is addressed to all ships.

Example:

Hello all ships, this is Pastoria, Pastoria. Ship approaching number four buoy, I am passing Belinda Bank Light.

2.2.2 Where a message is received and only acknowledgement of receipt is needed, say "received". Where a message is received and acknowledgement of the correct message is required, say "received, understood", and repeat message if considered necessary.

Example:

Message: Your berth will be clear at 08.30 hours.

Reply: Received, understood. Berth clear at 08.30 hours.

2.2.3 Where appropriate, the following message should be sent:

"Please use/ I will use IMO Standard Marine Communication Phrases".

When language difficulties exist which cannot be resolved by use of IMO Standard Marine Communication Phrases, the International Code of Signals should be used.

In this case the word "INTERCO" should precede the groups of the International Code of Signals.

Example:

"Please use/I will use the International Code of Signals".

2.2.4 Where the message contains instructions or advice, the substance should be repeated in the reply.

Example:

Message: Advise you pass astern of me.

Reply: I will pass astern of you.

2.2.5 If a message is not properly received, ask for it to be repeated by saying "Say again".

2.2.6 If a message is received but not understood, say "Message not understood".

2.2.7 If it is necessary to change to a different channel say "Change to channel ...." and wait for acknowledgement before carrying out the change.

2.2.8 During exchange of messages, a ship should invite a reply by saying "over".

2.2.9 The end of a communication is indicated by the word "out".

3 STANDARD MESSAGES

3.1 Since most ship-to-shore communications are exchanges of information, it is advisable to use standard messages which will reduce transmission time.

3.2 Commonly used standard messages are given in the IMO Standard Marine Communication Phrases (SMCP), which should be used whenever possible.

REFERENCE DOCUMENTS

SOLAS Convention, 1974, as amended, Chapter IV on Radiocommunications.
Radio Regulations, Appendix 18, Table of Transmitting Frequencies in the VHF Maritime Mobile Band.
Resolution A.917(22) on Guidelines for the Onboard Operational Use of Shipborne Automatic Identification Systems (AIS). Resolution A.918(22) on IMO Standard Marine Communication Phrases (SMCP).

RANGE OF VHF

It is most important to realise that the transmitting and receiving range of VHF signals is limited, in theory, to line of sight. This is because the radio waves of VHF do not normally bend around the curvature of the earth. The range may be affected to some degree by barometric pressure and/or increased humidity which often gives greater ranges than normally attained.

This atmospheric refraction results in the radio waves tending to follow curved rather than straight line paths.

The bending or refraction arises from a change of wave speed as the waves propagate through the atmosphere, the waves changing direction towards the region of lower wave speed. The degree of bending or refraction depends upon the rate at which the wave speed changes. This is governed by the refractive index of the air and its variation with height which, in turn, depends upon the pressure, temperature and humidity of the air.

Another significant factor in determining range is, generally, the height above sea level of the transmitting and receiving aerials. It shouldalso be noted that the fact that a transmitter and a receiver are within radio sight does not automatically guarantee that an acceptable signal will be received at that point. This will depend, amongst other things, on the power of the transmission, the sensitivity of the receiver and the quality and position of the transmitting and receiving aerials. **Figure 12** illustrates some typical VHF ranges that can be obtained from various transmitting and receiving stations.

THE USE OF MOBILE TELEPHONES IN DISTRESS AND SAFETY COMMUNICATIONS

The use of mobile telephones in the marine environment offshore is now well established, with users in all areas of the commercial, fishing and leisure communities.

A growing number of incidents have occurred where vessels requiring assistance from rescue services have used the inland emergency service, or alternatively telephoned direct to request assistance. (e.g. Lifeboat services). This procedure through a mobile telephone is **strongly discouraged**.

Use of mobile telephones bypasses the existing dedicated well established international marine distress communications systems.

Mobile telephone coverage offshore is limited and does not afford the same extensive safety coverage as VHF Channel 16. Consequently a greater risk exists of communications difficulties or even a complete breakdown if an accident should occur at the edge of a cell coverage area.

Subsequent on-scene communications would be restricted and delayed if mobile telephone communications were exclusively maintained throughout. There is always a risk that elements of vital information could be lost or misinterpreted by the introduction of further relay links in the communication chain. Mobile telephones are also highly susceptible to failure due to water ingress.

It is not possible to communicate direct to another vessel able to render assistance unless that vessel is also fitted with a mobile telephone and the telephone number is known. Requests for assistance cannot be monitored by other vessels in a position to render assistance. Valuable time would be lost whilst the relevant Coastguard Rescue Co-ordination Centre receives and then re-broadcasts the information to all ships on the appropriate distress channel(s).

In the interests of Safety Of Life At Sea (SOLAS), owners of vessels are urged to carry MARINE communications equipment onboard and to use this medium as the primary means of Distress and Safety communications.

Figure 12 - Typical VHF ranges

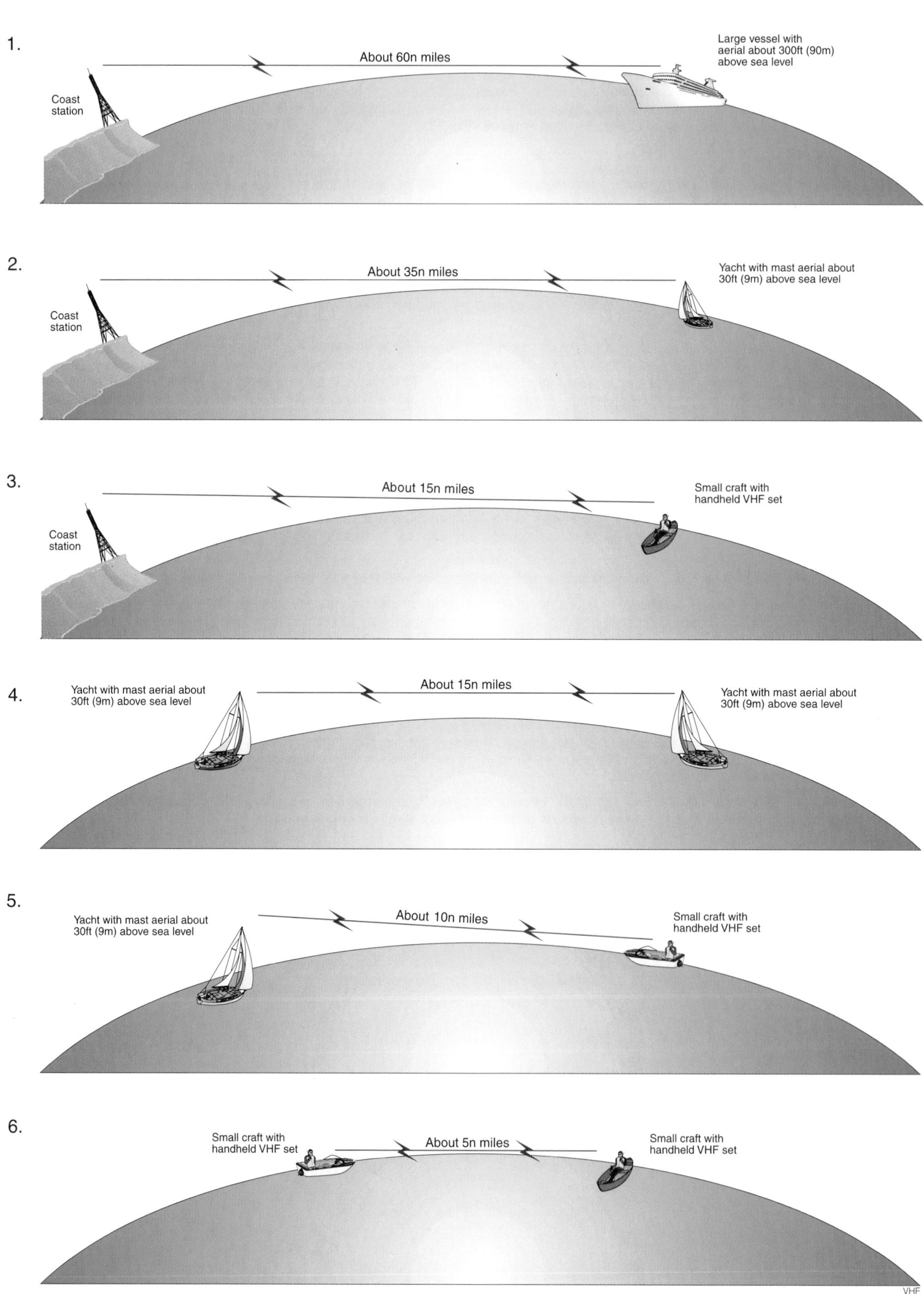

Table of Transmitting Frequencies in the VHF maritime mobile band

Channel designators	Notes	Transmitting frequencies (MHz)		Inter Ship	Port operations and ship movement		Public correspondence
		Ship stations	Coast stations		Single frequency	Two frequency	
60		156·025	160·625			x	x
01		156·050	160·650			x	x
61	*m), o)*	156·075	160·675		x	x	x
02	*m), o)*	156·100	160·700		x	x	x
62	*m), o)*	156·125	160·725		x	x	x
03	*m), o)*	156·150	160·750		x	x	x
63	*m), o)*	156·175	160·775		x	x	x
04	*m), o)*	156·200	160·800		x	x	x
64	*m), o)*	156·225	160·825		x	x	x
05	*m), o)*	156·250	160·850		x	x	x
65	*m), o)*	156·275	160·875		x	x	x
06	*f)*	156·300		x			
66		156·325	160·925			x	x
07		156·350	160·950			x	x
67	*h)*	156·375	156·375	x	x		
08		156·400		x			
68		156·425	156·425		x		
09	*i)*	156·450	156·450	x	x		
69		156·475	156·475	x	x		
10	*h)*	156·500	156·500	x	x		
70	*j)*	156·525	156·525	**Digital selective calling for Distress, Safety and Calling**			
11		156·550	156·550		x		
71		156·575	156·575		x		
12		156·600	156·600		x		
72	*i)*	156·625		x			
13	*k)*	156·650	156·650	x	x		
73	*h), i)*	156·675	156·675	x	x		
14		156·700	156·700		x		
74		156·725	156·725		x		
15	*g)*	156·750	156·750	x	x		
75	*n)*	156·775			x		
16		156·800	156·800		**Distress, Safety and Calling**		
76	*n)*	156·825			x		
17	*g)*	156·850	156·850	x	x		
77		156·875		x			
18	*m)*	156·900	161·500		x	x	x
78		156·925	161·525			x	x
19		156·950	161·550			x	x
79		156·975	161·575			x	x
20		157·000	161·600			x	x
80		157·025	161·625			x	x
21		157·050	161·650			x	x
81		157·075	161·675			x	x
22	*m)*	157·100	161·700		x	x	x
82	*m), o)*	157·125	161·725		x	x	x
23	*m), o)*	157·150	161·750		x	x	x
83	*m), o)*	157·175	161·775		x	x	x
24	*m), o)*	157·200	161·800		x	x	x
84	*m), o)*	157·225	161·825		x	x	x
25	*m), o)*	157·250	161·850		x	x	x
85	*m), o)*	157·275	161·875		x	x	x
26	*m), o)*	157·300	161·900		x	x	x
86	*m), o)*	157·325	161·925		x	x	x
27		157·350	161·950			x	x
87		157·375	161·975		x		
28		157·400	162·000			x	x
88	*h)*	157·425			x		
AIS 1	*l)*	161·975	161·975				
AIS 2	*l)*	162·025	162·025				

Note—For assistance in understanding the Table, see notes *a)* to *o)* on next page

NOTES REFERRING TO THE TABLE

General notes

a) Administrations may designate frequencies in the intership, port operations and ship movement services for use by light aircraft and helicopters to communicate with ships or participating coast stations in predominantly maritime support operations. However, the use of the channels which are shared with public correspondence shall be subject to prior agreement between interested and affected administrations.

b) The channels in this table, with the exception of Channels 06, 13, 15, 16, 17, 70, 75 and 76, **may** also be used for high-speed data and facsimile transmissions, subject to special arrangement between interested and affected administrations.

c) The channels in this table, but **preferably** Channel 28 and with the exception of Channels 06, 13, 15, 16, 17, 70, 75 and 76, may be used for direct-printing telegraphy and data transmission, subject to special arrangement between interested and affected administrations.

d) The frequencies in this table may also be used for radiocommunications on inland waterways.

e) Administrations having an urgent need to reduce local congestion may apply 12·5 kHz Channel interleaving on a non-interference basis to 25 kHz channels, provided:

— Recommendation ITU-R M.1084-2 shall be taken into account when changing to 12·5 kHz Channels;

— it shall not affect the 25 kHz Channels of the Appendix 18 maritime mobile distress and safety frequencies, especially the Channels 06, 13, 15, 16, 17, and 70, nor the technical characteristics mentioned in Recommendation ITU-R M.489-2 for those channels;

— implementation of 12·5 kHz channel interleaving and consequential national requirements shall be subject to prior agreement between the implementing administrations and administrations whose ship stations or services may be affected.

Specific notes

f) The frequency 156·300 MHz (Channel 06) **may** also be used for communication between ship stations and aircraft stations engaged in co-ordinated search and rescue operations. Ship stations shall avoid harmful interference to such communications on Channel 06 as well as to communications between aircraft stations, ice-breakers and assisted ships during ice seasons.

g) Channels 15 and 17 may also be used for on-board communications provided the effective radiated power does not exceed 1 W, and subject to the national regulations of the administration concerned when these channels are used in its territorial waters.

h) Within the European Maritime Area and in Canada, these frequencies (Channels 10, 67 & 73) may also be used, if so required, by the individual administrations concerned, for communication between ship stations, aircraft stations and participating land stations engaged in co-ordinated search and rescue and anti-pollution operations in local areas.

i) The preferred first three frequencies for the purpose indicated in note a) are 156·450 MHz (Channel 09), 156·625 MHz (Channel 72) and 156·675 MHz (channel 73).

j) Channel 70 is to be used exclusively for digital selective calling for distress, safety and calling.

k) Channel 13 is designated for use on a worldwide basis as a navigation safety communication channel, primarily for intership navigation safety communications. It may also be used for the ship movement and port operations service subject to the national regulations of the administrations concerned.

l) These Channels (AIS 1 and AIS 2) will be used for an automatic ship identification and surveillance system capable of providing worldwide operation on high seas, unless other frequencies are designated on a regional basis for this purpose.

m) These Channels (18 and 82 to 86) may be operated as single frequency channels, subject to special arrangement between interested or affected administrations.

n) The use of these Channels (75 and 76) should be restricted to navigation-related communications only and all precautions should be taken to avoid harmful interference to Channel 16, e.g. by limiting the output power to 1 W or by means of geographical separation.

o) These channels may be used to provide bands for initial testing and the possible future introduction of new technologies, subject to special arrangement between interested or affected administrations. Stations using these channels or bands for the testing and the possible future introduction of new technologies shall not cause harmful interference to, and shall not claim protection from, other stations operating in accordance with ITU Radio Regulations / Volume 1 / Chapter SII - Frequencies / Article S5 / Frequency allocations.

MARITIME SAFETY INFORMATION (MSI)

MSI is defined in general terms as "navigational and meteorological forecasts, and other urgent safety-related messages", of vital importance to all vessels at sea. The categories of MSI under the GMDSS have expanded considerably, in keeping with the requirements of world shipping and the capabilities of new technology. The new developments have offered the greatest potential benefit and improvement in safety services for all vessels.

There are seven basic categories of MSI within the GMDSS:

- Navigational warnings;
- Meteorological warnings;
- Ice reports;
- Search and rescue information;
- Meteorological forecasts;
- Pilot service messages (not in United States);
- Electronic navigational systems update messages.

Prior to the GMDSS, in order to receive all necessary messages in the above categories, operators would require the broadcast times and frequencies of the numerous radio stations and take time to copy each relevant broadcast. Under the GMDSS, a vessel anywhere in the world should be able to receive all types of information by just flipping the switch of two small receivers.

The MSI service, illustrated in the following diagram, is an internationally co-ordinated network of broadcasts of Maritime Safety Information from different Information Providers, such as:

- National Hydrographic Offices, for navigational warnings and electronic chart correction;
- National Meteorological Offices, for weather warnings and forecasts;
- Rescue Co-ordination Centres, for shore-to-ship distress alerts, and other urgent information;
- International Ice Patrol, for North Atlantic Ice hazards.

Only Information Providers approved by the IMO, the IHO or the WMO are given the authorization to make SafetyNET broadcasts.

Figure 13 - The International Maritime Safety Information service

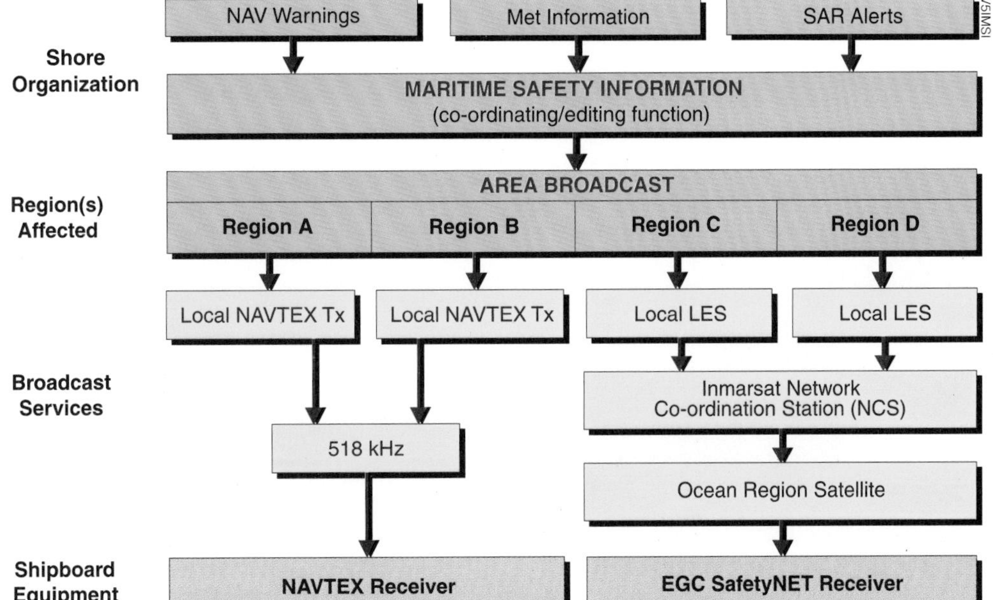

TWO INDEPENDENT SYSTEMS FOR BROADCASTING MSI

The GMDSS supports two independent systems for broadcasting MSI:

- **The International NAVTEX Service,** whereby the Information Provider forwards the MSI for a given area to a 518 kHz MF NAVTEX transmitter; note that reception of NAVTEX MSI is limited by the range of the MF transmitter to the coastal area immediately around the transmitter;
- **The International SafetyNET Service,** whereby the Information Provider forwards the MSI for a given area to an Inmarsat Land Earth Station (LES), for broadcasting via the satellite network over an entire Inmarsat Ocean Region; consequently, vessels can receive SafetyNET MSI anywhere in that Ocean Region, irrespective of their distance from the LES / Information Provider.

As indicated in **Figure 13**, MSI for a given area is generally broadcast over *either* NAVTEX *or* SafetyNET (except for some exceptional circumstances where a message may be broadcast using both services); vessels equipped with both a NAVTEX receiver and SafetyNET receiver should select the appropriate receiver to receive MSI for the area in which the vessel is operating. Where a coastal area is not covered by the International NAVTEX service, for example around Australia, MSI for that area will be broadcast on SafetyNET.

SCHEDULED AND UNSCHEDULED MSI BROADCASTS

To ensure that the user knows when to receive MSI for a given area and subject, many MSI broadcasts are *scheduled,* under IMO co-ordination, to a particular time, LES, and satellite. For example, all navigational warnings and meteorological forecasts are *scheduled broadcasts* (and given Safety priority, which does not produce an alarm at the terminal when received), while meteorological warnings and distress alerts are *unscheduled broadcasts* (and given urgent or distress priority, which produces an alarm at the terminal).

To be sure of receiving a scheduled MSI broadcast, the receiver must be tuned to the appropriate channel / satellite at the specified time, and programmed to receive information for the area concerned.

A smaller number of MSI messages are transmitted as *unscheduled broadcasts,* for example urgent navigational warnings, severe weather warnings, and distress alert relays. Unscheduled SafetyNET broadcasts are made over *all satellites covering an area,* so the receiver will not miss the message, no matter what satellite it is logged-in to. The user is advised of the receipt of an unscheduled broadcast by the terminal giving an alarm.

LANGUAGE USED FOR MSI BROADCASTS

All MSI broadcasts made on the International MSI service are printed in the English language (sometimes a local language is added after the English wording).

NAVAREAS / METAREAS

The 16 Navigational Areas (NAVAREAs), which are the same as the Meteorological Areas (METAREAs), into which the earth's navigable waters are sub-divided for the purpose of SafetyNET broadcasts. For each area, a NAVAREA Co-ordinator co-ordinates the broadcasting of navigational warnings, and a Meteorological Issuing Service co-ordinates the meteorological information throughout that area.

Figure 14 - Basic concept of the EGC services SafetyNET and FleetNET

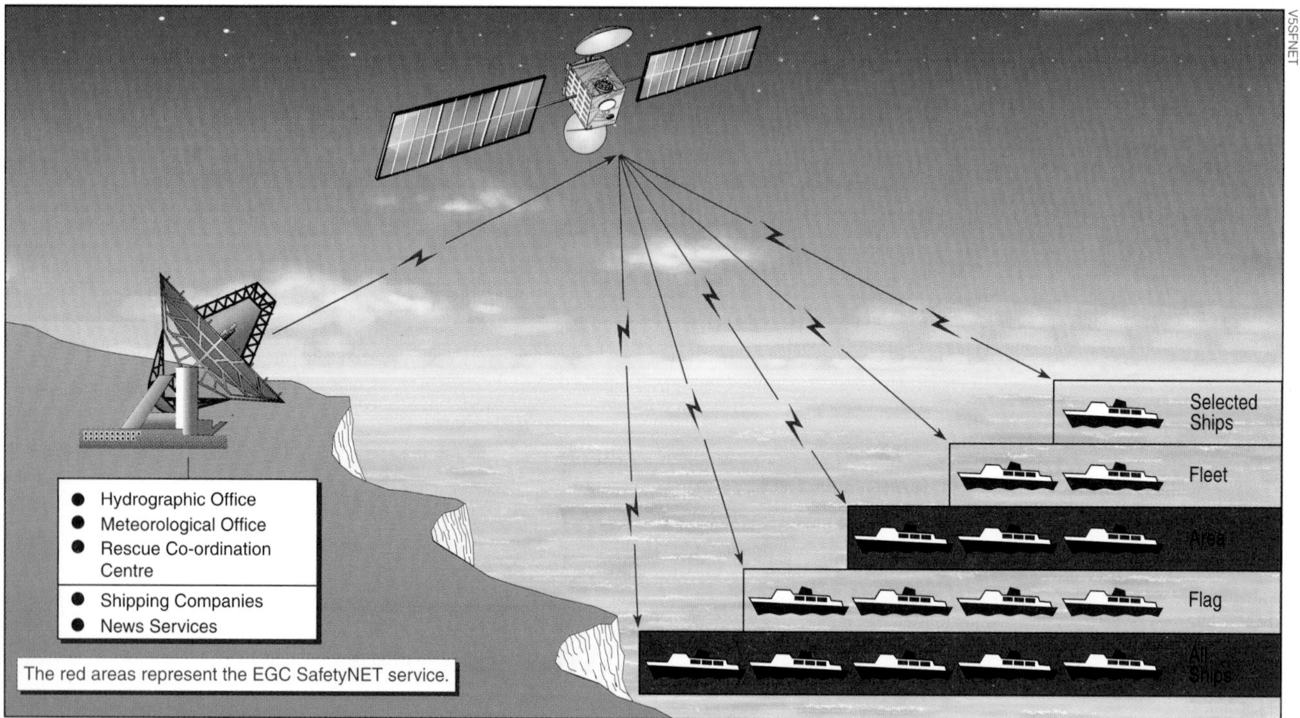

SAFETYNET

Figure 15 - The SafetyNET concept

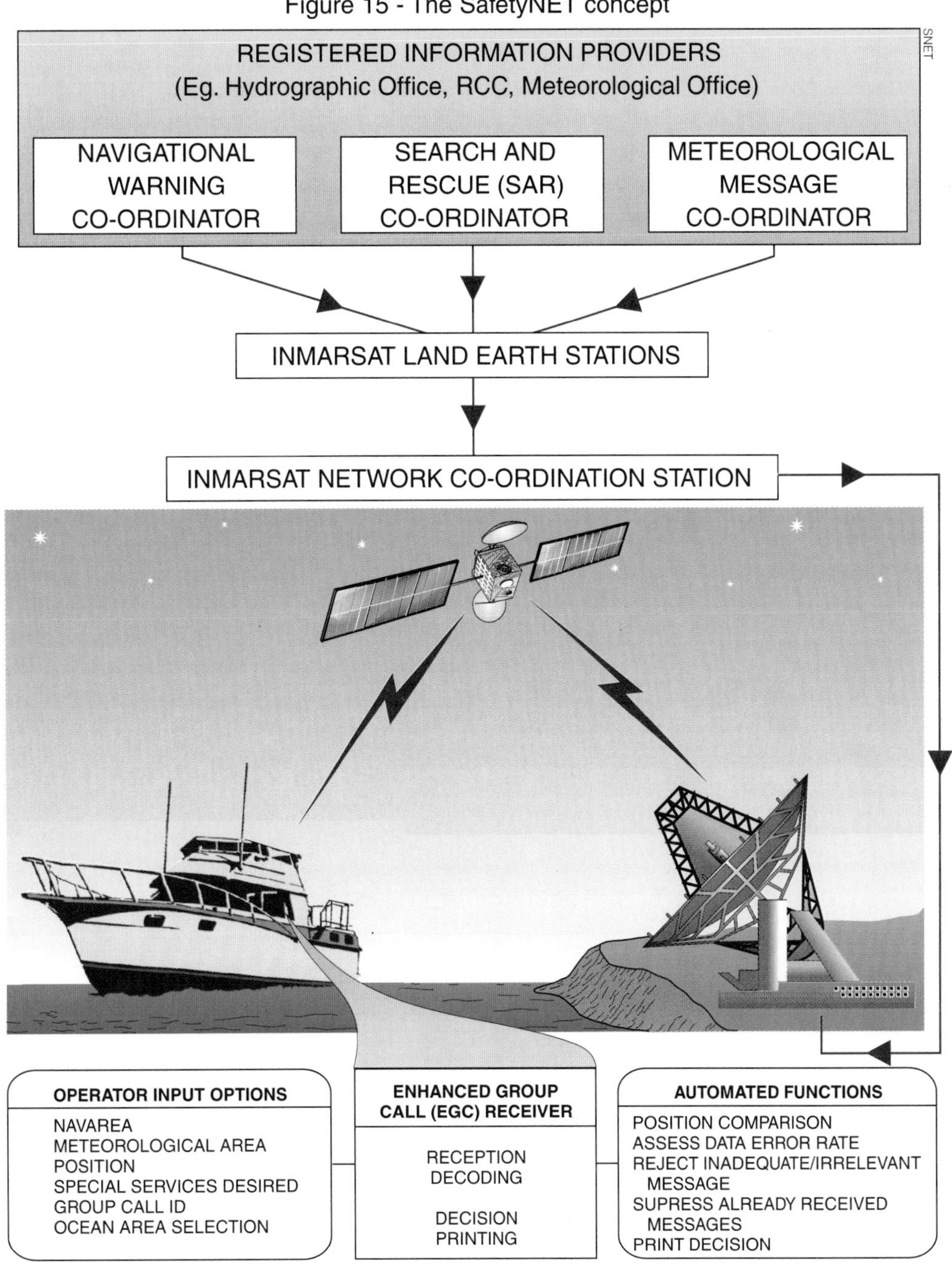

OPERATION OF THE SAFETYNET SERVICE - AN OVERVIEW

Operation of the SafetyNET service, illustrated in **Figure 15** involves a sequence of events:

1. A registered Information Provider, such as a national Hydrographic Office, Rescue Co-ordination Centre (RCC), or Meteorological Office, receives information from its specialized sources.
2. Each Information Provider prepares an MSI message in a standardized format, and submits it to the appropriate co-ordinator (Navigational Warning Co-ordinator, SAR Co-ordinator, or Meteorological Issuing Service).

3. The co-ordinator checks the message with any other information received, and edits it accordingly, then submits the finalized text to a selected Inmarsat C LES.

   Included with the message are the following codes (known as the "C" codes), to instruct the LES and MES on how to process the message automatically:

   - **Priority Code** (distress, urgency, safety, or routine);
   - **Service Code**, to identify the message type, for example a shore-to-ship distress alert, or meteorological forecast;
   - **Address Code**, to identify the geographical area for which the MSI is applicable - this may be a fixed geographical area, such as one of the 16 NAVAREAs / METAREAs, or a temporary area determined by the originator, such as a circular or rectangular area as shown in **Figures 16 and 17**:
   - **Repetition Code**, to indicate the number of times the message should be broadcast;
   - **Presentation Code**, to indicate the character set in which the message will be transmitted and printed. (The character set used is always the International Alphabet Number 5, which is also known as 7-bit ASCII).

4. The Information Provider may also choose the scheduled time(s) at which the message is to be broadcast, and, if a LES operates in more than one Ocean Region, the satellite to be used.
5. The LES receives the message with its instructions, and queues it with any other messages received, according to priority and scheduled time of transmission.
6. At the required time for transmission, the LES forwards the message over the Interstation Signalling Link (ISL) to the NCS for the Ocean Region.
7. The Network Co-ordination Station (NCS) automatically broadcasts the message on the NCS Common Signalling Channel over the entire Ocean Region.
8. All EGC receivers (that meet the requirements specified at the end of this chapter) will receive the MSI message, and print it out, unless the operator has chosen to reject messages of that type, or it has recently been printed out by that terminal.

MSI BROADCAST OVER THE SAFETYNET SERVICE

Coastal Warnings (see note 1)

- Navigational warnings;
- Meteorological warnings;
- Ice reports;
- Search and rescue information;
- Meteorological forecasts;
- SATNAV system messages;
- Other electronic navaid messages;
- Additional navigational warnings.

Meteorological and Navarea warnings and meteorological forecasts to ships within specified NAVAREAs / METAREAs.

Search-and-rescue co-ordination to fixed areas.

Search-and-rescue co-ordination to ships within specified circular areas.

Urgency messages, meteorological and navigational warnings to ships within specified circular areas.

Shore-to-ship distress alerts to ships within specified circular areas.

Urgency messages and navigational warnings to ships within specified rectangular areas.

Chart correction services

Notes:

1. The SafetyNET coastal warning broadcast facility is made available for the transmission of coastal information to areas where NAVTEX MSI is not provided.
2. MSI messages are generally broadcast with a key-word in their header indicating the priority of the message - for example DISTRESS or MAYDAY for priority 3, URGENT or PAN PAN for priority 2 and SAFETY or SECURITÉ for priority 1.

AVAILABILITY OF MSI IN DIFFERENT AREAS

To avoid excessive duplication of broadcasts, the IMO has authorised the following arrangements:

For a given NAVAREA/METAREA which is covered by more than one Ocean Region satellite, scheduled broadcasts of MSI, such as navigational warnings and meteorological information, are made only via a single nominated satellite/Ocean Region.

For a NAVAREA/METAREA which is covered by more than one Ocean Region satellite, unscheduled broadcasts of MSI, such as gale warnings and distress alert relays, are made via all satellites/Ocean Regions which cover the area concerned.

While the EGC SafetyNET service is continually being fine tuned, some Information Providers have not yet made the necessary arrangements to provide MSI through a Co-ordinator to an Inmarsat C Land Earth Station. This could result in some types of MSI not being provided in some NAVAREAs/METAREAs, or in a limited amount of MSI being provided through one satellite/Ocean Region compared to another. As the SafetyNET service continues, more Information Providers are expected to make arrangements to provide MSI.

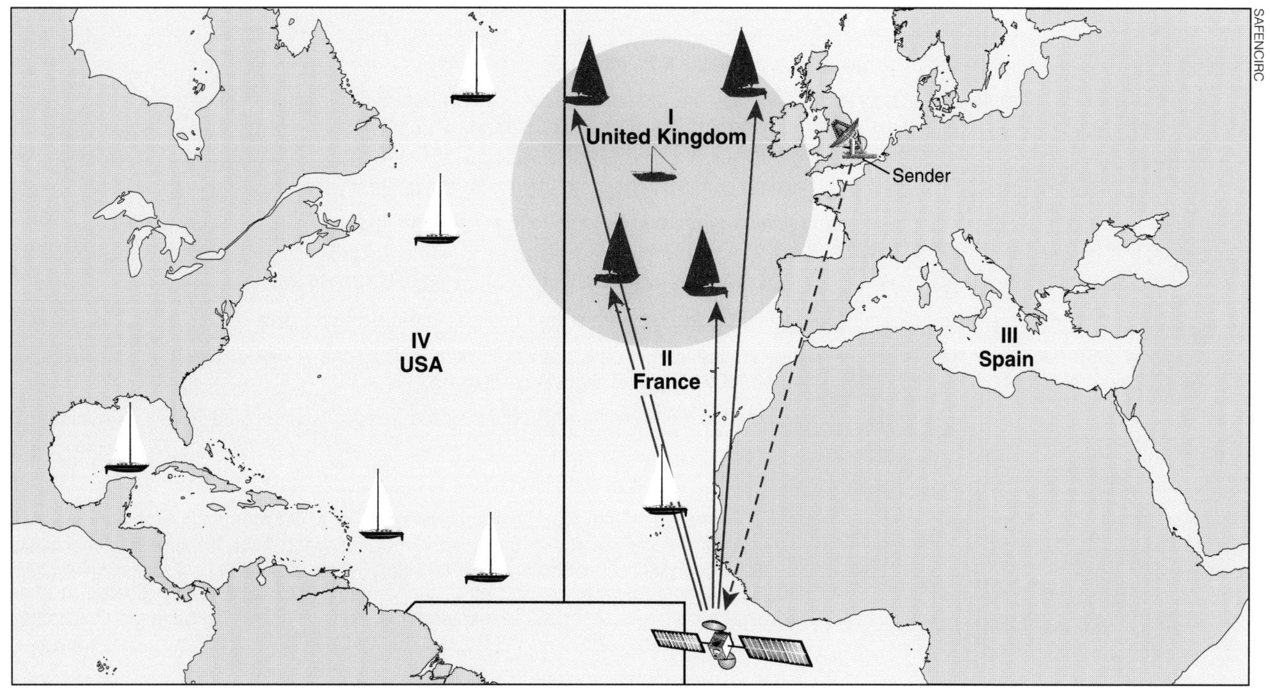

Figure 16 - SafetyNET message addressed to a circular area

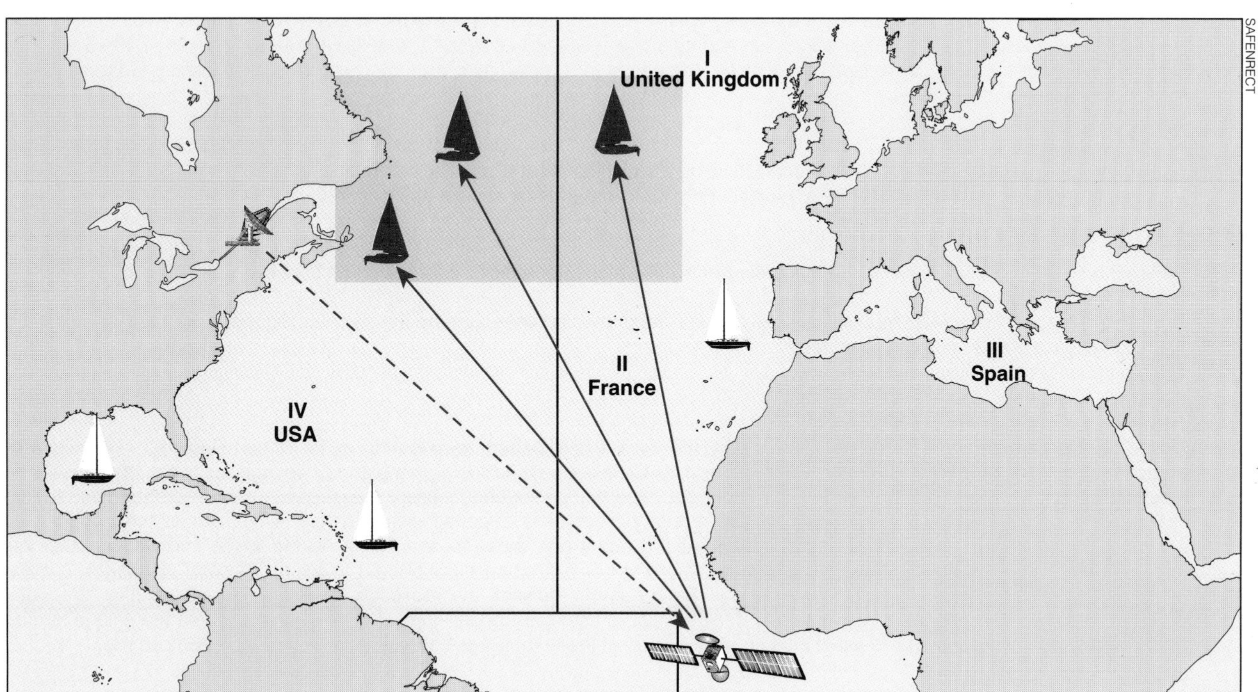

Figure 17 - SafetyNET message addressed to a rectangular area

REQUIREMENTS FOR RECEIVING SAFETYNET MSI BROADCASTS

For a vessel to be able to receive SafetyNET MSI broadcasts, certain technical and legal requirements must be met:

- The vessel must be equipped with a type-approved EGC receiver - this may be a standalone EGC receiver, or a receiver combined with an Inmarsat MES, as defined in the *Inmarsat Maritime Communications Handbook.*
- For optimal performance and GMDSS certification, the EGC receiver / MES should be installed in the vessel in accordance with the *Design and Installation Guidelines.* available from Inmarsat.
- For the vessel to be certificated in the GMDSS, the installation must comply with the GMDSS requirements of the national administration for the country in which the vessel is registered. (Note, however, that GMDSS certification is not necessary for the receipt of MSI broadcasts, which are free of charge to all ships).
- The MES with EGC receive capability must be *commissioned* into the Inmarsat system; this involves:

  Completing and submitting a *Commissioning Application Form* to the national Routeing Organization for the country of registration of the vessel;

  Performing *commissioning tests* on the SES, over the satellite link, to confirm that the MES is working correctly.

  More information on commissioning and testing is available from the Inmarsat Commissioning Unit.
- The EGC receiver / MES must be set-up as indicated in the manufacturer's instructions - this includes ensuring that the receiver / MES is tuned (synchronized) to the NCS Common Signalling Channel.
- The printer and any other peripherals connected to the receiver / MES must be made ready as indicated in their manufacturer's instructions.

REPEAT BROADCASTS OF MSI INFORMATION

Some classes of EGC receivers/MESs may not provide uninterrupted monitoring of the channel used for MSI broadcasts, and may switch to a different channel for normal commercial traffic. To improve the probability of these receivers receiving MSI broadcasts, Information Providers re-broadcast some messages: Unscheduled messages, such as distress alerts and gale warnings are re-broadcast six minutes after the initial broadcast; Scheduled broadcasts, such as navigational warnings and other longer-term information are repeated at every scheduled time, for as long as they remain in force. (Repeated broadcasts of the same message may, however, give some users the problem of receiving too many printed messages.)

TYPICAL MSI BROADCASTS

Figure 18 and **Figure 19** show typical MSI broadcasts which you may receive on your terminal. Note the following: The date and time of the message in UTC; The identifier of the LES sending the message - in **Figure 18**, STRATOS CSAT represents the STRATOS Inmarsat C LES. In **Figure 19**, LES 121 represents the Aussaguel Inmarsat C LES; A unique number identifying the message - in **Figure 18**, this is 929960, in **Figure 19**, this is 2498; The priority of the message - Safety in **Figure 18**, Urgent in **Figure 19**. (The terminal responds automatically to an urgent message by giving an audible/visual alarm.) The nature of the message - **Figure 18** is a navigational warning to NAVAREA I; **Figure 19** is a meteorological warning/forecast to METAREA II. Note also the term NoPos in **Figure 19** - some terminals include this with the message to tell the operator that the EGC receiver has not been updated with the ship's position within the last 12 hours. As explained in the section Managing your EGC receiver, this will result in the receiver accepting all geographically-addressed messages for the entire Ocean Region, instead of limiting reception of messages to the MET/ NAVAREAs specified. If your terminal gives this indication, you should make arrangements for regular position updates. **Figure 20** is an example of a message addressed to a circular area, centred on 40° South 112° East, and of radius 999 nautical miles. Messages may also be addressed to a rectangular area by giving the co-ordinates of the southwest corner, and degrees easterly and northerly.

EGC RECEIVER TYPES

EGC SafetyNET (and FleetNET) broadcasts can be received using a small Inmarsat C satellite communications terminal (or by fitting an EGC receiver to an Inmarsat A or Inmarsat B SES, or by a "receive-only" EGC receiver for special applications).

MANAGING YOUR EGC RECEIVER

The section should be read in conjunction with the manufacturer's instructions, for specific information on how to do the following:
Select a satellite/Ocean Region;
Program the receiver for specific NAVAREAs / METAREAs for which to print messages; Update the receiver regularly with the ship's position:
Specify the additional types of MSI message required.
Tune in at the scheduled times of MSI broadcasts.

SELECTIVE MESSAGE RECEPTION

Although an EGC receiver will receive and can print all SafetyNET broadcasts made throughout an entire Ocean Region, many messages may not be useful to the ship - for example those applicable to NAVAREAs beyond the ship's planned voyage, or those on subjects not relevant to the ship's circumstances. To avoid a receiver printing a large number of unnecessary messages, it can be programmed to print only essential messages, and to reject all other messages - every receiver is supplied with software which stores the geographical boundaries of the NAVAREAs; the receiver can use this information to print only those messages applicable to the current area, plus any other areas programmed by the operator. (Note, however, that the receiver cannot be programmed to reject "all ship" messages, such as some shore-to-ship distress alerts and Met/Nav warnings.) The receiver examines the message handling instructions (the "C" codes) included with each message, and uses this information to decide which messages to print. Similarly, the receiver stores the unique number included with each message, and uses this to avoid printing extra copies of those messages already received and printed correctly.

REGULAR POSITION UPDATES

Your EGC receiver **MUST** be updated regularly with the ship's position. The reasons for updating your EGC receiver regularly with the ship's position include: To decide if the receiver should print a message which it has received addressed to a specific geographic area; To print only messages for the required areas - if the ship's position has not been updated for 12 or 24 hours (depending on the model), the receiver will automatically print or store all geographically addressed messages within the entire Ocean Region; Another important reason for updating the terminal regularly with the ship's position, while not directly related to the SafetyNET service, is to ensure that the correct position is given if a distress alert has to be sent.

V9SAFENMSGS

```
***
EGC:              107  2002/02/14 18:14:35  SAFETY
***

STRATOS CSAT 46464 HYDRNW G 14-FEB-2002 18:14:07 929960
zczc
navarea one 075
baltic sea. kadetrenden. chart ba 2365. dangerous wreck located
53-43. On 12-24.6e marked by south cardinal lightbuoy 100 metres
southward.
nnnn
```

Figure 18 - Typical EGC SafetyNET navigational warning

```
EGC:  926         PAGE 1        UTC Time: 94-08-24 09:06:31
LES 121 -MSG 2498-MetWarn/Force Urgent Call to Area: 2 -NoPos
WARNING ON NAVAREA 2, ISSUED BY METEO-FRANCE, TOULOUSE
                        WIND SPEED IN BEAUFORTSCALE
WARNING N004
WEST OF FARADAY
FROM 24 AUGUST AT 09 UTC TO 24 AUGUST AT 18 UTC
SOUTHWEST 8.-
EGC.926
nnnn
```

Figure 19 - Typical EGC SafetyNET meteorology forecast

```
EGC    048    Page 1           UTC Time: 95-04-28 10:55:43
LES 302  -MSG 14314- Met/NavWarn Safety Call to Area:
40 S 112 E 999 Pos OK

IDW01W
SECURITE
=
WARNING ISSUED BY BUREAU OF METEOROLOGY PERTH
AT 04271000Z

AT 0600Z
COLD FRONT 39S105E 403117E 43S121E 50S132E MOVING ENE 35KN

AREA AFFECTED
BOUNDED BY SOUTH EAST OF ALINE FROM 50S113E 44S120E 43S129E
NW/SW WINDS 30/40KN VERY ROUGH HEAVY SWELL

=
+
EGC.048
```

Figure 20 - Typical message to a circular area

TWO WAYS ARE AVAILABLE TO UPDATE A TERMINAL WITH THE SHIP'S POSITION:

Automatically, using an electronic navigational device; the use of a GPS (Global Positioning System) receiver to provide position updates is highly recommended because of its accuracy and reliability. Some SES models can be purchased with an integral GPS receiver, whilst others can be interconnected with a separate on-board GPS receiver. (If, however, your terminal does not support GPS inter-connection, contact the manufacturer/agent about having it upgraded);

Manually, by keying the position co-ordinates directly into the terminal; IMO requires this be done every 4 hours. It is strongly recommended that automatic position updating is used whenever available.

REDUCING THE NUMBER OF ALARMS

Your receiver is programmed to give an audible/visual alarm on printing any distress alerts or urgent messages, to which you should respond immediately. To make sure that you do not get any unnecessary alarms, however, you should do the following: Keep the ship's position updated, to ensure that the receiver rejects messages for any geographic areas which do not include the ship's position; If your receiver is of a make which gives an alarm for messages other than of distress and urgent priority, you should set it to give an alarm only for distress and urgent messages.

GOOD OPERATING PRACTICE

The following advice is given to help you obtain the best possible use of the SafetyNET service:

Make sure all equipment associated with the EGC receiver is working properly, as indicated in the manufacturer's instructions, and that the printer is loaded with paper/ribbon.

Make sure that the terminal is not storing unwanted messages, and has storage space for new messages.
If your printer has an option for printing in a small font, consider selecting this option to reduce the amount of paper used for messages.
Make sure that your current position is entered into the terminal, and that it is regularly updated, to ensure that you only receive appropriate MSI throughout your voyage.

On the terminal, enter all NAVAREAs/METAREAs and coastal areas for which you want to receive MSI, considering your intended voyage. Also enter the MSI message types you want to receive, rejecting any unwanted types.

While in port, keep the EGC receiver in operation, to ensure that you have received all necessary MSI before sailing.

Find out the Class of your EGC receive facility (referring to the manufacturer's literature, or to the Inmarsat Maritime Communications Handbook), and note the following points:

Make sure your Inmarsat C MES monitors the appropriate satellite/Ocean Region at the time of a scheduled broadcast.

If the EGC receive facility shares a directional antenna with an Inmarsat A MES, make sure that the antenna is tracking the appropriate satellite at the time of a scheduled broadcast. (Note that Inmarsat does not recommend this configuration.)

Note that if you wish to continue to receive MSI information from a particular ocean region, you must set the automatic scan facility on your Inmarsat C MES to scan only that ocean region by making it the ***only preferred ocean region***. For details please refer to your Inmarsat C manufacturer's operating handbook.

Throughout your voyage, ensure that a written log is kept of the identities of all received messages, and a printed copy is kept of all distress traffic.

WHAT TO DO ABOUT MISSED MESSAGES

If you think you have missed any messages, for example at a scheduled broadcast time, you can:

Switch the terminal off and on again - this will clear the internal memory of all stored message IDs, so that if the message is re-broadcast, your receiver will not reject it as a repeated message, and will print/store it.

Check with the LES which broadcast the message whether they offer a re-broadcast facility (some LESs do this as a chargeable service).

The full version of the SafetyNET User's Handbook published by Inmarsat Ltd is available at www.inmarsat.com/safety/support/tools

FOR GENERAL INFORMATION ON THE INTERNATIONAL SAFETYNET SERVICE, AND THE GMDSS, CONTACT:

Telephone: +44(0)207 7357611 **Fax:** +44(0)207 5873210

FOR GENERAL INFORMATION ON THE INMARSAT SATELLITE NETWORKS, YOU CAN CONTACT THE INMARSAT CUSTOMER CARE CENTRE:

Telephone: +44(0)207 7281777 **Fax:** +44(0)207 7281746 **Website:** www.inmarsat.com/safety

The Customer Care Centre is normally manned between the hours 0600 to 2359, UK local time, Monday to Friday.

AREA OF RESPONSIBILITY FOR HIGH SEAS (GMDSS)

METAREA	Issuing service	Preparation service	Area LES of issuing service a) For scheduled broadcasts b) For unscheduled broadcasts	Notes
I	United Kingdom	United Kingdom, Norway	a) Goonhilly (For AOR-W) b) Goonhilly (For AOR-W, AOR-E)	1, 2
II	France	France	a) Aussaguel (For AOR-E) Aussaguel (For AOR-W) b) Aussaguel (For AOR-E) Aussaguel (For AOR-W)	1, 2
III	Greece	Greece, France	a) Thermopylae (For AOR-E) b) Thermopylae (For AOR-E & IOR)	1, 2
IV	USA	USA	a) Southbury (For AOR-W) b) Southbury (For AOR-W) Southbury (For AOR-E)	1, 2

Notes
1. Full coverage via SafetyNET for areas not covered by NAVTEX
2. Partial NAVTEX coverage

EGC SAFETYNET SYSTEM

Transmission schedule for full GMDSS service

NAV/MET AREA	NAV information		MET information		Satellite
	Co-ordinator	Times (UTC)	Issuing Country	Times (UTC)	
I	United Kingdom	1730 & as appropriate (AOR–E)	United Kingdom	0930, 2130 (AOR–E) Warnings only (AOR–W)	AOR–E / AOR–W
II	France	1630 (AOR–E)	France	0900, 2100 (AOR–E / AOR–W)	AOR–E / AOR–W
III	Spain	1200, 2400 & on receipt (AOR–E)	Greece	1000, 2200 (AOR-E)	AOR–E
IV	USA	1000, 2200 (0000, 1200 Ice reports N Atlantic)	USA	0430, 1030, 1630, 2230	AOR–W
V	Brazil	0400, 1230	Brazil	0130, 0730, 1330, 1930	AOR–E

Broadcast times for **MET information** published in the table above are for routine Weather Messages, Storm warnings are also broadcast on receipt. LT - Local Time.

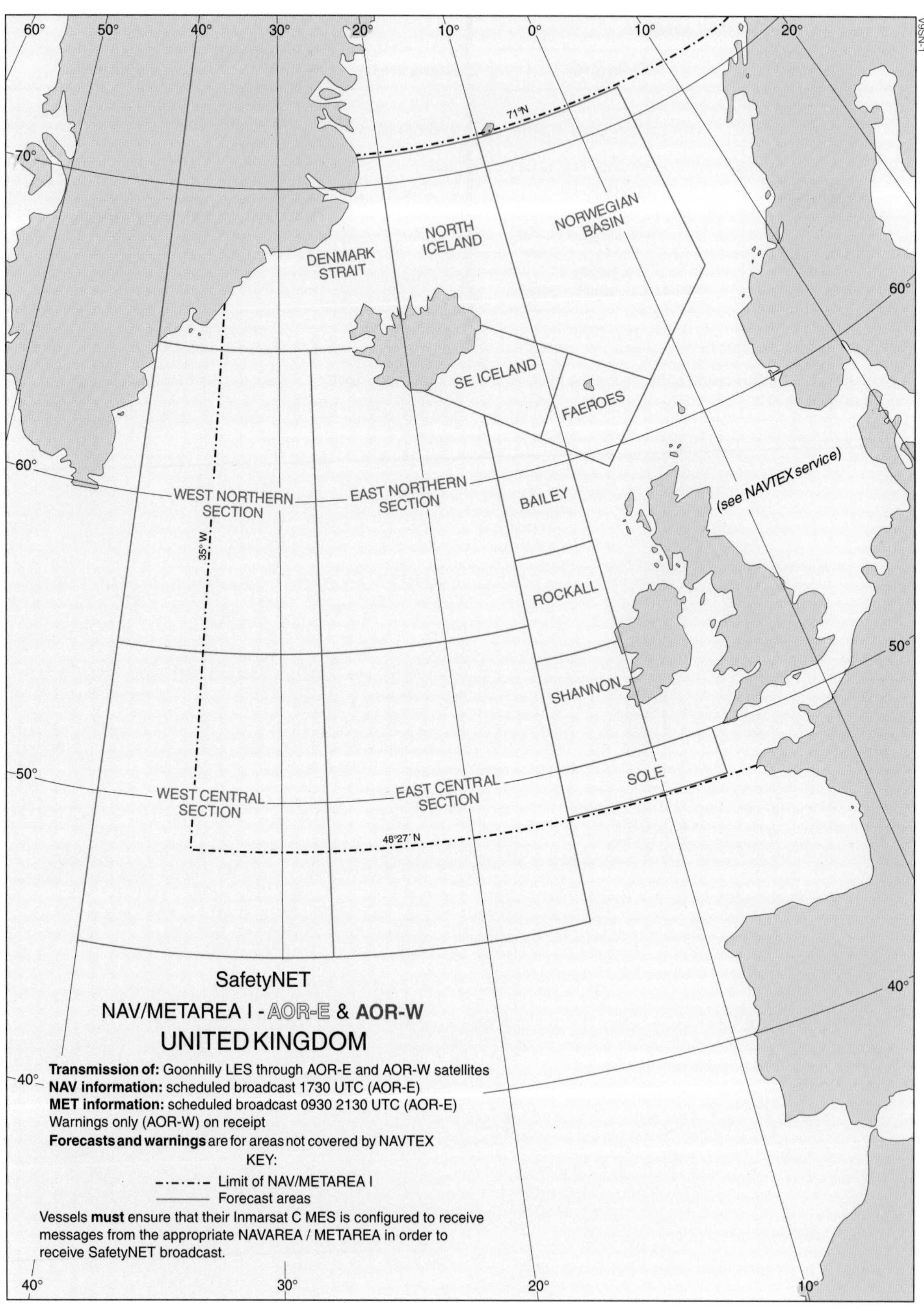

V9SN-1
60°
50°
40°
30°
20°
10°
0°
10°
20°
70°
60°
50°
40°
71°N
DENMARK
STRAIT
NORTH
ICELAND
NORWEGIAN
BASIN
SE ICELAND
FAEROES
WEST NORTHERN
SECTION
EAST NORTHERN
SECTION
BAILEY
(see NAVTEX service)
35° W
ROCKALL
SHANNON
SOLE
WEST CENTRAL
SECTION
EAST CENTRAL
SECTION
48°27' N
SafetyNET
NAV/METAREA I - AOR-E & AOR-W
UNITED KINGDOM
Transmission of: Goonhilly LES through AOR-E and AOR-W satellites
NAV information: scheduled broadcast 1730 UTC (AOR-E)
MET information: scheduled broadcast 0930 2130 UTC (AOR-E)
Warnings only (AOR-W) on receipt
Forecasts and warnings are for areas not covered by NAVTEX
KEY:
Limit of NAV/METAREA I
Forecast areas
Vessels must ensure that their Inmarsat C MES is configured to receive messages from the appropriate NAVAREA / METAREA in order to receive SafetyNET broadcast.
40°
30°
20°
10°

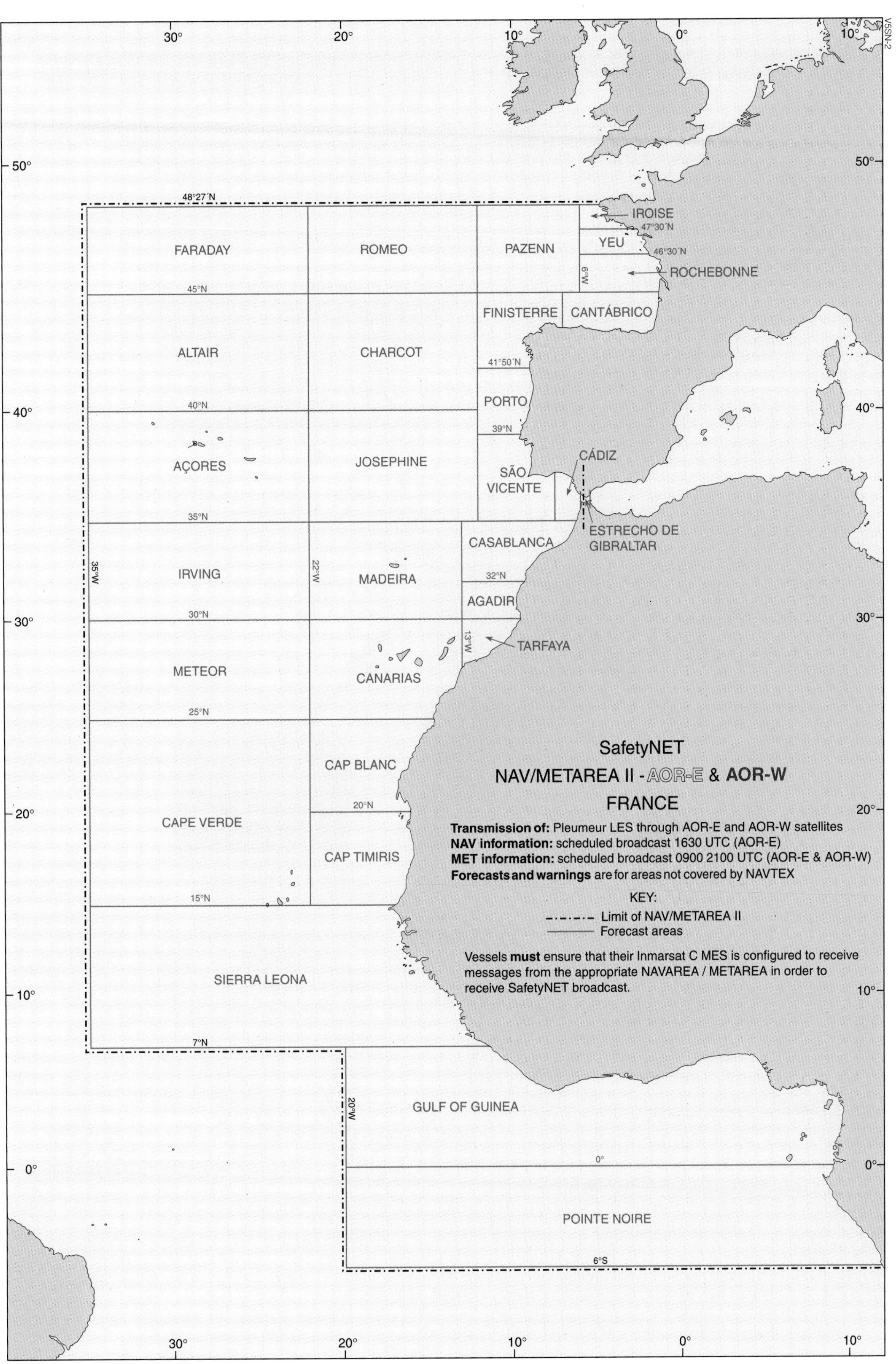
V5SN-2
30°
20°
10°
0°
10°
50°
40°
30°
20°
10°
0°
48°27′N
FARADAY
ROMEO
PAZENN
IROISE
47°30′N
YEU
46°30′N
ROCHEBONNE
6°W
45°N
FINISTERRE
CANTÁBRICO
ALTAIR
CHARCOT
41°50′N
PORTO
40°N
39°N
AÇORES
JOSEPHINE
CÁDIZ
SÃO VICENTE
35°N
ESTRECHO DE GIBRALTAR
CASABLANCA
35°W
22°W
IRVING
MADEIRA
32°N
AGADIR
30°N
13°W
TARFAYA
METEOR
CANARIAS
25°N
CAP BLANC
20°N
CAPE VERDE
CAP TIMIRIS
15°N
SIERRA LEONA
7°N
20°W
GULF OF GUINEA
0°
POINTE NOIRE
6°S
SafetyNET
NAV/METAREA II - AOR-E & AOR-W
FRANCE
Transmission of: Pleumeur LES through AOR-E and AOR-W satellites
NAV information: scheduled broadcast 1630 UTC (AOR-E)
MET information: scheduled broadcast 0900 2100 UTC (AOR-E & AOR-W)
Forecasts and warnings are for areas not covered by NAVTEX
KEY:
Limit of NAV/METAREA II
Forecast areas
Vessels must ensure that their Inmarsat C MES is configured to receive messages from the appropriate NAVAREA / METAREA in order to receive SafetyNET broadcast.

NAVTEX

INTRODUCTION

NAVTEX is an international automated direct-printing service for promulgation of navigational and meteorological warnings and urgent information to vessel. It has been developed to provide a low cost, simple and automated means of receiving maritime safety information on board vessels at sea and in coastal waters. The information transmitted is relevant to all sizes and types of vessel and the selective message-rejection feature ensures that every mariner can receive a safety information broadcast which is tailored to his particular needs.

NAVTEX fulfils an integral role in the GMDSS and is also a component of the World-Wide Navigational Warning Service (WWNWS).

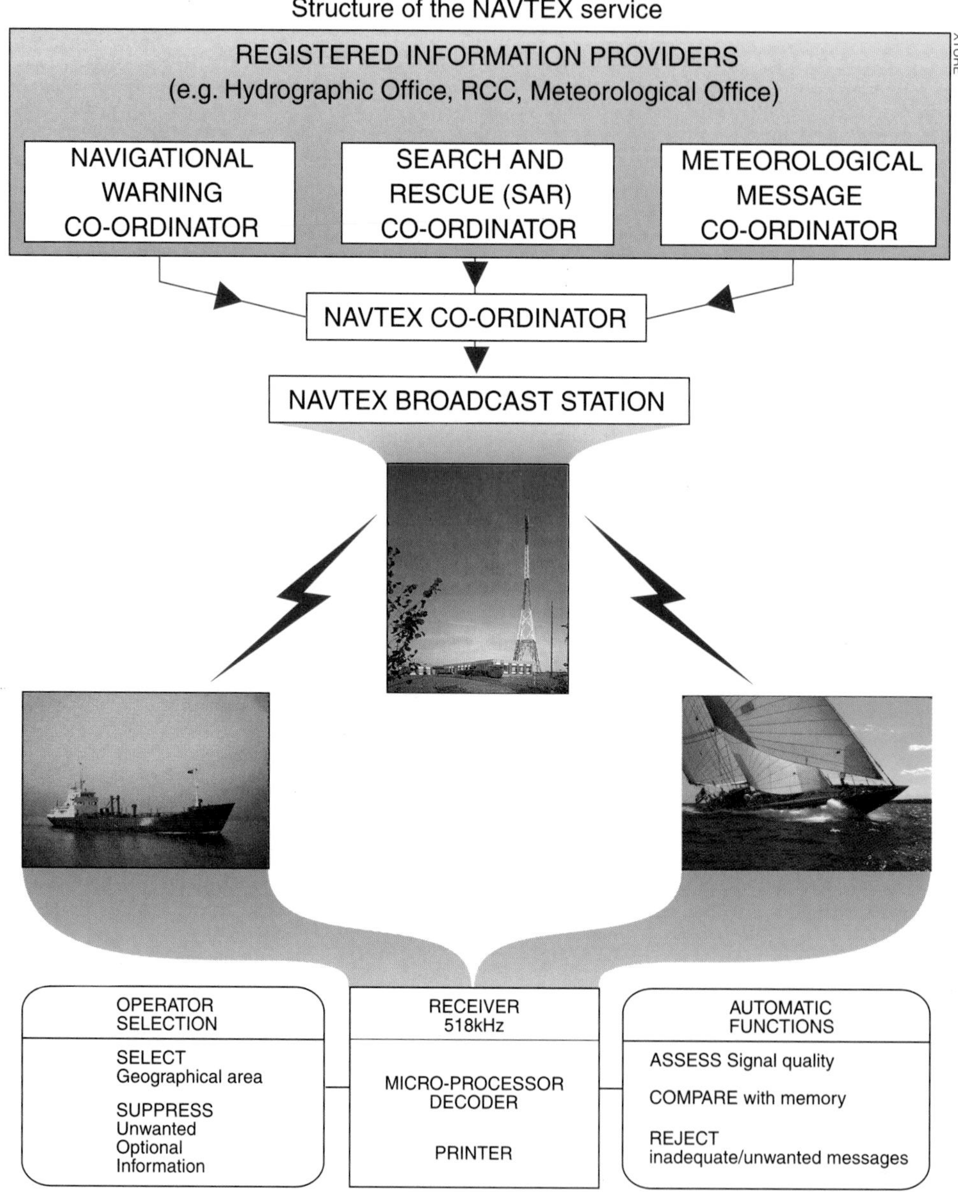

NAVTEX RECEPTION

Users should be aware that where there is a significant overland path between the transmitter site and the user, the strength of the signal will be markedly reduced, as will the range at which that signal may be received. Furthermore the topography of ports, harbours and marinas and the presence of high rise buildings may distort or preclude reception of NAVTEX. Up-to-date NAVTEX weather information SHOULD be available from all Harbour Masters, however, many do not provide such a service.

1. DEFINITIONS

(a) *NAVTEX* means the system for the broadcast and automatic reception of maritime safety information by means of narrow-band direct-printing telegraphy.

(b) *International NAVTEX service* means the co-ordinated broadcast and automatic reception on the frequency 518 kHz of maritime safety information by means of narrow-band direct-printing telegraphy using the English language.

(c) *National NAVTEX services* means the broadcast and automatic reception of maritime safety information by means of narrow-band direct-printing telegraphy using frequencies other than 518 kHz and languages decided by the Administrations concerned.

2. PRINCIPAL FEATURES OF NAVTEX

The service uses a single frequency with transmissions from nominated stations within each NAVAREA being arranged on a time-sharing basis to eliminate mutual interference. All necessary information is contained in each transmission.

The power of each transmitter is regulated so as to avoid the possibility of interference between transmitters.

A dedicated NAVTEX receiver which has the ability to select messages to be printed, according to:

(a) a technical code ($B_1B_2B_3B_4$), which appears in the preamble of each message; and

(b) whether or not the particular message has already been printed.

Certain essential classes of safety information such as navigational and meteorological warnings and search and rescue information are non-rejectable to ensure that ships using NAVTEX always receive the most vital information.

NAVTEX co-ordinators exercise control of messages transmitted by each station according to the information contained in each message and the geographical coverage required. Thus a user may choose to accept messages either from the single transmitter which serves the sea area around his position, or from a number of transmitters as appropriate.

3. LANGUAGE AND NATIONAL BROADCAST OPTIONS

There is often a requirement for broadcasts to be made in languages, in addition to English, for other types of messages. Methods of achieving these objectives are outlined below:

(a) Use of a separate transmitter identification character (B_1) on 518 kHz. (Subject to co-ordination procedures set out by IMO and ITU.)

(b) Use of additional subject indicator characters (B_2) V, W, X and Y on 518 kHz. (Subject to allocation by the NAVTEX Panel.)

(c) Use of national NAVTEX services as defined in paragraph 1(c).

(d) Provision of national NAVTEX services on the internationally adopted frequency for such services (490 kHz or 4209·5 kHz).

MESSAGE PRIORITIES

Three message priorities are used to dictate the timing of the first broadcast of a new warning in the NAVTEX service. In descending order of urgency they are:

VITAL — for immediate broadcast, subject to avoiding interference to ongoing transmissions;

IMPORTANT — for broadcast at the next available period when the frequency is unused;

ROUTINE — for broadcast at the next scheduled transmission period.

Note-Both VITAL and IMPORTANT warnings will normally need to be repeated, if still valid, at the next scheduled transmission period.

The standard format of NAVTEX messages

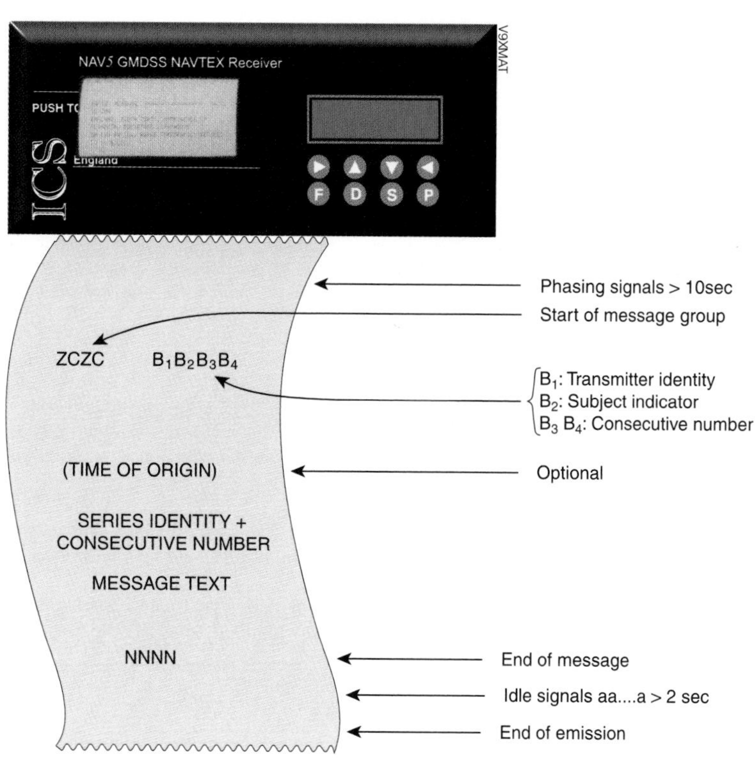

THE TRANSMITTER IDENTIFICATION CHARACTER (B_1)

The transmitter identification character B_1 is a single unique letter which is allocated to each transmitter. It is used to identify the broadcasts which are to be accepted by the receiver, and those which are to be rejected.

In order to avoid erroneous reception of transmissions from two stations having the same B_1 character, it is necessary to ensure that such stations have a large geographical separation. This is achieved by allocating B_1 characters in line with the general global scheme, within the IMO-adopted strategy for allocating B_1 characters by alphabetical sequence through each NAVAREA of the World-Wide Navigational Warning Service. NAVTEX transmissions have a designed range of about 400 nautical miles. The minimum distance between two transmitters with the same B_1 identifier is usually sufficient to ensure that a receiver cannot be within range of both at the same time.

SUBJECT INDICATOR CHARACTERS (B_2)

Information is grouped by subject on the NAVTEX broadcast, and each subject group is allocated a subject indicator character, B_2.
The subject indicator character is used by the receiver to identify different classes of messages as listed below. The indicator is also used to reject messages concerning certain optional subjects which are not required by the vessel. Receivers also use the B_2 character to identify messages which, because of their importance, may not be rejected. The following subject indicator characters are in use:

A = Navigational Warnings (cannot be rejected by the receiver)
B = Meteorological Warnings (cannot be rejected by the receiver)
C = Ice Reports
D = Search and Rescue information (cannot be rejected by the receiver)
E = Meteorological Forecasts
F = Pilot Service Messages
G = Defunct Service
H = LORAN Messages
I = Available
J = SATNAV Messages
K = Other Electronic Navaid Messages (messages concerning radio navigation services)
L = Navigational Warnings-additional to letter A (should not be rejected by the receiver (continuation of B_2 subject group "A"))
V = Special services-trial allocation
W= Special services-trial allocation
X = Special services-trial allocation
Y = Special services-trial allocation
Z = No messages on hand

Maritime Safety Information Broadcasts from **UK NAVTEX Stations** - Revised use of the Subject Indicator Character B_2.

The majority of UK originated Navigational Warnings (WZ and NAVAREA ONE messages) are currently transmitted using the NAVTEX subject indicator character B_2 "A". Full use is now being made of the following NAVTEX subject indicator characters:

A = Navigational Warnings, including Mobile Drilling Rig Movements (cannot be rejected by the receiver) see also "V"
B = Meteorological Warnings (cannot be rejected by the receiver)
C = Ice Reports
D = Search and Rescue information, including Piracy and Armed Robbery Warnings (cannot be rejected by the receiver)
E = Meteorological Forecasts
F = Pilot Service Messages
G = Defunct Service
H = LORAN Messages
I = Available
J = SATNAV Messages
K = Other Electronic Navaid Messages (messages concerning radio navigation services)
L = Subfacts / Gunfacts Warnings, brief message with details of VHF Channels and broadcast timings (should not be rejected by the receiver)
V = Amplifying Navigational Warning Information initially announced under "A"
W= Special services-trial allocation
X = Special services-trial allocation
Y = Special services-trial allocation
Z = No messages on hand

Navigational Warnings are designed to be brief and easily understood. Occasionally there is a requirement to supply amplifying details. To achieve this service any additional information will be broadcast as a NAVAREA ONE message using the NAVTEX subject indicator character "V" which can be programmed out if the detailed information is not required.

Example:

WZ 123
England East Coast. Great Yarmouth Approaches.
Extensive buoyage alterations will be implemented from 1200 UTC on 5 May 2003.
Full details in NAVAREA ONE 056 (GV32) - (the NAVTEX Code)

Attention is drawn to the NAVTEX handbook for details of programming the receiver to accept various subject indicator characters.

MESSAGE NUMBERING (B_3 B_4)

Each message within a subject group is allocated a serial number, B_3 B_4, between 01 and 99. This number will not necessarily relate to series numbering in other radio navigational warning systems. On reaching 99, numbering will re-commence at 01 but avoiding the use of message numbers still in force.
A shortage of numbers will, where possible, be alleviated by the allocation of messages to other, relevant subject groups. It has been found that 99 messages are not always enough for some subject groups, and B_2 = L may be used for additional navigational warnings, to receive the overflow from B_2 = A when necessary.

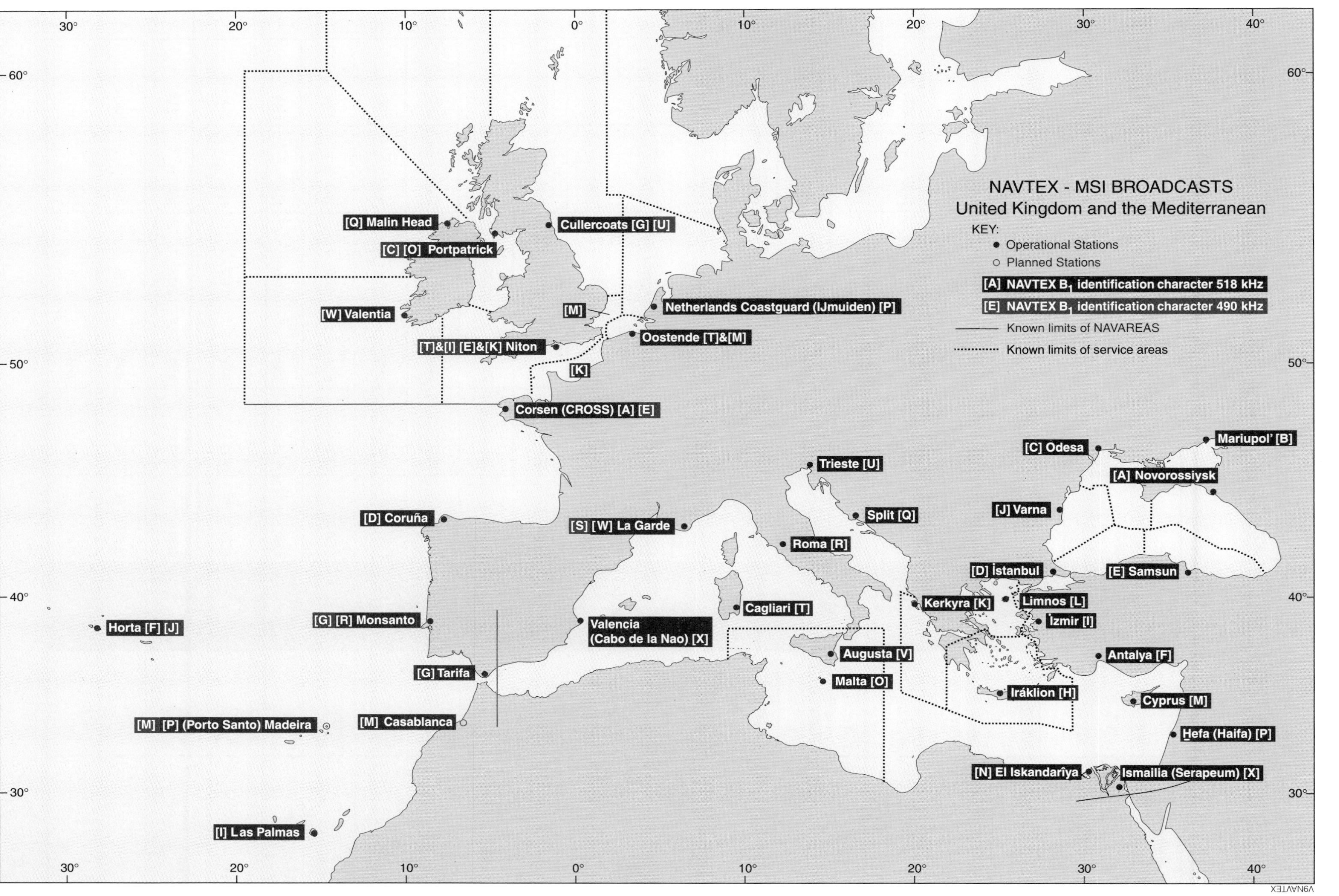

NAVTEX - MSI BROADCASTS
United Kingdom and the Mediterranean
KEY:
Operational Stations
Planned Stations
[A] NAVTEX B_1 identification character 518 kHz
[E] NAVTEX B_1 identification character 490 kHz
Known limits of NAVAREAS
Known limits of service areas
[Q] Malin Head
[C] [O] Portpatrick
Cullercoats [G] [U]
[W] Valentia
[M]
Netherlands Coastguard (IJmuiden) [P]
Oostende [T]&[M]
[T]&[I] [E]&[K] Niton
[K]
Corsen (CROSS) [A] [E]
[D] Coruña
[S] [W] La Garde
Trieste [U]
Split [Q]
Roma [R]
[C] Odesa
Mariupol' [B]
[A] Novorossiysk
[J] Varna
[D] İstanbul
[E] Samsun
Kerkyra [K]
Limnos [L]
İzmir [I]
Cagliari [T]
[G] [R] Monsanto
Valencia
(Cabo de la Nao) [X]
Horta [F] [J]
Augusta [V]
Antalya [F]
[G] Tarifa
Malta [O]
Iráklion [H]
Cyprus [M]
[M] [P] (Porto Santo) Madeira
[M] Casablanca
Hefa (Haifa) [P]
[N] El Iskandarîya
Ismailia (Serapeum) [X]
[I] Las Palmas
30°
20°
10°
0°
10°
20°
30°
40°
60°
50°
40°
30°
V9NAVTEX

NAVTEX MSI BROADCASTS 518 kHz

UK - MEDITERRANEAN (INCLUDING AZORES)

Station name	Position	B_1 ident	Transmission times every 4 hours. Weather bulletins in red					
Antalya **Turkey**	38°21′N 26°35′E	F	0050	0450	0850	1250	1650	2050
Augusta **Italy**	37°14′N 15°14′E	V	0330	0730	1130	1530	1930	2330
Cagliari **Italy**	39°14′N 09°14′E	T	0310	0710	1110	1510	1910	2310
Corsen **France**	48°28′N 05°03′W	A	0000	0400	0800	1200	1600	2000
Coruña **Spain**	43°21′N 08°27′W	D	0030	0430	0830	1230	1630	2030
Cullercoats **UK**	55°04′N 1°28′W	G	0100	0500	0900	1300	1700	2100
Cyprus	35°10′N 33°26′E	M	0200	0600	1000	1400	1800	2200
El Iskandariya **Egypt**	31°12′N 29°52′E	N	0210	0610	1010	1410	1810	2210
Ḥefa **Israel**	32°49′N 35°00′E	P	0020	0420	0820	1220	1620	2020
Horta **Azores**	38°32′N 28°38′W	F	0050	0450	0850	1250	1650	2050
Iraklion Kritis **Crete**	35°20′N 25°07′E	H	0110	0510	0910	1310	1710	2110
İstanbul **Turkey**	41°04′N 28°57′E	D	0030	0430	0830	1230	1630	2030
İzmir **Turkey**	38°21′N 26°35′E	I	0120	0520	0920	1320	1720	2120
Kerkyra **Greece**	39°45′N 19°52′E	K	0140	0540	0940	1340	1740	2140
La Garde **France**	43°06′N 05°59′E	W	0340	0740	1140	1540	1940	2340
Limnos **Greece**	39°52′N 25°04′E	L	0150	0550	0950	1350	1750	2150
Malin Head **Ireland**	55°22′N 07°21′W	Q	0240	0640	1040	1440	1840	2240
Malta	35°49′N 14°32′E	O	0220	0620	1020	1420	1820	2220
Monsanto **Portugal**	38°44′N 09°11′W	R	0250	0650	1050	1450	1850	2250
Niton **UK**	50°35′N 01°18′W	E	0040	0440	0840	1240	1640	2040
		K	0140	0540	0940	1340	1740	2140

Station name	Position	B_1 ident	Transmission times every 4 hours. Weather bulletins in red					
Oostende **Belgium**	51°11′N 02°48′E	T	0310	0710	1110	1510	1910	2310
		M	0200	0600	1000	1400	1800	2200
Porto Santo (PLANNED) **Madeira**	33°04′N 16°20′W	P	*0230*	*0630*	*1030*	*1430*	*1830*	*2230*
Portpatrick **UK**	54°51′N 05°07′W	O	0220	0620	1020	1420	1820	2220
Roma **Italy**	41°48′N 12°31′E	R	0250	0650	1050	1450	1850	2250
Split **Croatia**	43°30′N 16°29′E	Q	0240	0640	1040	1440	1840	2240
Tarifa **Spain**	36°01′N 05°35′W	G	0100	0500	0900	1300	1700	2100
Trieste **Italy**	45°41′N 13°46′E	U	0320	0720	1120	1520	1920	2320
Valencia **Spain**	39°27′N 0°20′W	X	0350	0750	1150	1550	1950	2350
Valentia **Ireland**	51°27′N 09°49′W	W	0340	0740	1140	1540	1940	2340

NAVTEX MSI BROADCASTS 490 kHz

UK - MEDITERRANEAN (INCLUDING AZORES)

Station name	Position	B_1 ident	**National Navtex Service.** Weather bulletins in BLUE					
Corsen (Language French) **France**	48°28′N 05°03′W	E	0040	0440	0840	1240	1640	2040
Cullercoats **UK**	55°04′N 01°28′W	U		0720			1920	
Horta (Language Portuguese) **Azores**	38°32′N 28°38′W	J	0130	0530	0930	1330	1730	2130
La Garde (Language French) **France**	43°06′N 05°59′E	S	0300	0700	1100	1500	1900	2300
Monsanto (Language Portuguese) **Portugal**	38°44′N 09°11′W	G	0100	0500	0900	1300	1700	2100
Niton **UK**	50°35′N 01°18′W	I		0520			1720	
Niton **UK** (Language French)		T	0310	0710	1110	1510	1910	2310
Porto Santo (PLANNED) (Language Portuguese) **Madeira**	33°04′N 16°20′W	M	*0100*	*0500*	*0900*	*1300*	*1700*	*2100*
Portpatrick **UK**	54°51′N 05°07′W	C			0820			2020

FURTHER DETAILED INFORMATION CAN BE FOUND IN THE RELEVANT MSI BROADCAST SECTION OF EACH COUNTRY

NAVTEX EQUIPMENT

The dedicated equipment typically comprises a small unit containing a receiver fixed-tuned to the broadcast frequency, a printer and a dedicated aerial. There are also a number of paperless units available based on a small microcomputer capable of receiving and storing NAVTEX information suitable for small craft, were space is at a premium. With the increasing use of the frequency 490 kHz for broadcasting weather services for small craft, manufactuers are introducing dual frequency receivers specifically aimed at the the leisure market. A recent advance is a PC based system which connects a NAVTEX antenna to the internal PC receiver via a spare serial (or USB) port .

The equipment should be left switched on continuously and may be programmed to receive only selected stations and/or categories of messages. A microprocessor control ensures that a routine message already received will not be reprinted on subsequent transmissions (provided that the equipment has not been switched off).

PRACTICAL INSTRUCTIONS FOR THE USE OF A NAVTEX RECEIVER

The NAVTEX receiver is a Narrow-Band Direct-Printing (NBDP) device operating primarily on the frequency 518kHz. Dual receivers can also receive on the supplementary *(National)* frequency 490 kHz (some equipment may also operate on 4209.5 kHz), and is a vital part of the GMDSS.

It automatically receives Maritime Safety Information such as Radio Navigational Warnings, Storm/Gale Warnings, Meteorological Forecasts, Piracy Warnings & Distress Alerts etc:

Each message begins with a start of message function (ZCZC) followed by a space then four B characters. The first, (B_1), identifies the station being received, the second (B_2), identifies the subject ie Navigational Warning, Met Forecasts etc, and the third and fourth, (B_3+B_4), form the consecutive number of the message from that station. This is followed by the text of the message and ends with an end of message function (NNNN).

The NAVTEX system broadcasts COASTAL WARNINGS which cover the area from the Fairway Buoy out to 250 nautical miles from the transmitter; the transmissions from some transmitters can be received out to 400 nautical miles and even further in unusual propagational conditions.

NAVTEX RECEIVER CHECK LIST

For a NAVTEX receiver to function effectively, it is essential that the operator should have a sound knowledge of how to programme and operate his/her particular receiver. This is not difficult provided the following practicable steps are followed:-

1. Make sure that there are sufficient rolls of NAVTEX paper on board; if this is not the case, replenish the stock immediately. Should you run out of paper and therefore not be able to receive vital safety information, you could seriously endanger your vessel.
2. Check that there is paper in the receiver.
3. Turn the NAVTEX receiver on at least 4 hours before sailing, or better still, leave it turned on permanently. This avoids the chance of losing vital information.
4. Make sure that you carry the **Equipment Operating Manual** onboard.
5. Programme only the B_1 character of the NAVTEX station which covers the area in which your vessel is currently sailing and the one covering the area into which you are about to sail. This will preclude the equipment printing information which has no relevance to your voyage and will avoid unnecessary waste of paper.
6. Programme the receiver with the B_2 characters (type of message) you wish to receive. It is recommended that most B_2 characters (A to Z) be programmed, but you may exclude those for navaid equipments (Loran C for example) with which your vessel is **NOT** fitted. Be aware that the characters A, B and D, are mandatory and cannot be rejected.
7. Take extra care not to confuse the programming of B_1 characters (station designators) with those of B_2 characters (type of messages). It is very easy for an operator to believe that he/she is programming B_1 characters when in fact they are programming B_2 characters. After programming **ALWAYS CHECK** the programme status to ensure that it is correct.
8. If information is received incomplete/garbled, inform the relevant NAVTEX station, giving the UTC and your vessel's position. You will obtain the information you require, and also help to improve the system. Any safety-critical occurences observed during the voyage should be passed to the National Co-ordinator responsible for the area in which you are sailing. This information may be used to update the Maritime Safety Information being broadcast over the NAVTEX service.

INMARSAT - LAND EARTH STATION OPERATORS CONTACTS AND SERVICES

The Inmarsat satellite services are available throughout the Atlantic, Pacific and Indian Oceans but not in certain parts of the polar regions. Communications are established through satellites in geostationary orbits, positioned over each of the four ocean areas.

LAND EARTH STATION OPERATORS CONTACTS AND SERVICES

Operator	Country	Services offered	Customer Services points of contact	Customer Service e-mail
Bezeq - The Israel Telecommunication Corp Ltd	Israel	**B,m,M,GAN**	Tel: +972 2 9904555 Fax: +972 2 9995490	c_s@sat711.com
CP Radio Marconi (Telecom Portugal)	Portugal	**C**	Tel: +351 1 21 9678760 Fax: +351 1 21 9279151	
France Telecom	France	**A,B,C,m,M, GAN,Fleet,c**	Tel: +33 5 56223231 Fax: +33 5 56836176 Telex: +42 560078	mobilesat@francetelecom.fr www.francetelecom-mobilsat.com
OTE SA	Greece	**A,B,C,m,M, GAN,Fleet,c**	Tel: +30 21 08114035 Fax: +30 21 06855880 Telex: +601 214171	customer_care@otesat.gr
Stratos Mobile Networks	Canada	**A,B,E,m,M, GAN**	Tel: +1 709 7484226 Fax: +1 709 7484320 Telex: +21 01921524	support@stratos.ca www.stratos.ca
Telecom Italia	Italy	**A,B,C,m,M,Fleet,c**	Tel: +39 06 36880397 Fax: +39 06 36872429	
Telenor Satellite Services AS	Norway	**A,B,C,m,M, GAN,Fleet,c**	Tel: +47 514 08060 Fax: +47 514 02240 Telex: +56 33280	eikvakt@telenor.com
Türk Telekom	Turkey	**A,C**	Tel: +90 312 3131579 Fax: +90 312 3131597	
Xantic	Netherlands	**A,B,C,D,m,M, GAN,Fleet,c**	Tel: +31 70 3434543 Fax: +31 70 3434796 Telex: +44 41400	services@xantic.net www.xantic.net

Key to services:

A: Inmarsat A **B: Inmarsat B** **C: Inmarsat C** **c: Inmarsat mini-C** **D: Inmarsat D/D+**
E: Inmarsat E **M: Inmarsat M** **m: Inmarsat mini-M** **GAN: Global Area Network**

HELP-LINE SERVICE

Inmarsat 'Help-lines', which contain information about the various Inmarsat services, are available to any person, ashore or afloat, who has access to the International telephone and telex networks.

The 'Help-line' is also available on UK telex number (51) 920327 INMHLP G, 24 hours a day, 7 days a week, and is available for access by anyone with a telex terminal. Inmarsat A and B users anywhere can obtain up-to-date information 24 hours a day. To use the telex 'Help-line', after connection wait for the system to exchange answerbacks; you will then be welcomed to the database. Do not type any message until you have received the welcome message. The option required should then be selected followed by . (full stop); the . (full stop) acts as the indication that you have finished your selection.

The following option facilities are available:

(1) **Information retrieval** – A menu-driven database that can be used to retrieve any generic information placed in the database including information on Land Earth Stations and the services offered.
(2) **Page Operator** – Whereby callers can have a 'live' telex conversation with Inmarsat Directorate personnel. This facility is available during normal UK working hours (0900-1700) when the Maritime Customer Relations Engineer will deal with answering enquiries using this facility. This facility is expected to be used when an immediate answer to a query is required.
(3) **Director of Retrievable information** – This option gives a listing of all information available for retrieval together with the date of origination. This is to enable users to see if they have the latest updated information.
(4) **Help** – This option contains instructions on how to use the Telex 'Help-line'.
(5) **Query Inmarsat Ship Directory** – This facility contains the main and second ID numbers of all Inmarsat A and Inmarsat C equipped vessels. If the ID number is listed as ex-directory the enquirer will see the indication 'Private' instead of the ID number.
(6) **Logoff**

GENERAL INFORMATION

The Inmarsat A, Inmarsat B and Inmarsat C maritime satellite services are available throughout the Atlantic, Pacific and Indian Oceans but not in certain parts of the polar regions. Communications are established through satellites in geostationary orbits, positioned over each of the four ocean areas (see page 71).

Each ocean region has the equivalent of a country area code which prefaces the telex or telephone (fax) or data number to be dialled. By ocean region, these codes are as follows: (Details on the Pacific Ocean Region can be found in NP290)

	ATLANTIC EAST (AOR–E)	ATLANTIC WEST (AOR–W)	INDIAN (IOR)
Telephone:	871	874	873
Telex:	581	584	583
Data (PSDN):	1111	1114	1113

INMARSAT A LAND EARTH STATION OPERATORS AND ACCESS CODES

Land Earth Station Operator	Country	AOR-E		AOR-W		IOR	
		Octal	Decimal	Octal	Decimal	Octal	Decimal
France Telecom	France	17	15	17	15	17	15
OTE	Greece	15	13	07	07	05	05
Stratos Mobile Networks	Canada	13-1	11-1			13-1	11-1
Stratos (Goonhilly LES)	Canada	02	02	02	02		
Telecom Italia	Italy	05	05	05	05	13-4	11-4
Türk Telekom	Turkey	10	08			10	08
Xantic	Netherlands	12	10	12	10	12	10

INMARSAT B LAND EARTH STATION OPERATORS AND ACCESS CODES

Land Earth Station Operator	Country	AOR-E	AOR-W	IOR
Bezeq	Israel	711		711
France Telecom	France	011	011	011
France Telecom (Ex DeteSat)	France	111	111	111
OTE	Greece	005	005	005
Stratos Mobile Networks	Canada	013	013	013
Stratos (Goonhilly LES)	Canada	002/202	002/202	002
Stratos (Laurentides LES)	Canada	113	113	
Telecom Italia	Italy	555	555	555
Xantic	Netherlands	012	012	012

INMARSAT C LAND EARTH STATION OPERATORS AND ACCESS CODES

Land Earth Station Operator	Country	AOR-E	AOR-W	IOR
Bezeq	Israel	127		327
CP Radio Marconi	Portugal	118		
France Telecom	France	121	021	321
France Telecom (Ex DeteSat)	France	115		333
OTE	Greece	120		305
Stratos (Goonhilly LES)	Canada	102	002	302
Telecom Italia	Italy	105		335
Türk Telekom	Turkey	110		310
Xantic	Netherlands	112	012	312

GMDSS SERVICES

Distress Alerting is available on all maritime MESs enabling the MES in distress to send distress information on the signalling channel to MRCC for the required actions. The distress alerting information includes the MES identity (Inmarsat C Mobile Number), date, latitude, longitude, course, speed, time of position update and nature of distress. The position is updated either from integrated or external GPS receiver or manually from a keyboard.

Distress Priority message is prepared in the MES text editor and sent on the messaging channel to MRCC regardless of the address given. The message may contain more detailed distress related information, eg. distress circumstances and assistance required.

The following services which relate directly to Distress and Safety are offered by all LESs as specified in the Radio Regulations under the GMDSS.

2 digit code	Service	Remarks
32	Medical Advice	Use this code to obtain medical advice. Some LES have direct connections with local hospitals when this code is used.
38	Medical Assistance	This code should be used if the condition of an ill or injured person on board the vessel requires urgent evacuation ashore or the services of a doctor aboard the vessel. This code will ensure that the call is routed to the appropriate agency/authority ashore to deal with the situation.
39	Maritime Assistance	This code should be used to obtain Maritime assistance if the vessel requires assistance or in cases of oil pollution, etc.
42	Navigational Hazards and Warnings	This code provides a connection to a navigational office for transmission of information from the vessel on any warnings hazards which could endanger safety of navigation (e.g. wrecks, derelicts, floating obstructions, defective radiobeacons or light vessels, icebergs, floating mines etc.).

For further information, contact Inmarsat customer services on +44(0)207 7281777.

SATELLITE ACQUISITION

To operate any Inmarsat equipment is it essential to acquire the satellite signal (Common Signalling Channel), and "lock" on to that signal before the equipment can operate. In principle, the satellite has to be "acquired" either manually or automatically by pointing the antenna accurately towards the satellite for the chosen Ocean Region.

Inmarsat C equipment uses a small omni-directional type of antenna which only requires an unobstructed line-of-sight view of the satellite.

Inmarsat A, B and M Mobile Earth Stations use a high gain parabolic dish or phased array antennæ which must be pointed at the required satellite quite precisely. Such antennæ must be steered and gyro-stabilised against the vessel's motion. The vessel's gyro input is fed into the Mobile Earth Station and allows the antenna to remain pointed at the satellite while the vessel is moving.

A manual means of antenna adjustment is usually available by which the azimuth and elevation of the antenna can be altered to "aim" at the satellite. The beamwidth of a typical antenna is wide enough that the antenna only needs to "see" the signal as the antenna is manually aimed towards the satellite for the terminal to acquire the common signalling channel signal.

Once the equipment has achieved an initial coarse acquisition of the satellite, the electronic circuits within the equipment, *(step track circuits)* perform the fine adjustment to obtain the strongest signal and lock on to the satellite.

Most Mobile Earth Stations are able to adjust their antennæ to find the satellite automatically after input of the vessel's latitude and longitude. Where the vessel's navigational system is linked directly to the terminal, the entire satellite acquisition sequence may be programmed to take place automatically at switch on. The full automated acquistion sequence may take several minutes to complete properly.

MARITIME RESCUE CO-ORDINATION CENTRES ASSOCIATED WITH INMARSAT LAND EARTH STATIONS (LESs)

Country	Associated LES	MRCC	Contact details
		Inmarsat Service	Ocean Region Satellite
		A B C E F77	AOR-E AOR-W IOR POR
France	Aussaguel	MRCC GRIS-NEZ **(SARNET)** CROSS Gris-Nez Audinghen F-62179 WISSANT	Tel: +33 3 21872187 Fax: +33 3 21877855 Inmarsat C: 422799256 grisnezmrcc@hotmail.com
		B C E F77	AOR-E AOR-W IOR
	Pleumeur Bodou	MRCC GRIS-NEZ **(SARNET)** CROSS Gris-Nez Audinghen F-62179 WISSANT	Tel: +33 3 21872187 Fax: +33 3 21877855 Inmarsat C: 422799256 grisnezmrcc@hotmail.com
		A	AOR-E AOR-W
Greece	Thermopylae	JRCC PEIRAIÁS **(SARNET)** Ministry of Mercantile Marine Hellenic Coast Guard RCC - Maritime Section 150, Gr. Lambraki Ave. 185 18 Peiraiás	Tel: +30 210 412500 (emergency) +30 210 4220772 (emergency) Fax: +30 210 4132398 Telex: +601 211588 RCC GR +601 211254 RCC GR Inmarsat A: 1133207 RCCG Inmarsat C: 423767310 RCCG jrccpgr@mail.yen.gr
		A B C	AOR-E IOR
Italy	Fucino	MRCC ROME Italian Coast Guard Viale dell'Arte,16 Roma I-00144	Tel: +39 06 5924145 +39 06 5923569 Fax: +39 06 5922737 & 59084793 Telex: +43 611172 COGECP I +43 614156 COGECP I cgcp3rep@transportinnavigacione.it
		A B C	AOR-E IOR

Country	Associated LES	MRCC	Inmarsat Service	Contact details	Ocean Region Satellite
			A B C E F77		AOR-E AOR-W IOR POR
Netherlands	**Burum**	JRCC DEN HELDER **(SARNET)** Netherlands Coastguard P.O. Box 10000 1780 CA Den Helder	A B C F77	Tel: +31 900 0111 (emergency) +31 223 542300 (watch officer) Fax: +31 223 658358 Telex: +44 71088 KUSTW NL Inmarsat C: 424426512 CGHQ X 424477710 NLCG X kwc@kustwacht.nl	AOR-E AOR-W IOR
Norway	**Eik**	JRCC STAVANGER **(SARNET)** Sikringbygget Sola N-4050	A B C F77	Tel: +47 51517000 (emergency) +47 51646000 Fax: +47 51652334 Telex: +56 33163 RCCS N Inmarsat C: 425899999 post@jrcc-stavanger.no	AOR-E AOR-W IOR
Portugal	**Sintra**	MRCC LISBOA Comando Naval Reduto Gomes Freire Estrada Da Medrosa Oeiras 2780-070	C	Tel: +351 21 4401919 Fax: +351 21 4401954 Telex: +404 60747 MRCCL P mrcclisboa@netc.pt	AOR-E
Turkey	**Ata**	MRCC ANKARA Denizcilik Mustesarligi Ana Arama Kurtama Koordinasyon Merkezi Gazi Mustafa Kemal Bulvari No: 128/ A P.K Maltepe 06100 Ankara	A C	Tel: +90 312 2319105 +90 312 2324783 Fax: +90 312 2320823 Telex: +607 44144 DZMS TR trmrcc@denizcilik.gov.tr	AOR-E IOR
United Kingdom	**Goonhilly**	MRCC FALMOUTH **(SARNET)** HMCG Pendennis Point Castle Drive Falmouth Cornwall TR11 4WZ	A B C E F77	Tel: +44 1326 317575 Fax: +44 1326 318342 Telex: +51 45560 FALMCG G Inmarsat A: AOR-E 1441532 Inmarsat C: AOR-E 423200158 Inmarsat C: AOR-W 423200159 dso_gmdss@mcga.gov.uk	AOR-E AOR-W IOR

SARNET - MRCCs associated with an Inmarsat LES that have been declared operational on Search and Rescue Network SARNET.

SARNET is a communication broadcast system to allow international MRCCs to exchange or seek SAR information by using Inmarsat C EGC FleetNET service. MRCC Turku (Finland), MRCC Göteburg (Sweden), MRCC Madrid (Spain), RCC Bermuda, MRCC Rīga (Latvia), MRCC Reykjavik (Iceland) and RCC Norfolk (USA) are not associated with Inmarsat LESs but have also been declared operational on SARNET.

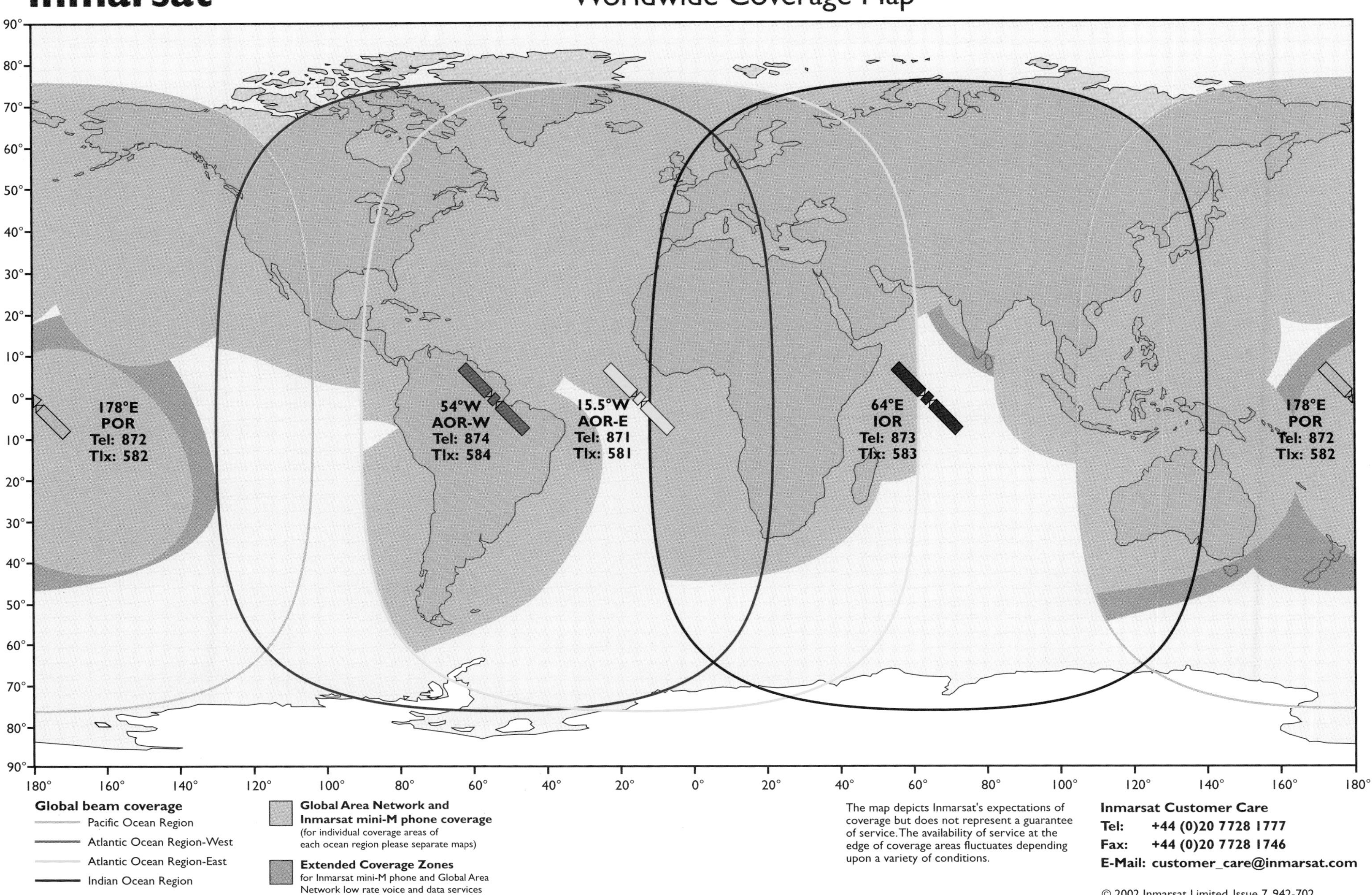
inmarsat
Mobile Satellite Communication
Worldwide Coverage Map
178°E
POR
Tel: 872
Tlx: 582
54°W
AOR-W
Tel: 874
Tlx: 584
15.5°W
AOR-E
Tel: 871
Tlx: 581
64°E
IOR
Tel: 873
Tlx: 583
178°E
POR
Tel: 872
Tlx: 582
90° 80° 70° 60° 50° 40° 30° 20° 10° 0° 10° 20° 30° 40° 50° 60° 70° 80° 90°
180° 160° 140° 120° 100° 80° 60° 40° 20° 0° 20° 40° 60° 80° 100° 120° 140° 160° 180°
Global beam coverage
Pacific Ocean Region
Atlantic Ocean Region-West
Atlantic Ocean Region-East
Indian Ocean Region
Global Area Network and
Inmarsat mini-M phone coverage
(for individual coverage areas of
each ocean region please separate maps)
Extended Coverage Zones
for Inmarsat mini-M phone and Global Area
Network low rate voice and data services
The map depicts Inmarsat's expectations of coverage but does not represent a guarantee of service. The availability of service at the edge of coverage areas fluctuates depending upon a variety of conditions.
Inmarsat Customer Care
Tel: +44 (0)20 7728 1777
Fax: +44 (0)20 7728 1746
E-Mail: customer_care@inmarsat.com
© 2002 Inmarsat Limited. Issue 7, 942-702

Spot Beam

Atlantic Ocean Region-West

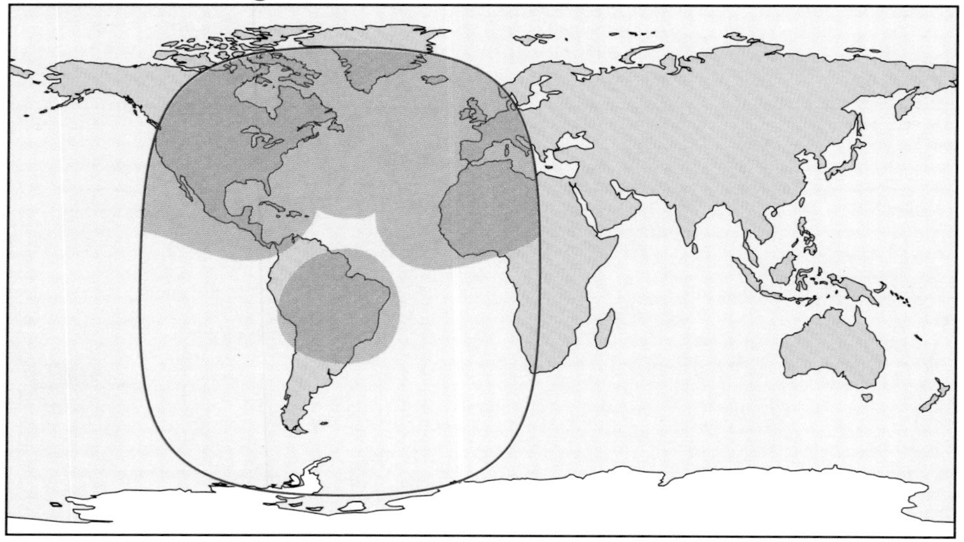

Indian Ocean Region

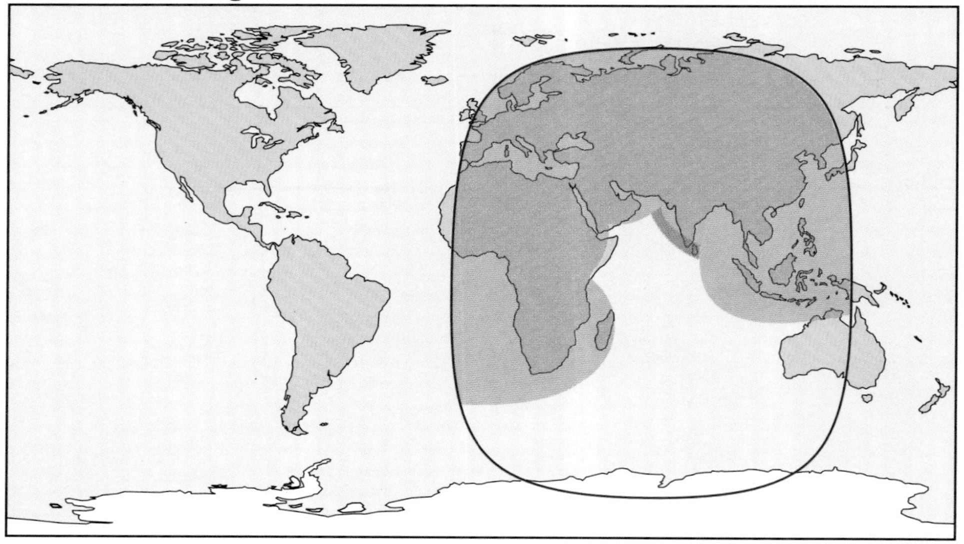

Atlantic Ocean Region-East

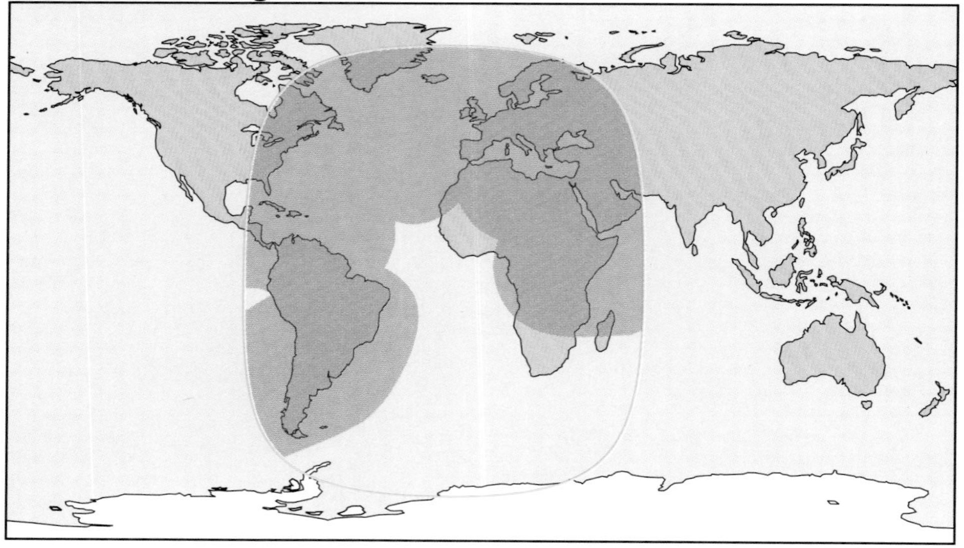

Pacific Ocean Region

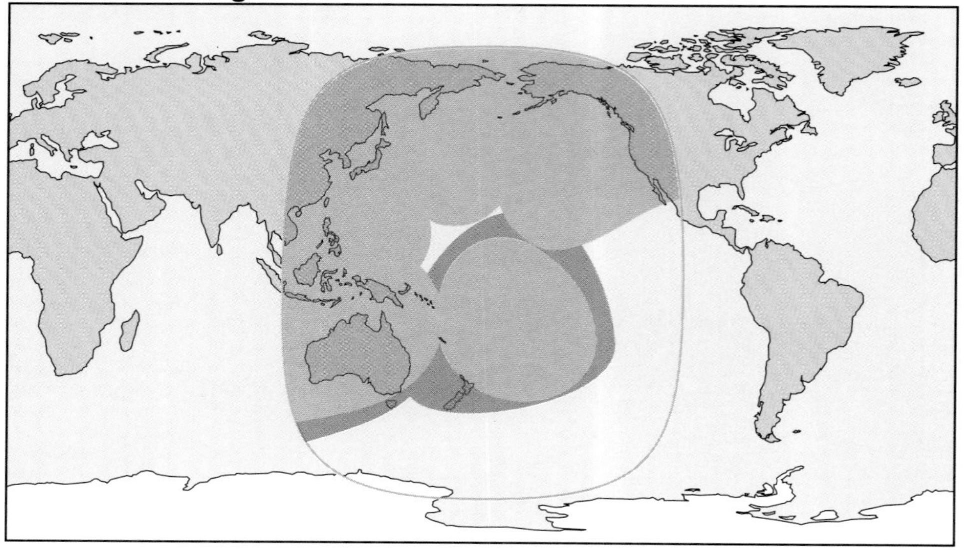

Global beam coverage
- Pacific Ocean Region
- Atlantic Ocean Region-West
- Atlantic Ocean Region-East
- Indian Ocean Region

Global Area Network and Inmarsat mini-M phone coverage

Extended Coverage Zones for Inmarsat mini-M phone and Global Area Network low rate voice and data services

The map depicts Inmarsat's expectations of coverage but does not represent a guarantee of service. The availability of service at the edge of coverage areas fluctuates depending upon a variety of conditions.

Issue 7 942-702

RADIO-FACSIMILE & RADIO TELEX

INTRODUCTION

These entries relate to facsimile transmissions of weather maps, ice charts and other information of interest to mariners.

Details are given of the frequencies employed, the times of the transmissions, the scale and limits of the map and the type of information broadcast.

The major symbols generally used on radio-facsimile weather charts are shown in the table on page 74.

EXAMPLE:

STATION NAME [FACSIMILE]				
	6446		Call Sign	Hours
	7907			1900-0600
	8444			
DIAGRAM: page reference				

Frequency (kHz) List

MAP AREAS

B	1:5,000,000 67°N.32°W 53°N.47°E 72°N.74°E 51°N.4°W	D	1:3,000,000 (a) 79°N.10°E 74°N.40°E 79°N.40°E 74°N.10°E	G	1:5,000,000 (a) 78°N.10°E 66°N.70°E 78°N.70°E 66°N.10°E	

An index diagram showing the coverage of **Map Areas** is included when possible

SCHEDULE

B	36 hour Forecast of Surface Pressure	0700(00)	120/576
G	Sea State Analysis for the Barents Sea.	0800(06)	
D	Surface Temperature Analysis / Iceberg positions for Barents Sea.	1400(12)	

EXPLANATION:

B D G	The letter identifies the transmitted base map.
1:5,000,000 1:3,000,000 (a) 1:5,000,000 (a)	The letter in parentheses following the scale identifies the projection: (a) = Mercator (b) = Lambert's Conical Orthomorphic (c) = Polar Stereographic In the case of (a) and (b) the scale is that at the standard parallel(s) of the map. The geographical co-ordinates of the map corners are usually stated.
0700(00) 0800(06) 1400(12)	Transmission times may be followed by observation times in parentheses.
120/576	The numbers relate to the drum speed, in revolutions per minute, and the Index of Co-operation, which is generally 576, although 288 with alternate line scanning is sometimes used. Frequencies refer to the centre value about which the frequency shift takes place. This shift is generally ± 400 Hz and is not stated. Other shifts are shown by means of a footnote.

Millibars / Hectopascals: In order to conform to the WMO's decision to adopt the hectopascal (hPa), as the international unit for atmospheric pressure measurement, the abbreviation hPa will now appear in schedules compiled from source data employing that term. It should be noted that: 1 hPa = 1 millibar.

SYMBOLS GENERALLY USED ON RADIO-FACSIMILE WEATHER CHARTS

FAXSYMS

FRONTAL AND PRESSURE-FEATURE SYMBOLS

Cold front at the surface

Cold front above the surface

Cold front frontogenesis

Cold front frontolysis

Warm front at the surface

Warm front above the surface

Warm front frontogenesis

Warm front frontolysis

Occluded front at the surface

Occluded front above the surface

Quasi-stationary front at the surface

Quasi-stationary front above the surface

Quasi-stationary front frontogenesis

Quasi-stationary front frontolysis

Instability line

Shear line

Convergence line

Intertropical convergence zone*

Intertropical discontinuity

Axis of trough

Axis of ridge

Centre of tropical cyclonic circulation (maximum winds of 34 - 63 knots)

Centre of tropical cyclonic circulation (maximum winds of 64 knots or more)

Fog

Continuous lines Isobars labelled in millibars/hectopascals

Crossed line segments Position of centre of high or low pressure given in millibars/hectopascals

H High pressure

** L Low pressure

f_8 f_8 Direction of movement of centres and fronts with speed in knots

* *Note:* The separation of the two lines gives a qualitative representation of the width of the zone: the hatched lines may be added to indicate areas of activity

** *Note:* The appropriate letter of the alphabet of the issuing country may be used

SEA TEMPERATURE CHARTS

Continuous lines Isotherms labelled in degrees Celsius

Note: Broken lines may be used to avoid confusion with other analysed parameters

ICE ACCRETION

Ice building slowly

Ice building rapidly

WAVE CHARTS

Continuous lines Significant wind-wave height (sea), or composite wind-wave and swell height, where so drawn, labelled in metres

Dashed lines Significant swell height, labelled in metres

MAX Centre of maximum wave height

MIN Centre of minimum wave height

Direction of sea waves

Direction of swell waves

NEPHANALYSIS CHARTS

Cumuliform cloud

Apparent Cu con. or Cb

Cirriform cloud

Stratiform cloud

Boundary of major cloud systems - fronts, vortices or other system dominating the scene viewed by the satellite

Definite boundary of more or less organized cloud masses

Indefinite boundary of more or less organized cloud masses

Striations

Striations, tenuous

Cloud lines

Building along the line

Cloud lines, tenuous cloud form denoted by

Direction of shear of Cirrus from Cb anvil or other source

Wave clouds (mountain or transverse)

Estimated location of jet stream

Vortex

Heavy cloud

Thin cloud

Cloud cells	Size n. mile	Open spaces
1	0 - 30	6
2	30 - 60	7
3	60 - 90	8
4	90 - 120	6

Cloud amount

Open (O) = Less than 20 per cent coverage

Mostly open (MOP) = 20 - 50 per cent coverage

Mostly covered (MCO) = 50 - 80 per cent coverage

Covered (C) = More then 80 per cent coverage

Note: Stippling is used to emphasize the area considered by the analyst to be of greatest synoptic significance

ATHINÁI (SVJ4) [FACSIMILE]

FREQUENCY & TIMES	4481 8105	0845-0945

SCHEDULE

C	30h & 36h Wave Prognosis	0845(12)	120/576
	42h & 48h Wave Prognosis	0902(12)	
B	30h & 36h WavePrognosis	0919(12)	
	42h & 48h Wave Prognosis	0936(12)	
A	24h Surface Analysis & Prognosis	0953(06)	

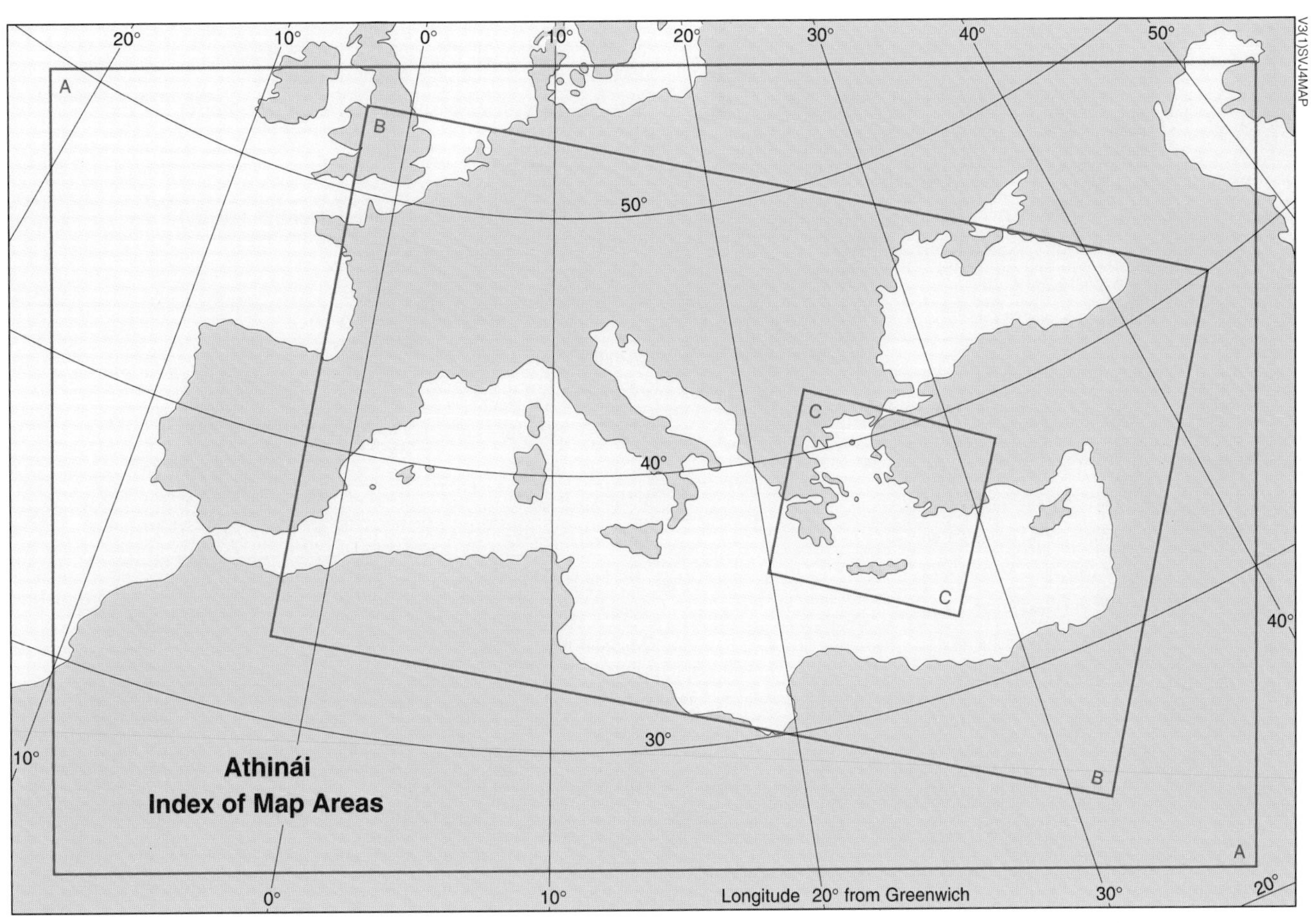

Athinái
Index of Map Areas

NORTHWOOD [FACSIMILE]

FREQUENCY & TIMES	2618·5			H24
	4610			
	8040			
	11086·5			
DIAGRAM: pages 77				

DIAGRAM: pages 77

MAP AREA

54°N.82°W 26°N.45°W 54°N.51°E 28°N.12°E	

SCHEDULE

	Surface Prognosis T + 72	0000(12) 0100(12) 0200(12) 0912(00) 1400(00) 2012(12)	
	Schedule	0236 1424	
	Surface Analysis	0300(00) 0400(00) 0500(00) 0900(06) 1100(06) 1200(06) 1500(12) 1800(12) 2100(18) 2300(18)	
	Gale Summary	0348(03) 0600(06) 0700(06) 1148(12) 1548(16) 1900(19)	
	500 hPa Height T + 0	0448(00) 1724(12)	
	500 hPa Height T + 24	0512(00) 1748(12)	
	Surface Prognosis T + 24	0524(00) 0800(00) 1000(06) 1300(06) 1736(12) 2200(18)	
	SCEXA TAFS (Summer only)	0536(06) 0548(06)	
	300 hPa Height T + 0	0612(00) 1812(12)	
	300 hPa Height T + 24	0624(00) 1824(12)	
	SCEXA TAFS	0636(07) 0648(07) 1436 1448	
	850 hPa WBPT T 24	0712(00) 1924(12)	
	500 / 1000 hPa Thickness T + 0	0724(00) 1836(12)	
	500 / 1000 hPa Thickness T + 24	0736(00) 1848(12)	
	Significant Wind Areas T + 24	0748(00) 2112(12)	
	Significant Wind Areas T + 48	0812(00) 2124(12)	
	Significant Wind Areas T + 72	0824(00) 2136(12)	
	Significant Wind Areas T + 96	0836(00) 2148(12)	120/576
	Surface Prognosis T + 48	0848(00) 1600(00) 1700(00) 2000(12)	
	Sea Swell T + 24	0924(00) 1912(12)	
	Spot Winds 850 hPa T + 24	0936(00) 2212(12)	
	Spot Winds 700 hPa T + 24	0948(00) 2224(12)	
	Spot Winds 500 hPa T + 24	1012(00) 2236(12)	
	Spot Winds 400 hPa T + 24	1024(00) 2248(12)	
	Spot Winds 300 hPa T + 24	1036(00) 2312(12)	
	Spot Winds 250 hPa T + 24	1048(00) 2324(12)	
	Surface Prognosis T + 96	1124(00) 2024(12)	
	Surface Prognosis T + 120	1136(00) 2036(12)	
	Sea Surface Temperature 10 percent ice edge	1212(Monday/Thursday)	
	Layer Depth	1224(Tuesday)	
	CZ Potential	1236(Tuesday)	
	Minimum Sound Channel Depth	1248(Tuesday)	
	Ship Ice Accretion 0 deg c level T + 24	1312(00)	
	Poor Visibility T + 24	1324(00)	
	Ocean Frontal Positions	1536(Thursday)	

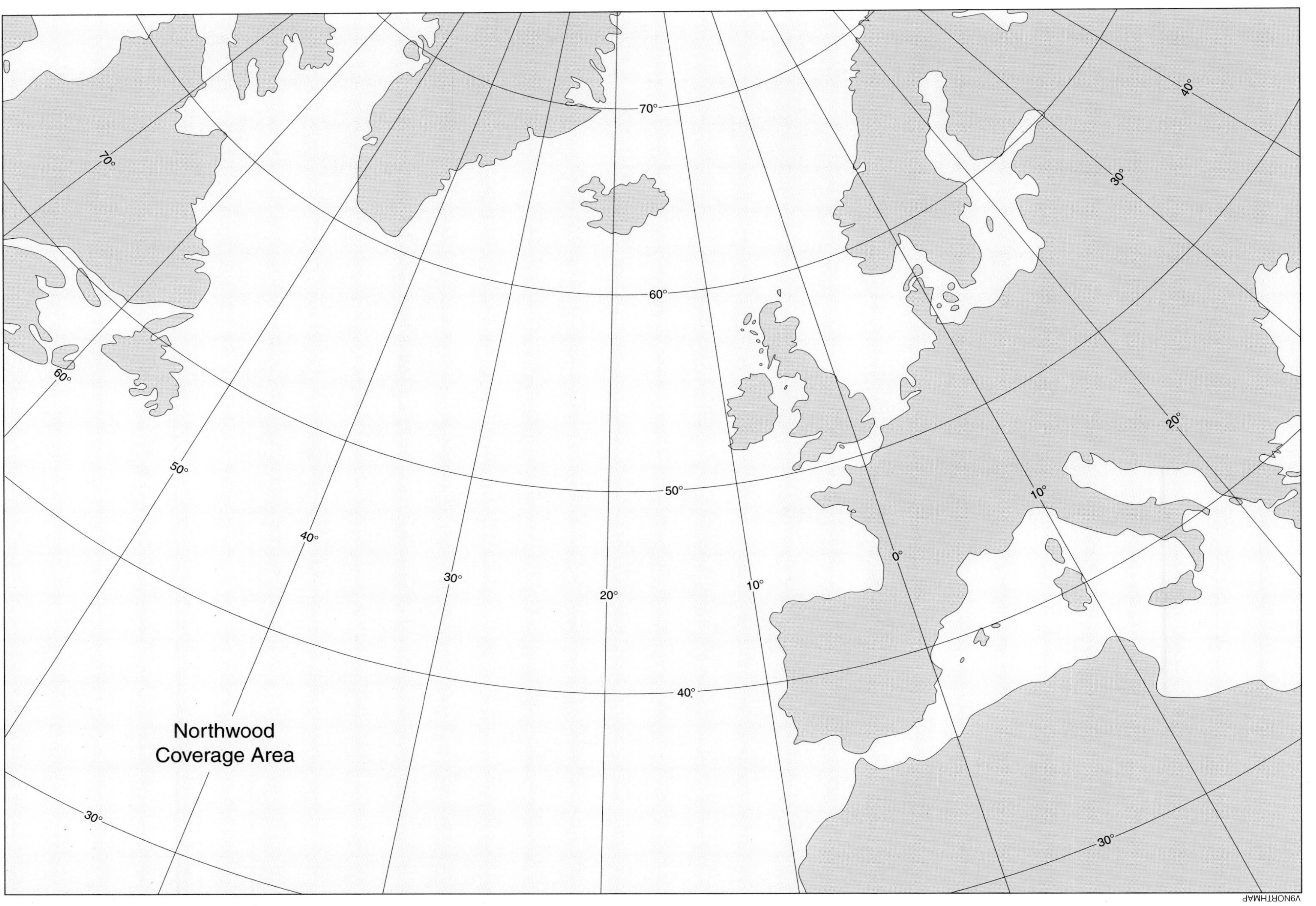
Northwood
Coverage Area
70°
60°
50°
40°
30°
40°
30°
20°
10°
0°
10°
20°
30°
40°
70°
60°
50°
40°
30°
V9NORTHMAP

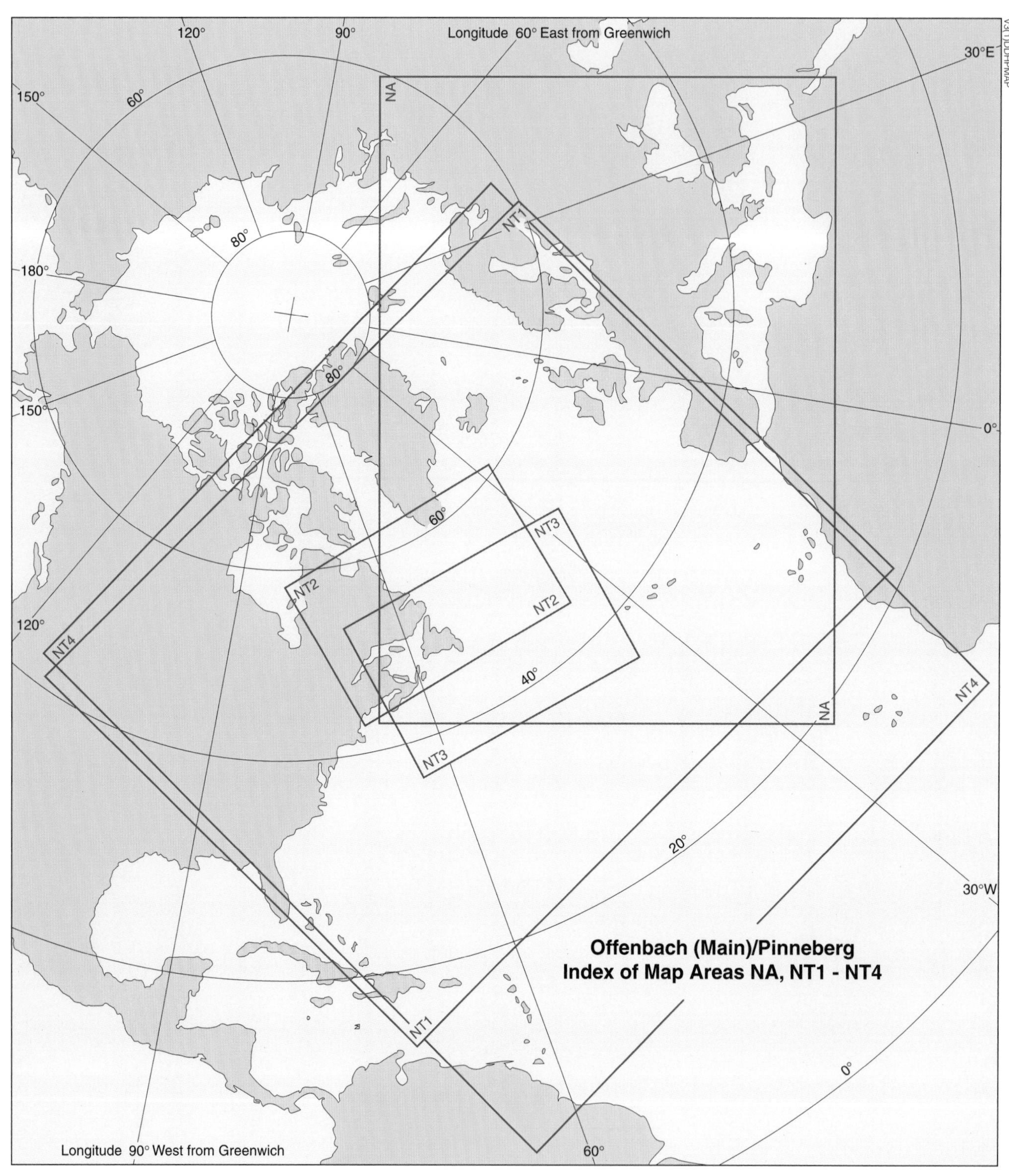

120°
90°
Longitude 60° East from Greenwich
30°E
V3(1)DDHPMAP
150°
60°
80°
180°
NA
NT1
80°
150°
0°
60°
NT3
NT2
NT2
120°
NT4
40°
NA
NT4
NT3
20°
30°W
Offenbach (Main)/Pinneberg
Index of Map Areas NA, NT1 - NT4
NT1
0°
Longitude 90° West from Greenwich
60°

OFFENBACH (MAIN) / PINNEBERG (DDH) (DDK) [FACSIMILE]

FREQUENCY & TIMES	3855		(DDH3)	
	7880		(DDK3)	
	13882·5		(DDK6)	
		DIAGRAM: page 78		

MAP AREAS

NA 1:20,000,000 (c) 1:15,000,000 (c) 43°N.67°W 61°N.79°E 19°N.27°W 27°N.33°E	NT1 1:15,000,000 (a) 41°N.114°W 60°N. 36°E 14°N. 70°W 21°N.13°W	NT2 (c) 59°N.82°W 61°N.28°W 43°N.70°W 44°N.35°W	NT3 (c) 53°N.70°W 52°N.26°W 36°N.63°W 36°N.33°E
NT4 1:15,000,000 (c) 48°N.117°W 63°N. 42°E 05°N. 63°W 10°N.18°W			

SCHEDULE

NA	Surface weather chart [1]	0430(00) 1050(06) 1600(12) 2200(18)	120/576
NA	30 hour Surface Pressure[1]	0512(18) 0717(18)	
NT1	Surface Pressure Analysis with plotted data	0525(00) 0743(00) 1800(12)	
NA	North Atlantic, information on Tropical Storms (seasonal)	0546(03) 1821(15)	
	12 hour & 24 hour 500 hPa (high, low) and Surface Pressure	0559(00)	
	12 hour & 24 hour 850 hPa (high, low) and 700 hPa Relative Humidity	0612(00)	
	36 hour & 48 hour 500 hPa (high, low) and Surface Pressure	0625(00)	
	36 hour & 48 hour 850 hPa (high, low) and 700 hPa Relative humidity	0638(00)	
	60 hour & 72 hour 500 hPa (high, low) and Surface Pressure	0651(00)	
	60 hour & 72 hour 850 hPa (high, low) and 700 hPa Relative Humidity	0704(00)	
	48 hour Surface pressure[1]	0730(00) 1847(00)	
	72 hour Surface pressure[1]	0804(00) 1900(00)	
	96 hour Surface pressure	0817(00)	
	48 hour Sea and Swell	1004(00) 2036(12)	
	72 hour Sea and Swell	1016(00) 2048(12)	
NT4	48 hour Wave prediction	1029(00) 2137(12)	
	Transmission Schedule	1111	
	Test Chart	1132	
NA	96 hour Sea and Swell	1206(00)	
NT2 & NT3	Ice chart (NW Atlantic)[2]	1219(00) 2100(00)	
NA	24 hour Surface pressure[1]	1834(12)	

1 If the manually modified chart is not available, then the automatically processed chart will be broadcast. The auto chart heading will have 'ii' = 98 instead of 'ii' = 89
2 Issued by Canadian Ice Service (Ottawa) or International Ice Patrol (USCG)
3 Issued by Bundesamt fuer Seeschiffahrt und Hydrographie
4 Only when the ice conditions so require
5 Prepared by SMHI Norrköping

OFFENBACH (MAIN) / PINNEBERG RADIO TELEX

A (English)	4583	Radio Telex	Programme 1	H24
	7646			
	10100·8			
B (German)	147·3		Programme 2	0500-2200
	11039			
	14467·3			

Weather Bulletins

A: 0415 1610	Time sequence reports, medium term weather reports for Mediterranean Sea, prognosis for 5 days for areas M1-M4, M8 and M9
A: 0955 2155	Time sequence reports for Western European waters (Southern Ireland - Islas Canarias), prognosis for 2 days
A: 1015 2215	Time sequence reports for Western Mediterranean Sea (Alboran - Tunis), prognosis for 2 days
A: 1115 2315	Time sequence reports for Eastern Mediterranean Sea (Eastern Tunis - Ródos/Cyprus), prognosis for 2 days
A: 1550	Weather reports for Mediterranean Sea in text format
B: 0535	Time sequence reports, medium term weather reports for Mediterranean Sea, prognosis for 5 days for areas M1-M4, M8 and M9
B: 0730 1030 1330 1630 1930	Station reports for Mediterranean Sea
B: 0820 1420 2020	Time sequence reports for Western European waters (Southern Ireland - Islas Canarias), prognosis for 2 days
B: 0840 1440 2040	Time sequence reports for Western Mediterranean Sea (Alboran - Tunis), prognosis for 2 days
B: 0930 1530 2130	Time sequence reports for Eastern Mediterranean Sea (Eastern Tunis - Ródos/Cyprus), prognosis for 2 days
B: 1010	Advice on the use of weather data
B: 1120 1735	Time sequence reports, medium term weather reports for Mediterranean Sea, prognosis for 5 days for areas M1-M4, M8 and M9
B: 1610	Weather reports for Mediterranean Sea in text format

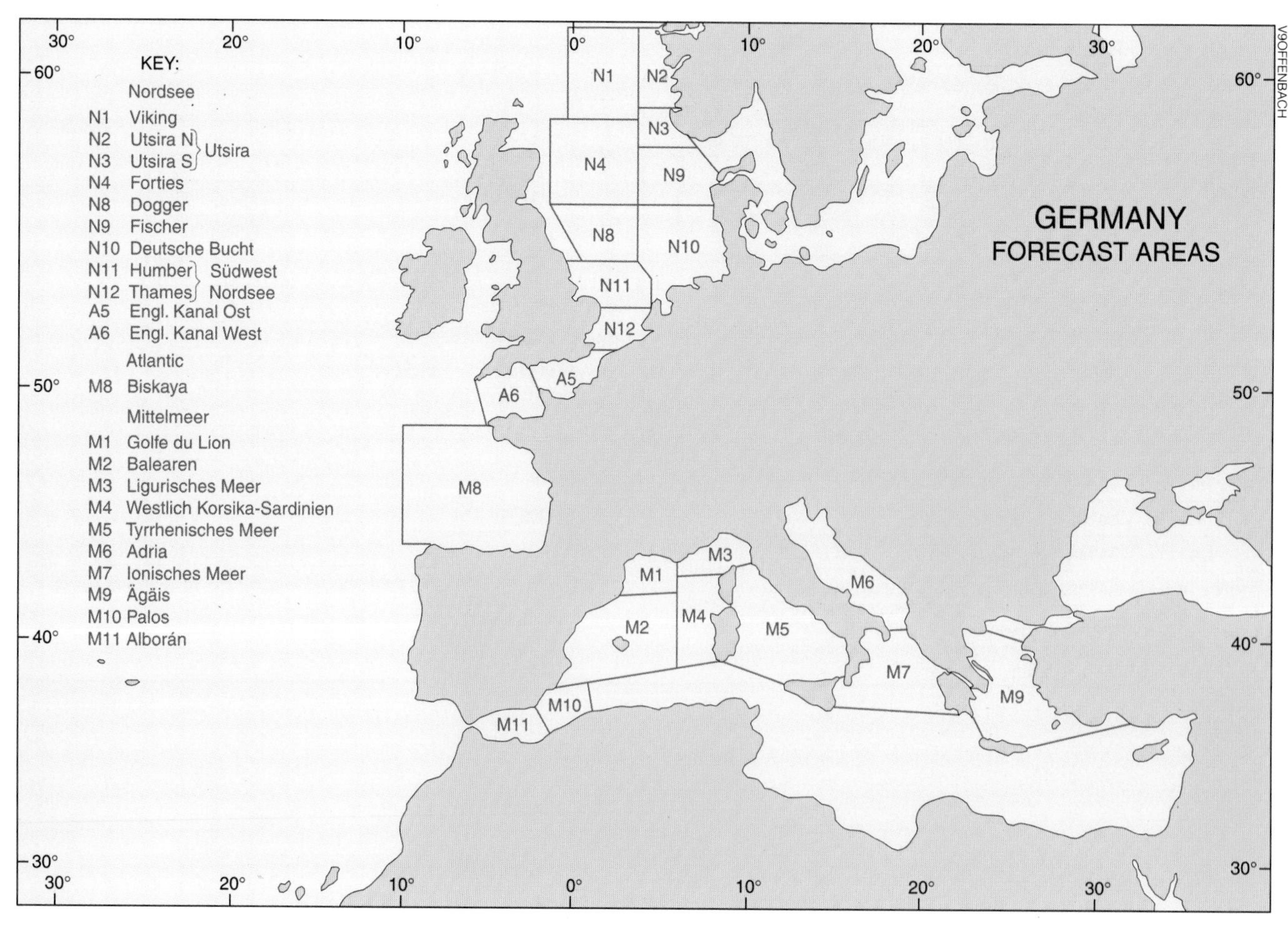

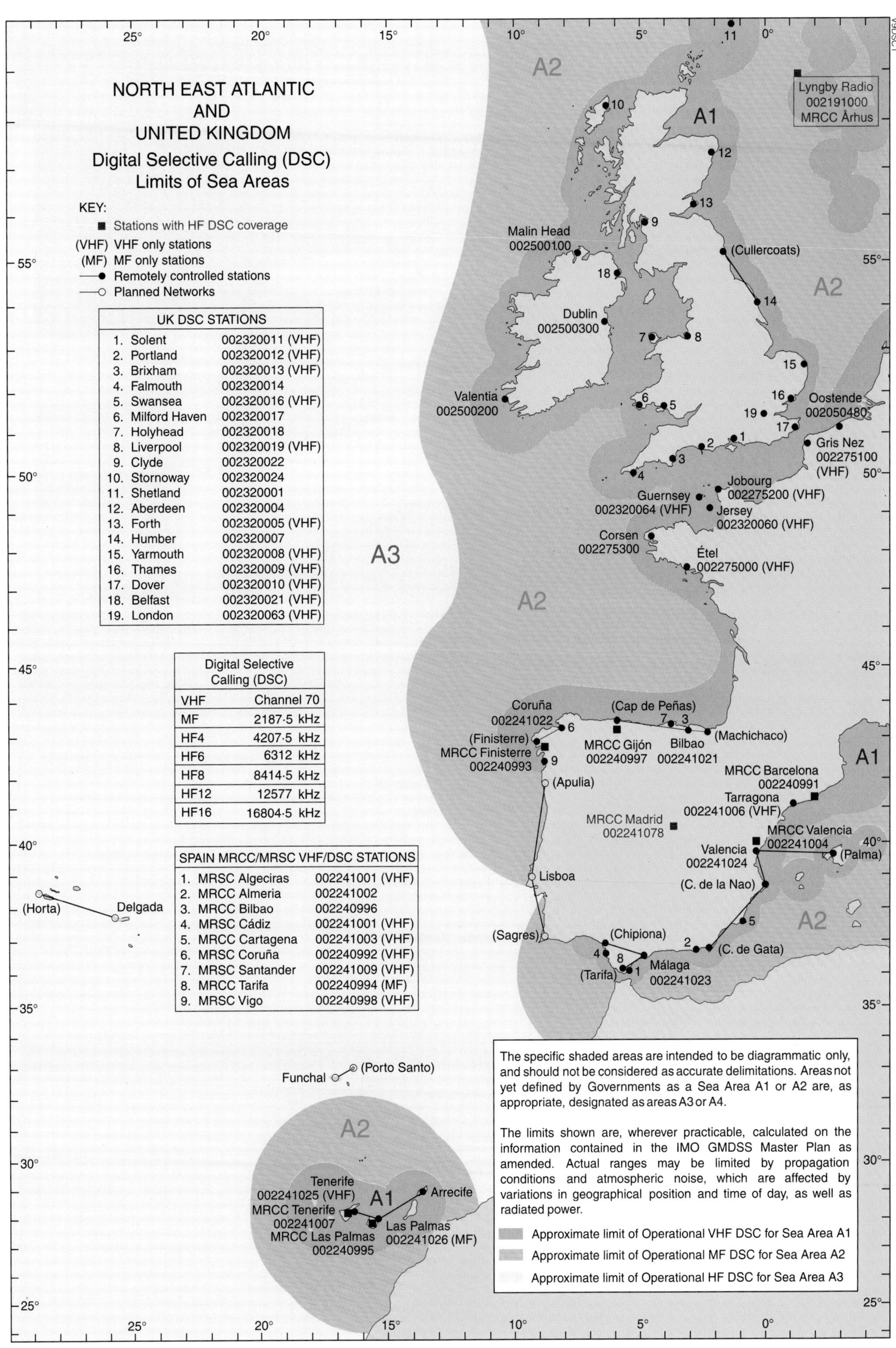

NORTH EAST ATLANTIC
AND
UNITED KINGDOM
Digital Selective Calling (DSC)
Limits of Sea Areas
KEY:
■ Stations with HF DSC coverage
(VHF) VHF only stations
(MF) MF only stations
Remotely controlled stations
Planned Networks
UK DSC STATIONS
1. Solent 002320011 (VHF)
2. Portland 002320012 (VHF)
3. Brixham 002320013 (VHF)
4. Falmouth 002320014
5. Swansea 002320016 (VHF)
6. Milford Haven 002320017
7. Holyhead 002320018
8. Liverpool 002320019 (VHF)
9. Clyde 002320022
10. Stornoway 002320024
11. Shetland 002320001
12. Aberdeen 002320004
13. Forth 002320005 (VHF)
14. Humber 002320007
15. Yarmouth 002320008 (VHF)
16. Thames 002320009 (VHF)
17. Dover 002320010 (VHF)
18. Belfast 002320021 (VHF)
19. London 002320063 (VHF)
Digital Selective Calling (DSC)
VHF Channel 70
MF 2187·5 kHz
HF4 4207·5 kHz
HF6 6312 kHz
HF8 8414·5 kHz
HF12 12577 kHz
HF16 16804·5 kHz
SPAIN MRCC/MRSC VHF/DSC STATIONS
1. MRSC Algeciras 002241001 (VHF)
2. MRCC Almeria 002241002
3. MRCC Bilbao 002240996
4. MRSC Cádiz 002241001 (VHF)
5. MRCC Cartagena 002241003 (VHF)
6. MRSC Coruña 002240992 (VHF)
7. MRSC Santander 002241009 (VHF)
8. MRCC Tarifa 002240994 (MF)
9. MRSC Vigo 002240998 (VHF)
A1
A2
A3
Lyngby Radio
002191000
MRCC Århus
Malin Head
002500100
Dublin
002500300
Valentia
002500200
(Cullercoats)
Oostende
002050480
Gris Nez
002275100
(VHF)
Jobourg
002275200 (VHF)
Guernsey
002320064 (VHF)
Jersey
002320060 (VHF)
Corsen
002275300
Étel
002275000 (VHF)
Coruña
002241022
(Cap de Peñas)
(Finisterre)
MRCC Finisterre
002240993
MRCC Gijón
002240997
Bilbao
002241021
(Machichaco)
(Apulia)
MRCC Barcelona
002240991
Tarragona
002241006 (VHF)
MRCC Madrid
002241078
MRCC Valencia
002241004
Valencia
002241024
(Palma)
Lisboa
(C. de la Nao)
(Horta)
Delgada
(Sagres)
(Chipiona)
(C. de Gata)
(Tarifa)
Málaga
002241023
Funchal
(Porto Santo)
Tenerife
002241025 (VHF)
MRCC Tenerife
002241007
MRCC Las Palmas
002240995
Las Palmas
002241026 (MF)
Arrecife
The specific shaded areas are intended to be diagrammatic only, and should not be considered as accurate delimitations. Areas not yet defined by Governments as a Sea Area A1 or A2 are, as appropriate, designated as areas A3 or A4.
The limits shown are, wherever practicable, calculated on the information contained in the IMO GMDSS Master Plan as amended. Actual ranges may be limited by propagation conditions and atmospheric noise, which are affected by variations in geographical position and time of day, as well as radiated power.
Approximate limit of Operational VHF DSC for Sea Area A1
Approximate limit of Operational MF DSC for Sea Area A2
Approximate limit of Operational HF DSC for Sea Area A3
V9DSC1

MARITIME SAFETY INFORMATION, MARINA AND PORT COMMUNICATIONS

AÇORES

NAVTEX [F]
NAVTEX [J]

F	Horta	518 kHz	38°32′N 28°38′W
J	Horta	490 kHz	38°32′N 28°38′W
DIAGRAMS: pages 133 and 138			
Weather Bulletins			
F: On receipt 0050 0450 0850 1250 1650 2050	Storm Warnings and Gale Warnings. Synopsis, 24 hour forecast for Areas Altair, Açores, Irvine, Milne and Marsala		
J: 0120 0520 0920 1320 1720 2120	In Portuguese		
Navigational Warnings			
F: 0050 0450 0850 1250 1650 2050	Warnings for Areas Altair, Açores, Irvine, Milne and Marsala		
J: 0120 0520 0920 1320 1720 2120	In Portuguese		

HORTA (RADIONAVAL)

A	2657	RT (MF)		
B	Ch 11	VHF		
DIAGRAM: page 133				
Weather Bulletins				
A: 0935 2135	Storm, gale and poor Visibility warnings. Synopsis and 24 hour forecast for Areas 3, 5, 7, 30 and 31. In Portuguese, repeated in English.			
B: 0900 2100	Local forecasts for Faial, Graciosa, Pico, São Jorge, and Terceira			
B: 1000 1900	Local forecasts for Corvo and Flores			
Navigational Warnings				
A: 0935 2135	Warnings within 200 n miles offshore coast of Açores. In Portuguese, repeated in English.			
B: 0900 2100	Local warnings for Faial, Graciosa, Pico, São Jorge, and Terceira			
B: 1000 1900	Local warnings for Corvo and Flores			

PONTA DELGADA (RADIONAVAL)

	Ch 11	VHF		
DIAGRAM: page 133				
Weather Bulletins				
0830 2000	Storm, gale and poor Visibility warnings. Synopsis and 24 hour forecast within 20 n miles of Santa Maria and São Miguel			
Navigational Warnings				
0830 2000	Local warnings for Santa Maria and São Miguel			

ANGRA DO HERÓISMO, ILHA TERCEIRA

Pilots and Port: CALL: Capimarangra — 38°39′N 27°13′W

Tel: Hr Mr: +351 295 540000
japah@mail.telepac.pt

Fax: Hr Mr: +351 295 540019

FREQUENCY: Ch 11 14 16 — HOURS: Ch 16: 0800-2000 LT

HORTA, ILHA DO FAIAL

Port: CALL: Capimarhorta — 38°31′·62N 28°37′·64W

Tel: Hr Mr: +351 292 293453
Mobile: 0936 6491223
portohorta@mail.telepac.pt

Fax: Port Auth: +351 292 208315
www.marina.jappdl.pt

FREQUENCY: Ch 11 16 — HOURS: 0800-2400 LT

Horta Marina da Horta — **Marina** 150 Berths

Depths: 1 - 4 m, Maximum LOA: 25 - 28 m

Tel: Marina: +351 292 391693
Mobile: 0936 6491291

Fax: +351 292 208315

FREQUENCY: Ch 06 **10** 11 16 — HOURS: 0800-1200 1300-2000 LT

Mid Atlantic Yacht Services — **Yacht Service Centre**

Tel: +351 292 391616
mays@mail.telepac.pt

Fax: +351 292 391656

MADALENA, ILHA DO PICO

Port: CALL: Policiamarmadalena — 38°32′N 28°31′W

Tel: +351 292 623303

FREQUENCY: Ch 11 16 — HOURS: Ch 16: Mon-Fri: 0900-1200 1400-1700 LT

PONTA DELGADA, ILHA DE SÃO MIGUEL

Marina 140-190 Berths (High Season) — 37°44′·12N 25°39′·40W

Depths: 3 - 8 m, Maximum LOA: 18 m

Tel: Port Capt: +351 296 285268
Marina Pêro de Teive: +351 296 281510, 281511 & 281512
marinapdl@jappdl.pt

Fax: Port Capt: +351 296 283050
Marina Pêro de Teive: +351 296 281311
www.marina.jappdl.pt

FREQUENCY: Port: Ch 16 Marina: Ch 16 **62** — HOURS: Ch **62** (Office hours) Ch 16 (H24)

SANTA CRUZ, ILHA DAS FLORES

Port: CALL: Capimarflores — 39°27′N 31°07′W

Tel: +351 292 592224

FREQUENCY: Ch 11 16 — HOURS: Ch 16: 0900-1200 1400-1700 LT

VILA DO PORTO, ILHA DE SANTA MARIA

Port: CALL: Capimarviporto — 36°56′N 25°09′W

Tel: +351 296 882157

FREQUENCY: Ch 11 16 — HOURS: Ch 16: Mon-Fri: 0800-1200 1400-1700 LT

FRANCE, ATLANTIC COAST

ÉTEL MMSI 002275000 DSC Ch 70	Centre Régional Opérationnel de Surveillance et du Sauvetage (CROSS):	47°39′N 3°12′W
DESCRIPTION: Provides a marine navigation, surveillance and information service		AREA: From Penmarc'h (Pointe d'Eckmühl) to the French-Spanish border
☎ +33(0)2 97553535	Inmarsat C 422799025	Fax +33(0)2 97554934
FREQUENCY: Call: CROSS Étel		HOURS: H24

Distress & Safety: VHF Ch 16 70 MF 2182 kHz	VHF facilities are located at the following: Étel CROSS	
SAR Co-ordination: Ch 15 67 **68** 73	Penmarc'h (Île de Eckmühl) (47°48′N 4°22′W) Étel (47°40′N 3°12′W)	Chassiron (46°03′N 1°25′W) Soulac (45°30′N 1°08′W)
Calling & Working: Ch **13** 80	Île de-Groix (Pen Men) (47°39′N 3°30′W) Saint-Nazaire (Kerrouault) (47°28′N 2°21′W)	Hourtin (45°08′N 1°10′W) Cap Ferret (44°39′N 1°15′W)
Information Broadcasts: VHF Ch 79 80 MF 2677 kHz	Belle Île (Goulphar) (47°19′N 3°14′W) Île d'Yeu (Grand Phare) (46°43′N 2°23′W) Les Sables d'Olonne (L'Armandèche) (46°29′N 1°48′W)	Contis (44°06′N 1°19′W) Biarritz (43°30′N 1°33′W)

INFORMATION BROADCASTS: Initial announcement on 2182 kHz and VHF Ch 16 will indicate working channel
(1) Urgent navigational information is broadcast on receipt then every 2h for the coastal zone between Raz de Sein and the French-Spanish border
(2) Non-urgent navigational information is broadcast after meteorological bulletins for the same zone

ÉTEL (CROSS) (MRCC)

A	Ch 80	VHF	Penmarc'h	47°48′N 4°22′W
B			Île de Groix	47°39′N 3°30′W
C			Belle-Île	47°19′N 3°14′W
D			Saint-Nazaire	47°28′N 2°21′W
E			Île d'Yeu	46°43′N 2°23′W
F			Les Sables d'Olonne	46°29′N 1°48′W
G	Ch 79		Chassiron	46°03′N 1°25′W
H			Soulac	45°30′N 1°08′W
I			Cap Ferret	44°39′N 1°15′W
J			Contis	44°06′N 1°19′W
K			Biarritz	43°30′N 1°33′W

BMS and warnings for the area affected, are only broadcast from the nearest transmitter site whilst the bulletin is in force

DIAGRAMS: pages 87, 99, 109 and 110

Weather Bulletins

A-K: On receipt	Storm warnings: Every H+03 Storm warnings and BMS. In French
A: 0703 1533 1903 LT **B:** 0715 1545 1915 LT **C:** 0733 1603 1933 LT **D:** 0745 1615 1945 LT **E:** 0803 1633 2003 LT **F:** 0815 1645 2015 LT	Storm warnings, situation, 24 hour forecast and outlook for a further 24 hours, for the coastal area from Penmarc'h to l'Anse de l'Aiguillon. In French
G: 0703 1533 1903 LT **H:** 0715 1545 1915 LT **I:** 0733 1603 1933 LT **J:** 0745 1615 1945 LT **K:** 0803 1633 2003 LT	Storm warnings, situation, 24 hour forecast and outlook for a further 24 hours, for the coastal area from l'Anse de l'Aiguillon to the Spanish frontier. In French

Navigational Warnings

G: 1903 LT **H:** 1915 LT **I:** 1933 LT **J:** 1945 LT **K:** 2003 LT	Warnings for Centre d'Essais des Landes (Firing Practice Area) and Cazaux

AMBÈS	**Port:** CALL: Ambès Port	45°02′N 0°35′W
☎ Port Office: +33(0)5 56771252		Fax Port Office: +33(0)5 56770431
FREQUENCY: Ch 12		HOURS: H24

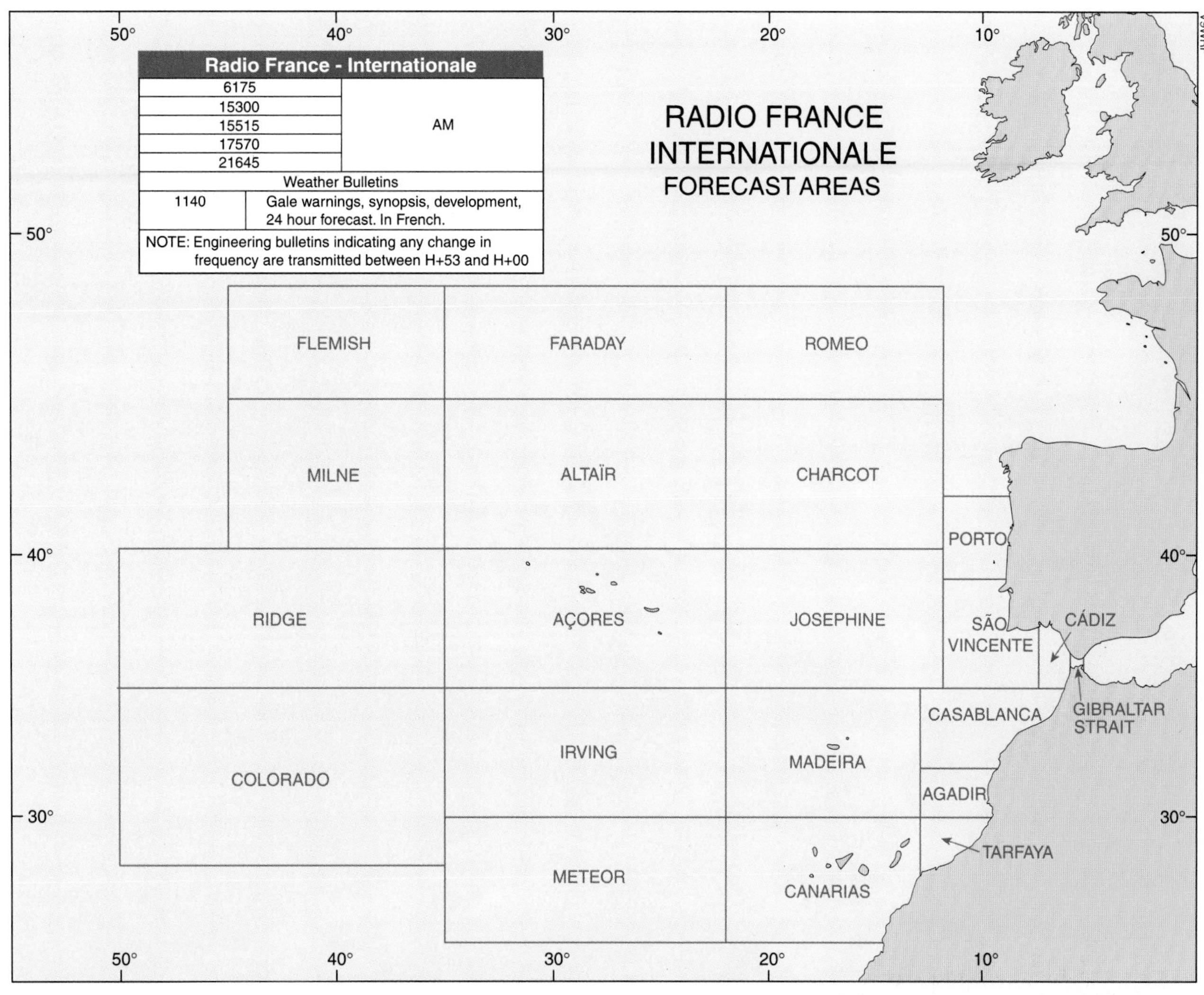

Radio France - Internationale	
6175	AM
15300	
15515	
17570	
21645	
Weather Bulletins	
1140	Gale warnings, synopsis, development, 24 hour forecast. In French.
NOTE: Engineering bulletins indicating any change in frequency are transmitted between H+53 and H+00	

ANGLET	Marina 425 Berths 58 Visitor Berths	43°31′·6N 1°30′·4W
☎ Capitainerie: +33(0)5 59630545 Yacht Club: +33(0)5 59631622	Maximum depth: 3 m, Maximum LOA: 18 m	Fax Capitainerie: +33(0)5 59521766
FREQUENCY: Pilotage de l'Adour: Ch 12		HOURS: Office hours

ARCACHON	Marina 2500 Berths 200 Visitor Berths	44°40′N 1°10′W
☎ Hr Mr: +33(0)5 56223675	Maximum depth: 2·5 m, Maximum LOA: 15 m	Fax Hr Mr: +33(0)5 56832619
FREQUENCY: Ch 09		HOURS: H24

ARS-EN-RÉ	Marinas Bassin del la Criée 225 Berths Bassin Prée 165 Berths	46°′12′·70N 1°30′·62W
☎ Bassin de la Criée: +33(0)5 46292510 Bassin Prée: +33(0)5 46290852		Fax
FREQUENCY: Ch 09		HOURS: HX

ARZAL-CAMOËL	**Marinaand Lock:** CALL: Écluse Arzal 827 Berths 50 Visitor Berths 25 on each side of the river	47°30′N 2°23′W
☎ Hr Mr: +33(0)2 97450297 Lock: +33(0)2 97450285 port-arzal-camoel@wanadoo.fr	Maximum depth: 4·5 m, Maximum LOA: 20 m.	Fax Hr Mr: +33(0)2 97450298
FREQUENCY: Ch 09 Lock: Ch 18		HOURS: Season: 0830-1230 1400-2000 LT Out of season: 0830-1230 1330-1730 LT
NOTE: Leisure craft should not call the lock but the Hr Mr at Arzal-Camoël marina to obtain the opening hours of the lock		

ARS-EN-RÉ

BARRAGE D'ARZAL AND ARZAL-CAMOËL

BAYONNE	Port	43°31′N 1°29′W
☎ Hr Mr: +33(0)5 59631157		Fax Hr Mr: +33(0)5 59420943
FREQUENCY: Ch 12		HOURS: H24

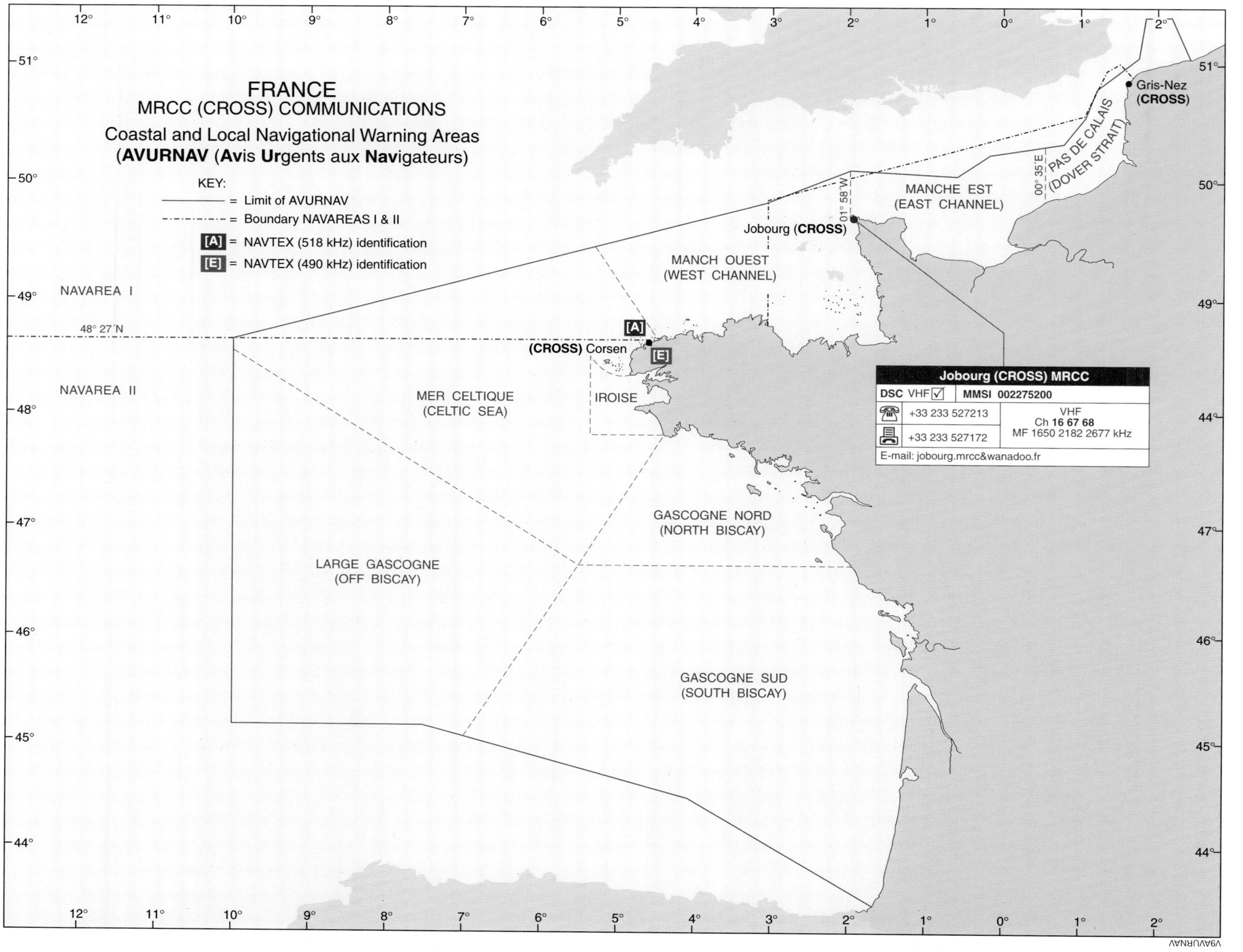
FRANCE
MRCC (CROSS) COMMUNICATIONS
Coastal and Local Navigational Warning Areas
(AVURNAV (Avis Urgents aux Navigateurs)
KEY:
= Limit of AVURNAV
= Boundary NAVAREAS I & II
[A] = NAVTEX (518 kHz) identification
[E] = NAVTEX (490 kHz) identification
NAVAREA I
NAVAREA II
48° 27´N
Gris-Nez
(CROSS)
PAS DE CALAIS
(DOVER STRAIT)
00° 35´E
01° 58´W
MANCHE EST
(EAST CHANNEL)
Jobourg (CROSS)
MANCH OUEST
(WEST CHANNEL)
[A]
(CROSS) Corsen
[E]
IROISE
MER CELTIQUE
(CELTIC SEA)
GASCOGNE NORD
(NORTH BISCAY)
LARGE GASCOGNE
(OFF BISCAY)
GASCOGNE SUD
(SOUTH BISCAY)
Jobourg (CROSS) MRCC
DSC VHF ✓ MMSI 002275200
+33 233 527213
+33 233 527172
VHF
Ch 16 67 68
MF 1650 2182 2677 kHz
E-mail: jobourg.mrcc&wanadoo.fr
V9AVURNAV

BÉNODET	Marinas 970 Berths Anse de Penfoul Marina: 550 Berths 79 Visitor Berths Saint Marine Marina: 420 Berths 70 Visitor Berths	47°53′N 4°07′W
☎ Anse de Penfoul Marina: +33(0)2 98570578 Sainte Marine Marina: +33(0)2 98563872 Yacht Club de l'Odet: +33(0)2 98572609		Fax: Anse de Penfoul Marina: +33(0)2 98570021 Sainte Marine Marina: +33(0)2 98519517
FREQUENCY: Ch 09		HOURS: Season: 0800-2000 LT Out of season: 0800-1200 1400-1800 LT

PORTS DE BÉNODET AND SAINTE MARINE - VIEW TO THE NW

BLAYE	Port: CALL: Port de Blaye	45°08′N 0°40′W
☎ Port Office: +33(0)5 57421363		Fax: Port Office: +33(0)5 57422819
FREQUENCY: Ch 12		HOURS: 0800-1200 1400-1800 LT

BONNE ANSE - PORT DE LA PALMYRE	Marina	45°′42′·00N 1°11′·30W
☎ Capitainerie: +33(0)5 46224431		Fax:
FREQUENCY: Ch 09		HOURS: HX

BONNE ANSE - PORT DE LA PALMYRE FROM S

BORDEAUX	Port and Marina: CALL: Bordeaux Traffic 230 Berths	44°51′N 0°33′W
☎ Hr Mr: +33(0)5 56525104 (H24) Marina: +33(0)5 56508414		Fax: Hr Mr: +33(0)5 56905996
FREQUENCY: Port: Ch 12 16 Marina: Ch 09		HOURS: Port: H24 Marina: Season: Office hours

BOURGENAY	Port and Marina 560 Berths 60 Visitor Berths	46°26′·38N 1°40′·57W
☎ Hr Mr: +33(0)2 51222036	Maximum depth: 2 m, Maximum LOA: 20 m	Fax: Hr Mr: +33(0)2 51222945
FREQUENCY: Ch 09 16		HOURS: Season 0800-2100 LT

BREST	Port de Commerce: CALL: Hr Mr: Capitainerie Brest	48°23′N 4°30′W
Tel Hr Mr: +33(0)2 98314147		Fax Hr Mr: +33(0)2 98460379
FREQUENCY: Ch 12 16		HOURS: H24
Port du Moulin Blanc	**Marina** 1325 Berths	48°23′·6N 4°25′·8W
Tel Hr Mr: +33(0)2 98022002 marc.lambert@soports.fr@wanadoo.fr		Fax Hr Mr: +33(0)2 98416791 www.portmoulinblanc.com
FREQUENCY: Ch 09 16	LOCATION: Port du Moulin Blanc	HOURS: Season: 0800-2000 LT Out of season: 0830-1800 LT Holidays: 0900-1200 1400-1900 LT

CAMARET-SUR-MER	Marina 180 Berths 80 Visitor Berths	48°17′N 4°35′W
Tel Hr Mr: +33(0)2 98279330 Marina Office: +33(0)2 98279599		Fax
FREQUENCY: Ch 09		HOURS: Season: 0730-2200 LT Out of season: 0830-1200 1330-1730 LT

CAP BRETON	Marina 950 Berths 61 Visitor Berths	43°39′N 1°27′W
Tel Hr Mr: +33(0)5 58722123	Maximum depth: 2·2 m, Maximum LOA: 25 m	Fax Hr Mr: +33(0)5 58724035
FREQUENCY: Ch 09		HOURS: Season: 0800-1900 LT Out of season: 0800-1200 1330-1830 LT Sat & holidays: 0800-1200 1330-1730 LT

CAP BRETON

CONCARNEAU	Port	47°52′N 3°55′W
Tel Hr Mr: +33(0)2 98605118 & 98605100 +33(0)2 98507991 & 6 80840183		Fax +33(0)2 98508541
FREQUENCY: Ch 12 16		HOURS: H24
NOTE: All vessels should maintain a listening watch on VHF Ch 16 before entering the Approach Channel		
	Marina 618 Berths 52 Visitor Berths	
Tel +33(0)2 98975796	Depth: 1 - 3 m, Maximum LOA: 12 m	Fax +33(0)2 98503863 (Indicate: for Port de Plaisance)
FREQUENCY: Ch 09		HOURS: Season: 0700-2100 LT Out of season & holidays: 0900-1200 1330-1730 LT

DONGES	Port: CALL: Donges Port	47°16′N 2°05′W
Tel Hr Mr: +33(0)2 40910513		Fax Hr Mr: +33(0)2 40910317
FREQUENCY: Ch 12 16 69		HOURS: H24

CONCARNEAU - VIEW TO THE N

DOUARNENEZ	Port: CALL: Douarnenez Port	48°06'N 4°20'W
Tel: Hr Mr: +33(0)2 98921485		Fax: Hr Mr: +33(0)2 98921485
FREQUENCY: Ch 12 16		HOURS: 0800-1200 1330-1730 LT
	Marina 400-450 Berths	
Tel: Hr Mr: +33(0)2 98740256		Fax: Hr Mr: +33(0)2 98740508
FREQUENCY: Ch 09	LOCATION: Tréboul (48°05'·9N 4°20'·3W)	HOURS: Season: 0700-1200 1330-2100 LT Out of season: 0800-1200 1300-1700 LT

DOUARNENEZ FROM WNW

ÉTEL	Marina 200 Berths 20 Visitor Berths	
Tel: Hr Mr: +33(0)2 97554662		Fax: Hr Mr: +33(0)2 97553414 (Indicate: for Capitainerie)
FREQUENCY: Ch 13 16		HOURS: (15 June-1 Sept): HW -3h to +2h

HENDAYE	Marina 720 Berths120 Visitor Berths	43°22'N 1°47'W
Tel: Port Office: +33(0)5 59480610	Depth: 4 m maximum, Maximum LOA: 16 m	Fax: Port Office: +33(0)5 59480601
FREQUENCY: Ch 09		HOURS: H24

ÉTEL

JARD SUR MER	Marina	46°'24'·45N 1°34'75W
☎ Hr Mr: +33(0)2 51334017		📠
FREQUENCY: Ch 09		HOURS: HX

JARD SUR MER FROM SW

LA GIRONDE	**Vessel Traffic Service:** CALL: Hr Mr: Bordeaux Traffic Radar: Radar Verdon	45°38'N 1°20'W
DESCRIPTION: The system is compulsory for all vessels (whatever their length). It ensures surveillance of marine and river traffic from seaward up to the port of Bordeaux. Information and radar assistance can be supplied on request for the entry to La Gironde		
AREA: The system covers the area extending from the BXA Lt buoy (45°37'·6N 1°28'·6W) to Bordeaux (Point de Pierre–44°50'·4N 0°33'·6W)		
☎ +33(0)5 56525104		📠 +33(0)5 56905879
FREQUENCY: Hr Mr: Ch 12 16 Radar: Ch 12	LOCATION: Harbour Master's Office, Bordeaux (44°51'·4N 0°33'·7W)	HOURS: H24
INFORMATION BROADCASTS: The height of water between Le Verdon and Bordeaux is broadcast automatically every 5 minutes on VHF Ch 17. The Control Centre issues a bulletin on meteorological conditions and also provides navigational information on request		

LA LOIRE	**Vessel Traffic Service:** CALL: Saint-Nazaire Port Control	47°14'N 2°16'W
DESCRIPTION: The system is compulsory for all commercial vessels. It ensures surveillance of marine and river traffic. Information and radar assistance can be supplied on request		
AREA: The system covers the area from Lt buoy SN1 (47°00'N 2°40'W) to the entrance to the Saint-Nazaire Access Channel up to the port of Nantes		
☎ +33(0)2 40004520		📠 +33(0)2 40004566

LA LOIRE (Continued)	Vessel Traffic Service: CALL: Saint-Nazaire Port Control	47°14′N 2°16′W
FREQUENCY: Ch 06 **12** 14 16 67 69	LOCATION: Harbour Master's Office, Saint-Nazaire (47°16′·30N 2°12′·15W)	HOURS: H24
INFORMATION: Tidal information between Saint-Nazaire and Nantes is automatically broadcast on VHF Ch 73 at H+00, H+15, H+30 and H+45 The Control Centre will provide on request information on tidal, meteorological and traffic conditions etc on VHF Ch 12 RADAR ASSISTANCE: The Control Centre will supply radar information on request on VHF Ch 12 to vessels relating their position from the pilot boarding position up to the Rade de Saint-Nazaire (Saint-Nazaire Roads)		

LA ROCHELLE-CHARENTE - VIEUX PORT	Port 350 Berths 120 Visitor Berths	46°09′N 1°14′W
☎ Hr Mr: +33(0)5 46413205 Out of Hours Contact: +33(0)5 46444120		Fax Hr Mr: +33(0)5 46423188
FREQUENCY: Ch **12** 16		HOURS: H24

LES MINIMES	Marina 3300 Berths 350 Visitor Berths	46°08′N 1°10′W
☎ Hr Mr: +33(0)5 46444120	Maximum Depth: 2 m, Maximum LOA: 25 m	Fax Hr Mr: +33(0)5 46443649
FREQUENCY: Ch 09		HOURS: H24

LA TRINITÉ-SUR-MER	Marina 1000 Berths 120 Visitor Berths	47°35′N 3°07′W
☎ +33(0)2 97527149 latrinite-sur-mer@wanadoo.fr	Depth: 0·3 - 5 m, Maximum LOA: 50 m	Fax +33(0)2 97558689
FREQUENCY: Ch 09		HOURS: Season: 0830-1900 LT Out of season: 0830-1230 1400-1800 LT

LA TURBALLE	Marina 310 Berths 20 Visitor Berths	47°21′N 2°31′W
☎ Port Office: +33(0)2 40628040		Fax Port Office: +33(0)2 40234764
FREQUENCY: Ch 09		HOURS: Season: 0700-1100 1500-2100 LT Out of season: 0800-1000 1600-1800 LT

LA TURBALLE TO THE N

LE CONQUET	Port	48°22′N 4°47′W
☎ Port Office: +33(0)2 98890807		Fax Port Office: +33(0)2 98891217 (Indicate: for Bureau du Port)
FREQUENCY: Ch 08 16		HOURS: Season: 0830-1200 1330-1800 LT

LE CROISIC	Marina 235 Berths 15 Visitor Berths	47°16′N 2°25′W
☎ +33(0)2 40231095		Fax
FREQUENCY: Ch 09		HOURS: Season: 0800-2000 LT Out of season: 0800-1700 LT

LE CROUESTY	Marina 1432 Berths 130 Visitor Berths	47°32′N 2°54′W
☎ Hr Mr: +33(0)2 97537333	Maximum depth: 2·5 m, Maximum LOA: 20 m	Fax Hr Mr: +33(0)2 97539022
FREQUENCY: Ch 09		HOURS: Season: 0800-2000 LT Out of season: 0900-1230 1330-1800 LT

LE CROUESTY

LE DOUHET	Marina 370 Berths 20 Visitor Berths	46°00'·15N 1°19'·18W
Hr Mr: +33(0)5 46767113	Maximum depth: 2·1 m, Maximum LOA: 15 m	Fax: Hr Mr: +33(0)5 46767826
FREQUENCY: Ch 09		

LE GUILVINEC-LÉCHIAGAT	Port 230 Berths Visitor Berths Available on Pontoons	47°48'N 4°17'W
+33(0)2 98580567 & 98581140		Fax: +33(0)2 98581794
FREQUENCY: Ch 12		HOURS: HX

LE PALAIS, BELLE-ÎLE	Marina 260 Berths	47°21'N 3°09'W
Hr Mr: +33(0)2 97314290	Depth 1·7 - 3 m in Basin, Maximum LOA: 30 m	Fax: Hr Mr: +33(0)2 97314921
FREQUENCY: Ch 09		HOURS: Season: 0800-1200 1500-2000 LT Out of season: 0830-1200 1400-1800 LT
BELLE ÎLE SAUZON	Port	47°22'·53N 3°12'·93W
Hr Mr: +33(0)2 97305717	Hr Mr only operates July/August	Fax: Hr Mr: +33(0)2 97528317 (Le Palais)
FREQUENCY: Ch 09 16		HOURS: Season 0800-2100 LT

LE POULIGUEN	Marina 750 Berths 30 Visitor Berths	47°16'N 2°25'W
+33(0)2 40603740		Fax:
FREQUENCY: Ch 09		HOURS: Season: 0900-1230 1400-1900 LT

LES SABLES-D'OLONNE	Port and Marina	46°31'N 1°48'W
Hr Mr: +33(0)2 51951179		Fax: Hr Mr: +33(0)2 51214004
FREQUENCY: Lock: Ch 12		HOURS: Hr Mr: Mon-Fri: 0800-1800 LT Lock: HW ± 2h or HW ± 1½ h
	Marina 1100 Berths 100 Visitor Berths	
Hr Mr: +33(0)2 51325116	Maximum depth: 3·5 m, Maximum LOA: 20 m	Fax: Hr Mr: +33(0)2 51323713
FREQUENCY: Ch 09	LOCATION: Port Olona	HOURS: H24

LE VERDON	Port: CALL: Radar Verdon	45°33'N 1°04'W
Hr Mr: +33(0)5 56096391		Fax: Hr Mr: +33(0)5 56737034 (Indicate: for Capitainerie)
FREQUENCY: Hr Mr & Radar: Ch 12		HOURS: H24

L' HERBAUDIÈRE, ÎLE DE NOIRMOUTIER	Marina 492 Berths 50 Visitor Berths	47°02'N 2°18'W
Tel: Hr Mr: +33(0)2 51390505	Maximum depth: 3 m, Maximum LOA: 15 m	Fax: Hr Mr: +33(0)2 51397597
FREQUENCY: Ch 09		HOURS: Season: 0830-1200 1530-2000 LT (July & August: 0730-2230 LT) Out of season: 0830-1200 1400-1800 LT

L'HERBAUDIÉRE FROM NE

LOCTUDY	Port	47°50'N 4°10'W
Tel: Hr Mr: +33(0)2 98874011 Capitainerie: +33(0)2 98879955		Fax: Hr Mr: +33(0)2 98879240 Capitainerie: +33(0)2 98874988
FREQUENCY: Ch 12 (portable VHF)		HOURS: Mon-Fri: 0630-1200 1400-1900 LT Sat: 0800-1200 LT
	Marina 722 Berths 116 Visitor Berths in the Principal and Secondary Basins	
Tel: Port de Plaisance: +33(0)2 98875136		Fax: Port Office: +33(0)2 98879677 Marina: +33(0)2 98665030
FREQUENCY: Ch 09		HOURS: Season: 0730-2100 LT Out of season: Mon-Sat: 0830-1200 1330-1800 LT

LOCTUDY

LORIENT	Port: CALL: Vigie Port Louis	47°44′N 3°22′W
☎ Hr Mr: +33(0)2 97371186		Fax Hr Mr: +33(0)2 97379073
FREQUENCY: Port: Ch 12 16	LOCATION: Vigie de Port-Louis (47°42′·7N 3°21′·8W)	HOURS: H24
	Marina 370 Berths 50 Visitor Berths	
☎ Hr Mr: +33(0)2 97211014		Fax Hr Mr: +33(0)2 97336356
FREQUENCY: Ch 09	LOCATION: Lorient-Ville	HOURS: See Kernével

KERNÉVEL	Marina 582 Berths 60 Visitor Berths	47°43′N 3°22′W
☎ Hr Mr: +33(0)2 97654825 port-kernevel@wanadoo.fr	Depth: 4 m, Maximum LOA: 25 m	Fax Hr Mr: +33(0)2 97336356
FREQUENCY: Ch 09		HOURS: Season: 0800-1230 1330-2000 LT Out of season: Mon-Sat: 0830-1230 1400-1800 LT Sun & holidays: 0900-1230 LT
PORT-LOUIS MARINA	180 Berths Visitor Berths Available	
☎ +33(0)2 97825955		Fax
FREQUENCY: Ch 09		HOURS: Season: 0830-1900 LT Out of season: 0830-1230 1400-1800 LT
LOCMIQUÉLIC MARINA	227 Berths Visitor Berths Available	
☎ +33(0)2 97335951		Fax +33(0)2 97338925
FREQUENCY: Ch 09		HOURS: Season: 0830-1900 LT Out of season: 0830-1230 1400-1800 LT

LOCMIQUÉLIC MARINA

MORGAT	Marina 597 Berths 50 Visitor Berths	48°14′N 4°30′W
☎ Hr Mr: +33(0)2 98270197 port-de-morgat@crozen.com		Fax Hr Mr: +33(0)2 98271976
FREQUENCY: Ch 09 16		HOURS: 0800-1200 1400-2000 LT ACCESS: Anytime for 1·5 m draft

NANTES	Port: CALL: Nantes Port	47°12′N 1°34′W
☎ Hr Mr: +33(0)2 40734147		Fax Hr Mr: +33(0)2 40442002
FREQUENCY: Ch 06 **12** 14 67 69		HOURS: H24

PAUILLAC	Port and Marina	45°12′N 0°44′W
☎ Port Office: +33(0)5 56590160		Fax Port Office: +33(0)5 56590161
FREQUENCY: Ch 12		HOURS: 0800-1200 1400-1800 LT
	Marina 150 Berths 50 Visitor Berths	
☎ Hr Mr: +33(0)5 56591216	Maximum depth: 4 m, Maximum LOA 16 m	Fax Hr Mr: +33(0)5 56592582
FREQUENCY: Ch 09		HOURS: 0800-1800 LT

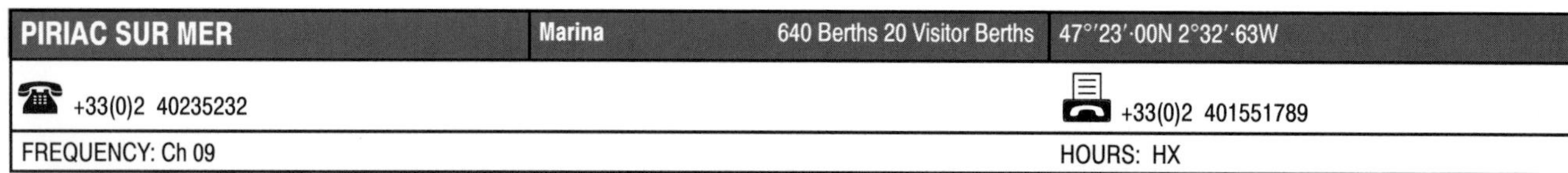

PIRIAC SUR MER	Marina 640 Berths 20 Visitor Berths	47°'23'·00N 2°32'·63W
☎ +33(0)2 40235232		Fax +33(0)2 401551789
FREQUENCY: Ch 09		HOURS: HX

PIRIAC SUR MER

PORNIC	Marina 920 Berths 120 Visitor Berths	47°06'N 2°07'W
☎ Hr Mr: +33(0)2 40820540	Maximum depth: 2 m, Maximum LOA: 20 m	Fax Hr Mr: +33(0)2 40825537
FREQUENCY: Ch 09	LOCATION: La Noëveillard	HOURS: H24

PORTS DE NOËVEILLARD AND PORNIC

PORNICHET	Marina 1150 Berths 150 Visitor Berths	47°15'N 2°21'W
☎ Hr Mr: +33(0)2 40610320	Maximum depth: 2·5 m, Maximum LOA: 25 m	Fax Hr Mr: +33(0)2 40618718
FREQUENCY: Ch 09		HOURS: Season: 0800-2100 LT Out of season: 0800-2000 LT

PORT DE BOURGENAY	Marina 560 Berths 60 Visitor Berths	46°27'N 1°41'W
☎ Hr Mr: +33(0)2 51222036		Fax Hr Mr: +33(0)2 51222945
FREQUENCY: Ch 09 16		

PORT DE LA FLOTTE	Marina	46°11′·35N 1°19′·25W
☎ Hr Mr: +33(0)5 46096766		Fax Hr Mr: +33(0)5 46767826

PORT-JOINVILLE, ÎLE D'YEU	Marina 500 Berths 170 Visitor Berths	46°44′N 2°21′W
☎ Hr Mr: +33(0)2 51583811 Lock: +33(0)2 51583701	Maximum depth: 2·5 m, Maximum LOA: 25 m Mooring is by arrangement with the Hr Mr	Fax Hr Mr: +33(0)2 51260349
FREQUENCY: Ch 09		HOURS: Season: 0730-2000 LT Out of season: 0830-1730 LT ACCESS: Wet basin HW ± 2h

PORT-JOINVILLE FROM SE

PORT-HALIGUEN	Marina 960 Berths	47°29′N 3°06′W
☎ Hr Mr: +33(0)2 97502056	Depth: 1·4 - 2·5 m, Maximum LOA: 16 m	Fax Hr Mr: +33(0)2 97305717
FREQUENCY: Ch 09		HOURS: Season: 0800-1230 1400-2000 LT Out of season: 0900-1200 1400-1800 LT

PORT-LA FORÊT	Marina 1010 Berths 100 Visitor Berths	47°54′N 3°58′W
☎ Port Office: +33(0)2 98569845		Fax +33(0)2 98568131
FREQUENCY: Ch 09		HOURS: Season: 0800-2000 LT Out of season: 0830-1200 1330-1830 LT

PORT TUDY (ÎLE DE GROIX)	Harbour 325 Berths Visitor Berths Available	47°38′·74N 3°26′·63W
☎ Capitainerie: +33(0)2 97865462	Depth: 1·7 - 3 m, Maximum LOA: 25 m	Fax +33(0)2 98271976
FREQUENCY: Ch 09 16		HOURS: 0800-1200 1400-1900 LT

ROCHEFORT	Port de Commerce	45°56′N 0°57′W
☎ Hr Mr: +33(0)5 46994493		Fax Hr Mr: +33(0)5 46994493
FREQUENCY: Hr Mr: Ch 12 16	LOCATION: Bassin No 1 (45°56′·6N 0°57′·3W)	HOURS: 0800-1200 1400-1800 LT
	Marina 300 Berths 20 Visitor Berths	
☎ Port Office: +33(0)5 46839996	Maximum depth: 2·5 m, Maximum LOA: 20 m	Fax
FREQUENCY: Ch 09		HOURS: HW ± 1h

PORT-LA-FORET MARINA

ROYAN	Marina 952 Berths 100 Visitor Berths	45°37′N 1°02′W
☎ Hr Mr: +33(0)5 46387222	Maximum depth: 2·5 m, Maximum LOA: 23 m	Fax Hr Mr: +33(0)5 46394247
FREQUENCY: Ch 09		HOURS: Season: 0800-2000 LT Out of season: 0900-1200 1400-1800 LT

SAINT-DENIS-D'OLÉRON	Marina 750 Berths 70 Visitor Berths	46°02′·16N 1°21′·97W
☎ +33(0)5 46479797	Depth: 2·5 m, Maximum LOA: 16 m	Fax +33(0)5 46478823
FREQUENCY: Ch 09		

SAINT-GILLES-CROIX-DE-VIE (PORT LA VIE)	Marina 800 Berths 80 Visitor Berths	46°42′N 1°56′W
☎ Hr Mr: +33(0)2 51558422 & 51553083	Maximum depth: 3 m, Maximum LOA: 20 m	Fax Hr Mr: +33(0)2 51553143
FREQUENCY: Ch 09		HOURS: Season: 0600-2200 LT Out of season: 0800-1200 1400-1800 LT

SAINT GUÉNOLE	Port	47°49′N 4°22′W
☎ Capitainerie: +33(0)2 98525132		Fax Capitainerie: +33(0)2 98585285
FREQUENCY: Ch 12		HOURS: HJ

SAINT-JEAN-DE-LUZ (CIBOURE)	Marina 75 Berths 6 Visitor Berths	43°23′N 1°40′W
☎ Capitainerie: +33(0)5 59472681	Maximum depth: 1·6 m, Maximum LOA: 15 m	Fax
FREQUENCY: Ch 09 16		HOURS: Season: 0630-1300 1330-2000 LT Out of season: 0730-1230 1330-1830 LT

SAINT-NAZAIRE	Port	47°16′N 2°12′W
☎ Hr Mr: +33(0)2 40004520		Fax Hr Mr: +33(0)2 40004566
FREQUENCY: Ch 06 **12** 14 67 69		HOURS: H24
NOTE: The Saint-Nazaire Hr Mr monitors traffic in the estuary and the seaward part of La Loire up to Pointe de Mindin Radar Station (47°16′·2N 2°09′·8W)		

TONNAY-CHARENTE	Port	45°57′N 0°53′W
☎ Hr Mr: +33(0)5 46887067		Fax
FREQUENCY: Ch 12 16		HOURS: HX

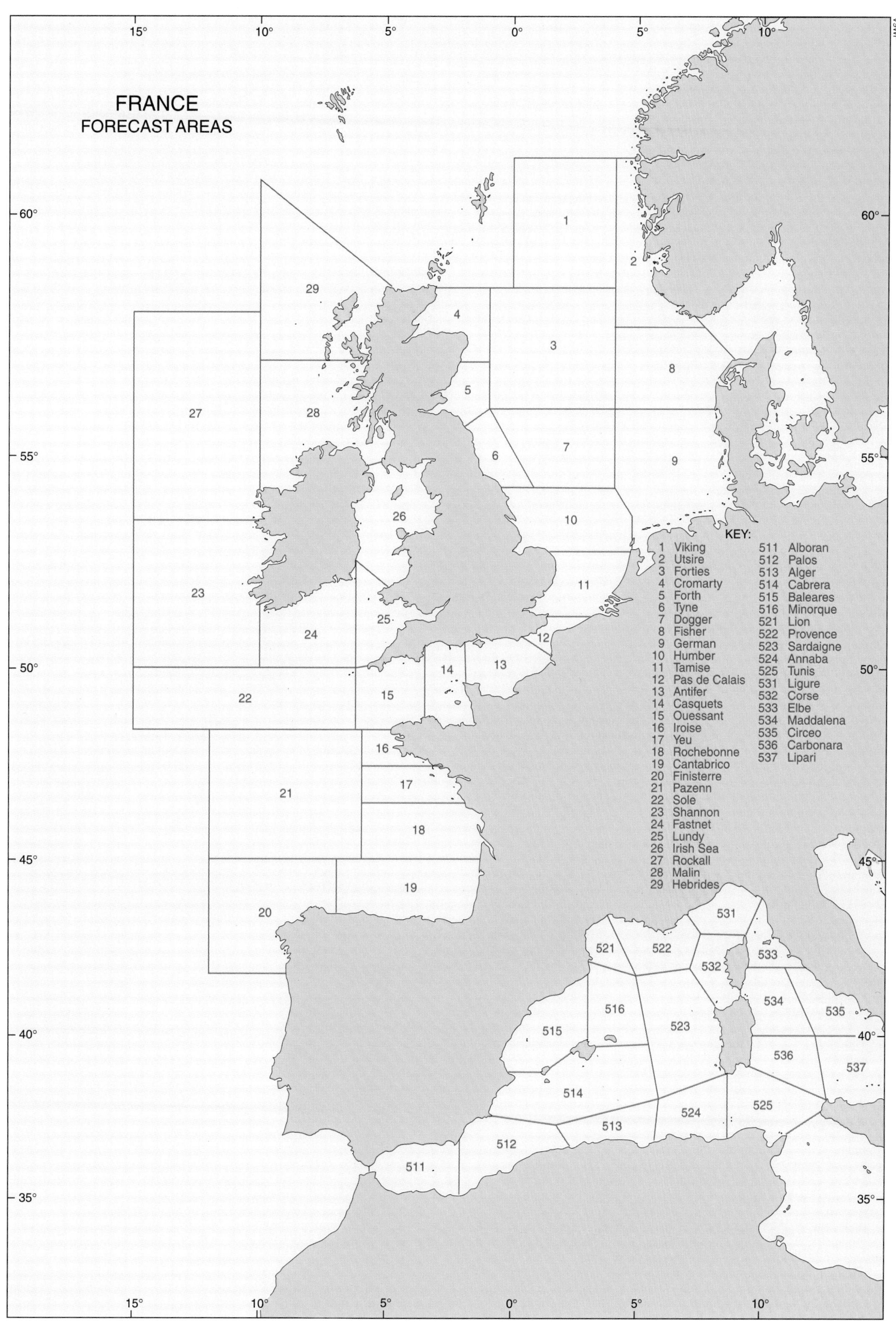
FRANCE
FORECAST AREAS
KEY:
1 Viking
2 Utsire
3 Forties
4 Cromarty
5 Forth
6 Tyne
7 Dogger
8 Fisher
9 German
10 Humber
11 Tamise
12 Pas de Calais
13 Antifer
14 Casquets
15 Ouessant
16 Iroise
17 Yeu
18 Rochebonne
19 Cantabrico
20 Finisterre
21 Pazenn
22 Sole
23 Shannon
24 Fastnet
25 Lundy
26 Irish Sea
27 Rockall
28 Malin
29 Hebrides
511 Alboran
512 Palos
513 Alger
514 Cabrera
515 Baleares
516 Minorque
521 Lion
522 Provence
523 Sardaigne
524 Annaba
525 Tunis
531 Ligure
532 Corse
533 Elbe
534 Maddalena
535 Circeo
536 Carbonara
537 Lipari
15°
10°
5°
0°
5°
10°
60°
55°
50°
45°
40°
35°
V9WF

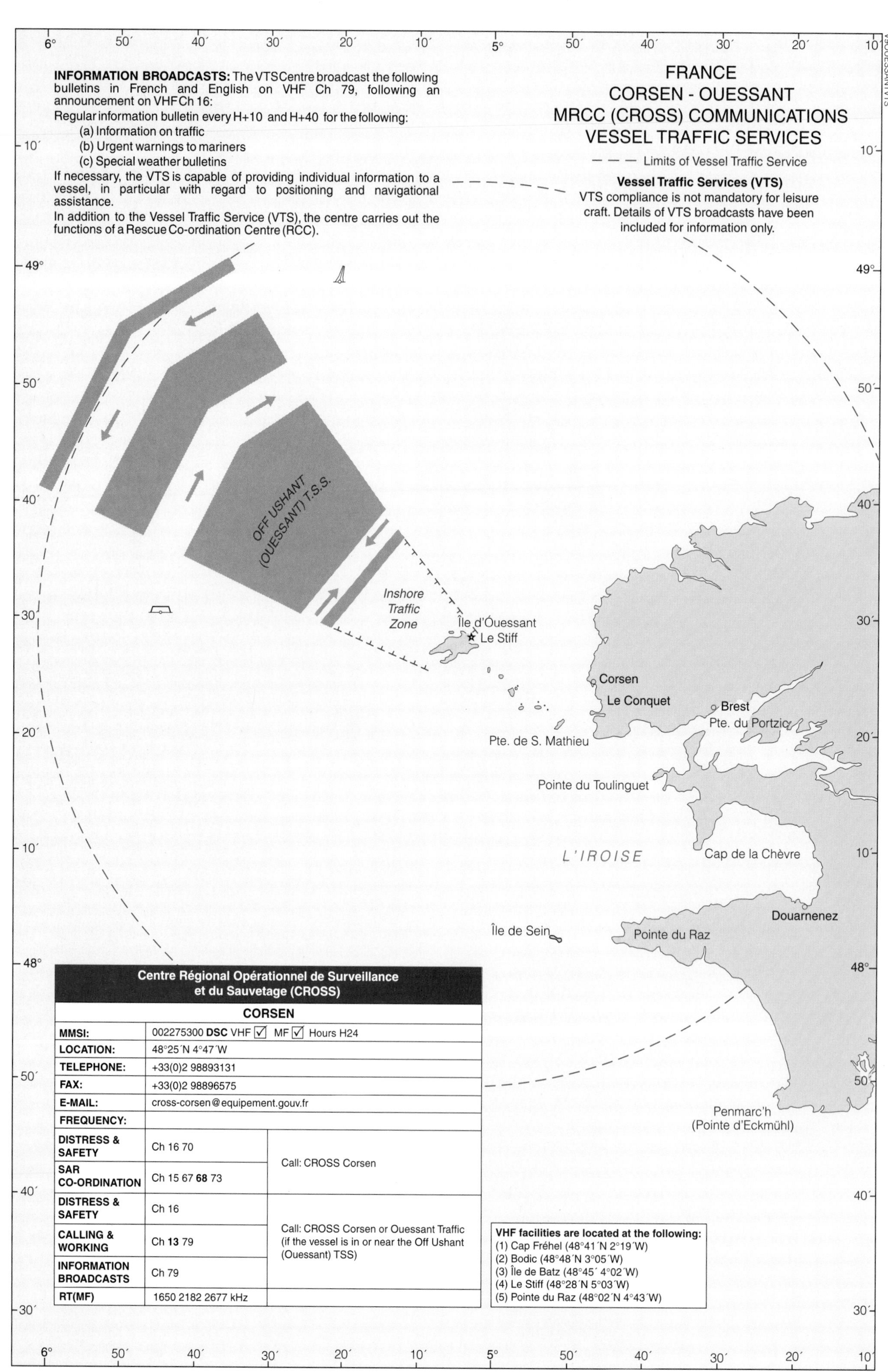

Centre Régional Opérationnel de Surveillance et du Sauvetage (CROSS)

CORSEN		
MMSI:	002275300 **DSC** VHF ☑ MF ☑ Hours H24	
LOCATION:	48°25′N 4°47′W	
TELEPHONE:	+33(0)2 98893131	
FAX:	+33(0)2 98896575	
E-MAIL:	cross-corsen@equipement.gouv.fr	
FREQUENCY:		
DISTRESS & SAFETY	Ch 16 70	Call: CROSS Corsen
SAR CO-ORDINATION	Ch 15 67 **68** 73	
DISTRESS & SAFETY	Ch 16	Call: CROSS Corsen or Ouessant Traffic (if the vessel is in or near the Off Ushant (Ouessant) TSS)
CALLING & WORKING	Ch **13** 79	
INFORMATION BROADCASTS	Ch 79	
RT(MF)	1650 2182 2677 kHz	

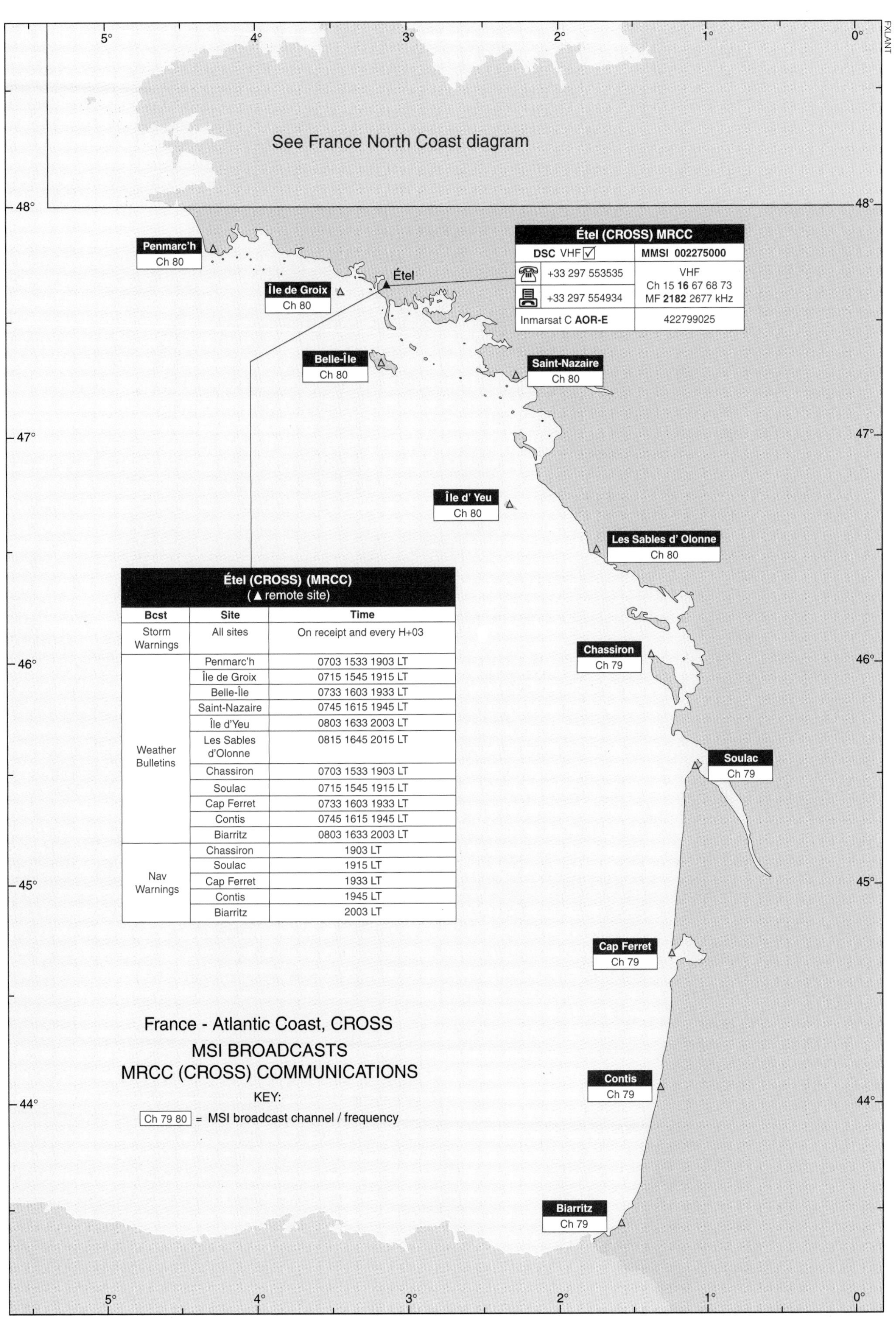

Étel (CROSS) (MRCC)
(▲ remote site)

Bcst	Site	Time
Storm Warnings	All sites	On receipt and every H+03
Weather Bulletins	Penmarc'h	0703 1533 1903 LT
	Île de Groix	0715 1545 1915 LT
	Belle-Île	0733 1603 1933 LT
	Saint-Nazaire	0745 1615 1945 LT
	Île d'Yeu	0803 1633 2003 LT
	Les Sables d'Olonne	0815 1645 2015 LT
	Chassiron	0703 1533 1903 LT
	Soulac	0715 1545 1915 LT
	Cap Ferret	0733 1603 1933 LT
	Contis	0745 1615 1945 LT
	Biarritz	0803 1633 2003 LT
Nav Warnings	Chassiron	1903 LT
	Soulac	1915 LT
	Cap Ferret	1933 LT
	Contis	1945 LT
	Biarritz	2003 LT

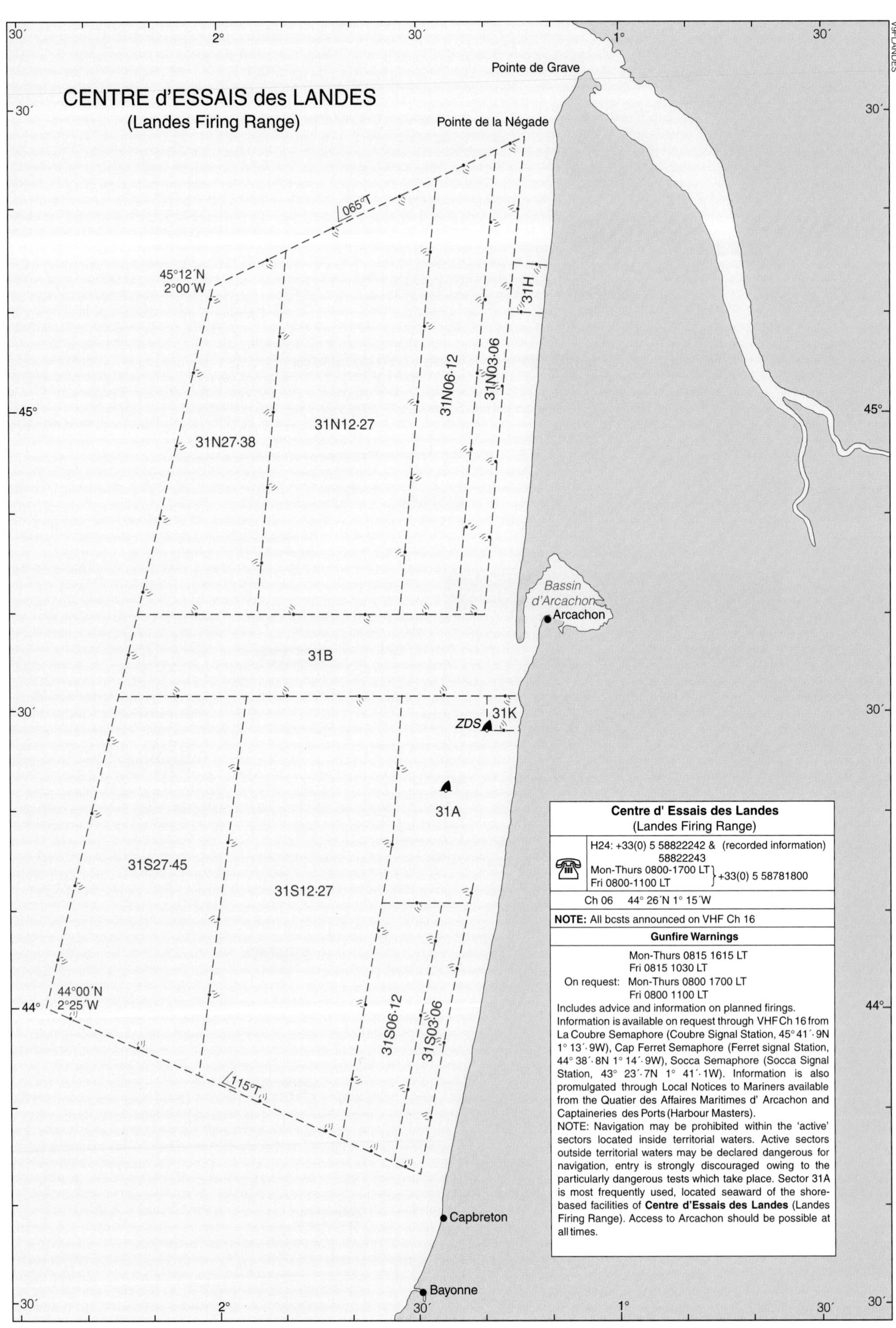
CENTRE d'ESSAIS des LANDES
(Landes Firing Range)
V9FLANDES
Pointe de Grave
Pointe de la Négade
065°T
45°12´N
2°00´W
31H
31N03·06
31N06·12
31N12·27
31N27·38
Bassin d'Arcachon
Arcachon
31B
31K
ZDS
31A
31S27·45
31S12·27
31S06·12
31S03·06
44°00´N
2°25´W
115°T
Capbreton
Bayonne
Centre d' Essais des Landes
(Landes Firing Range)
H24: +33(0) 5 58822242 & (recorded information) 58822243
Mon-Thurs 0800-1700 LT
Fri 0800-1100 LT
+33(0) 5 58781800
Ch 06 44° 26´N 1° 15´W
NOTE: All bcsts announced on VHF Ch 16
Gunfire Warnings
Mon-Thurs 0815 1615 LT
Fri 0815 1030 LT
On request: Mon-Thurs 0800 1700 LT
Fri 0800 1100 LT
Includes advice and information on planned firings. Information is available on request through VHF Ch 16 from La Coubre Semaphore (Coubre Signal Station, 45° 41´·9N 1° 13´·9W), Cap Ferret Semaphore (Ferret signal Station, 44° 38´·8N 1° 14´·9W), Socca Semaphore (Socca Signal Station, 43° 23´·7N 1° 41´·1W). Information is also promulgated through Local Notices to Mariners available from the Quatier des Affaires Maritimes d' Arcachon and Captaineries des Ports (Harbour Masters).
NOTE: Navigation may be prohibited within the 'active' sectors located inside territorial waters. Active sectors outside territorial waters may be declared dangerous for navigation, entry is strongly discouraged owing to the particularly dangerous tests which take place. Sector 31A is most frequently used, located seaward of the shore-based facilities of Centre d'Essais des Landes (Landes Firing Range). Access to Arcachon should be possible at all times.

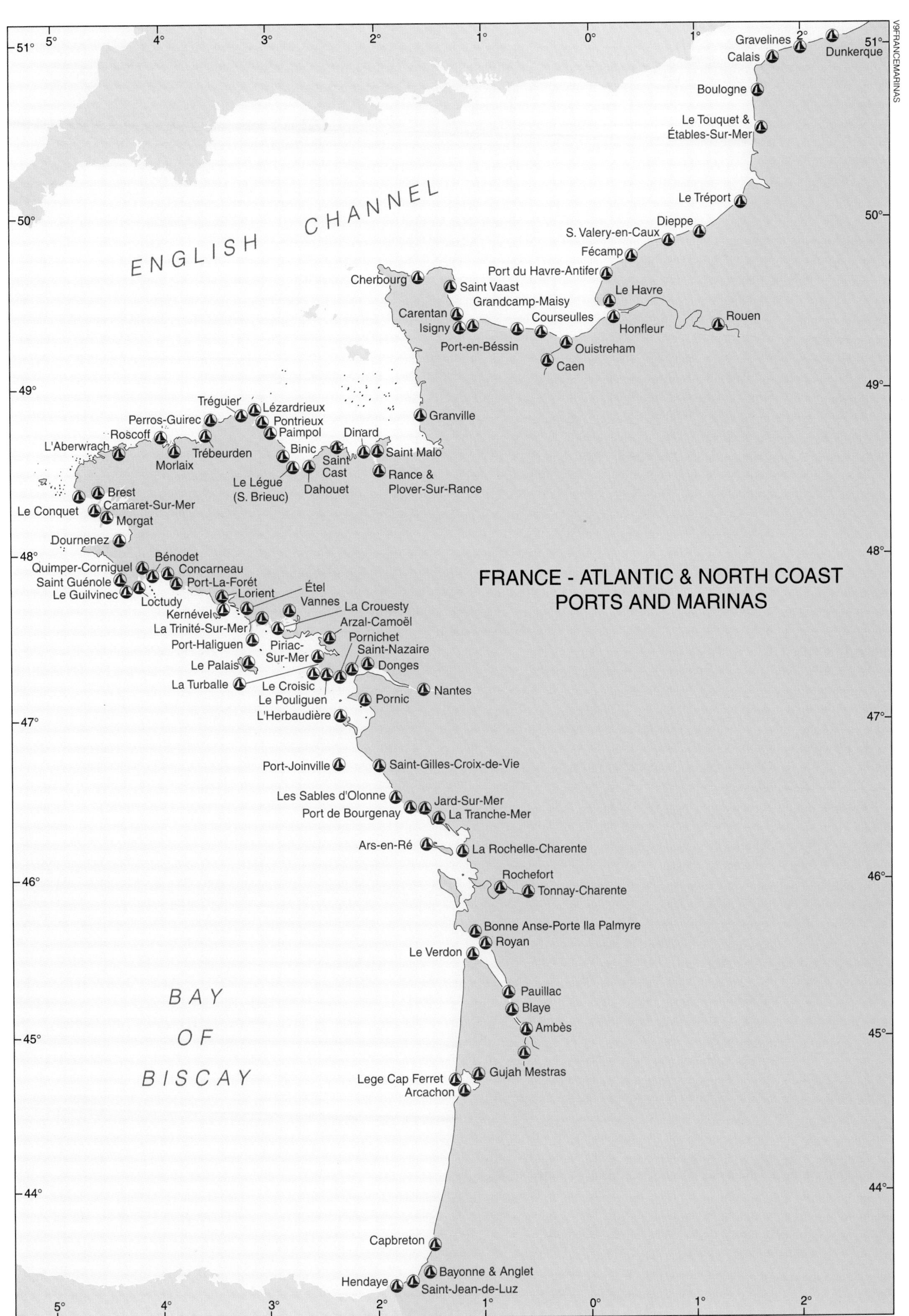

FRANCE - ATLANTIC & NORTH COAST
PORTS AND MARINAS
ENGLISH CHANNEL
BAY OF BISCAY
V9FRANCEMARINAS
Dunkerque
Gravelines
Calais
Boulogne
Le Touquet & Étables-Sur-Mer
Le Tréport
Dieppe
S. Valery-en-Caux
Fécamp
Port du Havre-Antifer
Le Havre
Rouen
Honfleur
Courseulles
Ouistreham
Caen
Cherbourg
Saint Vaast
Grandcamp-Maisy
Carentan
Isigny
Port-en-Béssin
Granville
Tréguier
Lézardrieux
Pontrieux
Paimpol
Perros-Guirec
Roscoff
L'Aberwrach
Morlaix
Trébeurden
Binic
Dinard
Saint Malo
Saint Cast
Dahouet
Le Légue (S. Brieuc)
Rance & Plover-Sur-Rance
Brest
Le Conquet
Camaret-Sur-Mer
Morgat
Dournenez
Bénodet
Concarneau
Quimper-Corniguel
Saint Guénole
Le Guilvinec
Loctudy
Port-La-Forét
Lorient
Kernével
Étel
Vannes
La Crouesty
Arzal-Camoël
La Trinité-Sur-Mer
Port-Haliguen
Le Palais
La Turballe
Piriac-Sur-Mer
Pornichet
Saint-Nazaire
Donges
Le Croisic
Le Pouliguen
Nantes
Pornic
L'Herbaudière
Port-Joinville
Saint-Gilles-Croix-de-Vie
Les Sables d'Olonne
Port de Bourgenay
Jard-Sur-Mer
La Tranche-Mer
Ars-en-Ré
La Rochelle-Charente
Rochefort
Tonnay-Charente
Bonne Anse-Porte lla Palmyre
Royan
Le Verdon
Pauillac
Blaye
Ambès
Lege Cap Ferret
Gujah Mestras
Arcachon
Capbreton
Bayonne & Anglet
Hendaye
Saint-Jean-de-Luz
51°
50°
49°
48°
47°
46°
45°
44°
5°
4°
3°
2°
1°
0°
1°
2°

VANNES	Marina 300 Berths 60 Visitor Berths	47°39′N 2°45′W
Port Office: +33(0)2 97541608	Maximum depth: 2·4 m, Maximum LOA: 25 m	Port Office: +33(0)2 97424800
FREQUENCY: Ch 09		HOURS: Season: 0830-2100 LT Out of season: HW ± 2½ h (Morning: 0900-1230 LT)

FRANCE, NORTH COAST

CENTRES RÉGIONAUX OPÉRATIONNELS DE SURVEILLANCE ET DE SAUVETAGE (CROSS)

National SAR Agency: Organisme d'études et de coordination pour la recherche et le sauvetage en mer (SECMAR) **Tel:** +33 1 53634159 **Fax:** +33 1 53634178

Centre Régionaux Operationels de Surveillance et de Sauvetage (CROSS)

Centres Régionaux Opérationnels de Surveillance et de Sauvetage (CROSS) are Maritime Rescue Co-ordination Centres (MRCC) and a Sous-CROSS is a Maritime Rescue Sub-Centre (MRSC). France has five MRCCs for its European coasts

CROSS provides a permanent, full time, all weather operational presence along the coast of France and co-operates with foreign MRCCs and MRSCs as required.

MRCC Gris Nez has been designated as the initial point of contact for foreign SAR authorities for any question concerning operational aspects of maritime SAR and when France is involved in an incident where a particular French MRCC is not clearly competent to deal with it

MRCC Gris Nez has also been designated as the MRCC associated to the French COSPAS-SARSAT Mission Control Centre (FMCC) and the Inmarsat LESs

Maritime Safety Information Broadcasts

Storm Warnings, Weather Bulletins, Navigational Warnings and Fog Warnings are announced by **Centre Régionaux Operationels de Surveillance et de Sauvetage (CROSS),** on 2182 kHz or VHF channel 16, before being broadcast on the scheduled frequency or channel number. All products broadcast by CROSS originate from Météo France

There are regular meterorological bulletins and special high winds bulletins (Bulletins Météorologique Spéciaux - BMS).

Regular morning and evening bulletins (or Weather Bulletins) are broadcast at fixed times. They consist of a repeat of any BMS warnings in force, a description of the general situation, a detailed forecast for the following 24 hours (actual situation, wind, sea state and visibility) further weather trends dependent on the forecast and where appropriate reports from signal stations

Regular bulletins are classed as follows:

'Coastal Waters' Bulletins - up to 20 n miles from the coast

'High Seas' Bulletins - up to 200 n miles

'Distant Waters' Bulletins - over 200 n miles

High Winds Bulletins, BMS (Storm Warnings), are included in any 'Coastal Waters', 'High Seas' or 'Distant Waters' bulletins. BMS are broadcast whenever the wind has risen to or is forecast to rise to Gale force 7 within coastal waters (BMS Coastal) or Gale force 8 in high seas and distant waters (BMS Offshore). Scheduled broadcasts may be suspended whilst SAR action is in progress

NAVTEX [A] [W]

A	Corsen (Le Stiff)	518 kHz	48°28′N 5°03′W
W	La Garde (Fort Ste Marguerite)	518 kHz	43°06′N 5°59′E

NAVTEX [E] [S]

E	Corsen (Le Stiff)	490 kHz	48°28′N 5°03′W
S	La Garde (Fort Ste Marguerite)	490 kHz	43°06′N 5°59′E

DIAGRAMS: pages 87, 99, 109 and 110

Weather Bulletins

A: On receipt 0000 0400 0800 1200 1600 2000	Storm warnings for areas Iroise, Yeu, Rochebonne, Cantabrico, Finisterre and Pazenn
A: 0000 1200	Gale warnings or storm warnings, synopsis and development, 24 hour forecast for areas Iroise, Yeu, Rochebonne, Cantabrico, Finisterre and Pazenn
W: On receipt 0340 0740 1140 1540 1940 2340	Storm warnings for Areas 514 (Eastern part), 515, 516, 521, 522, 523 & 531-534
W: 1140 2340	Storm warnings, synopsis and development, 24 hour forecast for areas 514 (Eastern part), 515, 516, 521, 522, 523 & 531-534. In English
E: 0040 0440 0840 1240 1640 2040	Storm warnings for areas Casquets, Ouessant, Iroise, Yeu, Rochebonne, Cantabrico, Finisterre, Pazenn, Sole, Shannon, Fastnet, Lundy, Irish Sea, Rockall, Malin and Hebrides. In French
E: 0840 2040	Gale warnings or storm warnings, synopsis and development, 24 hour forecast for areas Casquets, Ouessant, Iroise, Yeu, Rochebonne, Cantabrico, Finisterre, Pazenn, Sole, Fastnet, Shannon, Lundy and Irish Sea. In French
S: 0300 0700 1100 1500 1900 2300	Storm warnings for Areas 514 (Eastern part), 515, 516, 521, 522, 523 & 531-534. In French
S: 0700 1900	Storm warnings, synopsis and development, 24 hour forecast for areas 514 (Eastern part), 515, 516, 521, 522, 523 & 531-534. In French

Navigational Warnings

A: 0000 0400 0800 1200 1600 2000	AVURNAV Brest
W: 0340 0740 1140 1540 1940 2340	AVURNAV Toulon
E: 0040 0440 0840 1240 1640 2040	AVURNAV Brest. In French
S: 0300 0700 1100 1500 1900 2300	AVURNAV Toulon. In French

CORSEN (CROSS) (MRCC)

A	1650 2677	RT (MF)		
B	Ch 79	VHF	Pointe du Raz	48°02′N 4°52′W
C			Le Stiff	48°28′N 5°03′W
D			Île de Batz	48°54′N 4°02′W
E			Bodic	48°48′N 3°05′W
F			Cap Fréhel	48°41′N 2°19′W
DIAGRAMS: pages 87, 99, 109 and 110				
Weather Bulletins				
A: On receipt Every H+03	Storm warnings and Bulletins Météorologique Spéciaux (BMS) for Areas 13-29. In French			
A: 0815 2015 LT	Storm warnings in force. Synopsis and 24 hour forecast for Areas 13-29. Further 24 hour outlook. In French			
B-F: On receipt Every H+10 H+50	Storm warnings and BMS for Areas 14-17 . In French and English			
B-F: 0750 1950 1350 1650 1950 2250	24 hour forecast for Areas 14-17. In French and English			
B: 0445 0703 1103[1] 1533 1903 LT **C:** 0503 0715 1115[1] 1545 1915 LT **D:** 0515 0733 1133[1] 1603 1933 LT **E:** 0533 0745 1145[1] 1615 1945 LT **F:** 0545 0803 1203[1] 1633 2003 LT (1) 1 May - 30 September	Storm warnings and BMS in force. 24 hour forecast and reports from Signal Stations. For Area: Cap de la Hague to Penmarc'h extending 20 n miles from the coast. In French			
Navigational Warnings				
A: 0735 1935 LT	Local warnings			
B-F: Every H+10 H+40	General bulletin for Ouessant TSS. In English and French			
B-F: Broadcast when visibility conditions so require	Fog (Visibility) warnings for Ouessant TSS. In English and French			

GRIS-NEZ (CROSS) (MRCC)

A	1650 2677	RT (MF)		
B	Ch 79	VHF	S. Frieux	50°37′N 1°36′E
C			Dunkerque	51°03′N 2°21′E
D			L'Ailly	49°55′N 0°58′E
DIAGRAMS: pages 87, 99, 109 and 110				
Weather Bulletins				
A: On receipt Every H+03	Storm warnings and BMS for Areas 10-13. In French			
A: 0833 2033 LT	Storm warnings in force. Synopsis and 24 hour forecast for Areas 10-13. Further 24 hour outlook. In French			
B-D: On receipt Every H+03	Coastal BMS			
B: 0710 1545 1910 LT **C:** 0720 1603 1920 LT	Storm warnings and BMS in force. 24 hour forecast and reports from Signal Stations. For Area: Belgian frontier to Baie de la Somme extending 20 n miles from the coast. In French			
D: 0703 1533 1903 LT	Storm warnings and BMS in force. 24 hour forecast and reports from Signal Stations. For Area: Baie de la Somme to Cap de la Hague extending 20 n miles from the coast. In French			
Navigational Warnings				
B-D: Every H+10	Pas de Calais (Dover Strait) bulletin (includes vessel movement, vessel movement rule breakers, distress messages, BMS, buoyage irregularities, dangers to navigation). In French and English			
A: 0833 2033 LT	Cherbourg AVURNAVS 1-999. In French and English; Cherbourg Local AVURNAVS 1001–1999. In French			
B-D: Every H+25	Fog (Visibility) warnings: When visibility in the Pas de Calais (Dover Strait) falls below 2 n miles. In French and English. Supplementary bulletins are broadcast when required in addition to the scheduled broadcast times above.			

GRIS-NEZ	MMSI 002275100	Vessel Traffic Service: CALL: Gris-Nez Traffic	50°52′·2N 1°35′·1E
AREA: The Vessel Traffic Service covers the following areas: (1) The Pas de Calais Traffic Separation Scheme (2) The Inshore Traffic Zone			HOURS: H24
☎ +33(0)3 21872187 ops.cross-gris-nez@equipement.gouv.fr		Inmarsat C 422799256	Fax +33(0)3 21877855
FREQUENCY: Distress & Safety: Ch 16 CROSS Gris-Nez: Calling & Working: Ch **13** 79 Information Broadcasts: Ch 79		RT and VHF facilities are located at the following: (1) Dunkerque (51°03′N 2°21′E) Ch 16 67 70 79 (2) Gris-Nez (50°52′N 1°35′E) Ch 13 16 68 70 79 (3) Sainte-Frieux (50°37′N 1°36′E) Ch 13 16 67 70 79 (4) L'Ailly (49°55′N 0°58′E) Ch 16 68 70 79	LOCATION: Control Centre: CROSS Gris-Nez
INFORMATION BROADCASTS: The Control Centre broadcasts on VHF Ch 79, following an announcement on VHF Ch 16, in French and English. Broadcasts comprise: (1) Regular bulletin: every H+10 for traffic information, vessels contravening traffic regulations and nautical information for the area (2) Occasional bulletin: every H+25 when visibility is less than 2 n miles			
RADAR ASSISTANCE: On request, Gris-Nez Traffic provides radar information to vessels relative to their position on VHF Ch 79. The two radar stations at Gris-Nez (50°52′·2N 1°35′·1E) and Saint-Frieux (50°36′·6N 1°36′·6E) provide radar coverage extending approximately SW up to 0°30′E and NE up to 30 n miles from Gris-Nez			

JOBOURG (CROSS) (MRCC)

A	Ch 80	VHF	Granville	48°50′N 1°36′W
B			Jobourg	49°41′N 1°54′W
C			Port-en-Bessin	49°21′N 0°45′W
D			Antifer	49°41′N 0°10′E

DIAGRAMS: pages 87, 99, 109 and 110

Weather Bulletins	
A-D: On receipt H+20 H+50	Storm warnings and BMS Large (if winds are forecast to reach Force 8 or more) for Areas 13-14. In French and English
A-D: Every H+03	Coastal BMS in French
A: 0703 1533 1903 LT **B:** 0715 1545 1915 LT	Storm warnings and BMS in force. 24 hour forecast and reports from Signal Stations. For Area: Cap de la Hague to Pointe de Penmarc'h extending 20 n miles from the coast. In French
B: 0733 1603 1933 LT **C:** 0745 1615 1945 LT **D:** 0803 1633 2003 LT	Storm warnings and BMS in force. 24 hour forecast and reports from Signal Stations. For Area: Baie de Somme to Cap de la Hague extending 20 n miles from the coast. In French
Navigational Warnings	
A–D: Every H+20 H+50 On request	Regular bulletin for Casquets TSS and the area east to buoy number 'EC 2' (50°12′·0N 1°12′·5W). In French and English
A-D: 0915 2115 LT	Cherbourg AVURNAVS for Areas Manche Ouest and Manche Est. In French and English Cherbourg Local AVURNAVS for Area Manche Ouest. In French

JOBOURG	MMSI 002275200	Vessel Traffic Service: CALL: Jobourg Traffic	49°41′·1N 1°54′·5W
AREA: The Vessel Traffic Service covers the following areas: (1) The Off Casquets Traffic Separation Scheme (TSS) and the adjacent area (up to Lt buoy EC2 (50°12′·0N 1°12′·5W) to the east) (2) The Inshore Traffic Zone			HOURS: H24
☎ +33(0)2 33527213 jobourg.mrcc@wanadoo.fr			Fax +33(0)2 33 527172
FREQUENCY: Calling & Working: Ch 13 80 Information Broadcasts: Ch 80		RT and VHF facilities are located at the following: (1) Antifer (49°41′N 0°10′E) Ch 16 67 70 80 (2) Ver sur Mer Ch 70 (3) Port-en-Bessin (49°21′N 0°45′W) (4) Gatteville (49°42′N 1°16′W) Ch 16 68 70 80 (5) Jobourg (49°41′N 1°54′W) Ch 13 16 67 70 80 (6) Granville (48°50′N 1°36′W) Ch 16 68 70 80 (7) Roches-Douvres (49°06′N 2°49′W) Ch 70	LOCATION: Control Centre: CROSS Jobourg
INFORMATION BROADCASTS: The Control Centre broadcasts on VHF Ch 80, following an announcement on VHF Ch 16, in French and English. Broadcasts comprise: (1) Regular bulletin: every H+20 and H+50 for traffic information, vessels contravening traffic regulations and nautical information for the area (2) Occasional bulletin: when required			
RADAR ASSISTANCE: On request, Jobourg Traffic provides radar information to vessels relative to their position on VHF Ch 80. The area of radar coverage extends to 40 n miles between lines of bearing 270° and 000° from the Control Centre			

RADIO FRANCE (BULLETIN INTER-SERVICE-MER)			
A	162 (Long Wave)		France Inter
B	1404	AM	Ajaccio
	1494		Bastia
	1494		Bayonne
	1206		Bordeaux
	1404		Brest
	1242		Marseille
	1557		Nice
DIAGRAM: page 99			
Weather Bulletins			
A: 2003 LT **B:** 0655 LT	Gale warnings, synopsis, development, 24 hour forecast for Areas 1–29,514-516, 521–523 & 531–534. In French (NOTE: All stations transmit the same bulletin)		

BARFLEUR	Harbour 125 Berths 25 Visitor Berths	49°40′·40N 1°15′·40W
☎ Hr Mr: +33(0)2 33540829 Sailing Club: +33(0)2 33431662		Fax

BINIC	Marina 400 Berths 60 Visitor Berths	48°36′N 2°49′W
☎ Hr Mr: +33(0)2 96736186 (HX)	Depth: 1·5 - 3 m	Fax Hr Mr: +33(0)2 96737238
FREQUENCY: Ch 09		HOURS: Office hours ACCESS: Marina: HW -1 h to HW

BOULOGNE-SUR-MER	Port: CALL: Control Tower: Boulogne Port	50°44′N 1°35′E
☎ Hr Mr: +33(0)3 21807200 Control Tower: +33(0)3 21315243 (H24)		Fax Hr Mr: +33(0)3 21872879
FREQUENCY: Control Tower: Ch 12		HOURS: Control Tower: H24
	Marina 114 Berths 20 visitor berths	
☎ Marina: +33(0)3 21317001 Yacht Club:+33(0)3 21318067		Fax
FREQUENCY: Ch 09	LOCATION: 50°43′·5N 1°36′·0E	HOURS: HW ± 3h

CAEN	Port & Marina	49°11′N 0°21′W
☎ Hr Mr: +33(0)2 31971443 Operations: +33(0)2 31431500 Bassin de Plaisance: +33(0)2 31952447		Fax
FREQUENCY: Ch 12 68	LOCATION: Bassin Saint-Pierre	HOURS: Marina: 0745-1230 1400-1900 LT ACCESS: Caen Canal: HW ± 2-3 hrs

CALAIS	Port: CALL: Calais Port Traffic	50°58′N 1°51′E
☎ Hr Mr: +33(0)3 21963120		Fax Hr Mr: +33(0)3 21340892
FREQUENCY: Ch 12 16		HOURS: H24
NOTE: Vessels manoeuvring in the Access Channel, tidal port and its Bassins should maintain a listening watch on VHF Ch 12 at all times during the manoeuvre		
	Bridge	
PROCEDURE: Special requests for the opening of the Swing-Bridge; preferably for several vessels leaving together, may be made by contacting the Harbour Office at least 10 mins before departure on VHF Ch 12 or by telephone		
	Marina 350 Berths 400 Visitor Berths	
☎ Marina: +33(0)3 21345523 Yacht Club de Calais: +33(0)3 21970234 calais-marina@calais-port.com		Fax Marina: +33(0)3 21961078
FREQUENCY: Marina and Lock: (Écluse Carnot) Ch 12		HOURS: 0800-1200 1400-1800 LT

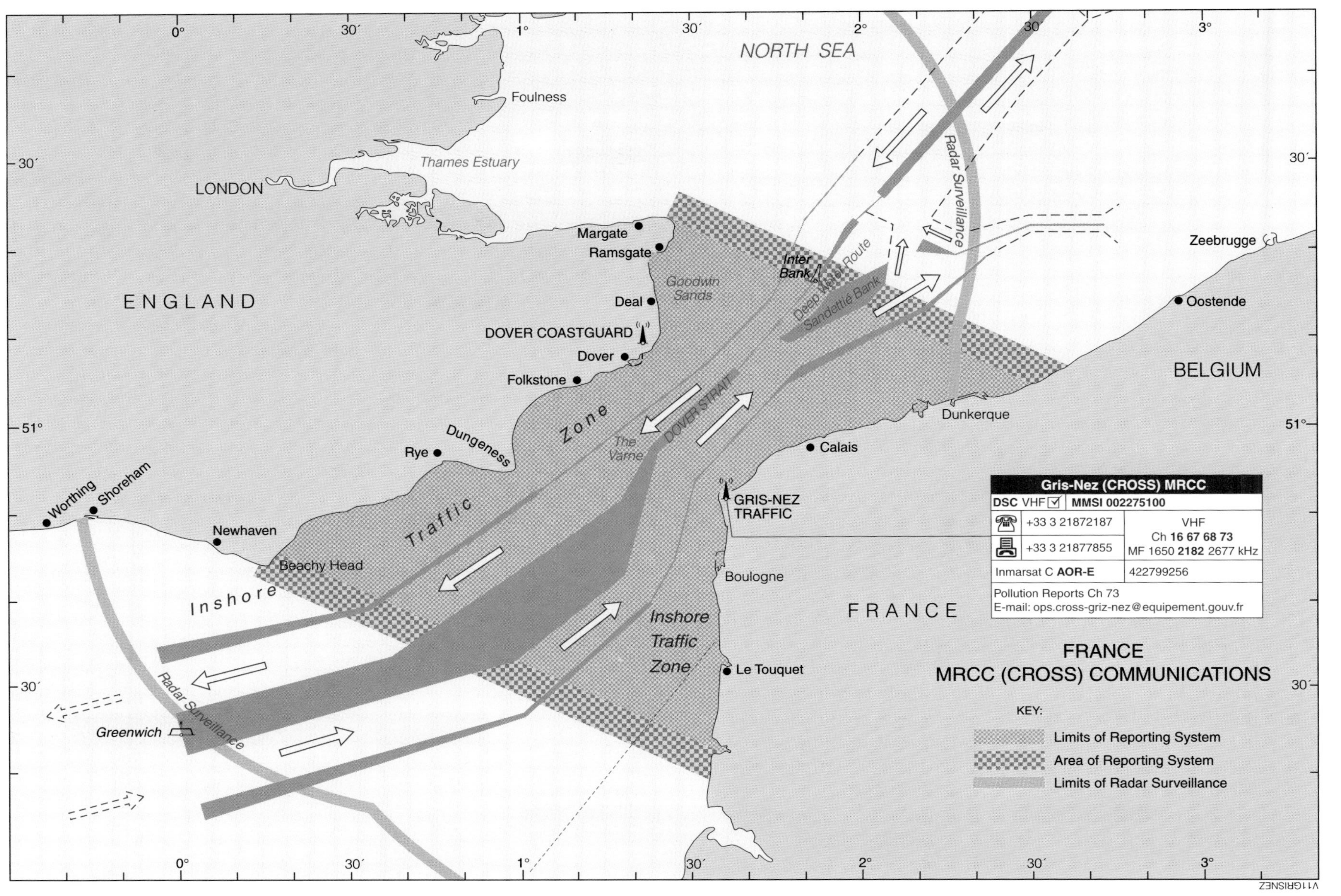
FRANCE
MRCC (CROSS) COMMUNICATIONS
Gris-Nez (CROSS) MRCC
DSC VHF ☑ MMSI 002275100
+33 3 21872187
+33 3 21877855
VHF
Ch 16 67 68 73
MF 1650 2182 2677 kHz
Inmarsat C AOR-E 422799256
Pollution Reports Ch 73
E-mail: ops.cross-griz-nez@equipement.gouv.fr
KEY:
Limits of Reporting System
Area of Reporting System
Limits of Radar Surveillance
NORTH SEA
ENGLAND
FRANCE
BELGIUM
LONDON
Foulness
Thames Estuary
Margate
Ramsgate
Goodwin Sands
Deal
DOVER COASTGUARD
Dover
Folkstone
Dungeness
Rye
Newhaven
Beachy Head
Shoreham
Worthing
Greenwich
Inshore Traffic Zone
DOVER STRAIT
The Varne
Inter Bank
Deep Water Route
Sandettie Bank
Radar Surveillance
Zeebrugge
Oostende
Dunkerque
Calais
GRIS-NEZ TRAFFIC
Boulogne
Le Touquet
Inshore Traffic Zone
V11GRISNEZ

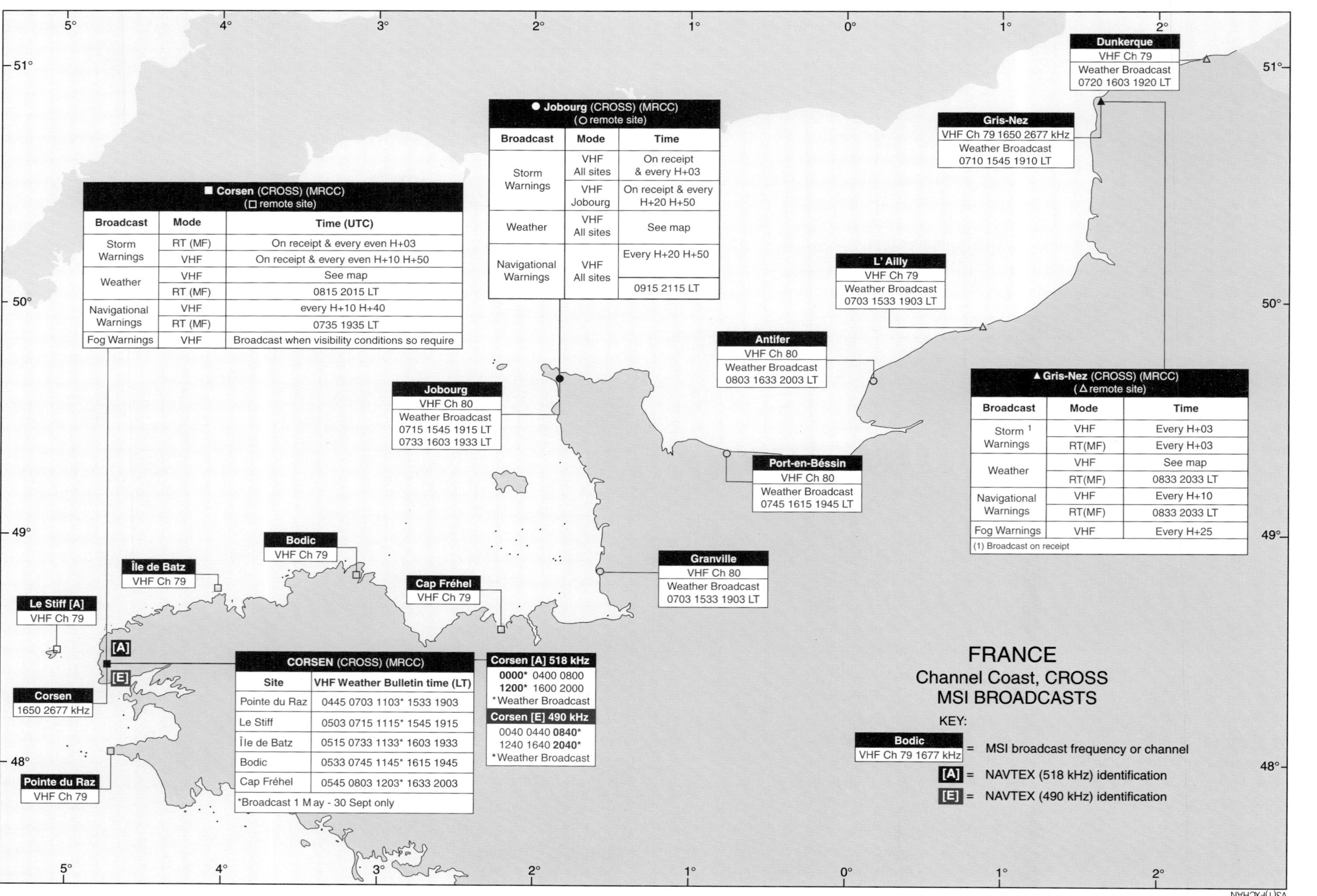
FRANCE
Channel Coast, CROSS
MSI BROADCASTS
KEY:
Bodic VHF Ch 79 1677 kHz = MSI broadcast frequency or channel
[A] = NAVTEX (518 kHz) identification
[E] = NAVTEX (490 kHz) identification
■ Corsen (CROSS) (MRCC) (□ remote site)
Broadcast | Mode | Time (UTC)
Storm Warnings | RT (MF) | On receipt & every even H+03
Storm Warnings | VHF | On receipt & every even H+10 H+50
Weather | VHF | See map
Weather | RT (MF) | 0815 2015 LT
Navigational Warnings | VHF | every H+10 H+40
Navigational Warnings | RT (MF) | 0735 1935 LT
Fog Warnings | VHF | Broadcast when visibility conditions so require
● Jobourg (CROSS) (MRCC) (○ remote site)
Broadcast | Mode | Time
Storm Warnings | VHF All sites | On receipt & every H+03
Storm Warnings | VHF Jobourg | On receipt & every H+20 H+50
Weather | VHF All sites | See map
Navigational Warnings | VHF All sites | Every H+20 H+50
0915 2115 LT
▲ Gris-Nez (CROSS) (MRCC) (Δ remote site)
Broadcast | Mode | Time
Storm [1] Warnings | VHF | Every H+03
Storm Warnings | RT(MF) | Every H+03
Weather | VHF | See map
Weather | RT(MF) | 0833 2033 LT
Navigational Warnings | VHF | Every H+10
Navigational Warnings | RT(MF) | 0833 2033 LT
Fog Warnings | VHF | Every H+25
(1) Broadcast on receipt
CORSEN (CROSS) (MRCC)
Site | VHF Weather Bulletin time (LT)
Pointe du Raz | 0445 0703 1103* 1533 1903
Le Stiff | 0503 0715 1115* 1545 1915
Île de Batz | 0515 0733 1133* 1603 1933
Bodic | 0533 0745 1145* 1615 1945
Cap Fréhel | 0545 0803 1203* 1633 2003
*Broadcast 1 May - 30 Sept only
Corsen [A] 518 kHz
0000* 0400 0800 1200* 1600 2000
*Weather Broadcast
Corsen [E] 490 kHz
0040 0440 0840* 1240 1640 2040*
*Weather Broadcast
Dunkerque VHF Ch 79 Weather Broadcast 0720 1603 1920 LT
Gris-Nez VHF Ch 79 1650 2677 kHz Weather Broadcast 0710 1545 1910 LT
L' Ailly VHF Ch 79 Weather Broadcast 0703 1533 1903 LT
Antifer VHF Ch 80 Weather Broadcast 0803 1633 2003 LT
Port-en-Béssin VHF Ch 80 Weather Broadcast 0745 1615 1945 LT
Granville VHF Ch 80 Weather Broadcast 0703 1533 1903 LT
Jobourg VHF Ch 80 Weather Broadcast 0715 1545 1915 LT 0733 1603 1933 LT
Cap Fréhel VHF Ch 79
Bodic VHF Ch 79
Île de Batz VHF Ch 79
Le Stiff [A] VHF Ch 79
Corsen 1650 2677 kHz
Pointe du Raz VHF Ch 79
[A]
[E]
5° 4° 3° 2° 1° 0° 1° 2°
51° 50° 49° 48°
V3(1)FXCHAN

CARENTAN	Marina 270 Berths 50 Visitor Berths	49°18′·4N 1°14′·0W
☎ +33(0)2 33422444 Lock: +33(0)2 33711085 port-carentan@wanadoo.fr	Depth: 3 m minimum	Fax: +33(0)2 33420003 www.sctel.fr/portcarentan/
FREQUENCY: Ch 09		HOURS: 0800-1200 1400-1800 LT ACCESS: Canal basin HW-2h to +3h

CARENTAN

CARTERET	Port and Marina: CALL: Semaphore 320 Berths 60 Visitor Berths	49°22′·7N 1°47′·0W
☎ Port de Plaisance: +33(0)2 33047084 Yacht Club: +33(0)2 33526073		Fax: Port de Plaisance: +33(0)2 33040837 Yacht Club: +33(0)2 33526098
FREQUENCY: Port & Marina: Ch 09	LOCATION: Port de Plaisance, Barneville-Carteret	HOURS: HW ± 2½h
NOTE: Traffic lights, situated next to the Harbour Office, indicate if the Marina is open or closed		

CHERBOURG	Port: CALL: Vigie Le Homet	49°39′N 1°37′W
☎ Hr Mr: +33(0)2 33204125 Lock: +33(0)2 33442318		Fax: Hr Mr: +33(0)2 33206929
FREQUENCY: Vigie du Homet (Homet Coastguard): Ch 12 16 Lock: Ch 06		HOURS: Vigie du Homet (Homet Coastguard): H24 Lock: HW ± 45 min
	Marina: CALL: Chantereyne 1200 Berths	
☎ +33(0)2 33876570 cherbourg.marina@wanadoo.fr		Fax: +33(0)2 33532112 (Indicate: for Capitainerie de Chantereyne) www.ville-cherbourg.fr
FREQUENCY: Ch **09** 72	LOCATION: Port de Chantereyne (49°38′·9N 1°37′·2W)	HOURS: 0800-1800 LT
PROCEDURE: Vessels should call Chantereyne on VHF 09 and provide ETA on entering the Grande Rade		

COURSEULLES-SUR-MER	Marina: CALL: Nouveau Bassin; Bassin Joinville 800 Places in Two Basins, Nouveau Bassin and Bassin Joinville Visitor Berths Available	49°20′N 0°27′W
☎ Port Office: 0900-1200: +33(0)2 31375169 Port du Plaisanciers: +33(0)2 31374834 Locks: +33(0)2 31374603		Fax: Port Office: +33(0)2 31371462 (Indicate: for Port de Plaisance)
FREQUENCY: Ch 09		HOURS: Nouveau Bassin: HW ± 3h Bassin Joinville: HW ± 2h

DAHOUËT	Marina 338 Berths	48°35′N 2°34′W
☎ Hr Mr: +33(0)2 96728285	Depth: 3 m	Fax
FREQUENCY: Ch 16		HOURS: Season: 0830-1215 LT and HW -2h +1h Out of season: 0830-1215 1400-1715 LT (except Sat afternoon & Sun)

COURSEULLES-SUR-MER TO THE WSW

DEAUVILLE-TROUVILLE	Port (Deauville)	49°22′N 0°04′E
☎ Municipal Port Office: +33(0)2 31985040 port-deauville-sa@wanadoo.fr		Fax
FREQUENCY: Port Office: Ch 09		HOURS: 0800-1730 LT ACCESS: HW ± 3h
Bassin du Vieux Port	**Marina** 400 Berths 80 Visitor Berths	
☎ Deauville Marina Club: +33(0)2 31985040 Lock: +33(0)2 31883621		Fax
FREQUENCY: Ch 09	LOCATION: Bassin Morny (49°21′·8N 0°04′·9E)	HOURS: 0900-1200 1400-1800 LT
	Marina 800 Berths 100 Visitor Berths	
☎ Hr Mr: +33(0)2 31983001 Lock: +33(0)2 31889566		Fax Hr Mr: +33(0)2 31887055 & 31819892
FREQUENCY: Ch 09	LOCATION: Port-Deauville (49°21′·8N 0°04′·4E)	HOURS: Mon-Fri (Closed Wed): 0900-1200 1400-1800 LT Sat: 0900-1200 1500-1800 LT Sun & holidays: 1000-1200 1500-1800 LT

DIÉLETTE	Marina 80 Berths	49°33′·34N 1°51′·90W
☎ Marina: +33(0)2 33536879		Fax +33(0)2 33536879
FREQUENCY: Ch 09		HOURS: 0800-2000 LT in season

DIEPPE	Port: CALL: Dieppe Port 50 berths in the Duquesne basin 15 Visitor Berths	49°56′N 1°05′E
☎ Hr Mr: +33(0)2 35841055 (HJ)	Maximum LOA: 15 m.	Fax Hr Mr: +33(0)2 35061256
FREQUENCY: Ch 12 16		HOURS: Ch 12: Office hours Ch 16: H24
Jehan Ango	**Marina** 380 Berths Visitor Berths Available.	
☎ +33(0)2 35401979 port.ango@wanadoo.fr		Fax
FREQUENCY: Ch 09		HOURS: 0900-1200 1400-1900 LT

DEAUVILLE FROM SE

DINARD	**Marina** 160 Berths	48°38′N 2°03′W
Port Office: +33(0)2 99466555 Yacht Club: +33(0)2 99461432		Port Office: +33(0)2 99466473
FREQUENCY: Ch 09		HOURS: Season: 0700-1200 LT Out of season: 0830-1200 1330-1800 LT

DUNKERQUE	**Port:** CALL: Dunkerque Port and Dunkerque Ouest	51°03′N 2°21′E
Port Control: +33(0)3 28297070 Central Hr Mr (E Dunkerque): +33(0)3 28297262 Hr Mr (W Dunkerque): +33(0)3 28297279 East Control Tr: +33(0)3 28297267		Port Control: +33(0)3 28297106 Central Hr Mr (E Dunkerque): +33(0)3 28297275 Hr Mr (W Dunkerque): +33(0)3 28297276 East Control Tr: +33(0)3 28297268
FREQUENCY: Ch 73		HOURS: H24
Vessels should maintain a continuous listening watch on VHF Ch 73 in the Approach Channel to Dunkerque Est, in Avant-Port and the Access Channel to Écluse Trystram. Radar coverage of the Pilot Embarkation Zone at the entrance to the Passe de l'Ouest is provided by the Pilot Station. Radar coverage of the Access Channels is provided by the Port		
	Marina: CALL: Bassin du Grand Large 315 Berths 25 Visitor Berths	
Hr Mr: +33(0)3 28632300	Maximum LOA: 20 m	Hr Mr: +33(0)3 28666662 www.dunkerque-marina.com
FREQUENCY: Ch 09	LOCATION: Bassin du Grand Large	HOURS: H24
Bassin du Commerce	**Marina** 200 Berths 15 Visitor Berths	
Hr Mr: +33(0)3 28211377	Depth: 5 m, Maximum LOA: 15 m	
FREQUENCY: Ch 09		HOURS: HX
	Marina 180 Berths 40 Visitor Berths	
Hr Mr: +33(0)3 28667990		Hr Mr: +33(0)3 28663662
FREQUENCY: Ch 09	LOCATION: Yacht Club de la Mer du Nord	HOURS: Season: Mon-Sat:: 0800-1200: 1400-2000: LT Out of season: Mon-Sat: 0900-1200 1400-1830 LT Sun: 1000-1200 1600-1800 LT

ÉTAPLES-SUR-MER	**Marina** 198 Berths 14 Visitor Berths	50°31′N 1°38′E
+33(0)3 21845433	Depth: 1·5 m, Maximum LOA: 11 m Anchorage at sea is recommended because of strong currents at certain times	
FREQUENCY: Ch 09		HOURS: HW ± 2h

FÉCAMP	Port: CALL: Bureau du Port Fécamp	49°46′N 0°22′E
☎ Port Office: +33(0)2 35282553		Fax
FREQUENCY: Ch 10 12 16		HOURS: HW -3h to +1h
Locks: Gayant Lock (Basin Freycinet): Bérigny Lock		
☎ Écluse Bérigny Hr Mr: +33(0)2 35282376		Fax
FREQUENCY: Ch 09		
	Marina	580 Berths 40 Visitor Berths
☎ Hr Mr: +33(0)2 35281358		Fax Hr Mr: +33(0)2 35286046 (Indicate: for Capitainerie du Port de Plaisance)
FREQUENCY: Ch 09		HOURS: Season: 0800-1200 1400-2000 LT Out of season: Mon-Sat: 0830-1200 LT ACCESS: Avant Port HW ±3½ h, Bassin Berigny HW -2h to HW +45 mins

FÉCAMP

GRANDCAMP-MAISY	Marina 240 berths 10 Visitor Berths	49°23′N 1°03′W
☎ Marina: +33(0)2 31226316 Lock: +33(0)2 31221917		Fax
FREQUENCY: Ch 09		HOURS: Season: 0600-2200 LT Out of season: Office hours

GRANDCAMP-MAISY TO THE NW

GRANVILLE	Marina 1000 Berths 150 Visitor Berths	48°50′·0N 1°36′·2W
Herel Marina: +33(0)2 33502006 Yacht Club: +33(0)2 33500425 cci@granville.cci.fr		Hr Mr: +33(0)2 33501701 www.granville.cci.fr
FREQUENCY: Ch 12	LOCATION: Port de Commerce	HOURS: HW -2½ h to +3½ h

GRANVILLE - VIEW OF PORT DE HEREL FROM S

GRAVELINES	Marina 450 Berths 40 Visitor Berths Berths include 150 in the Vauban Basin	50°59′N 2°07′E
Port de Plaisance: +33(0)3 28654524	Maximum LOA: 15 m	Port Office: +33(0)3 28230057
FREQUENCY: Ch 09		HOURS: Mon-Fri: 0800-1200 1330-1730 LT

HONFLEUR	Port: CALL: Honfleur Port 120 Berths 30 Visitor Berths	49°25′N 0°15′E
Hr Mr: +33(0)2 31892002 Capitainerie: +33(0)2 31146109 Mobile: 06859 36216 Marina Vieux Bassin: +33(0)2 31988713	Maximum LOA: 14m	Hr Mr: +33(0)2 31894210 Capitainerie: +33(0)2 31146109
FREQUENCY: Port: Ch 16 17 **73** Locks & Bridges: Ch 16 17		HOURS: Marina: 0700-1200 1700-2030 LT (Season) Locks & Bridges: H24

ISIGNY-SUR-MER	Marina 55 Berths 5 Visitor Berths	49°20′N 1°06′W
+33(0)2 31221067		
FREQUENCY: Ch 09		HOURS: 0900-1200 1400-1800 LT

L'ABERWRACH	Port and Marina 80 Berths 60 Visitor Berths	48°36′·75N 4°35′·30W
Hr Mr: +33(0)2 98049162		
FREQUENCY: Ch 09 16		HOURS: HW ± 2h

LE HAVRE (INCLUDING PORT DU HAVRE-ANTIFER)	**Le Havre Port de Commerce:** CALL: Control Tr: Le Havre Port **Vessel Traffic Service**	49°29′N 0°06′E
Hr Mr (Control Tr): +33(0)2 32747400		Hr Mr (Control Tr): +33(0)2 35217451 (Indicate: for Capitainerie du Havre)
FREQUENCY: Control Tr: 2182 kHz R/T Ch 12 16 20 22 Port Operations: Ch 67 69 Antifer Hr Mr: Ch 14 **22** Radar: Ch **12**		HOURS: H24
DESCRIPTION: The system, compulsory for all commercial vessels, provides maritime traffic surveillance; information and radar assistance can be supplied on request		

LE HAVRE (INCLUDING PORT DU HAVRE-ANTIFER)	Marina 1100 Berths 41 Visitor Berths	49°29′N 0°05′E
☎ Marina: +33(0)2 35212395 lehavre.plaisance@wanadoo.fr	Maximum LOA: 16 m	Fax Hr Mr: +33(0)2 35227272
FREQUENCY: Ch 09		Mon-Fri: 0800-1200 1400-1800 LT Sat: 0800-1200 LT. Sun & holidays: Closed

LE LÉGUÉ-SAINT-BRIEUC	Port: CALL: Hr Mr: Légué Port	48°32′N 2°44′W
☎ Hr Mr: +33(0)2 96333541		Fax Hr Mr: +33(0)2 96614694
FREQUENCY: Hr Mr: Ch 12 16		HOURS: 1-2h before to 1-1½ h after HW

LE TOUQUET	Port 115 Berths 15 Visitor Berths	50°32′N 1°35′E
☎ +33(0)3 21051277 & 21055977		Fax
FREQUENCY: Ch 09 77	LOCATION: 500 m SE of Pointe du Touquet	HOURS: HW -2h to +1h

LE TRÉPORT	Port & Marina 115 Berths 20 Visitor Berths	50°04′N 1°22′E
☎ Pilots & Hr Mr: +33(0)2 35861791 Marina: +33(0)2 35069672 Yacht Club: +33(0)2 35861993	Depth: 2.·5 - 4·5 m	Fax Pilots & Hr Mr: +33(0)2 35866011
FREQUENCY: Hr Mr: Ch 12 16 72		HOURS: Hr Mr: HW ± 3h

LÉZARDRIEUX	Marina 250 Berths	48°47′N 3°06′W
☎ +33(0)2 96201422	Depth: 2·3 m	Fax +33(0)2 96221831
FREQUENCY: Ch 09		

LÉZARDRIEUX

MORLAIX	Marina 183 Berths 30 Visitor Berths	48°35′N 3°50′W
☎ Hr Mr: +33(0)2 98621314 Lock: +33(0)2 98885492 (HW -1½h to +1h) plaisance@morlaix.cce.fr		Fax Hr Mr: +33(0)2 98888055
FREQUENCY: Ch 09 16		HOURS: HW ± 2h

OUISTREHAM	**Port:** CALL: Ouistreham Port	49°17'N 0°15'W
DESCRIPTION: The Hr Mr is responsible for the ports of Ouistreham and Caen		
☎ Hr Mr: +33(0)2 3136200 Bassin de Plaisance: +33(0)2 31969137 Lock: +33(0)2 31971443 p.auzou@oistreham.plaisance.com		Fax Hr Mr: +33(0)2 31963952 Bassin de Plaisance: +33(0)2 31969147 www.oistreham.plaisance.com
FREQUENCY: Port: Ch **68** 74 Lock: Ch 12 68	Depth: 2 - 3·8 m	HOURS: Port: H24 Lock: 2h before to 3h after HW
	Marina 600 Berths 65 Visitor Berths	
☎ Hr Mr: +33(0)2 31971305		Fax Hr Mr: +33(0)2 31963125
FREQUENCY: Ch 09	LOCATION: Riva Bella (49°16'·6N 0°14'·8W)	HOURS: Season: 0800-2000 LT Out of Season: 0800-1230 1400-1830 LT

OUISTREHAM - PORT DE PLAISANCE FROM SW

PAIMPOL	**Port** 300 Berths Visitor Berths Available	48°47'N 3°03'W
☎ Port Office: +33(0)2 96208077 Yacht Club: +33(0)2 96204765 Lock: +33(0)2 96209002 (HW ± 2h)		Fax Port Office: +33(0)2 96220074
FREQUENCY: Lock: Ch 09		HOURS: HW ± 2h

PERROS-GUIREC	**Marina** 700 Berths 80 Visitor Berths	48°48'N 3°26'W
☎ Hr Mr: +33(0)2 96233782 Marina: +33(0)2 96498050 port.perros.guirec@wanadoo.fr	Depth: 2·5 m, Maximum LOA: 20m.	Fax Port Office: +33(0)2 96474087 Marina: +33(0)2 96233719 www.port.perros.guirec.com
FREQUENCY: Ch 09 16		HOURS: Season: 0730-2100 LT Out of season: 0730-1730 LT ACCESS: Springs: HW ± 1½h Neaps: HW ± 30 m

PLOUËR-SUR-RANCE	**Marina** 240 Berths	48°33'N 1°59'W
☎ Marina: +33(0)2 96868315 Lock: +33(0)2 99462187		Fax Marina: +33(0)2 96891100
FREQUENCY: Ch 13	LOCATION: La Pointe de la Brebis Lock	HOURS: H24 ACCESS: ± 3½-4h HW in range

PONTRIEUX	**Port** 180 Berths	48°42'N 3°09'W
☎ Lock: +33(0)2 96956070 Port de Plaisance: +33(0)2 96953487		Fax Port de Plaisance: +33(0)2 96953487
FREQUENCY: Lock: Ch 12		HOURS: HW -2h to +1h

PERROS-GUIREC

PLOUËR-SUR-RANCE

PORT BAIL	Marina	200 Berths Visitor Berths Availables	49°20′N 1°42′W
Harbour Master: +33(0)2 33048348 Yacht Service Centre: +33(0)2 662585638 portbail@wanadoo.fr			Fax: +33(0)2 33043990 www.ville-portbail.fr
FREQUENCY: Ch 09			

PORT-EN-BESSIN	Port	69 Berths	49°21′N 0°45′W
Hr Mr: +33(0)2 31217049 Lock & Bridge: +33(0)2 31217177 (HW ± 2h)			Fax:
FREQUENCY: Lock & Bridge: Ch 18			HOURS: HW ± 2h

PORT DIÉLETTE	Port and Marina		49°33′·2N 1°51′·7W
Hr Mr: +33(0)2 33536878			Fax: Hr Mr: +33(0)2 33536879
FREQUENCY: Ch 09			HOURS: Winter: 0900-1200 1330-1800 LT Summer: 0800-1300 1400-2000 LT

PORT GUILLAUME, DIVES-SUR-MER	Marina	600 Berths 50 Visitor Berths	49°18′N 0°05′W
Capitainerie: +33(0)2 31244800 portguillaume@liberty-surf.fr	Maximum LOA: 29 m		Fax: +33(0)2 31247302 (H24)
FREQUENCY: Ch 09			HOURS: HW ± 3h

PORT GUILLAUME AND CABOURG TO THE WNW

ROSCOFF-BLOSCON	Port: & Marina	48°43′·5N 3°58′·8W
☎ Capitainerie: +33(0)2 98612784		Fax Hr Mr: +33(0)2 98611181
FREQUENCY: Hr Mr: Ch 12 16		HOURS: 0830-1200 1330-1800 LT

ROSCOFF-BLOSCON (Continued)	Port: & Marina	48°43′·5N 3°58′·8W
	Marina 300 Berths 20 Visitor Berths	
☎ Port de Plaisance: +33(0)2 98637307 Hr Mr: +33(0)2 98697637		Fax
FREQUENCY: Ch 09	LOCATION: Old Port: Vieux Port	HOURS: 0800-1200 1330-1730 LT

ROUEN	Port: CALL: Rouen Port	49°26′N 1°02′E
☎ Hr Mr: Office hours: +33(0)2 35525456 Outside office hours: +33(0)2 35525400		Fax Hr Mr: +33(0)2 35525402
FREQUENCY: Port: Ch 16 68 **73**		HOURS: H24

PROCEDURE:
(1) Within the limits of the port of Rouen, all vessels of 20m in length and over should be able to communicate by VHF on Ch 06 13 15 16 68 and **73**.
(2) The Harbour Master's Office must be kept informed of all movements within the Port Limits (arrivals, departures, transits, berthings and unberthings) together with all navigation incidents on VHF Ch 73. Vessels underway should maintain a continuous listening watch on VHF Ch 73
(3) VHF Channels used for clearance are as follows: (a) Upstream from Caudebec (Rouen Port): Ch 68 (b) Downstream from Caudebec (Radar Honfleur): Ch 15

ROUEN TO PARIS		Locks			
Name	**VHF Channel**	**Name**	**VHF Channel**	**Name**	**VHF Channel**
Andrésy	22	Mericourt	18	Poses-Amfreville	18
Bougival	22	Notre-Dame-de-la-Garenne	22	Suresnes	22
Chatou	18	Paris-Arsenal	09		

PROCEDURE:
(1) Vessels should send ETA by VHF 30 mins in advance to the lock-keepers
(2) In certain conditions the river level is such that some locks are left open
(3) During the summer months the locks operate from about 0700 to 1900 LT
(4) A red and green "Traffic Lights" system is also employed

SAINT CAST	Marina 110 Berths 10 Visitor Berths	48°38′·4N 2°14′·63W
☎ Hr Mr: +33(0)2 96418834		Fax
FREQUENCY: Ch 09		HOURS: 0900-1300 1400-2100 LT Season 0900-1200 1400-1800 LT out of season

SAINT MALO	Port	48°38'N 2°02'W
Tel: Hr Mr: +33(0)2 99202501		Fax: Hr Mr: +33(0)2 99402587
FREQUENCY: Ch **12** 16		HOURS: H24
	Marinas Bassin Vauban 350 Berths Les Bas Sablons 1280 Berths 64 Visitor Berths	
Tel: Bassin Vauban: Hr Mr: +33(0)2 99565191 Les Bas Sablons: Hr Mr: +33(0)2 99817134	Maximum LOA: 12 m	Fax: Bassin Vauban: Hr Mr: +33(0)2 99565781 Les Bas Sablons: Hr Mr: +33(0)2 99819181
FREQUENCY: Ch 09		HOURS: HX ACCESS: HW ± 3½-4h

SAINT-QUAY-PORTRIEUX	Marina 1000 Berths 100 Visitor Berths	48°39'N 2°49'W
Tel: Port Office: +33(0)2 96708130 & 95708131 Customs: +33(0)2 96704946 welcome@port-armor.com	Depth: 2 - 3 m, Maximum LOA: 18 m	Fax: Port Office: +33(0)2 96703872 www.port-armor.com
FREQUENCY: Ch 09		HOURS: H24

SAINT-QUAY-PORTRIEUX

SAINT-VAAST-LA HOUGUE	Marina 655 Berths 165 Visitor Berths	49°35'·2N 1°15'·4W
Tel: Hr Mr: +33(0)2 33236100 Club Nautique: +33(0)2 33545573 port-st-vasst@saint-vasst-reville.com		Fax: Hr Mr: +33(0)2 33236104 www.saint-vasst-reville.com
FREQUENCY: Ch 09		HOURS: Season: HW -2¼ h to +3h Out of Season: As season between 0800-1800 LT ACCESS: HW -2½ h to HW +3 - 3½ h

S. VALÉRY-EN-CAUX	Marina 580 Berths 20 Visitor Berths	49°52'N 0°43'E
Tel: +33(0)2 35970130	Maximum LOA: 14 m	Fax: +33(0)2 35977981
		ACCESS: (Lock) Day: HW ± 3h Night: HW ± ½ h

TANCARVILLE	Port	49°28'N 0°28'E
FREQUENCY: Port: Ch 16 Lock: Ch 18		HOURS: H24

TRÉBEURDEN	Marina 625 Berths 80 Visitor Berths	48°46'N 3°35'W
Tel: Port Office: +33(0)2 96236400 Marina: +33(0)2 96474015 Yacht Club: +33(0)2 96154597 port-trebeurden@wanadoo.fr	Depth: 3 m, Maximum LOA: 16 m	Fax: Port Office: +33(0)2 96474087 Marina: +33(0)2 96154087 www.port-trebeurden.com
FREQUENCY: Ch 09		HOURS: 0600-2400 LT. ACCESS: HW ± 3½ h at neaps and HW ± 4½ h at springs

TRÉGUIER	Marina 320 Berths 100 Visitor Berths	48°51′N 3°12′W
Tel: Hr Mr: +33(0)2 96924237 Club Nautique: +33(0)2 96924208	Depth: 2 m	Fax: Hr Mr: +33(0)2 96922925 (Indicate: for Port de Plaisance)
FREQUENCY: Ch 09		HOURS: Season: Mon-Sat: 0800-1200 1330-2100 LT Sun: 0800-1000 1600-1800 LT Out of season: Tues-Sat: 0800-1200 1330-1700 LT Sun & Mon: Closed

GIBRALTAR

BFBS GIBRALTAR

A	93·5 MHz	FM	BFBS 1	
	97·8 MHz			
B	89·4 MHz		BFBS 2	
	99·5 MHz			

Weather Bulletins

A, B: On receipt	Storm Warnings: Storm and gale warnings for the Gibraltar area
A: Mon-Fri: 0745 0845 1005 1605 Sat: 0845 0945 1202 Sun: 0845 0945 1202 1602 LT	Shipping forecast, wind, weather, visibility, sea state, swell High Water and Low Water times for local waters within 5 n miles of Gibraltar In English
B: Mon-Fri: 1200 LT	Shipping forecast, wind, weather, visibility, sea state, swell High Water and Low Water times for local waters within 5 n miles of Gibraltar In English

GIBRALTAR BROADCASTING CORPORATION

AM	1458	FM	91·3 MHz	
			92·6 MHz	
			100·5 MHz	

Weather Bulletins

Mon-Fri: 0530 0630 0730 1030 1230 Sat: 0530 0630 0730 1030 Sun: 0630 0730 1030	General synopsis, situation, forecast, wind direction and strength, sea state, visibility for area up to 5 n miles from Gibraltar In English

Vessel Traffic Services (VTS)
VTS compliance is not mandatory for leisure craft. Details of VTS control centres and their broadcast frequencies have been included for information only. Certain Ports and VTS areas request **all** vessels to monitor a certain VHF broadcast channel for navigational information and hazard warnings.

GIBRALTAR — Port — 36°08′N 5°21′W

Tel:
Port Captain (Hr Mr): +350 77254
Operations Room: +350 78134 & 77004
Fuel: +350 48232
Gibraltar Yacht Registry: +350 78343
RGYC: +350 78897

Fax:
Operations Room: +350 77011
Fuel: +350 48227
Gibraltar Yacht Registry +350 77044
RGYC: +350 40981

shipreg@gibnet.gi
info@rgyc.gi

www.rgyc.gi

FREQUENCY: Port: Ch 16; **06 12** 13 14 (Ch **12** is the Gibraltar Bay Working Channel)
LOCATION: Port Signal Station
HOURS: Port: H24

NOTE: 1) All vessels underway or at anchor in Gibraltar Bay should maintain a listening watch on VHF Ch 12.
2) On arrival all craft must report to the Yacht Reporting Station on Passenger Wharf in Waterport

MARINA BAY — CALL: Marina Bay — 209 Berths 150 Visitor Berths — 36°08′·5N 5°22′·5W

Depth: 4·5 m, Maximum LOA: 100 m

Tel:
Pier Office: +350 73300 (H24)
Head Office: +350 74322
Security: +350 588 79000 (H24)

Fax:
Pier Office: +350 42656
Head Office: +350 78373

mbcl@marinabay.gi
pieroffice@mainabay.gi

www.marinabay.gi

FREQUENCY: Ch 71
HOURS: Summer: 0830-2230 LT
Winter: 0830-2030 LT

QUEEN'S HARBOUR MASTER — CALL: Queen's Harbour Master — 36°08′·00N 5°21′·25W

Tel: +350 55901

Fax: +350 55981

FREQUENCY: Ch 08 (Gibraltar Military Port Operations and Tugs)
LOCATION: The Tower, HM Naval Base
HOURS: Mon-Thurs: 0800-1630 LT
Fri: 0800-1600 LT
At other times: can be contacted through Windmill Hill Signal Station

QUEENSWAY QUAY MARINA	CALL: Queensway Quay Marina 100 Berths	36°08'·1N 5°21'·3W
Tel: +350 44700 qqmarina@gibnet.gi	Depth: Minimum 3·5 m, Maximum LOA 50 m	Fax: +350 44699 www.taywood.gi
FREQUENCY: Ch 71	NOTE: Overnight reception pontoon available	HOURS: Summer: 0830-2145 LT Winter: 0830-2015 LT

PHOTOGRAPH - RCC PILOTAGE FOUNDATION

QUEENSWAY QUAY MARINA

SHEPHARD'S MARINA	CALL: Shephard's Marina 150 Berths 20 Visitor Berths	36°08'·5N 5°22'·5W
Tel: +350 75148 & 77183 info@sheppard.gi	Depth: Minimum 2 m, Maximum LOA: 20 m	Fax: +350 42535 www.sheppard.gi
FREQUENCY: Ch 71		HOURS: Mon-Fri: 0900-1300 1430-1800 LT Sat: 1000-1300 LT Duty staff until 1900 LT

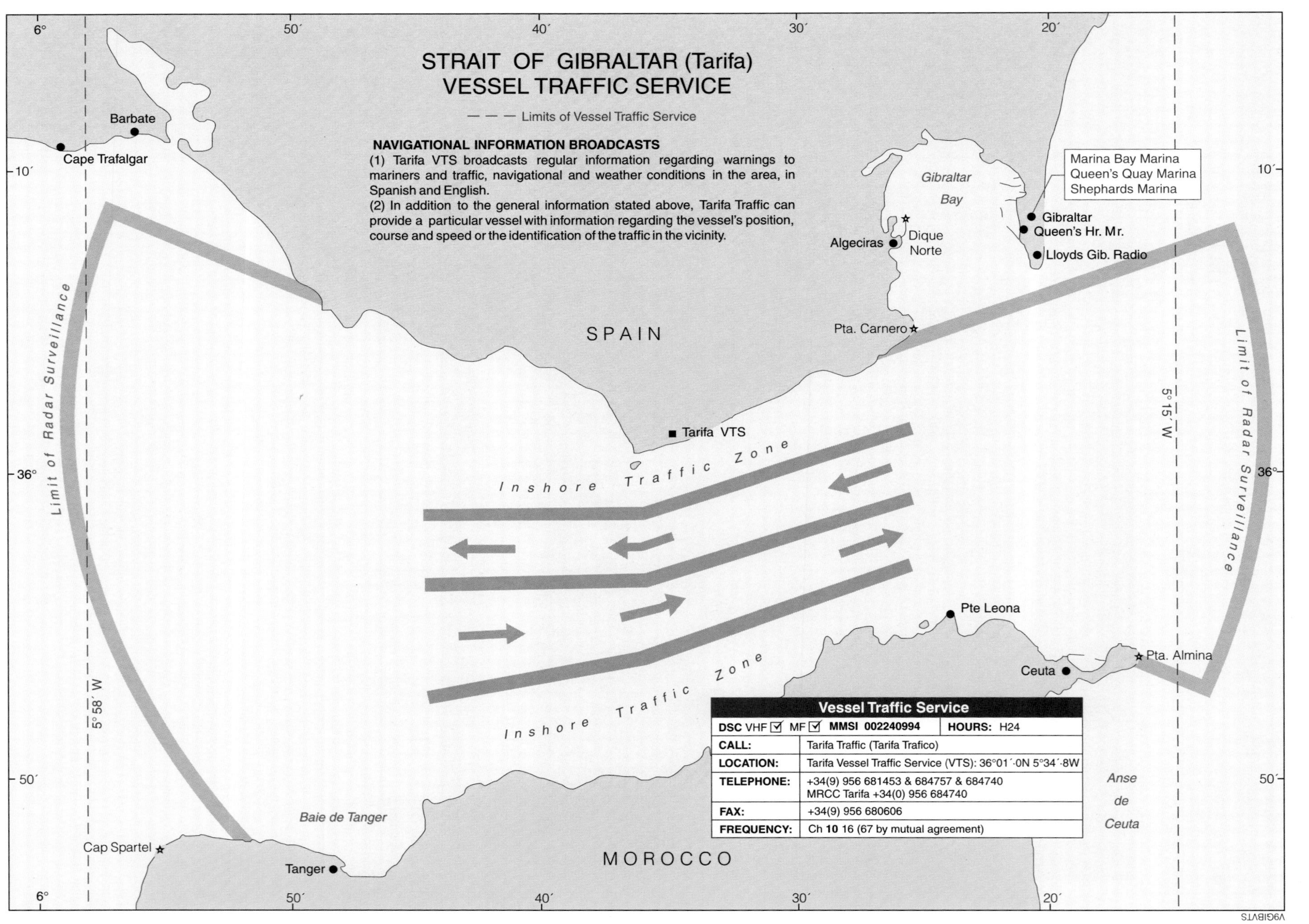

Vessel Traffic Service	
DSC VHF ☑ MF ☑ **MMSI 002240994**	**HOURS:** H24
CALL:	Tarifa Traffic (Tarifa Trafico)
LOCATION:	Tarifa Vessel Traffic Service (VTS): 36°01´·0N 5°34´·8W
TELEPHONE:	+34(9) 956 681453 & 684757 & 684740 MRCC Tarifa +34(0) 956 684740
FAX:	+34(9) 956 680606
FREQUENCY:	Ch **10** 16 (67 by mutual agreement)

IRELAND, REPUBLIC OF

National SAR Agency: Irish Coast Guard **Tel:** +353(0)1 662 0922 & 0923 **Fax:** +353(0)1 662 0795 **Telex:** 93039 IMES EI
The Irish Coast Guard has overall executive responsibility for co-ordinating Search and Rescue operations and is the location of MRCC Dublin. The co-ordination of Search and Rescue operations is conducted by the Irish Coast Guard centres at MRCC Dublin, MRSC Malin Head and MRSC Valentia, who are each responsible for a designated sub-region of the Ireland SRR. A continuous listening watch is maintained on VHF Ch 16, VHF DSC Ch 70 and MF DSC 2187·5 kHz for distress calls.

	Telephone +353	**Fax** +353	**Others**
MRCC DUBLIN (Coast Guard)	(0)1 6620922	(0)1 6620795	**Telex** +500 93039 IMES EI

NAVTEX [Q] [W]

Q	Malin Head	518 kHz	55°22′N 7°21′W
W	Valentia	518 kHz	51°27′N 9°49′W
DIAGRAMS: pages 63 and 159			
Weather Bulletins			
Q: On receipt 0240 0640 1040 1440 1840 2240	Gale warnings for Irish coastal waters up to 30 n miles offshore and the Irish Sea. Shannon, Rockall, Malin and Bailey		
Q: 0640 1840	Gale warnings and forecast for Shannon, Rockall, Malin and Bailey		
Q: 1040 2240	Gale warnings, synopsis and 24 hour forecast for Irish coastal waters up to 30 n miles offshore, Irish Sea, sea areas Atlantic-East, Northern and East Central sections		
W: On receipt 0340 0740 1140 1540 1940 2340	Gale warnings for Irish coastal waters up to 30 n miles offshore and the Irish Sea		
W: 0740 1940	Gale warnings, synopsis and 24 hour forecast for Irish coastal waters up to 30 n miles offshore, Irish Sea, sea areas Sole, Fastnet and Shannon		
W: 1140 2340	Forecast for Atlantic-East Central Section		
Navigational Warnings			
Q: On receipt 0240 0640 1440 1840	For North Channel, SW coast of Scotland, N, NW and W coasts of Ireland and approaches		
W: On receipt 0340 1140 1540 2340	For S, SW and W coasts of Ireland and approaches		

KILMORE QUAY - WEST

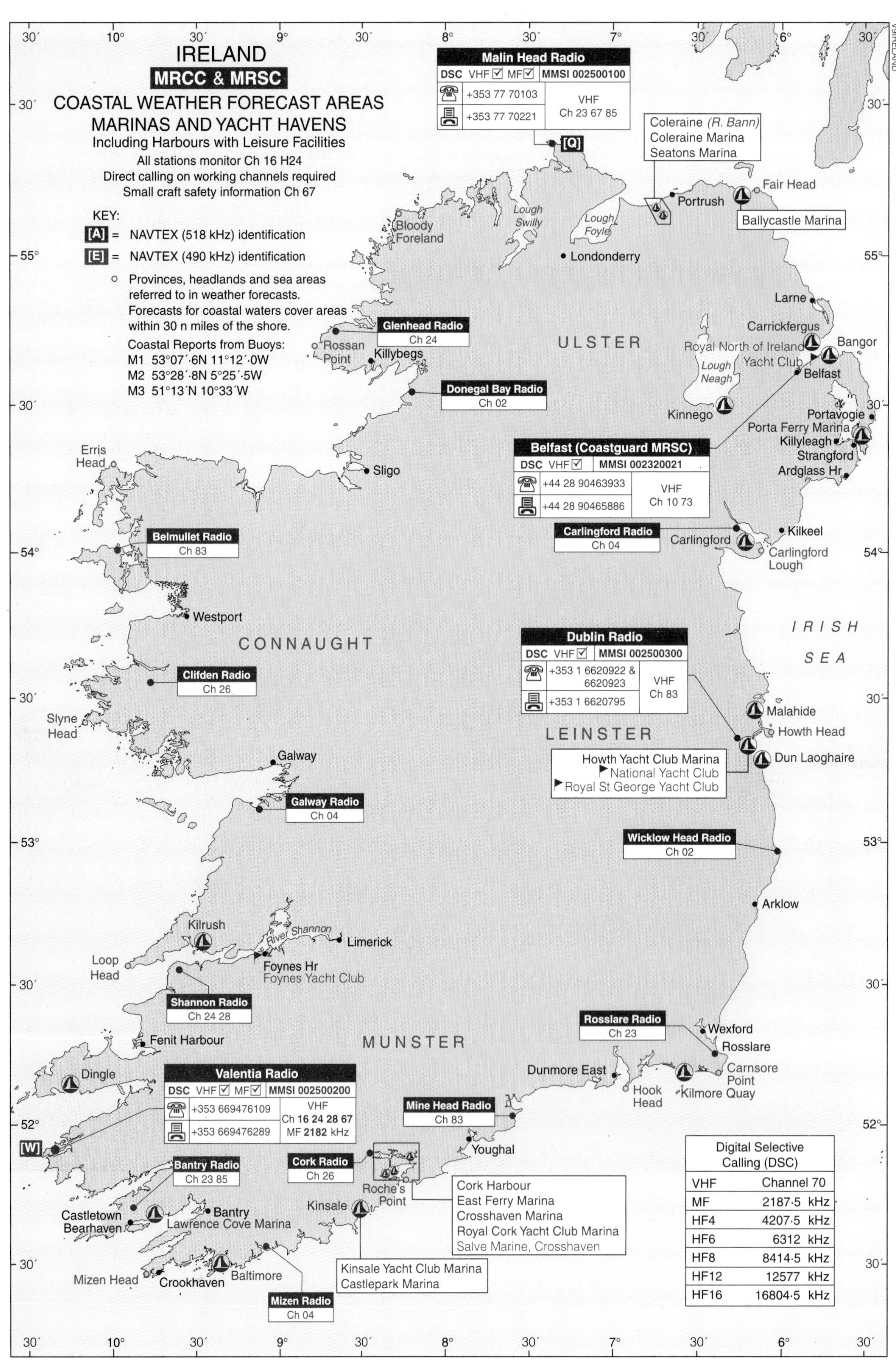

Digital Selective Calling (DSC)	
VHF	Channel 70
MF	2187·5 kHz
HF4	4207·5 kHz
HF6	6312 kHz
HF8	8414·5 kHz
HF12	12577 kHz
HF16	16804·5 kHz

DUBLIN (Coast Guard MRCC)

	VHF	Ch 04	Carlingford	54°05′N 6°19′W
		Ch 83	Dublin	53°23′N 6°04′W
		Ch 02	Wicklow Head	52°58′N 6°00′W
		Ch 23	Rosslare	52°15′N 6°20′W
		Ch 83	Mine Head	52°00′N 7°35′W
DIAGRAMS: pages 126, 159 and 161				
Weather Bulletins				
On receipt 0033 0633 1233 1833 after announcement on Ch 16	Storm warnings: Gale warnings for Irish coastal waters up to 30 n miles offshore and the Irish Sea			
0103 0403 0703 1003 1303 1603 1903 2203	Gale warnings, synopsis and 24 hour forecast for Irish coastal waters up to 30 n miles offshore and the Irish Sea			
On receipt 0033 0633 1233 1833 after announcement on Ch 16	Small Craft warning: Issued (Apr-Sept incl.) for Irish coastal waters if winds of Beaufort Force 6 are expected up to 10 n miles offshore			
NOTE: Broadcasts given 1 hour earlier when DST is in force				
Navigational Warnings				
0033 0433 0833 1233 1633 2033	For the E, SE and S coasts of Ireland and approaches			

MALIN HEAD (Coast Guard MRSC)

A	1677	RT (MF)	Malin Head	55°22′N 7°21′W
B	Ch 26	VHF	Clifden	53°30′N 9°56′W
	Ch 83		Belmullet	54°16′N 10°03′W
	Ch 24		Glen Head	54°44′N 8°43′W
	Ch 23		Malin Head	55°22′N 7°21′W
	Ch 02		Donegal Bay	54°22′N 8°31′W
DIAGRAMS: pages 126, 159 and 161				
Weather Bulletins				
B: On receipt 0033 0633 1233 1833 after announcement on Ch 16	Gale warnings, synopsis and 24 hour forecast for Irish coastal waters up to 30 n miles offshore, Irish Sea, sea areas Shannon, Rockall, Malin and Bailey			
B: On receipt 0033 0633 1233 1833 after announcement on Ch 16	Small Craft warning: Issued (Apr-Sept incl.) for Irish coastal waters if winds of Beaufort Force 6 are expected up to 10 n miles offshore			
B: 0103 0403 0703 1003 1303 1603 1903 2203	Gale warnings, synopsis and 24 hour forecast for Irish coastal waters up to 30 n miles offshore and the Irish Sea			
NOTE: Broadcasts given 1 hour earlier when DST is in force				
Navigational Warnings				
A[1], **B:** 0033 0433 0833 1233 1633 2033	For North Channel, SW coast of Scotland, N, NW and W coasts of Ireland and approaches			
1. When 1677 kHz is engaged at the scheduled time of broadcast, an alternative frequency will be announced on 2182 kHz				

VALENTIA (Coast Guard MRSC)

A	1752	RT (MF)	Valentia	51°56′N 10°21′W
B	Ch 24	VHF	Valentia	51°52′N 10°21′W
	Ch 26		Cork	51°51′N 8°29′W
	Ch 23		Bantry	51°38′N 10°00′W
	Ch 28		Shannon	52°31′N 9°36′W
	Ch 04		Mizen	52°34′N 9°33′W
			Galway	53°18′N 9°07′W
DIAGRAMS: pages 126, 159 and 161				

VALENTIA (Coast Guard MRSC) **(Continued)**	
Weather Bulletins	
B: On receipt 0033 0633 1233 1833	Storm warnings: Gale warnings for Irish coastal waters up to 30 n miles offshore and the Irish Sea
A, On receipt 0303 0903 1503 2103	Storm warnings: Gale warnings for Shannon, Fastnet
B: 0103 0403 0703 1003 1303 1603 1903 2203	Gale warnings, synopsis and 24 hour forecast for Irish coastal waters up to 30 n miles offshore, Irish Sea, sea areas Sole, Fastnet and Shannon
B: On receipt 0033 0633 1233 1833 after announcement on Ch 16	Small Craft warning: Issued (Apr-Sept incl.) for Irish coastal waters if winds of Beaufort Force 6 are expected up to 10 n miles offshore
A: 0833 2033	Gale warnings, synopsis, 24 hour forecast, for Shannon, Fastnet
NOTE: Broadcasts given 1 hour earlier when DST is in force	
Navigational Warnings	
A – B: 0233 0633 1033 1433 1833 2233	For S, SW and W coasts of Ireland and approaches

RADIO TELEFÍS ÉIREANN — RADIO 1 (RTE — RADIO 1)				
Cork	729 kHz	AM	Tullamore	567 kHz
Achill	89·3 MHz	FM	Holywell Hill	89·2 MHz
Athlone	89·9 MHz	FM	Kippure	89·1 MHz
Cahirciveen	89·5 MHz	FM	Limerick City	89·4 MHz
Castletownbere	88·3 MHz	FM	Maghera	88·8 MHz
Clermont Cairn	95·2 MHz	FM	Mount Leinster	89·6 MHz
Cork City	89·2 MHz	FM	Moville	88·3 MHz
Croaghmoyle, Mayo	89·8 MHz	FM	Mullaghanish	90 MHz
Dungarvan	88·5 MHz	FM	Three Rock	88·5 MHz
Fanad	89·8 MHz	FM	Truskmore	88·2 MHz

Weather Bulletins

Mon-Thurs 0605 1955 2355 Fri 0605 2355 Sat, Sun & Holidays 0605 1250 1955 2355 Broadcasts given 1 hour earlier when DST is in force	Sea Area Forecasts issued by Met Éireann contain the following standard elements: Description of synoptic situation Detailed forecast and current gale warnings for Irish coastal waters and the Irish Sea Outlook for further 24 hours The coastal reports include: (a) Wind direction (using 16 point compass) and speed in knots (b) Weather (c) Visibility in nautical miles and tenths of: (d) Pressure in hectopascals (millibars) (e) Pressure tendency, which describes the change in pressure over the past 3 hours, using the following scale: 0·0–0·4 hPa—steady 0·5–1·9 hPa—rising / falling slowly 2·0–3·4 hPa—rising / falling 3·5–5·9 hPa—rising or falling rapidly 6·0 hPa—rising or falling very rapidly

ARKLOW	**Marina** 70 Berths	52°48′N 6°09′W
☎ Marina: +353(0)402 39901/32610 Hr Office: +353(0)402 32466 Mobile: 0872 375189 technical@asl.ie		Fax Marina: +353(0)402 39902
FREQUENCY: Hr Office: Ch 16	LOCATION: North Bank	HOURS: 0800-1830 LT ACCESS: H24

BALTIMORE	**Harbour** 30 Berths	51°29′·0N 9°22′·5W
☎ +353(0)28 22145 Mobile: 0872 351485 info@atlanticboat.ie		Fax +353(0)28 22145 www.atlanticboat.ie
FREQUENCY: Ch 09 16		HOURS: 0900-1700 LT (May to September 0900-2100 LT)

BANTRY	Port — Tourist Moorings Bantry Inner Harbour 12 Glengarriff Harbour 6 Adrigole 5 Trafrask 1	51°42′N 9°28′W
Hr Mr: +353(0)27 53277 Mobile: 0879 532777 harbourmaster@bantrybayport.com		Fax: Hr Mr: +353(0)27 51202 www.bantrybayport.com
FREQUENCY: Ch 11 14 16		HOURS: H24

BURTONPORT	Port — Leisure Berths Available	54°59′N 8°26′W
Hr Mr: +353(0)75 42155 Mobile: 0868 310121 manuscecilygallagher@hotmail.com		Fax: Port Auth: +353(0)74 41205
FREQUENCY: Ch 06 12 16		

CARLINGFORD MARINA	130 Berths	54°03′·1N 6°11′·5W
+353(0)4293 73073 Mobile: 0872 321567 info@carlingfordmarina.com		Fax: +353(0)4293 73075 www.carlingfordmarina.com
FREQUENCY: Ch 16 **M**		

CASTLETOWN BEARHAVEN	Port	51°39′N 9°54′W
Hr Mr: Office hours: +353(0)27 70220 harbourmaster@eircom.net	Commercial port with few leisure facilities	Fax: +353(0)27 70329
FREQUENCY: Ch 12 14 16		

CORK	**Port Operations and Information Service:** CALL: Cork Harbour Radio	51°50′N 8°17′W
PORT LIMITS: Seaward limit: line joining Cork Head (51°44′·6N 8°18′·0W) and Power Head (51°47′·0N 8°10′·4W)		
Port Operations: +353(0)214 811380 Deputy Hr Mr: +353(0)214 273125 Mobile: 086 2556278 Royal Cork Yacht Club (Crosshaven): +353(0)214 831023 RCYC Marina: +353(0)214 831025 info@portofcork.ie office@royalcork.iol.ie		Fax: Port Auth: +353(0)214 276484 Royal Cork Yacht Club (Crosshaven): +353(0)21 4831586 & 4831025 www.royalcork.iol.ie www.portofcork.ie
FREQUENCY: Ch 12 14 16 RCYC: Ch M		HOURS: H24
EAST FERRY MARINA	85 Berths 15 Visitor Berths	51°51′·9N 8°12′·8W
+353(0)214 811342		Fax:
FREQUENCY: Ch M		
ROYAL CORK YACHT CLUB MARINA	15 Visitor Berths	51°48′·3N 8°18′·2W
+353(0)214 831023 office@iroyalcork.iol.ie	Depth: 3 - 4 m, LOA: 20 m	Fax: +353(0)214 831586 www.iol.ie/royalcork
FREQUENCY: Ch M		HOURS OF WATCH: 0900-2300 LT

COURTMACSHERRY		51°38′·22N 8°40′·90W
+353(0)23 46311/40394		Fax:

CROSSHAVEN BOATYARD MARINA	100 Berths	51°48′·3N 8°17′·7W
+353(0)214 831161 Mobile: +0868 563095 cby@eircom.net	Depth: 3·5 m, 35 m LOA	Fax: +353(0)214 831603 www.crosshavenboatyard.com
FREQUENCY: Ch M		

SALVE MARINE, CROSSHAVEN	Marina and Boatyard	51°48′·3N 8°18′·0W
Tel: +353(0)214 831145 salvemarine@eircom.net	Depth: 4·5 m, Maximum LOA 40 m	Fax: +353(0)214 831747
FREQUENCY: Ch M		

DINGLE	Marina	52°08′·2N 10°16′·5W
Tel: Hr Mr: +353(0)66 9151629 Mobile: 0872 830380 Hr Mr: ifarrell@eircom.net dinglemarina@eircom.net	Channel Depth: 2·6 m, Berth 5 m	Fax: +353(0)66 9151629 www.homepage.eircom.net/ifarell/dinglemarina
FREQUENCY: Ch 11 **M**		

DROGHEDA	**Port:** CALL: Drogheda Port	53°43′N 6°21′W
Tel: Hr Mr: +353(0)42 9334136 Outside Office hours: +353(0)41 9838385 Mobile: 0862 547827 maritimehouse@droghedaport.ie		Fax: Port Auth: +353(0)41 9832844
FREQUENCY: Port: Ch 11		HOURS: Port: Mon-Fri: 0900-1700 LT

DUBLIN	**Port:** CALL: Dublin Port Radio	53°21′N 6°16′W
Tel: Berthing Master: +353(0)1 8555779 Harbour Office: 0900-1700 (Office hours): +353(0)1 8550888 & 8555771 Port Radio: Outside Office Hours: +353(0)1 8555776, 8557961 & 8556714 info@dublinport.ie		Fax: Harbour Office: Office hours: +353(0)1 8553423 www.dublinport.ie
FREQUENCY: Port Operations Ch **12** 13 16	LOCATION: Eastern Breakwater Lt	HOURS: Dublin Port Radio: H24
EAST-LINK LIFTING BRIDGE		53°20′·7N 6°13′·6W
FREQUENCY: Ch 12 13	20 minutes notice required	
DUBLIN CITY MOORINGS	25 Visitor Berths	
Tel: +353(0)1 818 3300 Mobile: 0868 568113 info@ddda.ie info@dublindocklands.ie	Depth: 3.2 m	Fax: +353(0)1 818 3399 www.ddda.ie
	LOCATION: Custom House Quay	HOURS: Liffey Bridge Opening 0900 1100 1500 LT

DUNDALK	Port	54°00′N 6°24′W
Tel: +353(0)4293 34096 dundalkport@eircom.net		Fax: +353(0)4293 35481
FREQUENCY: Hr Mr: Ch 14 16		HOURS: Hr Mr: Mon-Fri: 0900-1700 LT ACCESS: HW ± 3

DUN LAOGHAIRE	Port and Marina 450 Berths 30 Visitor Berths	53°18′N 9°53′W
Tel: Marina: +353(0)1 2020047 Hr Mr: +353(0)1 2809278 dlmarina@indigo.ie	Depth: 40 m	Fax: Marina: +353(0)1 2020043 Hr Mr +353(0)1 2808062 www.ddda.ie
FREQUENCY: Marina: Ch M **80** Port Operations: Ch **14** 16		HOURS: H24

FENIT	Port and Marina 110 Berths 30 Visitor Berths	52°17′N 9°53′W
Tel: Hr Office & Marina: +353(0)66 7136231 Mobile: Marina Manager: +0874 60516 fenitmarina@eircom.net	Maximum LOA: 30 m	Fax: Hr Office: +353(0)66 7136231 Marina: +353(0)66 7136473 www.sailingireland.com
FREQUENCY: Port: Ch 14 16 Marina: Ch 16 M 80		HOURS: Open: 0900-2100 LT ACCESS: H24

FOYNES HARBOUR

Port: CALL: Shannon Estuary Radio — 52°37'N 9°07'W

Tel: Hr Mr: +353(0)69 73103
Hr Mr Mobile: 0872 560427
Outside Office Hours: 0872 542266
marineops@sfpc.ie

Landing slips at yacht club and moorings SE side of Foynes Island

Fax: Hr Mr: +353(0)69 65552

FREQUENCY: Ch **12** 13 16

HOURS: Office Hours

GALWAY

Port: CALL: Harbour Master Galway — 53°16'N 9°03'W

Tel: Port & Hr Mr: +353(0)91 562329 & 561874
Hr Mr: Outside office hours: +353(0)91 520034
galwayharbour@eircom.net

Fax: Port & Hr Mr: +353(0)91 563738
www.portofgalway.com

FREQUENCY: Ch 12 16

Pilot Vessel MMSI 250113440

HOURS: Office Hours and 2h before HW

GREENORE

Port: CALL: Ferry Greenore — 54°02'N 6°08'W

Tel: Port: +353(0)4293 73170

Fax: Port: +353(0)4293 73567

FREQUENCY: Ch 16

HOURS: HJ

HOWTH MARINA

53°23'·4N 6°03'·9W

Tel: Marina: +353(0)1839 2777
Hr Mr: +353(0)1832 2252
marina@hyc.ie
hmhowth@eircom.net

Fax: +353(0)1839 2430
Hr Office: +353(0)1832 6948
www.hyc.ie

FREQUENCY: Marina: Ch M 16 80

HOURS: Mon-Fri: 0700-2300 LT Sat & Sun: HX

KILLYBEGS

Port — 54°38'N 8°26'W

Tel: Hr Mr: +353(0)73 31032
harbourm@eircom.net

Fax: Port Auth: +353(0)73 31840

FREQUENCY: Ch 14 16

HOURS: HX

KILMORE QUAY MARINA

55 Berths — 52°11'N 6°35'W

Tel: +353(0)53 29955
hmkilmore@eircom.net

Fax: +353(0)53 29915

FREQUENCY: Ch 09 16 M

KILRUSH CREEK MARINA, SHANNON ESTUARY

120 Berths — 52°38'·0N 9°29'·5W

Tel: Marina: +353(0)6590 52072
Mobile: 0872 313870
Lock Gate: +353(0)6590 52155
kcm@shannon-dev.ie

Fax: +353(0)6590 51692
www.kilrushcreekmarina.ie

FREQUENCY: Ch 80

ACCESS: H24

KINSALE

Port: CALL: Kinsale Harbour Radio — 51°42'N 8°31'W

Tel: Hr Office: +353(0)21 4772503
Outside office hours: +353(0)21 4773047
kharbour@iol.ie

Fax: Hr Office: +353(0)21 4774695
www.indigo.ie/ipress/mt/welcome.htm

FREQUENCY: Ch 06 **14** 16

LOCATION: Customs Quay

CASTLE PARK MARINA, KINSALE

51°41'·80N 8°30'·90W

Tel: +353(0)21 4774959
maritime@indigo.ie

Fax: +353(0)21 4774958
www.activeireland.com

FREQUENCY: Ch 06 16

KINSALE YACHT CLUB MARINA	90 Berths 20 Visitor Berths	51°42′N 8°31′W
Tel: +353(0)21 4772196 Mobile: 0876 787377 kyc@iol.ie	Depth: 10 m, Maximum LOA: 20 m	Fax: +353(0)21 4774455 www.kyc.ie
FREQUENCY: Ch 16 M		HOURS: 0830-2330

LAWRENCE COVE MARINA		51°38′·28N 9°49′·28W
Tel: +353(0)27 75044 Mobile: 0872 506429 lcm@iol.ie		Fax: +353(0)27 75044 www.lawrencecovemarina.com
FREQUENCY: Ch 16	LOCATION: N side of Bear Island	

MALAHIDE MARINA	Call: Malahide Marina 350 Berths	53°27′·2N 6°08′·9W
Tel: +353(0)1 845 4129 info@malahidemarina.net	LOA: 75 m	Fax: +353(0)1 845 4255 www.malahidemarina.net www.crestnicholsonmarinas.co.uk
FREQUENCY: Ch M 80		HOURS: H24

ROSSLARE	**Port:** CALL: Rosslare Harbour	52°16′N 6°20′W
Tel: +353(0)53 33162		Fax: +353(0)53 33206
FREQUENCY: Ch 06 **12** 14 16		HOURS: H24

SLIGO	**Port** Leisure Moorings Available	54°16′N 8°28′W
Tel: Hr Office: +353(0)71 61197 Hr Mr: 0868 526233 sligoharbour@eircom.net sligoharbourmaster@indigo.ie		Fax: Hr Mr: +353(0)71 61197 www.imdo.ie
FREQUENCY: Ch **12** 14 16		HOURS: 0900-1700 LT

WATERFORD	**Port and Marina**	52°07′N 6°55′W
Tel: Hr Mr: +353(0)51 874499 Hr Office: +353(0)51 874907 Marina: +353(0)51 873501 Mobile: 0872 384944 pc@portofwaterford.com		Fax: Hr Office: +353(0)51 874908 www.portofwaterford.com
FREQUENCY: Port: Ch 12 14 16		HOURS: HJ

WICKLOW	**Port**	52°59′N 6°02′W
Tel: Hr Office: Office hours: +353(0)404 67455 Outside office hours: +353(0)404 69466		Fax:
FREQUENCY: Port: Ch 12 **14** 16		

YOUGHAL	**Port**	51°56′N 7°50′W
Tel: +353(0)24 92577		Fax: +353(0)24 92747
FREQUENCY: Ch 14 16	LOCATION: Green's Quay	HOURS: HW ± 3h

PORTUGAL

NAVTEX [R]			
R	Monsanto	518 kHz	38°44′N 9°11′W
NAVTEX [G]			
G	Monsanto	490 kHz	38°44′N 9°11′W
DIAGRAM: page 133			
Weather Bulletins			
R: On receipt 0250 0650 1050 1450 1850 2250	Storm warnings and gale warnings, synopsis, 24 hour forecast for Areas Charcot, Josephine, Finisterre, Porto, S. Vicente and Cádiz. In English		
G: 0100 0500 0900 1300 1700 2100	In Portuguese		
Navigational Warnings			
R: 0250 0650 1050 1450 1850 2250	Warnings for for Areas Charcot, Josephine, Finisterre, Porto, S. Vicente and Cádiz. In English		
G: 0100 0500 0900 1300 1700 2100	In Portuguese		

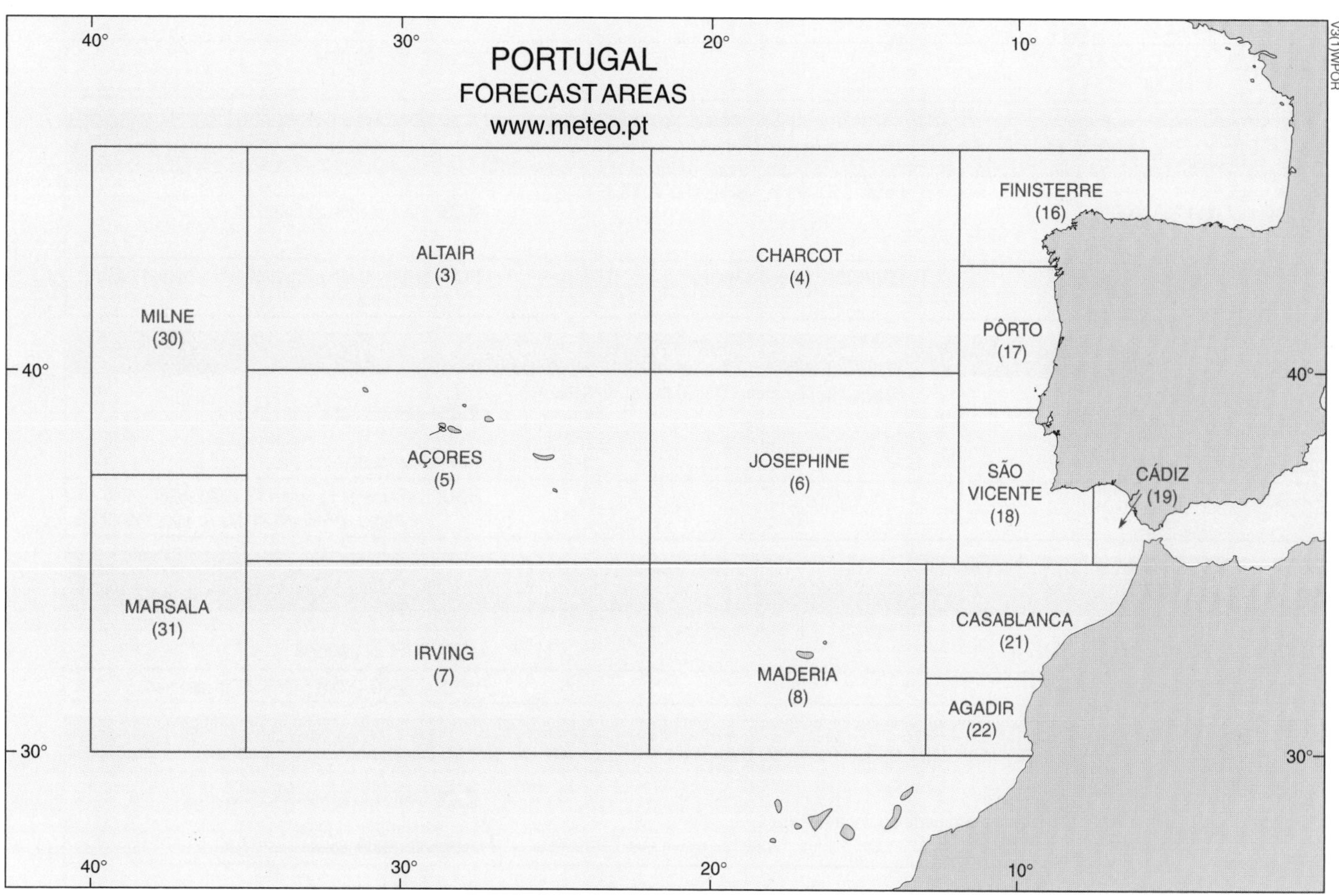

RADIONAVAL PORTUGAL			
A	2657	RT (MF)	Monsanto
A	Ch 11	VHF	Monsanto
B			Leixões
C			Faro
DIAGRAM: page 133			

RADIONAVAL PORTUGAL (CONTINUED)

Weather Bulletins	
A: 0905 2105	Storm, gale and poor Visibility warnings. Synopsis and 24 hour forecast for Areas 4, 6 & 16-19. In Portuguese, repeated in English.
B: 0705 1905	Storm, gale and poor Visibility warnings. Synopsis and 24 hour forecast for Portuguese coastal waters within 20 n miles covering area Rio Minho to Cabo de São Vicente. In Portuguese repeated in English.
C: 0805 2005	Storm, gale and poor Visibility warnings. Synopsis and 24 hour forecast for Portuguese coastal waters within 20 n miles covering area Cabo Carvoerio to Rio Guadiana. In Portuguese repeated in English.
Navigational Warnings	
A: 0905 2105	Warnings for area within 200 n miles offshore coast of Portuguese continent. In Portuguese, repeated in English.
B: 0705 1905	Coastal warnings within 20 n miles offshore. In Portuguese, repeated in English.
C: 0805 2005	

CASCAIS (MARINA DE CASCAIS)

Marina 638 Berths 125 Visitors Berths		38°42'N 9°25'W
☎ Marina: +351 214 824800 reception@marinacascais.pt	Depth: 6 - 8 m, Maximum LOA: Inside 37 m, Outside 46 m, Fuel available	Fax Marina: +351 214 824899
FREQUENCY: Ch 62		HOURS: Summer: 0900-2000 LT Winter: 0900-1800 LT

FARO

Port: CALL: Postradfaro		37°01'N 7°56'W
☎ Port Captain: +351 289 803601 portfaro@mail.telepac.pt	Depth: 4 m, fuel available	Fax Port Captain: +351 289 860666
FREQUENCY: 2182; **2252** 2657 kHz MF Ch 11 16		HOURS: Ch 16: H24

FIGUEIRA DA FOZ

Port: & Marina CALL: Capimarfoz 200 Berths Visitor Berths Available		40°09'N 8°52'W
☎ Marina: +351 233 402910 japff.gapoio@mail.telepac.pt	Depth: 2·5 - 3·5 m, Maximum LOA: 16 m	Fax Marina: +351 233 402920
FREQUENCY: Port: Ch 11 16 Marina: Ch 62	LOCATION: Doca de Recreo	HOURS: Ch 16: Mon-Fri: 0900-1200 1400-1700 LT Marina: HX

LAGOS

Marina: CALL: Marina de Lagos 462 Berths		37°06'N 8°40'W
☎ Port Capt: +351 282 762826 Marina: +351 282 770210 marlagos@mail.telepac.pt	Depth: 3 m, Maximum LOA: 30 m, fuel available	Fax Marina: +351 282 770219 www.marlagos.pt
FREQUENCY: Ch 16 **62**		HOURS: Summer (1 June-15 Sept): 0800-2200 LT Winter (16 Sept-31 May): 0900-1900 LT

LEIXÕES

Marina Porto Atlantico 240 Berths Visitor Berths Available		41°11'N 8°42'W
☎ +351 22 9964895	Depth: 3 - 5 m, Maximum LOA: 35 m	Fax +351 22 9964899
FREQUENCY: Ch 62		HOURS: 0900-1830 LT (2000 LT in summer)

LISBOA

Port: CALL: Port Control		38°41'N 9°13'W
☎ Control: +351 213 922026 **Contact above number for leisure craft berthing instructions** admin.junqueira@porto-de-lisboa.pt		Fax Control: +351 213 922028 www.porto-de-lisboa.pt
FREQUENCY: Calling: Ch 16 Working: Ch **64** Listening: Ch 12 13 **61**		HOURS: H24
INFORMATION BROADCASTS: Harbour Police broadcast in Portuguese as follows: Local Navigational Warnings: VHF Ch 11 at 1030 and 1630. Storm Warnings: VHF Ch 16 then VHF Ch 11 on receipt and every H+00		
Marinas		
Doca do Bom Sucesso	161 Berths	
☎ +351 21 3013027	Depth: 2·5 - 3 m, Maximum LOA: 15 m	Fax +351 21 3020092
Doca de Belém	198 Berths	
☎ +351 21 3631246	Depth: 2·5 - 3 m	Fax +351 21 3624578

LISBOA (Continued)	Port: CALL: Port Control		38°41'N 9°13'W
Doca de Santo Amaro		161 Berths	
☎ +351 21 3922011 & 20112	Depth: 4 m, Maximum LOA: 12·5 m Dock for visitors		Fax +351 21 3922038
Doca de Alcântara		348 Berths	
☎ +351 21 3922048	Depth: 10 m		Fax +351 21 3922085
MarinaExpo		200 Berths	
☎ +351 21 3825800 marinaexpo@mail.telepac.pt			Fax +351 21 3825808
FREQUENCY: Ch 62			
Administraçéo do Porto de Lisboa			
☎ +351 21 3611000			Fax +351 21 3611005
FREQUENCY: Ch 12			

NAZARÉ	Marina	14 Visitor Berths	39°36'N 9°05'W
☎ Hr Mr: +351 262 561401 Marina Mobile: 0968 074254 (Celtic Marine Services) celticmarine@clix.pt	Depth: 5 m, Maximum LOA: 25 m		Fax Hr Mr: +351 262 561402
FREQUENCY: Ch 11 16			HOURS: Ch 16: Mon-Fri: 0900-1700 LT

OLHÃO	Port: CALL: Capimarolhão	50 Berths	37°02'N 7°50'W
☎ Port Captain: +351 289 703160 Recreation port: +351 289 703519	Depth: 2 m, fuel available		Fax
FREQUENCY: Ch 11 16			HOURS: Mon-Fri: 0900-1230 1400-1730 LT

PENICHE	Port: and Marina CALL: Capimarpeniche	140 Berths	39°21'N 9°22'W
☎ Port Captain: +351 262 784109 Marina: +351 262 781153	Depth: 3 - 3·5 m, Maximum LOA: 15 m, fuel available		Fax +351 262 784225
FREQUENCY: Ch 11 16 62			HOURS: Ch 16: Mon-Fri: 0900-1200 1400-1700 LT

PENICHE LOOKING NNE

PHOTOGRAPH - RCC PILOTAGE FOUNDATION

PORTIMÃO	Marina 620 Berths	37°02'N 7°50'W
☎ +351 282 400680 marinaportimao@mail.telepac.pt	Depth: 3 - 4 m, Maximum LOA: 30 m, fuel available	Fax +351 282 400681 www.marina-portimao.com
FREQUENCY: Ch 62		HOURS: 1 June to 30 Sept: 0900 - 2100 LT 1 Oct - 31 May 0900 - 1800 LT

PÓVOA DE VARZIM	Marina 241 Berths 70 Visitor berths	41°22'N 8°46'W
☎ +351 252 688121 marinadapova@clix.pt	Depth: 3 m, Maximum LOA: 18 m, fuel available	Fax +351 252 688123 www.clubenavalpovoense.com
FREQUENCY: Port: Ch 11 16 Marina: Ch 62		HOURS: Ch 16: Mon-Fri: 0900-1200 1400-1700 LT

PUERTO DEPORTIVO DEL GUARDIANA	Marina 360 Berths	37°11'N 7°24'W
☎ Port Services: +351 281 513769 Marina: +351 281 541571	Depth: 2 m, Maximum LOA: 20 m	Fax +351 281 511140
FREQUENCY: Ch 12		HOURS: HX

SESIMBRA	Marina Visitor Berths Available	38°26'N 9°06'W
☎ +351 212 233451 secretaria@naval-sesimbra.pt		Fax +351 212 281039
FREQUENCY: Ch 11 16		HOURS: Mon-Fri: 0900-1200 1400-1700 LT

SETÚBAL	Marina 150 Berths	38°28'N 8°59'W
☎ Doca de Recreio das Fontainhas: +351 265 542076	Depth: 3 - 4 m, Maximum LOA: 15 m	Fax +351 265 230992
FREQUENCY: Ch 62		

SINES MARINA LOOKING E

PHOTOGRAPH - RCC PILOTAGE FOUNDATION

SINES	Port: CALL: Capimarsines	37°57'N 8°53'W
☎ Hr Mr: +351 269 860600 dcom@portodesines.pt		Fax Hr Mr: +351 269 860790 www.portodesines.pt
FREQUENCY: Port: Ch 11 13 16		HOURS: Ch 16: H24
	Marina 230 Berths	
☎ Marina: +351 269 860631	Depth: 4 m, Maximum LOA: 20 m, fuel available	Fax Marina: +351 269 860691
FREQUENCY: Port: Ch 12		

VIANA DO CASTELO	Marina 150 Berths 30 Visitor Berths	41°40′·5N 8°50′·3W
Viana Marina: +351 258 359546 Port Auth: +351 258 3503500 marina@ipnorte.pt	Maximum LOA: 14 m, Fuel available	Fax: Viana Marina: +351 258 359535 & 3503550 Port Auth: +351 2583535 www.ipnorte.pt
FREQUENCY: Marina: Ch 12 Ch 11 16		HOURS: Ch 16: Mon-Fri: 0900-1200 1400-1700 LT

VILAMOURA	Marina: CALL: Vilamoura Radio 1300 Berths	37°04′·4N 8°07′·3W
Hr Mr: +351 289 313214 Marina: +351 289 310560 marinavilamoura@mail.telepac.pt	Depth: 2 - 3·3 m, Entry Basin 4 m, Maximum LOA: 50 m, Fuel available	Fax: +351 289 310580 www.vilamour.net
FREQUENCY: Ch 16 62 Weather Information Broadcasts: Ch 20 (1000 LT)		HOURS: Ch 62: H24

VILA REAL DE SANTO ANTÓNIO	Marina 370 Berths	37°11′N 7°25′W
Port Capt: +351 281 512035 +351 281 541571 Port Service: +351 281 513769 (H24)	Depth: 2 m, Maximum LOA: 20 m	Fax: +351 281 511140
FREQUENCY: Marina: Ch 12 Port: Ch 11 16		HOURS: Mon-Fri: 0900-1200 1400-1700 LT

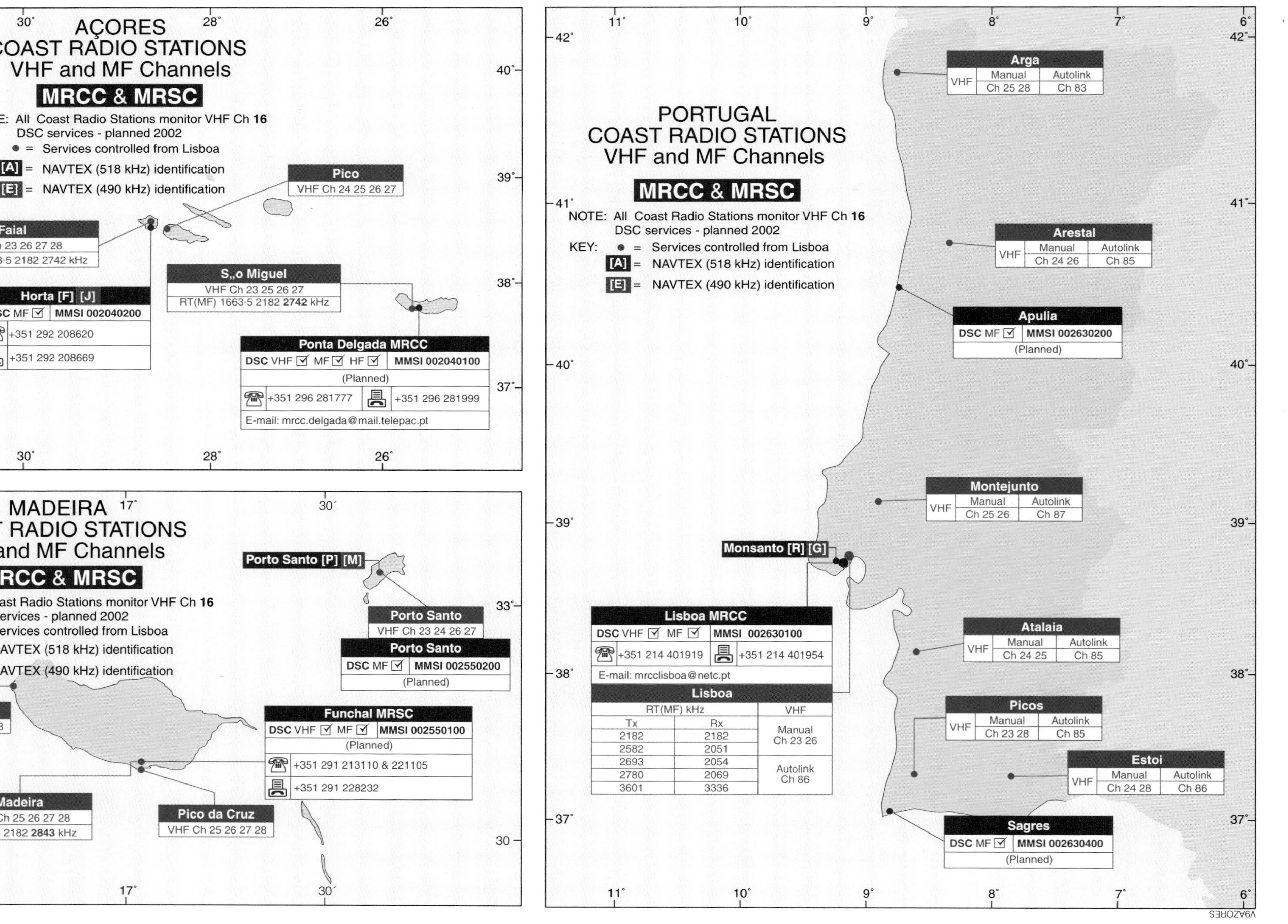

Lisboa		
RT(MF) kHz		VHF
Tx	Rx	
2182	2182	Manual Ch 23 26
2582	2051	
2693	2054	Autolink Ch 86
2780	2069	
3601	3336	

SPAIN, ATLANTIC COAST

National SAR Agency: Sociedad de Salvamento y Seguridad Marítima **Tel:** 91 7559132 & 91 7559133 **Fax:** 91 5261440 **Website:** www.sasemar.es
MRCC Madrid is responsible for co-ordinating Search and Rescue operations and has twentytwo MRCCs and MRSCs, divided into the North Coast, South Coast, Mediterranean Coast and Islas Canarias regions, under its control. All the MRCCs and MRSCs are manned on a 24 hour basis. A network of Coast Radio Stations, connected by telephone to all Spanish MRCCs, maintains a continuous listening watch on international distress frequencies.
Maritime Safety Information Broadcasts (Storm Warnings, Weather Bulletins and Navigational Warnings) are announced by Spanish CRS and MRCCs / MRSCs on either 2182 kHz or VHF Ch 16, before being broadcast on the scheduled frequency or channel number.

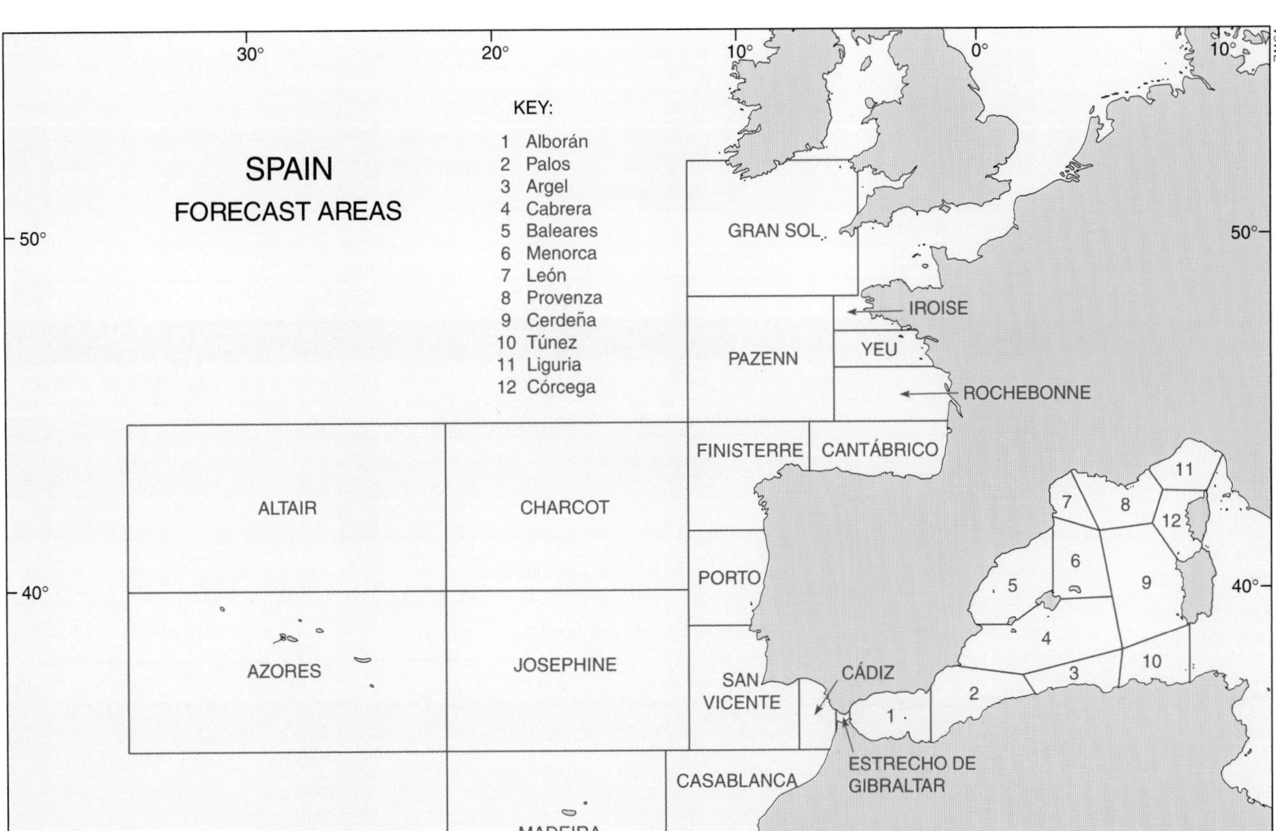

NAVTEX [D] [G]

D	Coruña	518 kHz	43°21′N 8°27′W
G	Tarifa		36°01′N 5°34′W
DIAGRAMS: pages 139 and 147			
Weather Bulletins			
D: 0830	Storm warnings, synoptic situation and development, forecast valid for the following 18 hours for N Atlantic within 450 n miles from coast		
D: 2030	Storm warnings, synoptic situation and development, forecast valid for the following 36 hours for N Atlantic within 450 n miles from coast		
G: 0900	Storm warnings, synoptic situation and development, forecast valid for the following 18 hours for N Atlantic and West Mediterranean Sea within 450 n miles from coast		
G: 2100	Storm warnings, synoptic situation and development, forecast valid for the following 36 hours for N Atlantic and West Mediterranean Sea within 450 n miles from coast		
Navigational Warnings			
D: 0030 0430 1230 1630	NAVAREA II warnings and local warnings in Spanish and English		
G: 0100 0500 1300 1700	NAVAREA II warnings; coastal warnings from Portuguese border to Europa Point (Gibraltar), in English		

BILBAO (CCR Group IV)

A	1677	RT (MF)	Cabo Peñas	43°39′N 5°51′W
	1707		Machichaco	43°27′N 2°45′W
B	Ch 26	VHF	Bilbao	43°22′N 3°02′W
			Cabo Peñas	43°39′N 5°51′W
	Ch 60		Navia	43°25′N 6°50′W
	Ch 27		Pasajes	43°17′N 1°55′W
	Ch 24		Santandar	43°25′N 3°36′W

DIAGRAMS: pages 139 and 147

Weather Bulletins	
A: 0703 1903	24 hours forecast for Atlantic areas in Spanish
A: 1303	48 hours forecast for Atlantic areas in Spanish
B: 0840 2010	Forecast for coastal areas in Spanish
B: 1240	48 hours forecast for coastal areas in Spanish
Navigational Warnings	
A: 0703 1903	General warnings
B: 0840 2010	Coastal warnings

BILBAO (MRCC)

	Ch 10	VHF		43°21′N 3°02′W

DIAGRAMS: pages 139 and 147

Weather Bulletins	
On receipt Every even H+33	Storm warnings
0033 0433 0833 1233 1633 2033	Coastal waters: Gale warnings and forecast in Spanish and English
0233 0633 1033 1433 1833 2233	High seas: Gale Warnings and Forecast in Spanish and English

CORUÑA (CCR GROUP III)

A	1698	RT (MF)	Coruña	43°22′N 8°27′W
	1764		Finisterre	42°54′N 9°16′W
B	Ch 02	VHF	Cabo Ortegal	43°35′N 7°47′W
	Ch 26		Coruña	43°22′N 8°27′W
	Ch 22		Finisterre	42°54′N 9°16′W
	Ch 21		La Guardia	41°53′N 8°52′W
	Ch 65		Vigo	42°10′N 8°41′W

DIAGRAMS: pages 139 and 147

Weather Bulletins	
A: 0703 1903	Forecast for Atlantic areas in Spanish
A: 1303	48 hours forecast for Atlantic areas in Spanish
B: 0840 2010	Forecast for coastal areas in Spanish
B: 1240	48 hours forecast for coastal areas in Spanish
Navigational Warnings	
A: 0703 1903	General warnings
B: 0840 2010	Coastal warnings

CORUÑA (MRSC)

	Ch 13	VHF		43°22′N 8°23′W

DIAGRAMS: pages 139 and 147

Weather Bulletins	
0005 0405 0805 1205 1605 2005	In Spanish and English

CORUÑA (MRSC) **(Continued)**				
Navigational Warnings				
0205 0605 1005 1405 1805 2205	NAVAREA II warnings and local warnings in Spanish and English			

FINISTERRE (MRCC)				
	Ch 11	VHF		42°42′N 8°59′W
DIAGRAMS: pages 139 and 147				
Weather Bulletins				
H+33 every 4 hours commencing 0233	In Spanish and English			
Navigational Warnings				
H+33 every 4 hours commencing 0033	In Spanish and English			

GIJÓN (MRCC)				
	Ch 10	VHF		43°34′N 5°42′W
DIAGRAMS: pages 139 and 147				
Weather Bulletins				
Every even H+15 (0215-2215)	In Spanish and English			
Navigational Warnings				
Every H+15	In Spanish and English			

HUELVA (MRSC)				
	Ch 11	VHF		
Weather Bulletins and Navigational Warnings				
0415 0815 1215 1615 2015 UTC	In Spanish and English			

SANTANDER (MRSC)				
	Ch 11	VHF		43°27′N 3°49′W
DIAGRAMS: pages 139 and 147				
Weather Bulletins				
0245 0645 1045 1445 1845 2245	In Spanish and English			
Navigational Warnings				
0045 0445 0845 1245 1645 2045	In Spanish and English			

TARIFA (MRCC)				
	Ch 10 67	VHF		36°01′N 5°35′W
DIAGRAMS: pages 139 and 147				
Weather Bulletins				
Every even H+15	Actual wind and visibility at Tarifa, followed by forecast for Strait of Gibraltar, Cádiz Bay and Alborán in Spanish and English			
Navigational Warnings				
On receipt	For the Strait of Gibraltar between the meridians of Cabo Espartel Lt (35°47′N 5°56′W) and Punta Almina Lt (35°54′N 5°17′W), in Spanish and English			
Every even H+15	**Fog (Visibilty) Warnings**: Broadcasts are more frequent when visibility falls below 2 n miles, in Spanish and English			

VIGO (MRSC)				
	Ch 10	VHF		42°14′N 8°44′W
DIAGRAMS: pages 139 and 147				
Weather Bulletins				
0015 0415 0815 1215 1615 2015	In Spanish and English			

VIGO (MRSC) (Continued)

Navigational Warnings	
0215 0615 1015 1415 1815 2215	In Spanish and English

TELEPHONE MARINE WEATHER INFORMATION SERVICE

A recorded telephone marine weather information service is provided by the Instituto Nacional de Meteorología. This service is only available within Spain and also vessels' equipped with Autolink, dedicated Autolink VHF Channels and RT (MF) frequencies. The following bulletins are available:

TELEPHONE: 906 365372
Coastal Waters Bulletin for the Cantábrico and Galicia coasts

TELEPHONE: 906 365373
Coastal Waters Bulletin for the Atlantic coast of Andalucía and Islas Canarias

TELEPHONE: 906 365374
High Seas Bulletin for the Atlantic Forecast Areas

AYAMONTE	Marina 174 Berths	37°12′N 7°20′W
Tel: +34 959 321694	Depth: 3 m	Fax: +34 959 321694
FREQUENCY: Ch 09		HOURS: HX

BARBATE	Marina 256 Berths	36°10′N 5°55′W
Tel: +34 956 431907 barbate@eppa.es	Depth: 3 m, Maximum LOA: 30 m	Fax: +34 956 431918 www.eppa.es
FREQUENCY: Ch 09 16		

CÁDIZ, REAL CLUB NAUTICO DE CÁDIZ	Marina and Port 160 Berths	36°31′N 6°17′W
Tel: Marina: +34 956 213262 Hr Mr: +34 956 224011 cadiz@lcadiz.portel.es	Depth: 3·4 m	Fax: +34 956 221040
FREQUENCY: Marina: Ch 09 16 Port: Ch 11 12 14 16		HOURS: HX

CENTRO NAUTICO ELCANO	Marina 234 Berths	36°30′N 6°15′W
Tel: +34 956 290012 cnelcano@teleline.es	Depth: 2 m	Fax: +34 956 290099
FREQUENCY: Ch 09		HOURS: HX

CHIPIONA (PUERTO de CHIPIONA)	Marina 355 Berths	36°45′N 6°25′·40W
Tel: +34 956 373844 hipiona@eppa.es	Depth: 3·5 m, Maximum LOA: 30 m	Fax: +34 956 370037 www.eppa.es
FREQUENCY: Ch 09		HOURS: HX

EL ROMPIDO	Marina	37°13′N 7°07′W
Tel: Port: +34 955 390728 Marina: +34 955 331742 Nautical Club: +34 955 399217		Fax:
FREQUENCY: Ch 09 16		HOURS: HX

HUELVA	Port	37°15′·1N 6°57′·5W
Tel: Port: +34 955 248611 Punta Umbría Club: +34 955 311899		Fax: Port Auth: +34 955 213101
FREQUENCY: Port: Ch 06 11 12 14 16; Punta Umbria Club: Ch 09 16		HOURS: H24
	Marina	
Tel: Marina: +34 955 248199		Fax:
FREQUENCY: Ch 09 16		HOURS: HX

PUERTO DEPORTIVO MAZAGON (PALOS DE LA FRONTERA - HUELVA)	Marina 497 Berths	37°13′·04N 6°57′·81W
Tel +34 959 536251 magazon@eppa.es	Depth: 4 m, Maximum LOA: 30 m	Fax +34 959 376237 www.eppa.es

Bridge Drawbridge across the Estero de Burro
PROCEDURE: Can be opened after a call (on VHF) to Huelva Pilots or, by telephone, to the Huelva Port Office

ISLA CRISTINA	Marina 203 Berths	37°11′·57N 7°19′·36W
Tel +34 959 343501 islachristinad@eppa.es	Depth: 2 m, Maximum LOA: 20 m	Fax +34 959 343511 www.eppa.es
FREQUENCY: Ch 09		HOURS: HX

PHOTOGRAPH - RCC PILOTAGE FOUNDATION

MARINA ISLA CRISTINA LOOKING ESE

MARINA ISLA CANELA	Marina 231 Berths	37°11′·3N 7°20′·3W
Tel +34 959 479000 marina@islacanela.es	Depth: 2·5 m, Maximum LOA: 12 m	Fax +34 959 479020
FREQUENCY: Ch 09		

PUERTO AMÈRICA	Marina 152 Berths	36°32′·36′N 6°16′·42W
Tel +34 956 223666 puertoamerica@eppa.es	Depth: 7·5 m, Maximum LOA: 25 m	Fax +34 956 224220 www.eppa.es
FREQUENCY: Ch 09 16	LOCATION: San Felipe Point (Commercial Basin)	

PUERTO DE SANTA MARIA (REAL CLUB NAUTICO)	Marina 175 Berths Visitors Berths on Outside Pontoons	36°35′N 6°15′W
Tel +34 956 852527	Depth: 5 m, Maximum LOA: 22 m	Fax +34 956 874400
FREQUENCY: Ch 09 16		HOURS: HX

PUERTO GELVES MARINA	Marina	133 Berths	37°20′·37N 6°01·38′W
☎ +34 955 761212 puertogelves@teleline.es	Depth: 3 m, Maximum LOA: 16 m		Fax +34 955 761538 www.puertogelves.com
FREQUENCY: Ch 09			

PUERTO SHERRY	Marina	753 Berths	36°35′N 6°15′W
☎ +34 956 870103	Depth: 4·5 m, Maximum LOA: 50 m		Fax +34 956 873902
FREQUENCY: Ch 09 16			HOURS: HX

PHOTOGRAPH - RCC PILOTAGE FOUNDATION

PUERTO SHERRY LOOKING NE

ROTA	Marina	496 Berths	36°36′·′60N 6°20′·57W
☎ Marina: +34 956 840069 Port: +34 956 813811 rota@eppa.es	Depth: 4·5 m, Maximum LOA: 32 m		Fax +34 956 813811 www.eppa.es
FREQUENCY: Ch 09			

SEVILLE (RÍO GUADALQUIVIR)	Marinas		37°25′N 6°00′W
Club Nàutico de Sevilla	Access through bridge which opens at 1000, 2000 and 0830 LT during festivals.		
☎ +34 95 4454777			Fax +34 95 4284693
Puerto Deportivo de Gelves	**Marina**	156 Berths	
☎ +34 955 761212	Maximum LOA: 16 m		Fax +34 955 761583
Marina Yachting Sevilla S.A.	**Marina**	200 Berths	
☎ +34 95 4230326	Maximum LOA: 16 m		Fax +34 954 230172
FREQUENCY: Marinas: Ch 09 Locks: Ch 12			HOURS: Lock opening times: Season: 0100, 0400, 0700, 0900, 1100, 1300, 1600, 1900 and 2100 LT Out of season opens: 0100, 0400, 0700, 0930, 1030, 1300, 1600, 1800 and 2000 LT

SANCTI PETRI	Marina	88 Berths	36°23'N 6°12'W
☎ +34 956 496169	Depth: 5 m		Fax +34 956 495434
sanctipetri@eppa.es			www.eppa.es
FREQUENCY: Ch 09 16			

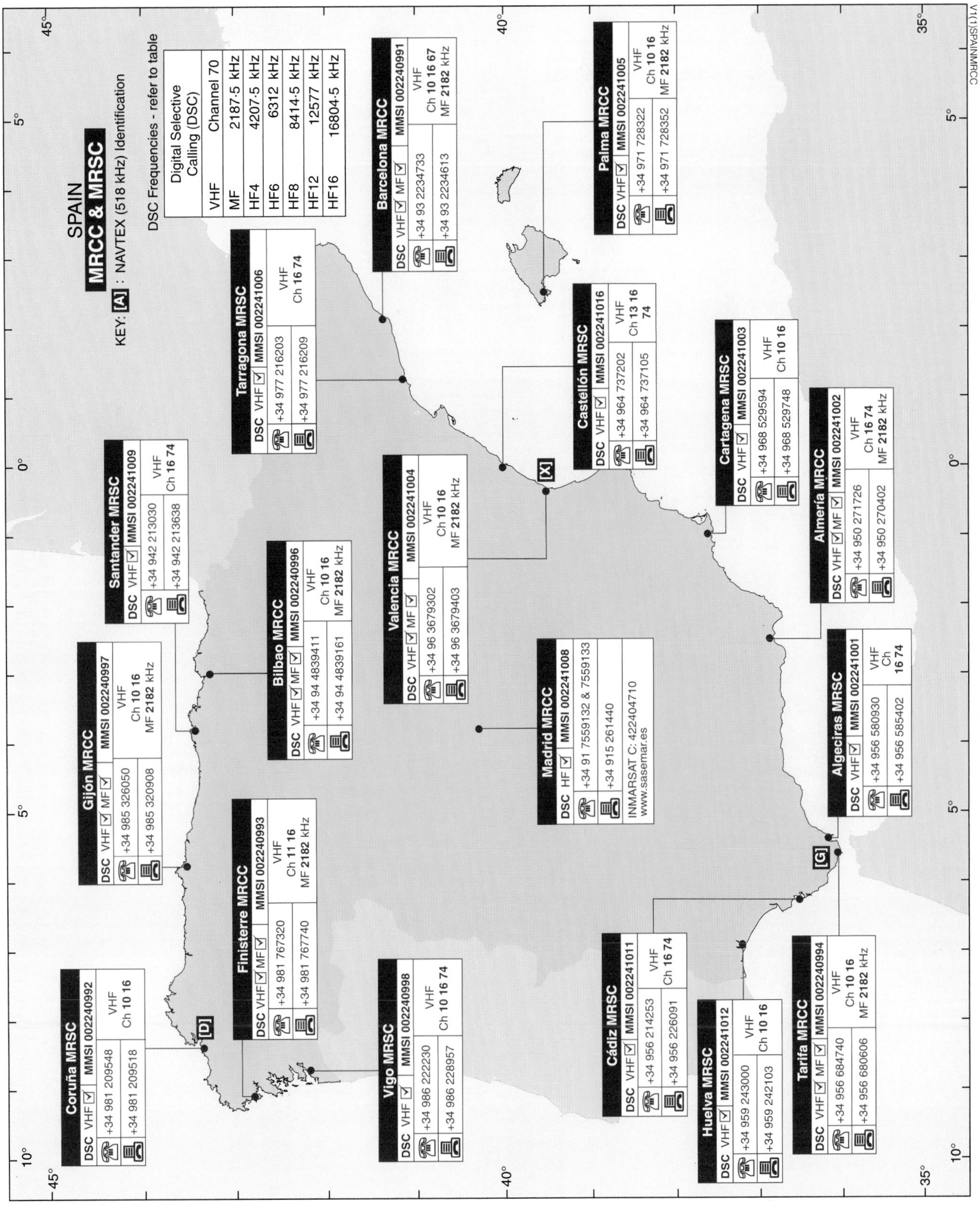

SPAIN MRCC & MRSC

KEY: [A] : NAVTEX (518 kHz) Identification

DSC Frequencies - refer to table

	Digital Selective Calling (DSC)
VHF	Channel 70
MF	2187·5 kHz
HF4	4207·5 kHz
HF6	6312 kHz
HF8	8414·5 kHz
HF12	12577 kHz
HF16	16804·5 kHz

Coruña MRSC – DSC VHF☑ – MMSI 002240992
☎ +34 981 209548 – Fax +34 981 209518 – VHF Ch 10 16

Finisterre MRCC – DSC VHF☑ MF☑ – MMSI 002240993
☎ +34 981 767320 – Fax +34 981 767740 – VHF Ch 11 16, MF 2182 kHz

Vigo MRSC – DSC VHF☑ – MMSI 002240998
☎ +34 986 222230 – Fax +34 986 228957 – VHF Ch 10 16 74

Gijón MRCC – DSC VHF☑ MF☑ – MMSI 002240997
☎ +34 985 326050 – Fax +34 985 320908 – VHF Ch 10 16, MF 2182 kHz

Santander MRSC – DSC VHF☑ – MMSI 002241009
☎ +34 942 213030 – Fax +34 942 213638 – VHF Ch 16 74

Bilbao MRCC – DSC VHF☑ MF☑ – MMSI 002240996
☎ +34 94 4839411 – Fax +34 94 4839161 – VHF Ch 10 16, MF 2182 kHz

Madrid MRCC – DSC HF☑ – MMSI 002241008
☎ +34 91 7559132 & 7559133 – Fax +34 915 261440
INMARSAT C: 422404710
www.sasemar.es

Tarragona MRSC – DSC VHF☑ – MMSI 002241006
☎ +34 977 216203 – Fax +34 977 216209 – VHF Ch 16 74

Valencia MRCC – DSC VHF☑ MF☑ – MMSI 002241004
☎ +34 96 3679302 – Fax +34 96 3679403 – VHF Ch 10 16, MF 2182 kHz

Barcelona MRCC – DSC VHF☑ MF☑ – MMSI 002240991
☎ +34 93 2234733 – Fax +34 93 2234613 – VHF Ch 10 16 67, MF 2182 kHz

Castellón MRSC – DSC VHF☑ – MMSI 002241016
☎ +34 964 737202 – Fax +34 964 737105 – VHF Ch 13 16 74

Palma MRCC – DSC VHF☑ – MMSI 002241005
☎ +34 971 728322 – Fax +34 971 728352 – VHF Ch 10 16, MF 2182 kHz

Cartagena MRSC – DSC VHF☑ – MMSI 002241003
☎ +34 968 529594 – Fax +34 968 529748 – VHF Ch 10 16

Almería MRCC – DSC VHF☑ MF☑ – MMSI 002241002
☎ +34 950 271726 – Fax +34 950 270402 – VHF Ch 16 74, MF 2182 kHz

Algeciras MRSC – DSC VHF☑ – MMSI 002241001
☎ +34 956 580930 – Fax +34 956 585402 – VHF Ch 16 74

Cádiz MRSC – DSC VHF☑ – MMSI 002241011
☎ +34 956 214253 – Fax +34 956 226091 – VHF Ch 16 74

Huelva MRSC – DSC VHF☑ – MMSI 002241012
☎ +34 959 243000 – Fax +34 959 242103 – VHF Ch 10 16

Tarifa MRCC – DSC VHF☑ MF☑ – MMSI 002240994
☎ +34 956 684740 – Fax +34 956 680606 – VHF Ch 10 16, MF 2182 kHz

[D] [X] [G]

V1(1)SPAINMRCC

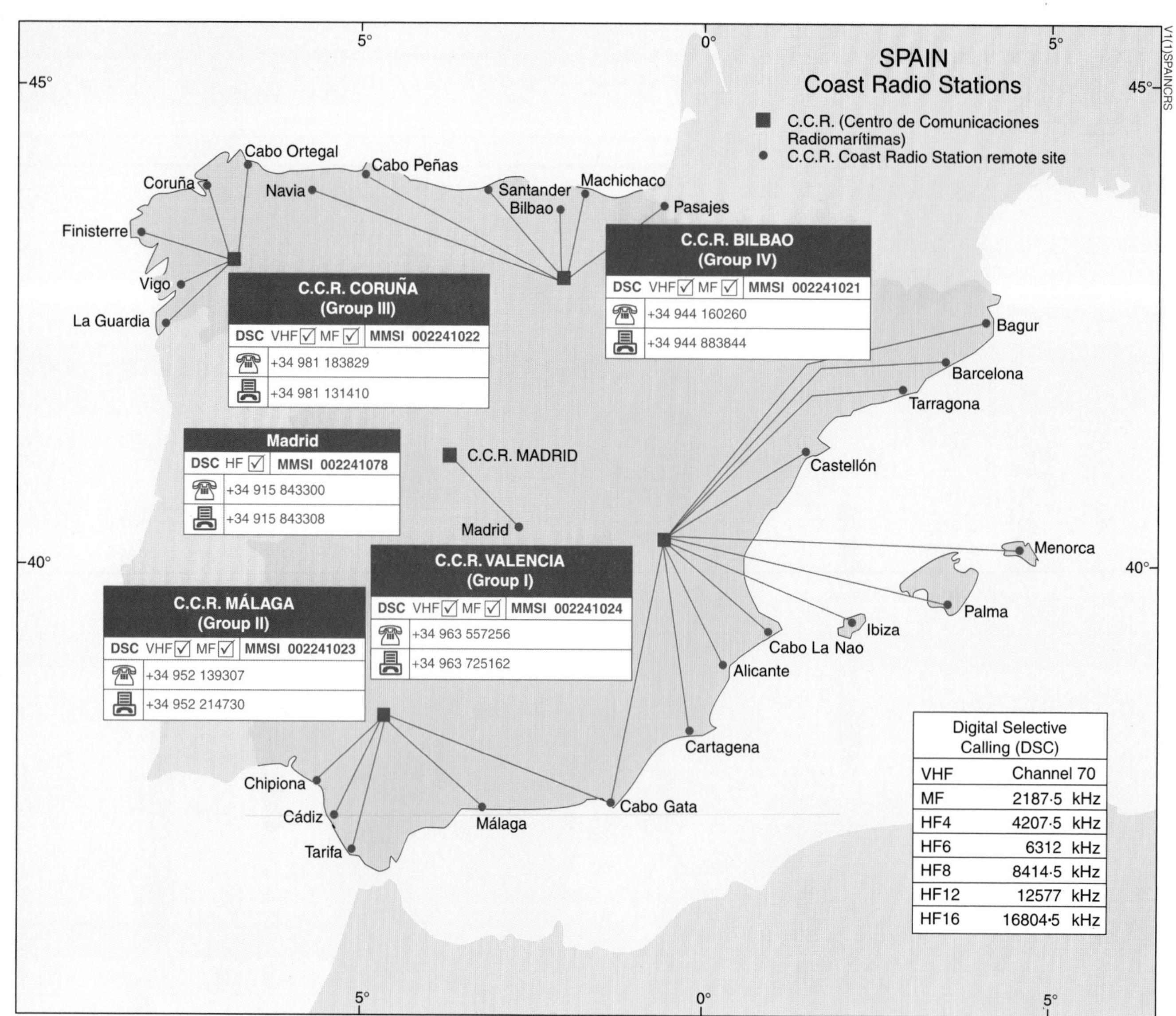

Primary Working Frequencies

	RT (MF)				VHF Ch	
	Manual		Autolink			
CRS Name	**Tx**	**Rx**	**Tx**	**Rx**	**Man**	**Auto**
Pasajes					27	25
Machichaco	1707	2132	2586	3287		
Bilbao					26	04
Santander					24	
Cabo Peñas	1677	2102	2649	3231	26	25
Navia					60	
Cabo Ortegal					02	
Coruña	1698	2123	2806	3283	26	28
Finisterre	1764	2108	2596	3280	22	27
Vigo					65	62
La Guardia					21	
Chipiona	1656	2081				
Cádiz					26	61
Tarifa	1704	2129	2610	3290	81	23
Málaga					26	25
Cabo Gata	1767	2111			27	20

	RT (MF)				VHF Ch	
	Manual		Autolink			
CRS Name	**Tx**	**Rx**	**Tx**	**Rx**	**Man**	**Auto**
Cartagena					04	65
Alicante					85	
Cabo La Nao					01	61
Castellón					25	63
Tarragona					23	26
Barcelona					60	60
Bagur					23	23
Menorca					85	85
Palma	1755	2099	2799	2099	20	83
Ibiza					03	

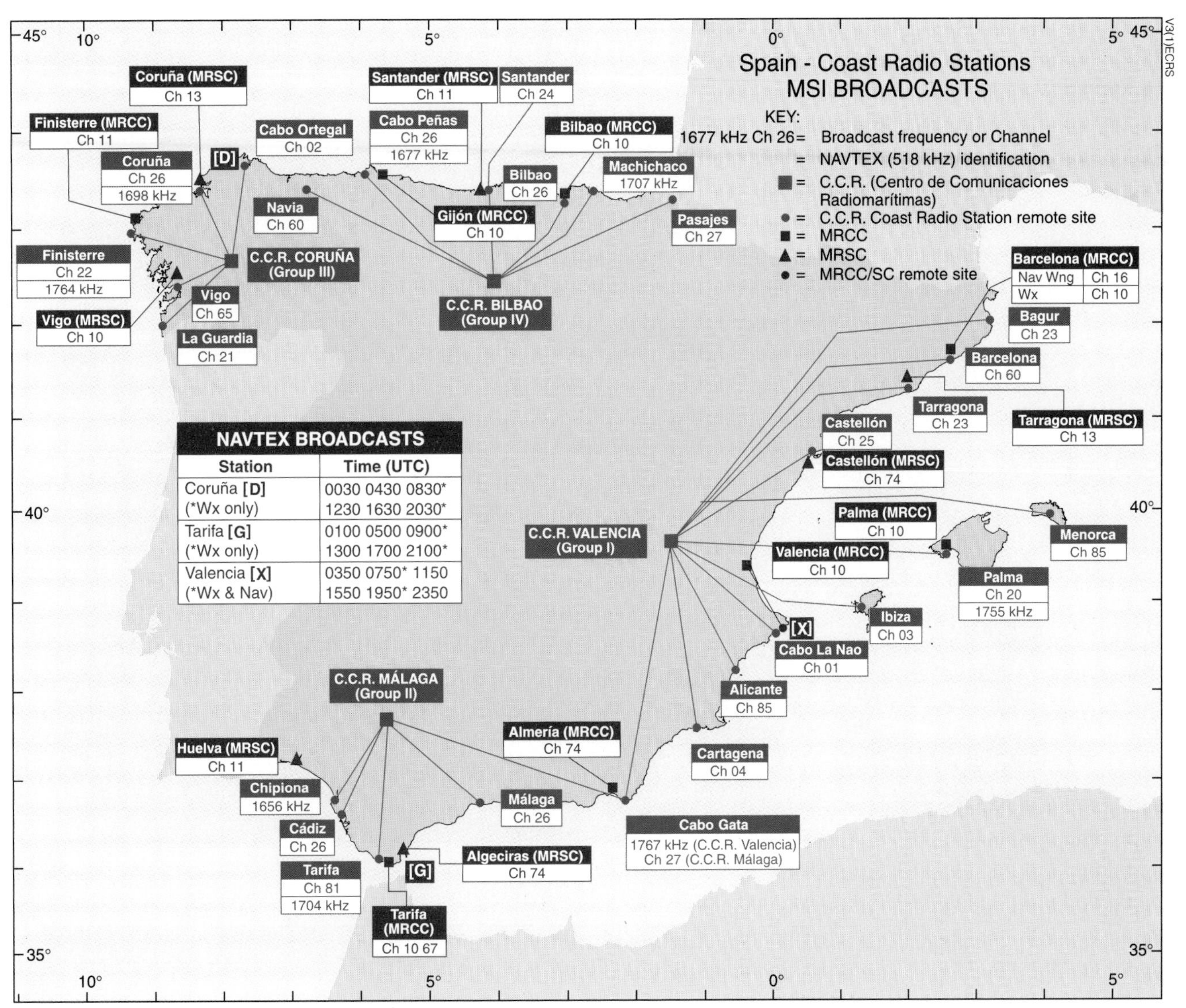

VHF/MF RADIOTELEPHONE MSI BROADCAST SCHEDULE

CRS Name	Weather Bulletin RT (MF)	Weather Bulletin VHF	Navigational Warnings RT (MF)	Navigational Warnings VHF
Alicante		0910 1410 2110		0910 2110
Algeciras (MRSC)		0315 0515 0715 1115 1515 1915 2315		On request
Almería (MRCC)		Odd H+15		Odd H+15
Bagur		0910 1410 2110		0910 2110
Barcelona		0910 1410 2110		0910 2110
Barcelona (MRCC)		0700 1100 1600 2100 LT		0700 1100 1600 2100 LT
Bilbao		0840 1240 2010		0840 2010
Bilbao (MRCC)		0033 0433 0833 1233 1633 2033		0233 0633 1033 1433 1833 2233
Cabo Gata	0750 1303 1950	0833 1133 2033	0750 1950	0833 2003
Cabo la Nao		0910 1410 2110		0910 2110
Cabo Ortegal		0840 1240 2010		0840 2010
Cabo Peñas	0703 1303 1903	0840 1240 2010	0703 1903	0840 2010
Cádiz		0833 1133 2033		0833 2003
Cartagena		0910 1410 2110		0910 2110
Castellón		0910 1410 2110		0910 2110
Castellón (MRSC)		Summer: 0503 0903 1503 1903 Winter: 0603 1003 1603 2003		
Chipiona	0733 1233 1933		0733 1933	
Coruña	0703 1303 1903	0840 1240 2010	0703 1903	0840 2010
Coruña (MRSC)		0005 0405 0805 1205 1605 2005		0205 0605 1005 1405 1805 2205
Finisterre	0703 1303 1903	0840 1240 2010	0703 1903	0840 2010
Finisterre (MRCC)		0233 0633 1033 1433 1833 2233		0033 0433 0833 1233 1633 2033

CRS Name	Weather Bulletin RT (MF)	Weather Bulletin VHF	Navigational Warnings RT (MF)	Navigational Warnings VHF
Gijón (MRCC)		Even H+15 (0215-2215)		Every H+15
Huelva (MRSC)		0415 0815 1215 1615 2015		
Ibiza		0910 1410 2110		0910 2110
La Guardia		0840 1240 2010		0840 2010
Machichaco	0703 1303 1903		0703 1903	
Málaga		0833 1133 2033		0833 2003
Menorca		0910 1410 2110		0910 2110
Navia		0840 1240 2010		0840 2010
Palma	0750 1303 1950	0910 1410 2110	0750 1950	0910 2110
Palma (MRCC)		Summer: 0635 0935 1435 1935 Winter: 0735 1035 1535 2035		
Pasajes		0840 1240 2010		0840 2010
Santander		0840 1240 2010		0840 2010
Santander (MRSC)		0245 0645 1045 1455 1845 2245		0045 0445 0845 1245 1645 2045
Tarifa	0733 1233 1933	0833 1133 2033	0733 1933	0833 2003
Tarifa (MRCC)		Even H+15		On receipt
Tarragona		0910 1410 2110		0910 2110
Tarragona (MRSC)		0630 1030 1630 2130 LT		0630 1030 1630 2130 LT
Valencia (MRCC)		Even H+15		Even H+15
Vigo		0840 1240 2010		0840 2010
Vigo (MRSC)		0015 0415 0815 1215 1615 2015		0215 0615 1015 1415 1815 2215

SPAIN, NORTH COAST

LUARCA HARBOUR LOOKING S

PHOTOGRAPH - RCC PILOTAGE FOUNDATION

BAYONA	Marina 210 Berths 50 Visitor Berths	42°07′N 8°51W
Monte Real Club de Yates: +34 986 355234	Depth: 3·5 m, Maximum LOA: 40 m Fuel available	Fax: +34 986 355061
FREQUENCY: Ch 09 16		HOURS: HX

BILBAO	Port	43°19′N 3°01′W
Capitanía de Puerto: +34 944 241416		Fax: Capitanía de Puerto: +34 944 248057
FREQUENCY: 06 12 16		HOURS: H24
Abra de Bilbao	**Marina** 150 Berths	43°20·4N 3°00′8W
+34 944 637600 puertobilbao@bilbaoport.es	Depth: 0·8 - 2 m, Maximum LOA: 16 m	Fax: +34 944 638061
FREQUENCY: Ch 06 12 16		
Getxo (Bilbao)	**Marina** 827 Berths	43°20′·5N 3°01′W
+34 944 912367	Depth: 1·5 - 2 m, Maximum LOA: 18 m	Fax: +34 944 911818
FREQUENCY: Ch 09 16		

CARAMIÑAL	Port & Marina 150 Berths 30 Visitor Berths	42°36′N 8°56W
+34 981 830970 & 877317	Depth: 2·5 m, Fuel available	Fax:
FREQUENCY: Ch 09 16		HOURS: HX

CAMARIÑAS	Marina 30 Berths Pontoons Available	43°7′·60N 9°10′·90W
+34 981 737130		Fax: +34 981 736325
FREQUENCY: Ch 09 16		HOURS: HX

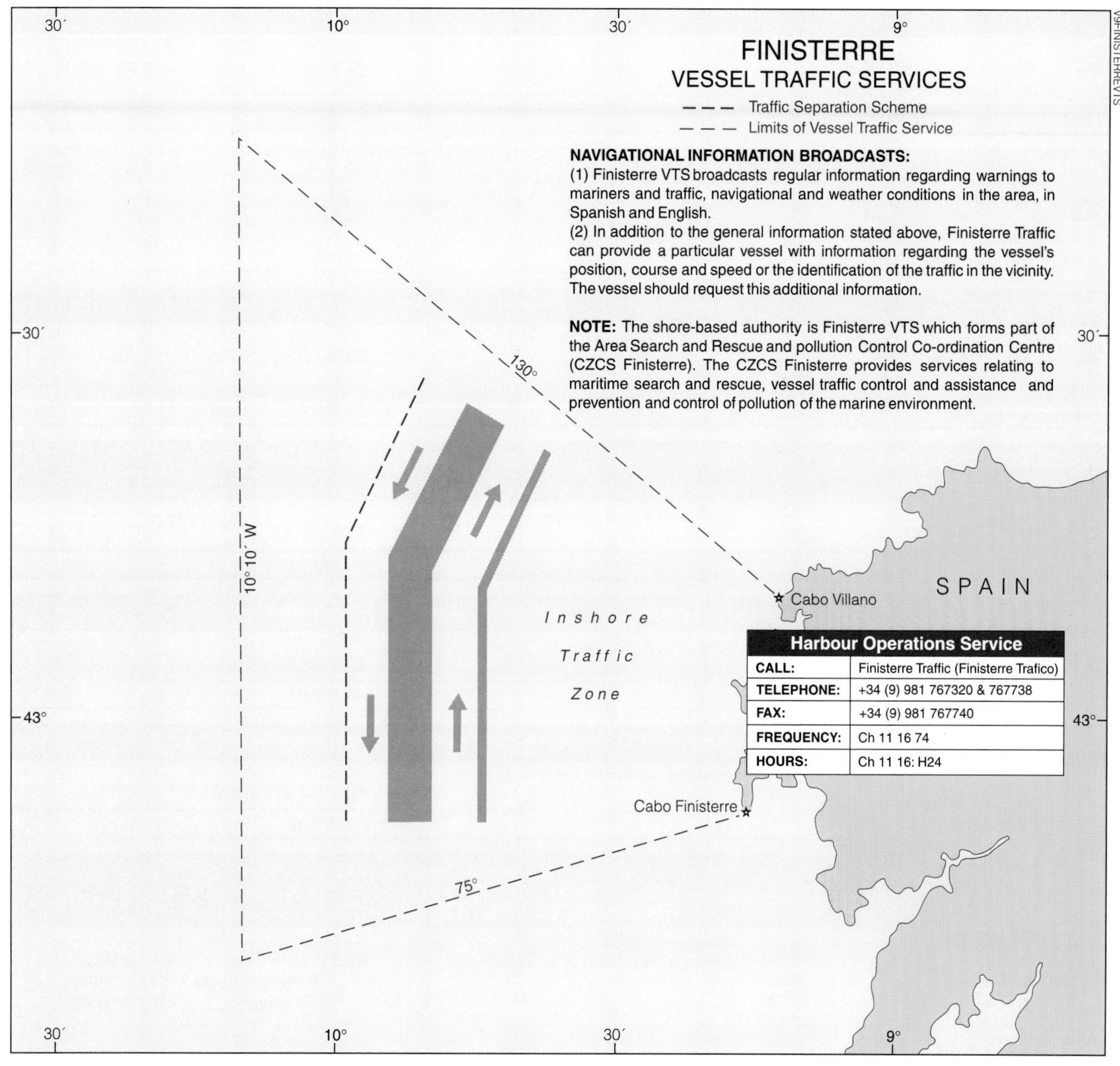

Harbour Operations Service

CALL:	Finisterre Traffic (Finisterre Trafico)
TELEPHONE:	+34 (9) 981 767320 & 767738
FAX:	+34 (9) 981 767740
FREQUENCY:	Ch 11 16 74
HOURS:	Ch 11 16: H24

GIJÓN	Port & Marina 657 Berths 100 Visitor Berths	43°33′N 5°40′W
☎ Port: +34 985 354945 Marina: +34 985 344543	Maximum LOA: 16m.	Fax Port: +34 985 359917 Marina: +34 985 350027
informacion@puertogijon.es		www.portel.es

GUETARIA	Marina CALL: Guetaria Náutico 300 Berths 5 Berths for Visiting Yachts	43°18′N 2°12′W
☎ Port: +34 943 140201 & 943 140413 Marina: +34 943 580959	Maximum LOA: 14 m	Fax Marina: +34 943 580959
FREQUENCY: 2182; 2700 kHz MF & VHF Ch 09		HOURS: HX

HONDARRIBIA	Marina 600 Berths	43°23′N 1°47′·40W
☎ +34 943 641711	Maximum LOA: 16 m	Fax +34 945 213686
FREQUENCY: Ch 09 16		HOURS: HX

LA CORUÑA	Port & Marina CALL: Dársena Radio Torre Hércules 150 Berths 40 Visitor Berths	43°23′N 8°22′W
☎ Port Captain: +34 981 226001 Real Club Náutico: +34 981 203265	Maximum LOA: 15 m, Larger yachts anchor off the club	Fax Real Club Náutico: +34 981 203008
FREQUENCY: Port: Ch 09 12 16		HOURS: HX

PASAJES	Port	43°20′N 1°55′W
☎ Hr Mr: +34 943 351816 Club Maritimo +34 986 439069 Port Auth: ppasajes@sarenet.es		Fax Hr Mr: +34 943 351348

PORTOSIN	Marina 240 Berths 35 Visitor Berths	42°45′·8N 8°54′·9W
☎ +34 981 766583 & 766598 cnp@arrakis.es	Depth: 2 m, Maximum LOA: 20 m	Fax +34 981 766389
FREQUENCY: Ch 09 16		HOURS: HX

PORTO PEDRAS NEGRAS (SAN VICENTE DO MAR)	Marina 135 Berths 12 Visitor Berths	42°27′N 8°55′W
☎ Marina: +34 981 873801	Depth: 3 - 4 m, Fuel available	Fax Marina: +34 981 873801
FREQUENCY: Club Nautico: Ch 09		HOURS: HX

RIANJO	Port & Marina 80 Berths 10 Visitors Berths	42°39′N 8°49′W
☎ Marina: +34 981 866107	Depth: 2 - 4 m, Maximum LOA: 10 m	Fax +34 981 860620
FREQUENCY: Club Náutico: Ch 09		HOURS: HX

SADA	Marina 650 Berths 45 Visitor Berths	43°21′·44N 8°14′·92W
☎ +34 981 619015	Depth: 2 m - 3 m, Maximum LOA: 20 m	Fax +34 981 619287
FREQUENCY: Ch 09 16		HOURS: HX

SANTANDER	Port: Club Náutico La Horadada 100 Berths Marina de Santander 900 Berths Real Club Maritimo de Santander 250 Berths	43°28′N 3°47′W
☎ Hr Mr: +34 942 223900 Club Náutico La Horadada: +34 942 273013 Marina de Santander: +34 942 36288 R.C. Santander: +34 942 214050 Marina: marisan@nexo.es	Marina de Santander: 7 - 10 m, Anchorage Real Club Maritimo de Santander: Depth: 12 m	Fax Hr Mr: +34 942 362413 Marina de Santander: +34 942 369286 R.C. Santander: +34 942 261972 www.puertosantander.com
FREQUENCY: Ch 09 16		HOURS: H24

SANTA EUGENIA DE RIVIERA	Port & Marina 220 Berths 40 Visitor Berths	42°34′N 8°59′W
☎ Hr Mr: +34 982 501340 Marina: +34 981 873801 Club Náutico: +34 981 830970	Depth: 3 - 5 m, Maximum LOA: 12 - 16 m, fuel available	Fax Hr Mr: +34 982 507923 Marina +34 981 873290
FREQUENCY: Club Nautico: Ch 09 16		HOURS: HX

SAXENXO (SANGENJO) MARINA	Marina 700 Berths 70 Visitor Berths Planned	42°24′N 8°48′W
☎ +34 986 720517	Depth: 3·5 m, Maximum LOA: 60 m	Fax +34 986 720578
FREQUENCY: Ch **09** 16		HOURS: HX

VIGO	Port: CALL: Vigo Prácticos 413 Berths	42°14′N 8°43′W
☎ Port: +34 986 432055 Real Club Náutico: +34 986 447441 Liceo Maritimo: +34 986 232442 rcnauticovigo@cibermedia.com	Depth: 2 - 2·5 m, Maximum LOA 25 m, fuel available at Real Club Náutico	Fax Port: +34 986 434807 Real Club Náutico: +34 986 449695
FREQUENCY: Port: Ch 14 16 Real Club Nautico: Ch 06	LOCATION: Muelle de Transatlánticos	HOURS: HX

VIGO LOOKING N

PHOTOGRAPH - RCC PILOTAGE FOUNDATION

VILLAGARCIA DE AROSA	Port 460 Berths 60 Visitor Berths	42°36′N 8°46′W
Port Commario: +34 986 501340 Marina: +34 986 511175 marinavilagarcia@marinavilagarcia.com	Depth: 3 - 5 m, Maximum LOA: 25 m, fuel available	Fax: Marina: +34 986 512792 www.vilagarcia.com
FREQUENCY: Ch 09 12 16		HOURS: HX

ZUMAIA	Marina 230 Berths	43°18′N 2°15′W
+34 943 862078 portua01@sarenet.es	Depth: 3·5 m, Maximum LOA: 16 m	Fax: +34 943 862078
FREQUENCY: Ch 09 16		HOURS: HX

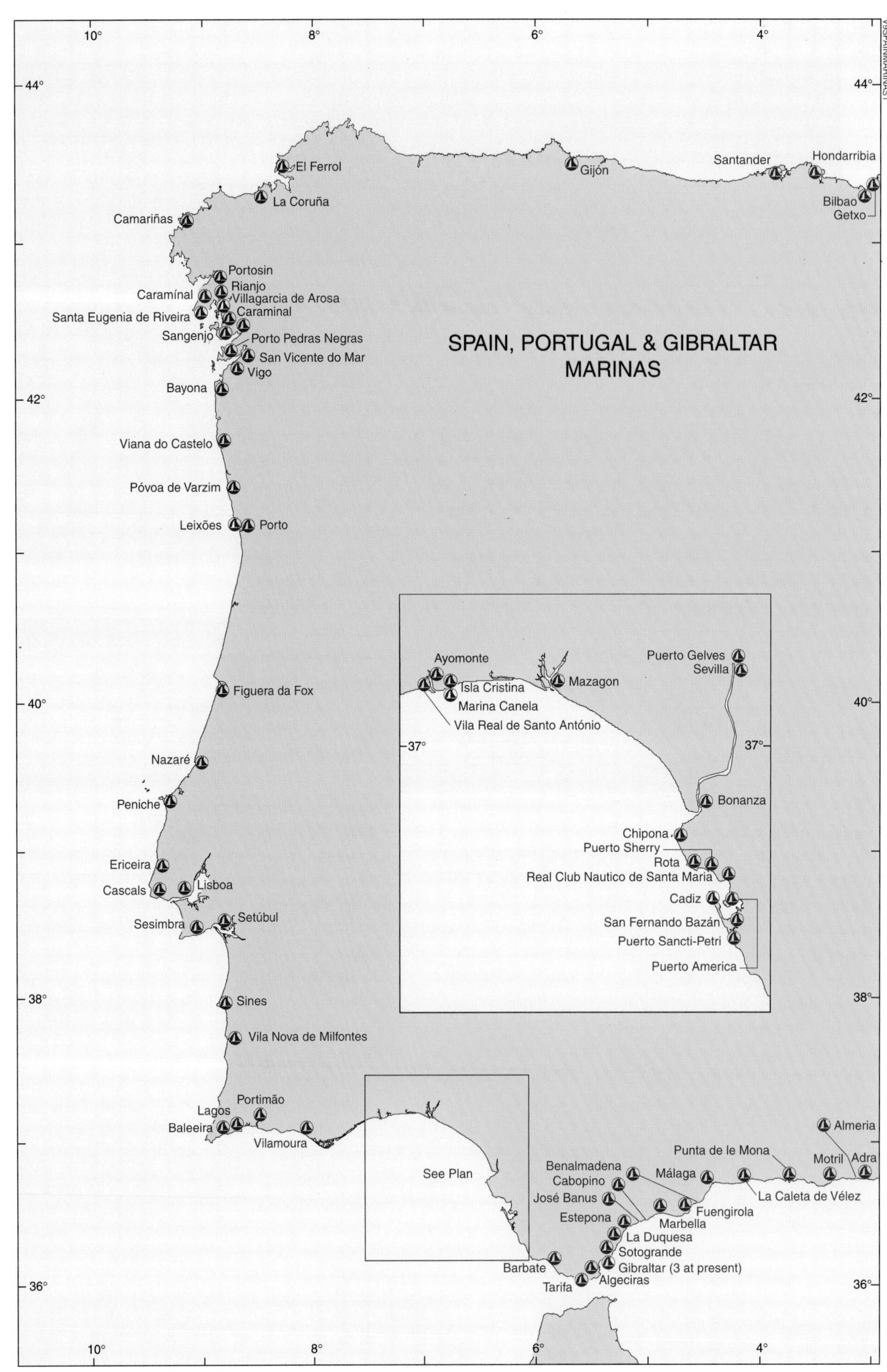
SPAIN, PORTUGAL & GIBRALTAR MARINAS
V9SPAINMARINAS1
El Ferrol
La Coruña
Camariñas
Gijón
Santander
Hondarribia
Bilbao
Getxo
Portosin
Rianjo
Caramínal
Villagarcia de Arosa
Santa Eugenia de Riveira
Caraminal
Sangenjo
Porto Pedras Negras
San Vicente do Mar
Vigo
Bayona
Viana do Castelo
Póvoa de Varzim
Leixões
Porto
Figuera da Fox
Nazaré
Peniche
Ericeira
Cascals
Lisboa
Sesimbra
Setúbul
Sines
Vila Nova de Milfontes
Portimão
Lagos
Baleeira
Vilamoura
See Plan
Ayomonte
Isla Cristina
Marina Canela
Vila Real de Santo António
Mazagon
Puerto Gelves
Sevilla
Bonanza
Chipona
Puerto Sherry
Rota
Real Club Nautico de Santa Maria
Cadiz
San Fernando Bazán
Puerto Sancti-Petri
Puerto America
Almeria
Punta de le Mona
Motril
Adra
Benalmadena
Cabopino
Málaga
La Caleta de Vélez
José Banus
Fuengirola
Estepona
Marbella
La Duquesa
Sotogrande
Gibraltar (3 at present)
Barbate
Algeciras
Tarifa
10°
8°
6°
4°
44°
42°
40°
38°
36°
37°

UNITED KINGDOM

<table>
<tr><th colspan="5">UNITED KINGDOM</th></tr>
<tr><td colspan="2">National SAR Agency - Administrative Centre
Maritime and Coastguard Agency
Tel: +44 (0) 2380 329100
Fax: +44(0) 2380 329488 Telex: 47655
E-MAIL: infoline@mcga.gov.uk www.mcagency.gov.uk
24-Hour information telephone line 0870 6006505</td><td colspan="3">In addition to regional responsibilities, MRCC Falmouth plays an important role in the GMDSS established by the IMO. MRCC Falmouth is the UK Single Point of Contact (SPOC) for world wide RCCs outside of the European theatre. MRCC Falmouth is also the link for Inmarsat alerts and satellite traffic via the LES at Goonhilly. All EPIRB alerts on 406, 121·5 and 243 MHz from within the UK SRR are passed to MRCC Falmouth for action through the UKMCC at RAF Kinloss</td></tr>
<tr><td>International SAR Co-ordination</td><td>Telephone +44</td><td>Telex +51</td><td>Fax +44</td><td>Others</td></tr>
<tr><td>MRCC FALMOUTH
VHF & MF DSC : MMSI 002320014</td><td>(0)1326 317575</td><td>45560</td><td>(0)1326 318342</td><td>Inmarsat A (AOR-E) 1441532
Inmarsat C (AOR-E) 423200158
Inmarsat C (AOR-W) 423200159</td></tr>
</table>

<table>
<tr><th colspan="2">VOLUNTARY SAFETY IDENTIFICATION SCHEME</th></tr>
<tr><td>FORM CG66</td><td>The Voluntary Safety Identification Scheme is a means of registering details of your vessel or craft with HM Coastguard for use in an emergency for Search and Rescue purposes. The owner of any type of water borne craft of any size may partake in the scheme - free of charge. Should anyone ashore have any concern for the safety of your vessel, or should you get into difficulty at sea, HM Coastguard will be able to call up detailed information relating to your vessel, that will greatly assist you, and the Coastguard should you be reported overdue or in need of assistance. The form is also available from all Coastguard Stations, MCA Marine Offices, RNLI Lifeboat Boathouses, Marinas and Yacht Clubs. Alternatively, go to the MCAs website at www.mcagency.org.uk complete the form and mail it to your local Co-ordination Centre.</td></tr>
<tr><th colspan="2">406 MHz EPIRB - NEW OR CHANGE OF REGISTRATION</th></tr>
<tr><td>EPIRB REGISTRATION</td><td>Emergency Beacons (EPIRBS): Although conventional marine radio is the best means of alerting nearby shipping and SAR services of a distress situation, the carriage of an Emergency Beacon will much improve the chances of a vessel being located should conventional means fail. The EPIRB Registry, HM Coastguard Southern (Falmouth), Pendennis Point, Castle Drive, Falmouth, Cornwall, TR11 4WZ Tel: 01326 211569 Fax: 01326 319264</td></tr>
</table>

SOVEREIGN HARBOUR MARINA

NAVTEX

HM COASTGUARD NAVIGATIONAL AND WEATHER BROADCASTS

NAVTEX [G] [E] [K] [O] (remotely controlled by Falmouth Coastguard)			
G	Cullercoats	518 kHz	55°04′N 1°28′W
E	Niton		50°35′N 1°18′W
K	Niton		50°35′N 1°18′W
O	Portpatrick		54°51′N 5°07′W
DIAGRAMS: pages 266, 267, 268, 303, 304 and 343			
Weather Bulletins			
G: On receipt and repeated once during next routine broadcast	Gale warnings for Viking, Forties, Cromarty, Forth, Tyne, Dogger, Humber, Thames and Fair Isle		
G: 0900 2100	Shipping Forecast: general synopsis, 24 hour forecast and 24 hour outlook (hazards) for Viking, Forties, Cromarty, Forth, Tyne, Dogger, Humber, Thames and Fair Isle		
G: 0100	Extended Outlook daily, signalling expected hazards (gales and/or extensive sea fog) for a further two or three days, for the North Sea and Eastern English Channel		
E: On receipt and repeated once during next routine broadcast	Gale warnings for Thames, Dover, Wight, Portland, Plymouth, Biscay, FitzRoy, Sole, Lundy and Fastnet		
E: 0840 2040	Shipping Forecast: general synopsis, 24 hour forecast and 24 hour outlook (hazards) for Thames, Dover, Wight, Portland, Plymouth, Biscay, FitzRoy, Sole, Lundy and Fastnet		
E: 0040	Extended Outlook daily, signalling expected hazards (gales and/or extensive sea fog) for a further two or three days, for Thames, Dover, Wight, Portland, Plymouth, Biscay, FitzRoy, Sole, Lundy, Fastnet, Irish Sea and Shannon		
O: On receipt and repeated once during next routine broadcast	Gale warnings for Lundy, Fastnet, Irish Sea, Rockall, Malin, Hebrides, Bailey, Fair Isle, Faeroes and SE Iceland		
O: 0620 1820	Shipping Forecast: general synopsis, 24 hour forecast and 24 hour outlook (hazards) for Lundy, Fastnet, Irish Sea, Rockall, Malin, Hebrides, Bailey, Fair Isle, Faeroes and SE Iceland		
O: 0220	Extended Outlook daily, signalling expected hazards (gales and/or extensive sea fog) for a further two or three days, for Lundy, Fastnet, Irish Sea, Shannon, Rockall, Malin, Hebrides, Fair Isle, Faeroes and SE Iceland		
Navigational Warnings			
G: 0100 0500 0900 1300 1700 2100	For areas Kilo, Lima, Mike & November NAVAREA I warnings are included at 0500 and 1700		
G: On receipt	Warnings of negative tidal surges in the Southern North Sea & Thames		
E: On receipt	Warnings of negative tidal surges in the Dover Strait		
E: 0040 0440 0840 1240 1640 2040	For areas Delta, Foxtrot, Golf, Hotel and India NAVAREA I Warnings are included at 0300 and 1500		
E: 0440 1640 (General Information)	**Submarine Exercises (SUBFACTS—South Coast)** Broadcasts are after any gale warnings or weather forecasts and will cover any planned submarine activity for the following 24 hours and will refer to the exercise areas depicted on the SUBFACTS diagrams		
E: 0440 1640 (General Information)	**Gunnery Exercises (GUNFACTS—South Coast)** Broadcasts are after any gale warnings or weather forecasts and SUBFACTS and will cover controlled underwater explosions, planned gunnery and missile firings of 20mm calibre and above, for the following 24 hours. Broadcasts will refer to the exercise areas depicted on the GUNFACTS diagrams		
K: 0140 0540 0940 1340 1740 2140	In English for areas Golf, Hotel and India south of the Channel median		
O: 0220 0620 1020 1420 1820 2220	For areas Alfa, Bravo, Charlie and Echo NAVAREA I Warnings are included at 0220 and 1420		
O: 0620 1820 (General Information)	**Submarine Exercises (SUBFACTS—Clyde)** Broadcasts are after any gale warnings or weather forecasts and will cover any planned submarine activity for the following 16 hours and will refer to the exercise areas depicted on the SUBFACTS diagrams		

NAVTEX [U] [I] [T] [C] (remotely controlled by Falmouth Coastguard)			
U	Cullercoats	490 kHz	55°04′N 1°28′W
I	Niton		50°35′N 1°18′W
T	Niton		50°35′N 1°18′W
C	Portpatrick		54°51′N 5°07′W
DIAGRAMS: pages 266, 267, 268, 303, 304 and 343			
Weather Bulletins			
U: 0720 1920	Inshore Waters 24 hour forecast, 24 hour outlook, wind, weather, visibility and sea state for: Cape Wrath to Rattray Head including Orkney, Rattray Head to Berwick-upon-Tweed, Berwick- upon-Tweed to Whitby, Whitby to The Wash and The Wash to North Foreland. **National 3 day outlook**		
I: 0520 1720	Inshore Waters 24 hour forecast, 24 hour outlook, wind, weather, visibility and sea state for: The Wash to North Foreland, North Foreland to Selsey Bill, Selsey Bill to Lyme Regis, Lyme Regis to Land's End including the Isles of Scilly, Land's End to S. David's Head including the Bristol Channel and S. David's Head to Colwyn Bay including S. George's Channel. **National 3 day outlook**		
T: 0310 0710 1110 1510 1910 2310	**Storm Warnings,** Bulletins Météorologique Spéciaux (BMS) for areas: Humber, Tamise, Pas de Calais, Antifer, Casquets and Ouessant. In French		
T: 0710 1910	**Gale Warnings** or **Storm Warnings,** synopsis and development, 24 hour forecast for areas: Humber, Tamise, Pas de Calais, Antifer, Casquets and Ouessant. In French		
C: 0820 2020	Inshore Waters 24 hour forecast, 24 hour outlook, wind, weather, visibility and sea state for: S. David's Head to Colwyn Bay including S.George's Channel, Colwyn Bay to the Mull of Galloway including the Isle of Man, Lough Foyle to Carlingford Lough, the Mull of Galloway to the Mull of Kintyre including the Firth of Clyde and the North Channel, Mull of Kintyre to Ardnamurchan Point, Ardnamurchan Point to Cape Wrath including the Outer Hebrides and the Shetland Islands. **National 3 day outlook**		
Navigational Warnings			
T: 0310 0710 1110 1510 1910 2310	In French, for areas Antifer, Casquets and Ouessant, south of the Channel median to the French coast		

BRITISH BROADCASTING CORPORATION — RADIO 4				
A	198	AM	United Kingdom Long Wave	
B	603		Tyneside	
C	720		London	
D	720		N Ireland	
E	756		Redruth	
F	774		Plymouth	
F	774		Enniskillen	
G	1449		Aberdeen	
H	1485		Carlisle	
I	92·4-94·6MHz	FM	England	
	92·4-94·6MHz, 92·4-96·1MHz or 103·5-104·9MHz		Scotland, Wales and N Ireland	
DIAGRAM: page 159				
Weather Bulletins				
A-I: At the first available programme junction	**Storm Warnings:** Gale warnings for all United Kingdom Forecast Areas, including Trafalgar			
A-I: 0048 0535	Gale warnings in force, synopsis, 24 hour forecast for United Kingdom Forecast Areas. Reports from selected observation stations. Forecast valid until 1800, from observations up to 0500. For coastal waters of the United Kingdom and Northern Ireland up to 12 n miles offshore. Following the general synopsis, forecasts for wind direction and force, visibility and weather are broadcast. Reports from selected observation stations. Long Range Forecast of particular interest to mariners			
A: 1201 **A:** Mon-Fri: 1754 **A-I:** Sat-Sun: 1754	Gale warnings in force, synopsis, 24 hour forecast for United Kingdom Forecast Areas. Reports from selected observation stations			
A-I: Sun: 0542	Long Range Forecast of particular interest to mariners			
A-I: Sat: 0556	Topical Leisure Forecast for the UK and other parts of Europe			
NOTE: Broadcasts given 1 hour earlier when DST is in force				

VHF BROADCAST CHANNEL FOR SAFETY AND WEATHER INFORMATION

Vessels should listen to the announcement on VHF Ch 16 indicating which of the following VHF channels will be used for the broadcast:

VHF Ch: 10 23 73 84 86

Certain HM CG stations also broadcast on Medium Frequencies (MF) after a prior announcement on 2182 kHz

MSI broadcasts and contact details of all UK MRCC AND MRSC Stations operated by the MCA can be found in the following sections:
UK Navtex and Weather Forecast Areas
England East Coast : Berwick-upon-Tweed to Ramsgate
England South Coast : Ramsgate to S. Mary's, Isles of Scilly including the Channel Islands
England West Coast : S. Ives to Solway Firth
Northern Ireland: Londonderry to Warrenpoint
Scotland: Solway Firth to Grangemouth
Wales: Newport to Conwy

The first broadcast of any new Gale (Storm) Warning or Navigational Warning will be announced through DSC on 2187·5 kHz / VHF Ch 70 and RT through 2182 kHz / VHF Ch 16, including details of the scheduled RT broadcast frequency / channel.
Scheduled VHF RT MSI broadcasts are announced through VHF Ch 16 before being broadcast through a combination of channels 10, 23, 73, 84 and 86 as directed by the initial announcement on Ch 16. Broadcasts may be suspended whilst SAR action is in progress.

Broadcasts are made sequentially from some *or* all remote transmitter sites throughout the CG district, and may include some or all of the following:

- **Gale (Storm) Warnings**
- **Strong Wind Warnings** (force 6 and above) for the coastal waters out to 5 n miles of the coast will be broadcast if issued unexpectedly or forecast conditions adversly at variance with the Inshore Forecast
- **Local Inshore Forecast** (UK waters within 12 n miles of the coast) — divided into 16 areas
- **WZ Navigational Warnings** — including any Negative Tide Surges
- **SUBFACTS / GUNFACTS** — from selected stations only

This information is of importance to virtually all craft, no matter what their size or function.

HM COASTGUARD MSI BROADCASTS

VHF/MF RADIOTELEPHONE BROADCASTS

Coastguard	1st VHF Broadcast (UTC)	Shipping Forecast VHF/MF (UTC)	SUBFACTS (S) GUNFACTS (G)	1st MF Broadcast (UTC)
Aberdeen	0320	0720 1920		0320
Belfast	0305	0705 1905	(S)	
Brixham	0050	0850 2050	(S/G)	
Clyde	0020	0820 2020	(S)	0020
Dover	0105	0905 2105		
Falmouth	0140	0940 2140	(S/G)	0140
Forth	0205	1005 2205		
Holyhead	0235	0635 1835		0235
Humber	0340	0740 1940		0340
Liverpool	0210	1010 2210		
Milford Haven	0335	0735 1935		0335
Portland	0220	1020 2220		
Shetland	0105	0905 2105		0105
Solent	0040	0840 2040		0040
Stornoway	0110	0910 2110	(S/G)	0110
Swansea	0005	0805 2005		
Thames	0010	0810 2010		
Yarmouth	0040	0840 2040		0040

All stations monitor DSC Ch 70. Stations in Red also monitor DSC MF 2187·5

Maritime Safety Information consisting of Gale Warnings, the Local Inshore Forecast, the Extended Outlook, Area Forecasts, WZ Navigation Warnings and SUBFACTS/GUNFACTS are broadcast every 4 hours on VHF and on MF from selected co-ordination centres commencing at the times shown. Additionally, Gale Warnings, WZ Navigational Warnings and selected Strong Wind Warnings are broadcast on receipt. Area forecasts are broadcast twice daily at the times shown.

The order the broadcast is made in is determined by local considerations and may differ from station to station.

MSI broadcasts will be announced on Channel 16 VHF and on 2182 kHz on MF. The announcement will indicate which working frequency the mariner should select for the actual broadcast depending on location. Working frequencies used may include Channels 10, 23, 73, 84 and 86.

A 3 day forecast for fishing fleets in the North Sea and South West Approaches is transmitted by NAVTEX 490 kHz between October and March.

NAVTEX BROADCASTS

Station	Time (UTC)
Cullercoats [G] (*Wx only)	0100* 0500 0900* 1300 1700 2100*
Portpatrick [O] (*Wx/SUBFACTS)	0220* 0620* 1020 1420 1820* 2220
Niton [E] (*Wx/SUBFACTS)	0040* 0440 0840* 1240 1640 2040*

KEY:

■ = MRCC

▲ = MRSC

——— = District Boundary

[A] = NAVTEX (518 kHz) identification

[E] = NAVTEX (490 kHz) identification

Refer to NAVTEX Section for 490 kHz broadcasts

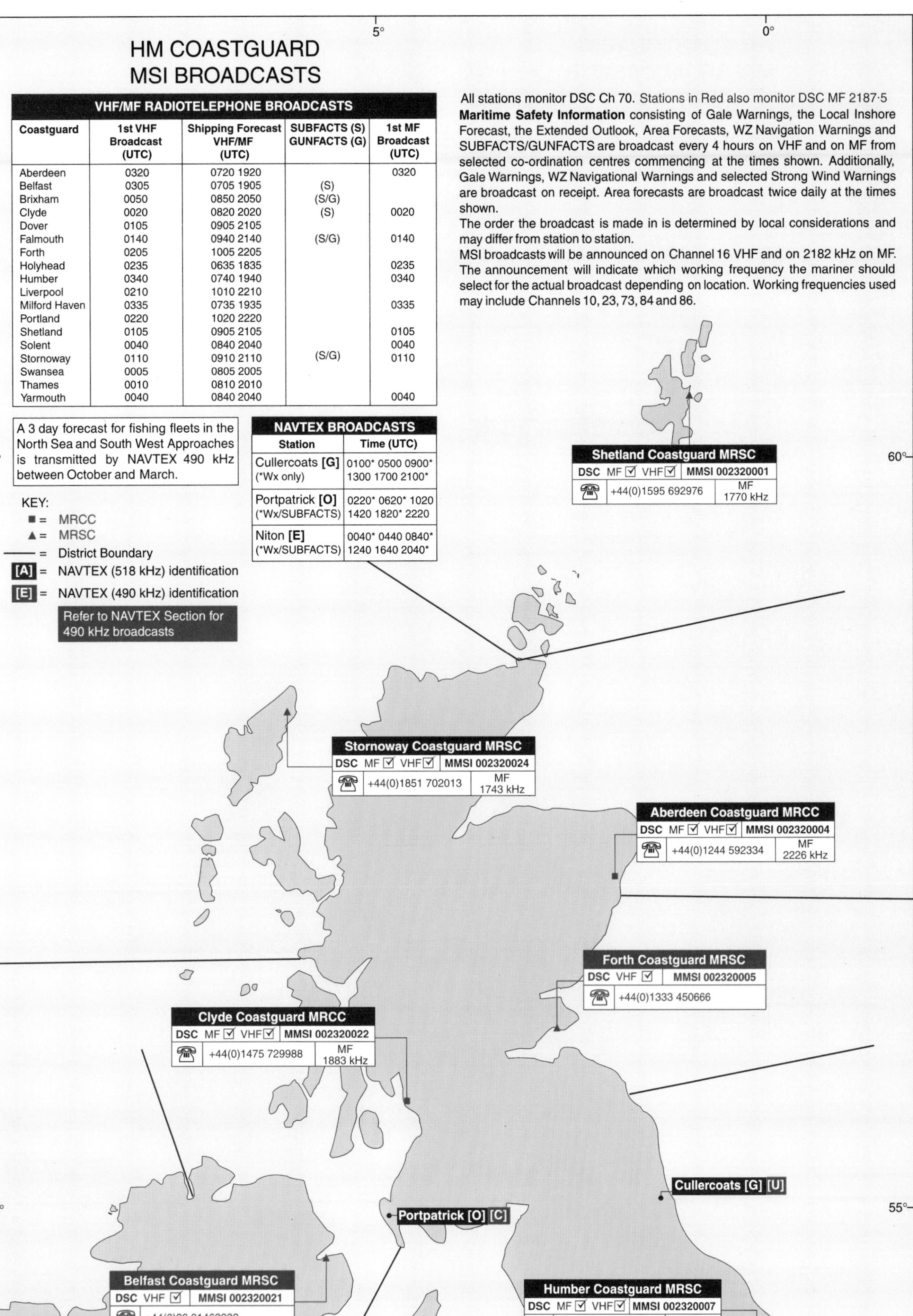

HM COASTGUARD MSI BROADCASTS

VHF/MF RADIOTELEPHONE BROADCASTS

Coastguard	1st VHF Broadcast (UTC)	Shipping Forecast VHF/MF (UTC)	SUBFACTS (S) GUNFACTS (G)	1st MF Broadcast (UTC)
Aberdeen	0320	0720 1920		0320
Belfast	0305	0705 1905	(S)	
Brixham	0050	0850 2050	(S/G)	
Clyde	0020	0820 2020	(S)	0020
Dover	0105	0905 2105		
Falmouth	0140	0940 2140	(S/G)	0140
Forth	0205	1005 2205		
Holyhead	0235	0635 1835		0235
Humber	0340	0740 1940		0340
Liverpool	0210	1010 2210		
Milford Haven	0335	0735 1935		0335
Portland	0220	1020 2220		
Shetland	0105	0905 2105		0105
Solent	0040	0840 2040		0040
Stornoway	0110	0910 2110	(S/G)	0110
Swansea	0005	0805 2005		
Thames	0010	0810 2010		
Yarmouth	0040	0840 2040		0040

NAVTEX BROADCASTS

Station	Time (UTC)
Niton **[S]** (*Wx/SUBFACTS)	0040* 0440 0840* 1240 1640 2040*
Oostende **[T]** (Weather Forecast)	0310 0710* 1110 1510 1910* 2310
Oostende **[M]** (Nav Warnings)	0200 0600 1000 1400 1800 2200

All stations monitor DSC Ch 70. Stations in Red also monitor DSC MF 2187·5
Maritime Safety Information consisting of Gale Warnings, the Local Inshore Forecast, the Extended Outlook, Area Forecasts, WZ Navigation Warnings and SUBFACTS/GUNFACTS are broadcast every 4 hours on VHF and on MF from selected co-ordination centres commencing at the times shown. Additionally, Gale Warnings, WZ Navigational Warnings and selected Strong Wind Warnings are broadcast on receipt. Area forecasts are broadcast twice daily at the times shown.
The order the broadcast is made in is determined by local considerations and may differ from station to station.
MSI broadcasts will be announced on Channel 16 VHF and on 2182 kHz on MF. The announcement will indicate which working frequency the mariner should select for the actual broadcast depending on location. Working frequencies used may include Channels 10, 23, 73, 84 and 86.

KEY:

■ = MRCC
▲ = MRSC
——— = District Boundary
[A] = NAVTEX (518 kHz) identification
[E] = NAVTEX (490 kHz) identification

Refer to NAVTEX Section for 490 kHz broadcasts

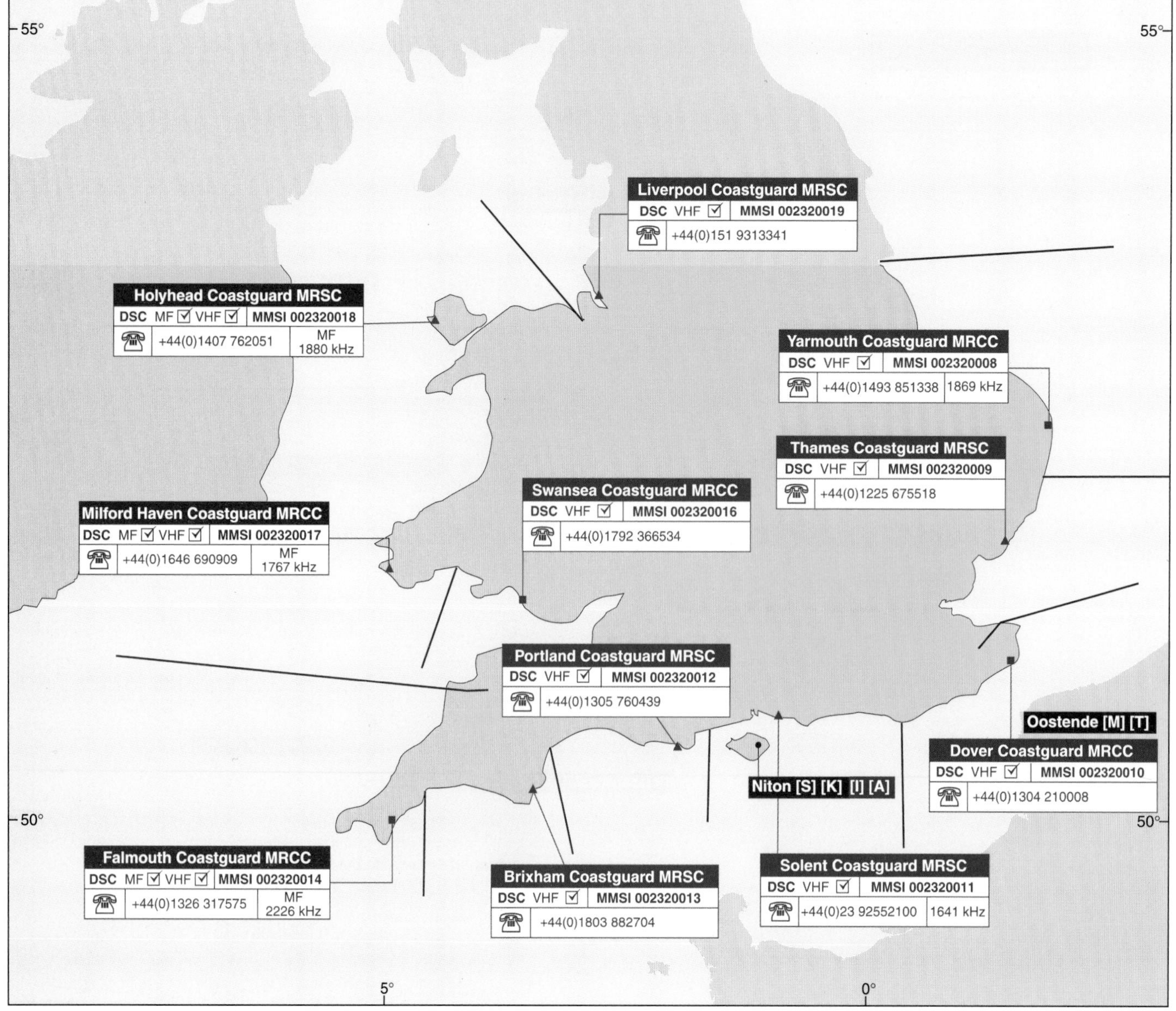

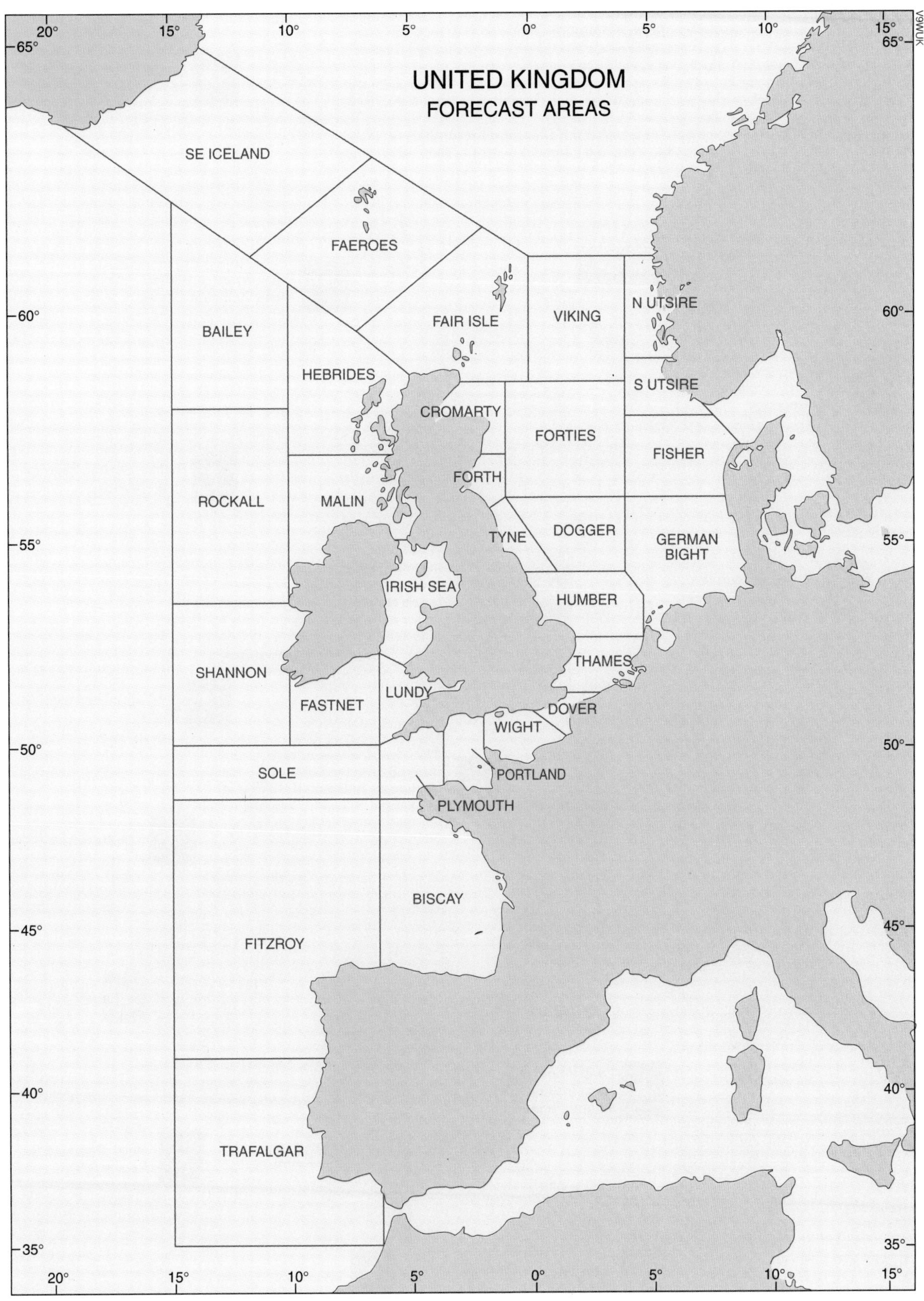
UNITED KINGDOM
FORECAST AREAS
SE ICELAND
FAEROES
BAILEY
FAIR ISLE
VIKING
N UTSIRE
S UTSIRE
HEBRIDES
CROMARTY
FORTIES
FISHER
ROCKALL
MALIN
FORTH
TYNE
DOGGER
GERMAN
BIGHT
IRISH SEA
HUMBER
THAMES
SHANNON
FASTNET
LUNDY
DOVER
WIGHT
PORTLAND
SOLE
PLYMOUTH
BISCAY
FITZROY
TRAFALGAR
20°
15°
10°
5°
0°
65°
60°
55°
50°
45°
40°
35°
V9WUK

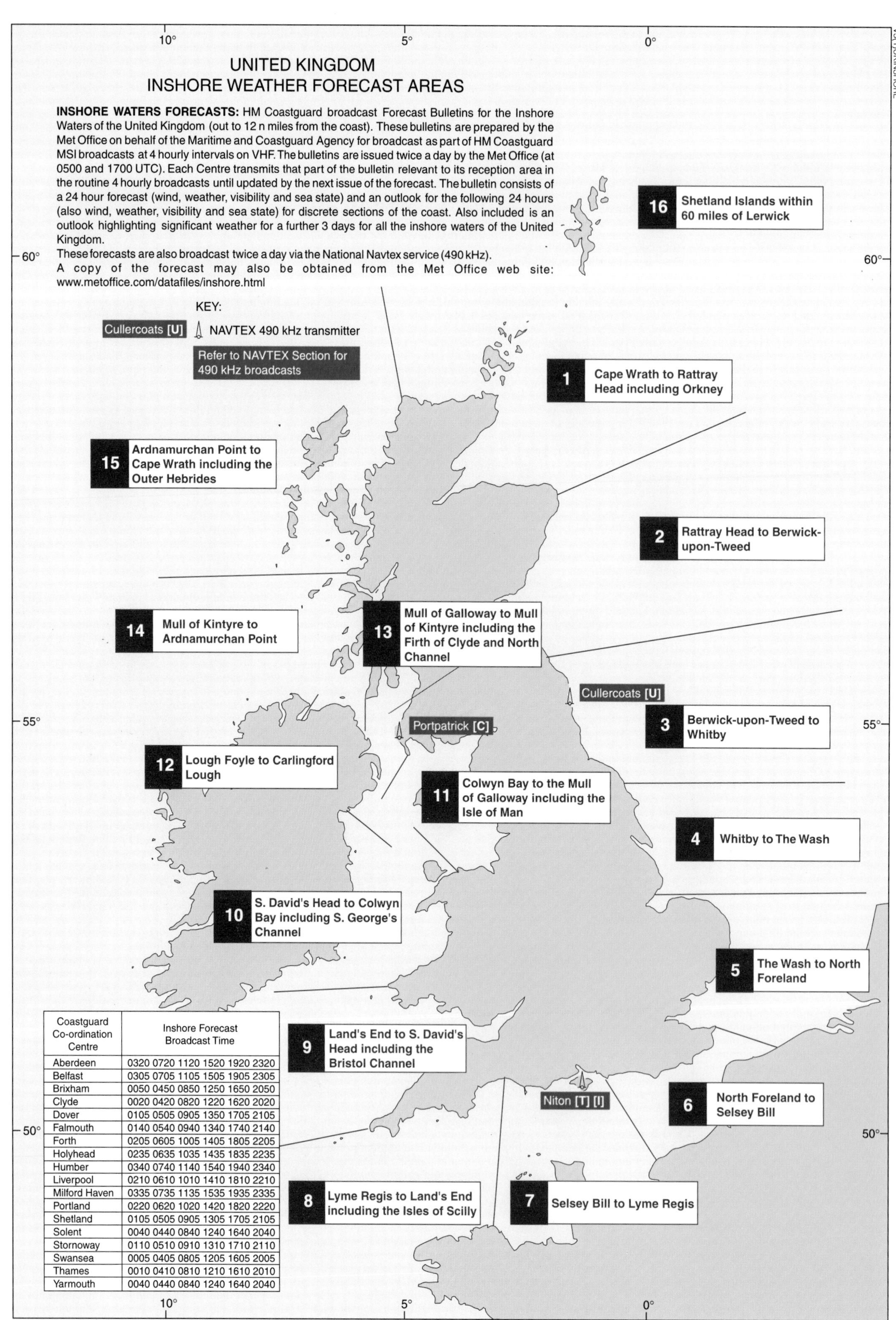

Coastguard Co-ordination Centre	Inshore Forecast Broadcast Time
Aberdeen	0320 0720 1120 1520 1920 2320
Belfast	0305 0705 1105 1505 1905 2305
Brixham	0050 0450 0850 1250 1650 2050
Clyde	0020 0420 0820 1220 1620 2020
Dover	0105 0505 0905 1350 1705 2105
Falmouth	0140 0540 0940 1340 1740 2140
Forth	0205 0605 1005 1405 1805 2205
Holyhead	0235 0635 1035 1435 1835 2235
Humber	0340 0740 1140 1540 1940 2340
Liverpool	0210 0610 1010 1410 1810 2210
Milford Haven	0335 0735 1135 1535 1935 2335
Portland	0220 0620 1020 1420 1820 2220
Shetland	0105 0505 0905 1305 1705 2105
Solent	0040 0440 0840 1240 1640 2040
Stornoway	0110 0510 0910 1310 1710 2110
Swansea	0005 0405 0805 1205 1605 2005
Thames	0010 0410 0810 1210 1610 2010
Yarmouth	0040 0440 0840 1240 1640 2040

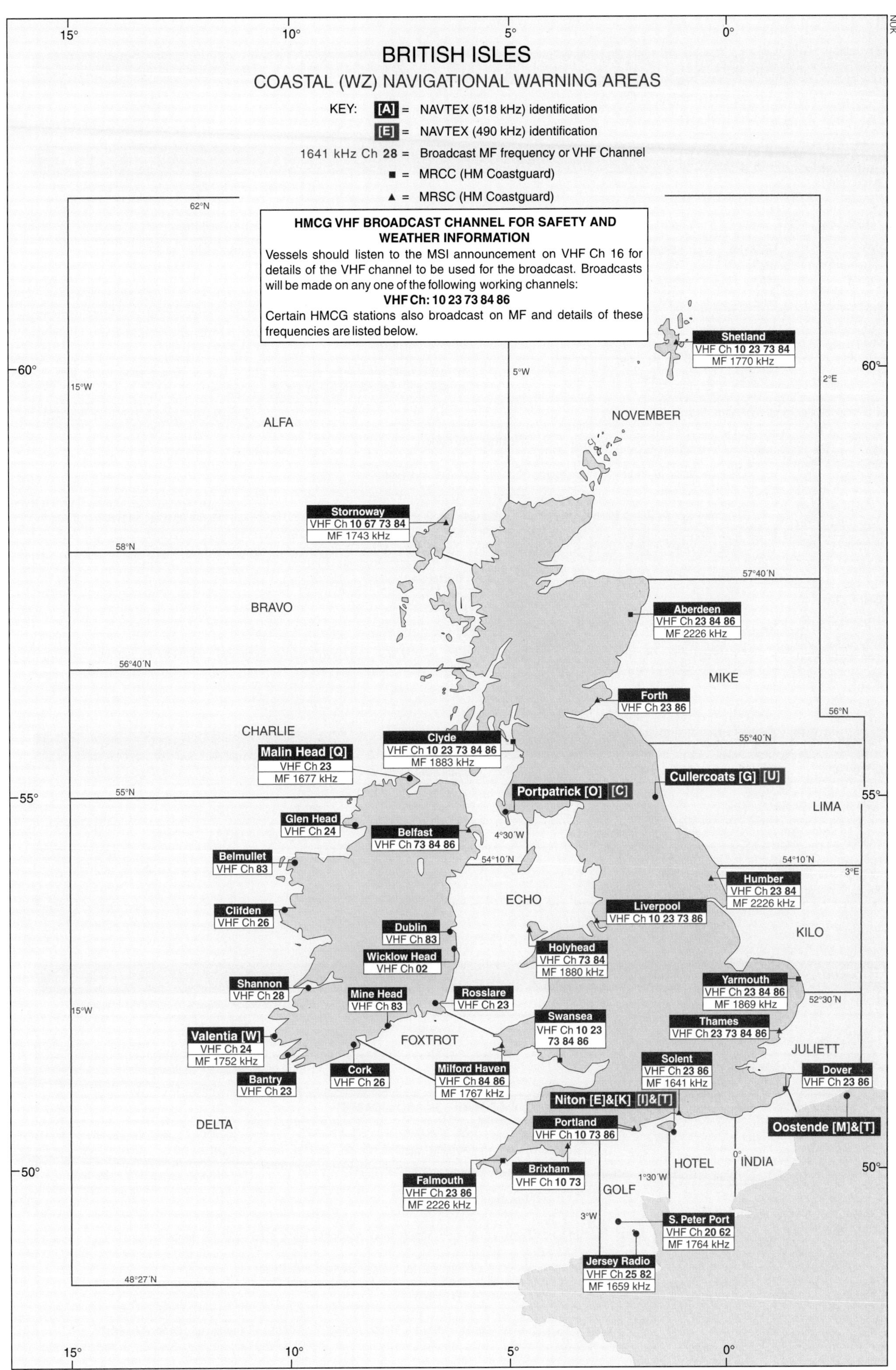

BRITISH ISLES
COASTAL (WZ) NAVIGATIONAL WARNING AREAS
KEY: [A] = NAVTEX (518 kHz) identification
[E] = NAVTEX (490 kHz) identification
1641 kHz Ch 28 = Broadcast MF frequency or VHF Channel
■ = MRCC (HM Coastguard)
▲ = MRSC (HM Coastguard)
HMCG VHF BROADCAST CHANNEL FOR SAFETY AND WEATHER INFORMATION
Vessels should listen to the MSI announcement on VHF Ch 16 for details of the VHF channel to be used for the broadcast. Broadcasts will be made on any one of the following working channels:
VHF Ch: 10 23 73 84 86
Certain HMCG stations also broadcast on MF and details of these frequencies are listed below.
ALFA
BRAVO
CHARLIE
DELTA
ECHO
FOXTROT
GOLF
HOTEL
INDIA
JULIETT
KILO
LIMA
MIKE
NOVEMBER
Shetland VHF Ch 10 23 73 84 MF 1770 kHz
Stornoway VHF Ch 10 67 73 84 MF 1743 kHz
Aberdeen VHF Ch 23 84 86 MF 2226 kHz
Forth VHF Ch 23 86
Clyde VHF Ch 10 23 73 84 86 MF 1883 kHz
Malin Head [Q] VHF Ch 23 MF 1677 kHz
Cullercoats [G] [U]
Portpatrick [O] [C]
Glen Head VHF Ch 24
Belfast VHF Ch 73 84 86
Belmullet VHF Ch 83
Humber VHF Ch 23 84 MF 2226 kHz
Clifden VHF Ch 26
Liverpool VHF Ch 10 23 73 86
Dublin VHF Ch 83
Wicklow Head VHF Ch 02
Holyhead VHF Ch 73 84 MF 1880 kHz
Yarmouth VHF Ch 23 84 86 MF 1869 kHz
Shannon VHF Ch 28
Mine Head VHF Ch 83
Rosslare VHF Ch 23
Swansea VHF Ch 10 23 73 84 86
Thames VHF Ch 23 73 84 86
Valentia [W] VHF Ch 24 MF 1752 kHz
Cork VHF Ch 26
Bantry VHF Ch 23
Milford Haven VHF Ch 84 86 MF 1767 kHz
Solent VHF Ch 23 86 MF 1641 kHz
Dover VHF Ch 23 86
Niton [E]&[K] [I]&[T]
Portland VHF Ch 10 73 86
Oostende [M]&[T]
Brixham VHF Ch 10 73
Falmouth VHF Ch 23 86 MF 2226 kHz
S. Peter Port VHF Ch 20 62 MF 1764 kHz
Jersey Radio VHF Ch 25 82 MF 1659 kHz
62°N
58°N
56°40′N
55°N
57°40′N
56°N
55°40′N
54°10′N
52°30′N
48°27′N
15°W
5°W
4°30′W
2°E
3°E
1°30′W
3°W
0°
15°
10°
5°
60°
55°
50°

UNITED KINGDOM, ENGLAND - EAST COAST

HUMBER (Coastguard MRSC) MMSI 002320007 — DSC VHF √ MF √

54°06′N 0°11′W			Operational area: Scottish Border to Haile Sand Fort	
☎ +44(0)1262 672317			Fax +44(0)1262 606915	
RT (MF)	Transmits: 1925, 2182, **2226**	Receives: 1925, 2182, **2226**	**VHF** Ch 06 10 **16** **23** 67 73 **84** 86	
MARITIME SAFETY INFORMATION BROADCASTS				
A	2226	RT (MF)	CG District	
B	VHF Ch **23 84**	An announcement will be made on VHF Channel 16 indicating which VHF working channel will be used for the broadcast		
Weather and Navigational Warnings broadcast on receipt			DIAGRAMS: pages 157, 159 and 161	
Weather Bulletins				
A: 0340 0740 1140 1540 1940 2340	Gale warnings for Areas Tyne, Dogger, Humber and German Bight			
B: 0340 0740 1140 1540 1940 2340	Gale warnings for Areas Tyne, Dogger, Humber and German Bight. Local area strong wind warnings. Inshore forecast for Regions 3 and 4			
A, B: 0740 1940	Shipping forecast: gale warnings, synopsis, 24 hour forecast for Areas Tyne, Dogger, Humber and German Bight			
Navigational Warnings				
A: 0340 0740 1140 1540 1940 2340	For Areas Kilo and Lima			
B: 0340 0740 1140 1540 1940 2340	For Areas Kilo and Lima. Local warnings as and when agreed with the Hydrographer, Lighthouse Authority or Harbour Authority			

LONDON Coastguard MMSI 002320063

51°30′N 0°05′E	Operational area: River Thames from Shell Haven Point (North Bank) and Egypt (South Bank) to Teddington
☎ +44(0)208 3127380	Fax +44(0)208 3127679
	VHF Ch 06 10 **16** 23 67 73 84 86

NOTES:
(1) This station does not broadcast MSI
(2) London Coastguard is based at Woolwich Radio

THAMES (Coastguard MRSC) MMSI 002320009 — DSC VHF √

51°51′N 1°17′E			Operational area: Southwold to Reculver Towers
☎ +44(0)1255 675518			Fax +44(0)1255 675249
RT (MF)	Transmits: 2182	Receives: 2182	**VHF** Ch 06 **10** **16** **23** 67 **73** **84** **86**
MARITIME SAFETY INFORMATION BROADCASTS			
	VHF Ch **23 73 84 86**	An announcement will be made on VHF Channel 16 indicating which VHF working channel will be used for the broadcast	
Weather and Navigational Warnings broadcast on receipt			DIAGRAMS: pages 157, 159 and 161
Weather Bulletins			
0010 0410 0810 1210 1610 2010	Gale warnings for Areas Thames and Dover. Local area strong wind warnings. Inshore forecast for Region 5		
0810 2010	Shipping forecast: gale warnings, synopsis, 24 hour forecast for Areas Thames and Dover		
Navigational Warnings			
0010 0410 0810 1210 1610 2010	For Area Juliett. Local warnings as and when agreed with the Hydrographer, Lighthouse Authority or Harbour Authority		

YARMOUTH (Coastguard MRCC) MMSI 002320008 — DSC VHF √

52°37′N 1°43′E — Operational area: Haile Sand Fort to Southwold

Tel: +44(0)1493 851338 — Fax: +44(0)1493 852307

RT (MF)	Transmits	Receives	VHF Ch 06 **10** 16 **23** 67 **73 84 86**
	1869	**1869**	
	2182	2182	
	2596	2596	

MARITIME SAFETY INFORMATION BROADCASTS

A	**1869**	RT (MF)
B	VHF Ch **23 84 86**	An announcement will be made on VHF Channel 16 indicating which VHF working channel will be used for the broadcast

Weather and Navigational Warnings broadcast on receipt — DIAGRAMS: pages 157, 159 and 161

Weather Bulletins

A: 0040 0440 0840 1240 1640 2040	Gale warnings for Areas Humber and Thames
B: 0040 0440 0840 1240 1640 2040	Gale warnings for Areas Humber and Thames. Local area strong wind warnings. Inshore forecast for Region 5
A, B: 0840 2040	Shipping forecast: gale warnings, synopsis, 24 hour forecast for Areas Humber and Thames

Navigational Warnings

A: 0040 0440 0840 1240 1640 2040	For Areas Juliett and Kilo
B: 0040 0440 0840 1240 1640 2040	For Areas Juliett and Kilo. Local warnings as and when agreed with the Hydrographer, Lighthouse Authority or Harbour Authority

AMBLE MARINA LTD — CALL: Amble Marina — 55°20′·1N 1°35′·0W

Tel: Marina: +44(0)1665 712168
Port: +44(0)1665 710306
marina@amble.co.uk

Fax: +44(0)1665 713363
www.amble.co.uk

FREQUENCY: Port: Ch 14 16 Marina: Ch 80 — LOCATION: Hr Office: Quayside, Amble — HOURS OPEN: H24 ACCESS: HW ± 4h

BERWICK-UPON-TWEED — Port — Commercial Port — 55°45′N 2°00′W

Tel: +44(0)1289 307404 & 308344 — Fax:

FREQUENCY: Ch **12** 16 — LOCATION: Hr Mr Office: Tweed Dock — HOURS: HX

BLACKWATER MARINA, RIVER BLACKWATER — 51°41′·4N 0°45′·3E

Tel: +44(0)1621 740264 — Fax: +44(0)1621 742122

FREQUENCY: Ch M — LOCATION: Maylandsea — HOURS OPEN: 0900-1700 ACCESS: HW ± 2½ h

BLYTH — Port: CALL: Blyth Harbour — 55°07′N 1°29′W

Tel: Hr Mr: +44(0)1670 352678
Royal Northumberland Yacht Club: +44(0)1670 353636

Fax: Hr Mr: Office hours: +44(0)1670 368540
www.rnyc.org.uk

FREQUENCY: Ch 11 12 16 — Visitor berths available in South Harbour — HOURS: H24

BOSTON — Port: CALL: Boston Dock — 52°58′N 0°01′W

Tel: Hr Mr: +44(0)1205 362328
Dock Office: +44(0)1205 365571 (5 lines)
Grand Sluice: +44(0)1205 364864
Denver Sluice: +44(0)1366 382340

Fax: Hr Mr: +44(0)1205 351852
Dock Office: +44(0)1205 310126

FREQUENCY: Ch 12 16 Grand Sluice: Ch 16 74
Denver Sluice: Ch 16 74

HOURS: Mon-Fri: 0800-1730 LT
Other times: HW -2½h to +1½h

BOSTON MARINA — CALL: Boston Marina — 52°59′·1N 0°01′·8W

Tel: +44(0)1205 364420 — Fax:

FREQUENCY: Ch 06 M — HOURS OPEN: 0900-1700 LT
ACCESS: HW ± 2h through the lock

BRADWELL MARINA, RIVER BLACKWATER

51°43′·9N 0°53′·2E

+44(0)1621 776235 & 776391

Fax: +44(0)1621 776393

FREQUENCY: Ch M 80

HOURS OPEN: Mon-Fri: 0830-1700 LT
Sat-Sun: 0830-2000 LT
ACCESS: LW ± 1½ h

BRENTFORD DOCK MARINA, RIVER THAMES

51°29′N 0°18′W

+44(0)208 2328941
Hr Mr Mobile: 0797 0143987

Fax: +44(0)207 5605486

FREQUENCY: Ch M

HOURS OF WATCH: 0800-1800 LT
ACCESS: HW ± 2½ h

BRIDLINGTON

Port: CALL: Bridlington Harbour

+44(0)1262 670148 & 670149

New 500 berth marina planned

Fax: +44(0)1262 602041

FREQUENCY: Ch **12** 16

HOURS: HX ACCESS: HW ± 3h

BRIGHTLINGSEA

Port: CALL: Brightlingsea Port Radio

51°48′N 1°02′E

Port Office: +44(0)1206 302370

Fax: Port Office: +44(0)1206 305243
Harbour: +44(0)1208 308533

FREQUENCY: Ch 68

HOURS: 0800-1700 LT

BURNHAM YACHT HARBOUR, RIVER CROUCH

51°37′·5N 0°48′·3E

Hr Mr: +44(0)1621 786832
Hr Mr (Mobile): 07761 282894
Yacht Harbour: +44(0)1621 782150
Bridgemarsh Marine: +44(0)1621 740414

Fax: +44(0)1621 785848
Bridgemarsh Marina: +44(0)1621 742216

FREQUENCY: Ch 80

HOURS OPEN: 0700-1800 LT ACCESS: H24

CADOGAN PIER, RIVER THAMES

51°28′·95N 0°09′·87W

+44(0)207 2652656

Fax: +44(0)207 2652699

FREQUENCY: Ch 14

LOCATION: Chelsea Embankment

HOURS OPEN: 0900-1700 LT

CHATHAM MARITIME MARINA

300 Berths

51°24′·25N 0°32′·05E

+44(0)1634 899200
chatham@mdlmarinas.co.uk

Depth 4 m, Maximum LOA 24 m

Fax: +44(0)1634 899201
www.marinas.co.uk

FREQUENCY: Ch 80

LOCATION: Chatham off Upnorcastle

HOURS: HX

CHELSEA HARBOUR MARINA, RIVER THAMES

CALL: Chelsea Harbour

51°28′·5N 0°10′·8W

Hr Mr: +44(0)207 7618606
Hr Mr: Mobile: 07770542783
Office: +44(0)207 3514433

Fax: +44(0)207 3527868

FREQUENCY: Ch 80

HOURS OPEN: 0900-1700 LT ACCESS: HW ± 1½ h

CHISWICK QUAY MARINA LTD, RIVER THAMES

51°28′·55N 0°16′·15W

+44(0)208 9948743

Fax: +44(0)208 9948743

FREQUENCY: Ch 14

ACCESS: HW ± 2h (Lock)

CONYER MARINA

50 Berths

51°20′·9N 0°49′·0E

+44(0)1795 521285

Depth 1·8 m, Maximum LOA 15 m

Fax: +44(0)1795 521384

FREQUENCY: Ch 80

HOURS OPEN: On request ACCESS: HW ± 1½ h

CUXTON MARINA, ROCHESTER

150 Berths plus Visitors

51°20′·9N 0°49′·0E

+44(0)1634 721941

Fax: +44(0)1634 250853

ELMHAVEN MARINA, ROCHESTER	CALL: Elmhaven Marina 60 Berths	51°21'·8N 0°27'·0E
Tel: +44(0)1634 240489		Fax: +44(0)1322 555665
elmhaven-marina@talk21.com		www.elmhaven-marina.co.uk
FREQUENCY: Ch M	LOCATION: North Halling, Rochester	HOURS OPEN: H24 ACCESS: HW ± 4h

ESSEX MARINA, RIVER CROUCH	CALL: Essex Marina 400 Berths	51°37'·3N 0°47'·9E
Tel: +44(0)1702 258531		Fax: +44(0)1702 258227
FREQUENCY: Ch M 80		HOURS OPEN: Season: H24 Out of season: 0900-1800 LT ACCESS: H24

FELIXSTOWE FERRY	**Port:** CALL: ODD TIMES	51°59'·35N 1°23'·69E
Tel: +44(0)1394 270106 Mobile: 0780 3476621		Fax:
FREQUENCY: Ch 08		HOURS: HX

FELIXSTOWE FERRY BOAT YARD	CALL: Deben Worker	51°59'·35N 1°23'·50E
Tel: +44(0)1394 282173		Fax:
FREQUENCY: Ch 08 16		HOURS: HX

FOX'S MARINA IPSWICH, RIVER ORWELL	CALL: Fox's 100 Berths	52°02'·0N 1°09'·2E
Tel: +44(0)1473 689111	Maximum LOA: 35 m	Fax: +44(0)1473 601737
FREQUENCY: Ch M 80		HOURS OPEN: 0800-1700 LT ACCESS: H24

IPSWICH HAVEN MARINA		52°03'N 1°10'E
Tel: +44(0)1473 236644 Hr Mr: +44(0)1473 231010 Marina: +44(0)1473 215204		Fax: +44(0)1473 236645 Hr Mr: +44(0)1473 230914 Marina: +44(0)1473 215206
ipswich@abports.co.uk enquiries@neptuns-marina.com		www.abports.co.uk
FREQUENCY: Ch M 80	LOCATION: Wetdock, Ipswich	HOURS: Office Hours. ACCESS: H24

INFORMATION:
IPSWICH ENCLOSED DOCK
All inward bound leisure craft should contact Lock Control on VHF Ch 68 for up-to-date information on lock times at the Orwell bridge.
ARRIVAL:
It is accessable, through a lock entrance, at all states of the tide for vessels up to 2 m draft. Vessels over 2 m draft should contact Lock Control, VHF Ch 68. Once through the lock contact either: Ipswich Haven Marina on VHF Ch 80 or 37 or Neptune Marina on VHF Ch 80 or 37 for allocation of a pontoon berth.
DEPARTURE:
All vessels to call Lock Control prior to leaving the marina berth. The duty officer will inform you when there is free flow or when you can lock out.

DEBBAGE YACHTING, RIVER ORWELL		
Tel: +44(0)1473 601169		Fax:
NOTE: Repairs/Fuel	LOCATION: The Quay, New Cut, Ipswich	HOURS: HX

WARNING: Within the entrance to NEW CUT is a Water Velocity Control Structure which is raised, when required from the river bed. When raised the top of the structure may be just below the water level. 3 Vertical Red Lights, when lit, warn vessels that they **MUST NOT PROCEED**.

GALLIONS POINT MARINA, RIVER THAMES	CALL: Gallions Point Marina	51°30'·3N 0°04'·4E
Tel: +44(0)207 4767054		Fax: +44(0)207 4747056
FREQUENCY: Ch 80	LOCATION: Royal Albert Basin	HOURS OPEN: H24 ACCESS: HW ± 5h

IPSWICH HAVEN MARINA

GILLINGHAM MARINA	CALL: Gillingham Marina Lock 250 Berths Lock Basin 250 Berths Tidal Basin	51°23′·8N 0°33′·6E
☎ +44(0)1634 280022 berthing@gillingham-marina.co.uk	Depth 2·5 m, Maximum LOA 21 m	Fax +44(0)1634 280164 www.gillingham-marina.co.uk
FREQUENCY: Ch 80		HOURS OPEN: 0700-2300 LT ACCESS: Tidal Basin (HW ± 2h) Locked Basin (HW ± 4½ h)

GOOLE	140 Berths	53°42′N 0°52′W
☎ Dock Master: +44(0)1405 762691 Yacht Basin: +44(0)1405 763985 goole@abports.co.uk	Access via Lock and Swing bridge (River Ouse)	Fax Dock Master: +44(0)1405 766029
FREQUENCY: Ch 09 (Bridge/Lock) 14 (Dock)	LOCATION: Basin off the Aire and Calder Canal	HOURS: H24

GREAT YARMOUTH	**Port:** CALL: Yarmouth	52°34′N 1°44′E
☎ Port Control: +44(0)1493 335511 (H24) Burgh Castle Marina (Breydon Water): +44(0)1493 780331 gypa@gypa.demon.co.uk		Fax Port Control: +44(0)1493 653464
FREQUENCY: Port: 09 11 **12** 16		HOURS: H24

GREENWICH YACHT CLUB, RIVER THAMES		51°29′·5N 0°00′·2E
☎ +44(0)208 8587339		Fax
FREQUENCY: Ch M		HOURS OF WATCH: HX

GRIMSBY	**Docks:** CALL: Grimsby Docks Radio	53°35′N 0°04′W
☎ Dock Master: +44(0)1469 571555 & 1472 359181 Mobile: 07885 498561		Fax Dock Master: +44(0)1469 571559 Port Manager: +44(0)1472 348275
FREQUENCY: Docking Instructions: Ch 18 **74** 79		HOURS: H24
PROCEDURE: Vessels Inward-Bound should obtain permission by VHF before entering the lock		

GRIMSBY MARINA (MERIDIAN QUAY)	CALL: Fish Dock	53°35′·12N 0°05′·97W
☎ +44(0)1472 268424		Fax
FREQUENCY: Ch 74		ACCESS: HW -3½h to +2½h

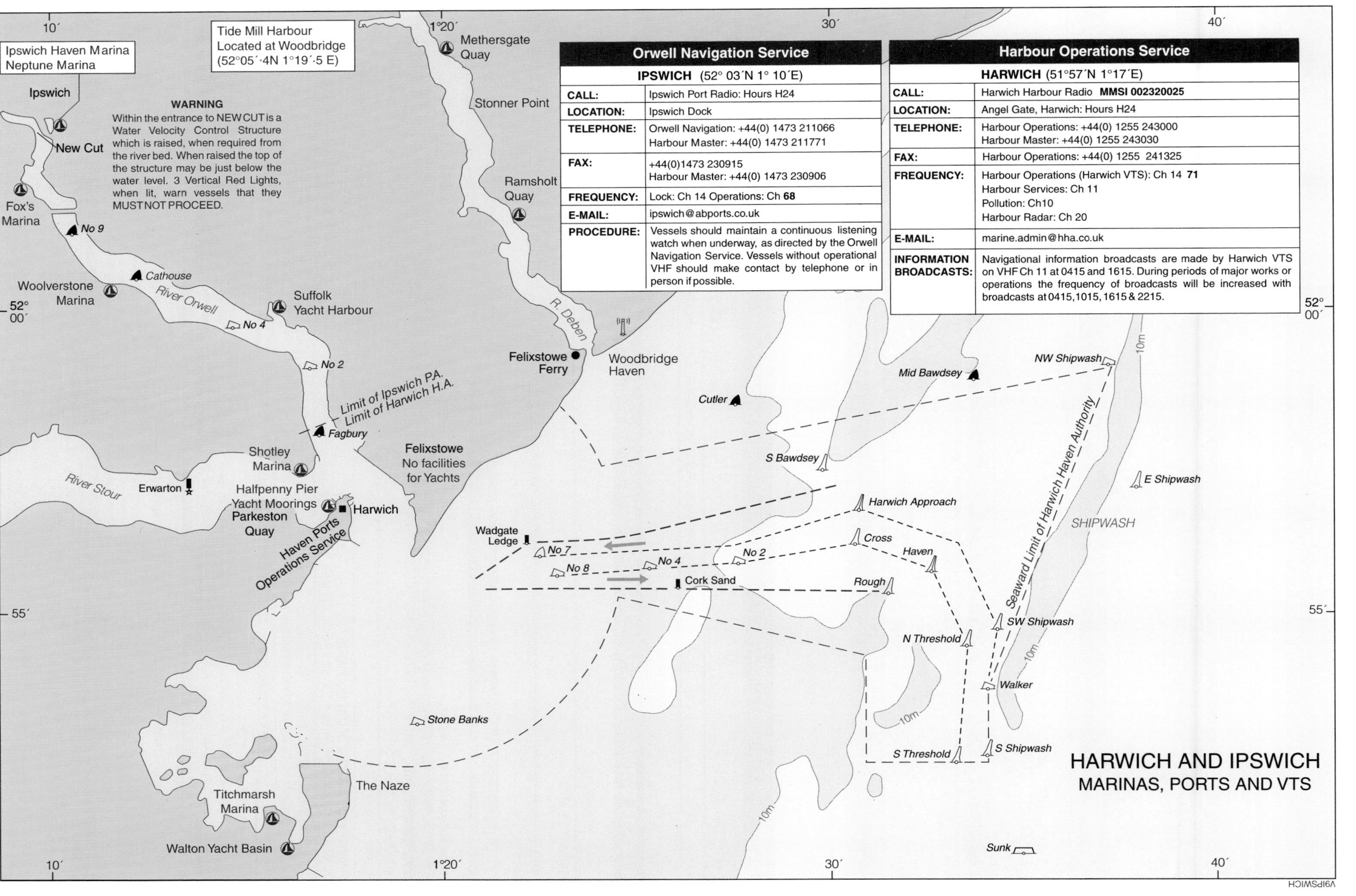

Orwell Navigation Service

IPSWICH (52° 03´N 1° 10´E)

CALL:	Ipswich Port Radio: Hours H24
LOCATION:	Ipswich Dock
TELEPHONE:	Orwell Navigation: +44(0) 1473 211066 Harbour Master: +44(0) 1473 211771
FAX:	+44(0)1473 230915 Harbour Master: +44(0) 1473 230906
FREQUENCY:	Lock: Ch 14 Operations: Ch **68**
E-MAIL:	ipswich@abports.co.uk
PROCEDURE:	Vessels should maintain a continuous listening watch when underway, as directed by the Orwell Navigation Service. Vessels without operational VHF should make contact by telephone or in person if possible.

Harbour Operations Service

HARWICH (51°57´N 1°17´E)

CALL:	Harwich Harbour Radio **MMSI 002320025**
LOCATION:	Angel Gate, Harwich: Hours H24
TELEPHONE:	Harbour Operations: +44(0) 1255 243000 Harbour Master: +44(0) 1255 243030
FAX:	Harbour Operations: +44(0) 1255 241325
FREQUENCY:	Harbour Operations (Harwich VTS): Ch 14 **71** Harbour Services: Ch 11 Pollution: Ch10 Harbour Radar: Ch 20
E-MAIL:	marine.admin@hha.co.uk
INFORMATION BROADCASTS:	Navigational information broadcasts are made by Harwich VTS on VHF Ch 11 at 0415 and 1615. During periods of major works or operations the frequency of broadcasts will be increased with broadcasts at 0415,1015,1615 & 2215.

GRIMSBY

HALCON MARINE LTD, CANVEY ISLAND		51°31′·25N 0°37′·30E
☎ +44(0)1268 511611		Fax:
FREQUENCY: Ch M	LOCATION: Small Gains Creek, Canvey Island	HOURS OPEN: 0800-1700 LT ACCESS: HW ± 2h

HARTLEPOOL MARINA	CALL: Hartlepool Marina	54°41′·4N 1°11′·9W
☎ +44(0)1429 865744		Fax: +44(0)1429 865947
FREQUENCY: Ch M 80		HOURS OPEN: H24 ACCESS: H24 through the lock

HARWICH (Operations MMSI 002320025)	Leisure Craft Procedures	51°57′N 1°17′E
☎ Operations: +44(0)1255 243000 Hr Mr: +44(0)1255 243030 harbour.house@hha.co.uk marine.admin@hha.co.uk		Fax: Operations: +44(0)1255 507177 Harbour Office: +44(0)1255 243302 www.hha.co.uk
FREQUENCY: Ch 09 **11** 20 **71**		HOURS: H24
HALFPENNY PIER VISITORS' YACHT MOORINGS Facility for visiting yachts available from 29th March to 20th October for a maximum stay of 72 hours.		

Information Broadcasts: Navigational information broadcasts are made by Harwich VTS on VHF Ch 11 at 0415 and 1615. During periods of major works or operations the frequency of broadcasts will be increased with broadcasts at 0415, 1015, 1615 and 2215

FOG: Recommended procedure for leisure craft in visibility of five cables or less:

(1) All craft with VHF radio should maintain a listening watch on VHF Ch 71
(2) Provided you are aware of your position and you intend staying on the yacht track, just monitor the commercial activity as reported on VHF Ch 71
(3) If you are uncertain of your position, it may be prudent to anchor clear of the shipping channel until visibility improves
(4) If you do not have radar and intend crossing any shipping lane, and you are in serious doubt as to the commercial movements, call Harwich Harbour Radio on VHF Ch 71. In summertime, or at times of peak commercial activity, you will probably be directed to VHF Ch 11
(5) If you pass a craft without radio which asks you for guidance, you should advise Harwich Harbour Radio of the details

NOTE: Harwich Harbour Radio cannot undertake control of small craft in reduced visibility but the operators will give whatever assistance is possible at the time

The Harbour Operations frequency, VHF Ch 71 is extremely busy with commercial shipping. Yachts are requested not to use this Port Operations Channel, except in an emergency, although it is beneficial to monitor this frequency in order to obtain information on commercial vessels movements

HARBOUR PATROL: The Harwich Haven Authority maintains a regular patrol of the Haven throughout the year. In addition, during the summer months weekends, between the hours of 0800-1800, these patrols are maintained to provide assistance and advice to yachtsmen, and to ensure that the main channel is kept clear for the transit of commercial shipping. The weekend Harbour Patrol launch maintains a listening watch on VHF Ch 11. The crew will be pleased to offer advice and information on the harbour and its approaches. A separate launch patrol may operate to regulate Shotley Point Marina traffic at peak summer weekends

HAVENGORE BRIDGE	**Bridge Keeper:** CALL: Shoe Bridge **Radar Control:** CALL: Shoe Radar* **Range Officer:** CALL: Shoe Base	51°34'N 0°51'E
☎ Bridge Keeper: +44(0)1702 383436 Range Operations: +44(0)1702 383211 & 383212 Admin Office: +44(0)1702 383200		Fax: +44(0)1702 383477
FREQUENCY: Ch 16 **72**		HOURS OPEN: Office hours

PROCEDURE:
Bridge will be opened for vessels from 2h before to 2h after HW during daylight hours, (1h before sunrise to 1h after sunset BST, ½h before sunrise to ½h after sunset UT), provided Shoeburyness Firing Range is not in use. Information may be obtained from the Range Operations Officer or the Bridge Keeper
*NOTE: Radar Surveillance is maintained while the Firing Range is in use

HEYBRIDGE LOCK, RIVER BLACKWATER	51°43'·70N 0°42'·64E
☎ +44(0)1621 853506	Fax:
FREQUENCY: Ch 80	HOURS OPEN: 0900-2300 LT ACCESS: HW -2 to +1h

HOO MARINA, RIVER MEDWAY	CALL: Hoo Marina — 120 Berth Pontoon, 125 Berths Drying	51°24'·6N 0°33'·8E
☎ +44(0)1634 250311	Depth 2 m, Maximum LOA 20 m	Fax: +44(0)1634 251761
FREQUENCY: Ch M 80	LOCATION: Rochester	HOURS OPEN: H24 ACCESS: HW ± 3½h

HULL MARINA	CALL: Hull Marina	53°44'·3N 0°20'·1W
☎ +44(0)1482 609960		Fax: +44(0)1482 224148 (Lock)
FREQUENCY: Ch 80		HOURS OF WATCH: H24 ACCESS: HW ± 3h through the lock

HULL MARINA

KING'S LYNN	**Pilots and Port:** CALL: Pilots & Hr Radio: **KLCB**	52°45'N 0°24'E
☎ Hr Office: +44(0)1553 773411 Port Manager's Office: +44(0)1553 691555 harbourmaster@portauthoritykingslynn.fsnet.co.uk		Fax: Port Operations: +44(0)1553 763431 Port Manager's Office: +44(0)1553 761335 www.portauthoritykingslynn.fsnet.co.uk
FREQUENCY: Hr Office: Ch 11 **14** 16	LOCATION: Hr Mr's Office (52°45'·35N 0°23'·65E)	HOURS: Port: Mon-Fri: 0800-1730 LT Other times: HW -4h to +1h

HUMBER
VESSEL TRAFFIC SERVICES

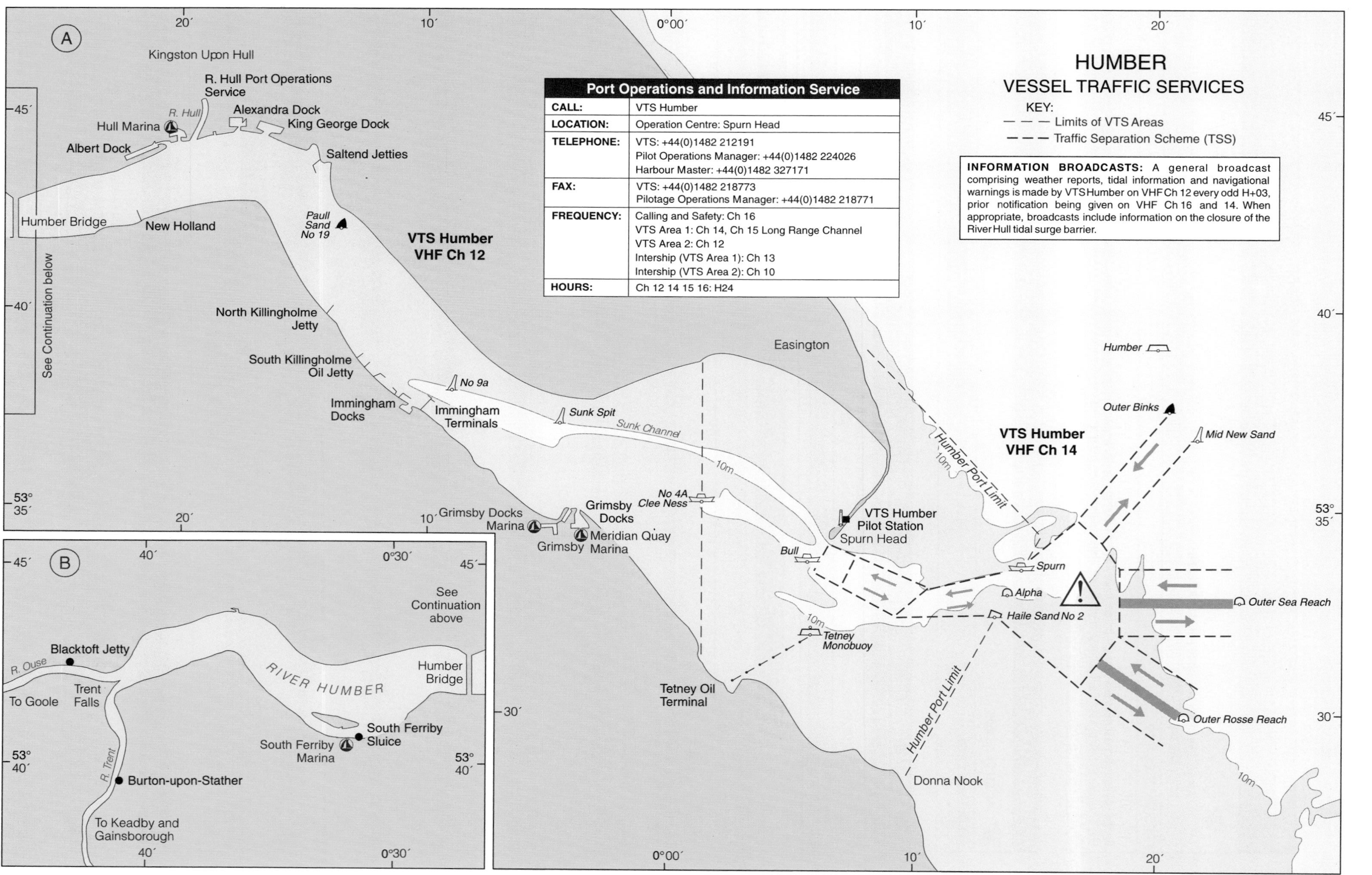

Port Operations and Information Service	
CALL:	VTS Humber
LOCATION:	Operation Centre: Spurn Head
TELEPHONE:	VTS: +44(0)1482 212191 Pilot Operations Manager: +44(0)1482 224026 Harbour Master: +44(0)1482 327171
FAX:	VTS: +44(0)1482 218773 Pilotage Operations Manager: +44(0)1482 218771
FREQUENCY:	Calling and Safety: Ch 16 VTS Area 1: Ch 14, Ch 15 Long Range Channel VTS Area 2: Ch 12 Intership (VTS Area 1): Ch 13 Intership (VTS Area 2): Ch 10
HOURS:	Ch 12 14 15 16: H24

INFORMATION BROADCASTS: A general broadcast comprising weather reports, tidal information and navigational warnings is made by VTS Humber on VHF Ch 12 every odd H+03, prior notification being given on VHF Ch 16 and 14. When appropriate, broadcasts include information on the closure of the River Hull tidal surge barrier.

LIMEHOUSE BASIN, RIVER THAMES	CALL: Limehouse Marina 350 Berths	51°30'·65N 0°02'·10W
Hr Mr: +44(0)207 3089930 marina@cruising.org.uk		Fax: Marina: +44(0)207 3630428 Office: +44(0)207 5372266 www.cruising.org.uk
FREQUENCY: Ch 80		HOURS OPEN: Summer (1 April-31 Oct): 0800-1800 LT Winter (1 Nov-31 Mar): 0800-1600 LT ACCESS: HW ± 1-1½h

LONDON AND THE RIVER THAMES		51°30'N 0°05'E
PORT CONTROL		www.portoflondon.co.uk
PLA's VTS (Vessel Traffic Service) is based at Gravesend and the Thames Barrier Navigation Centre at Woolwich		
Vessels of 20 metres or more in length, irrespective of vessel type, must carry a VHF radiotelephone capable of communicating with the Harbour Master at the Thames Navigation Service. Each such vessel must maintain a continuous listening watch on the VHF channel appropriate for that part of the Thames in which it is navigating and must use VHF to make any communications necessary If no VHF is carried on vessels under 20m they should telephone the PLA Navigation Centre at Woolwich (208 855 0315) to report to the Duty Officer immediately before and again on completion of the transit		
RADIO AND RADAR: PORT RADIO FREQUENCIES		
Port Control London **(Area - Crayfordness to Seaward Limit)**	Tel: Gravesend +44(0)1474 560311	Fax: +44(0)1474 352996
VHF Channels	Thames Seaward Approaches to Sea Reach No 4 Lt buoy: Ch **12** Sea Reach No 4 Lt buoy to Crayfordness: Ch **68**.	INFORMATION BROADCASTS: Ch 12: H+15 H+45 Ch 68: H+00 H+30 See Note 1
Radar Coverage	Erith to the Seaward limits of The Port of London	
Tidal Information	For Walton-on-Naze, Margate, Shivering Sands, Southend and Tilbury	
Woolwich Radio, including Barrier Control Zone **(Area - Upriver of Crayfordness)**	Tel: London: +44(0)20 88550315	Fax: +44(0)20 88547422
VHF Channels	**14**, 16 and 22	INFORMATION BROADCASTS: Ch 14: H+15 H+45 See Notes 1, 2 and 3
Radar Coverage	Crayfordness to Greenwich	
Tidal Information	For Woolwich (Silvertown), Tower Pier and Richmond	
Medway Radio **(Area - River Medway and approaches)**	Tel: Sheerness +44(0)1795 663025	
VHF Channels	**74**, 16 and 22	
Radar Coverage	River Medway and approaches	
Tidal Information	For Sheerness	
PATROL LAUNCHES	Callsign Thames Patrol	**Port of London Authority**
	VHF Channels 12 14 16 and 68	
NOTES: 1. During fog, more detailed information will be broadcast 2. Spans open for navigation will be included 3. Notification of actual or intended closure of the Thames flood defence barriers will be included when appropriate		

INCIDENT PROCEDURES:

(1) **POLACAP** (Port of London Authority Combined Accident Procedure)
Details of a major incident (alongside or underway) in the river between Sea Reach No. 1 buoy and Crayfordness will be broadcast by Port Control London and will include the code word POLACAP. This signifies that the Port of London Authority has initiated the Combined Accident Procedure agreed between the Port emergency services.

(a) All vessels should maintain current communications watch, minimise all radio traffic and be prepared for traffic regulation instructions.
(b) Vessels involved in or assisting at the scene of the incident may be ordered to switch to an alternate channel and report to Port Control London.
(c) A forward control craft or vessel may be designated by the Port of London Authority using callsign Forward Control.
(d) When the incident is under control and POLACAP is no longer in force, a broadcast will be made by Port Control London including the words 'Cancel POLACAP'. Vessels should then revert to normal working.

(2) **POLASEA**
Details of a major incident to seaward of Sea Reach No. 1 and Medway buoys will be broadcast by Port Control London and include the code word POLASEA. This signifies that the Port of London Authority has initiated the procedure agreed between the Port of London Authority and HM Coastguard.

(a) All vessels should maintain current communications watch, minimise all radio traffic, and be prepared for traffic regulation instructions.
(b) If necessary the Port of London Authority will establish an On Scene Zone centered on the incident, the radius of which will be broadcast on VHF Ch 12 by Port Control London and Medway Radio.
(c) Vessels operating in the On Scene Zone should keep watch on VHF Ch 16 and 2182 kHz.
(d) Vessels not involved in the incident should avoid passing through the On Scene Zone.
(e) Vessels outside the On Scene Zone and those passing through but not actively engaged should keep watch on VHF Ch 12 with duplicate watch on VHF Ch 16 if possible. (As necessary, vessels will be transferred to VHF Ch 20 or Ch 18 to ease message congestion).

THAMES ESTUARY & RIVER THAMES MARINAS AND YACHT HAVENS

Including Harbours with Small Craft Facilities

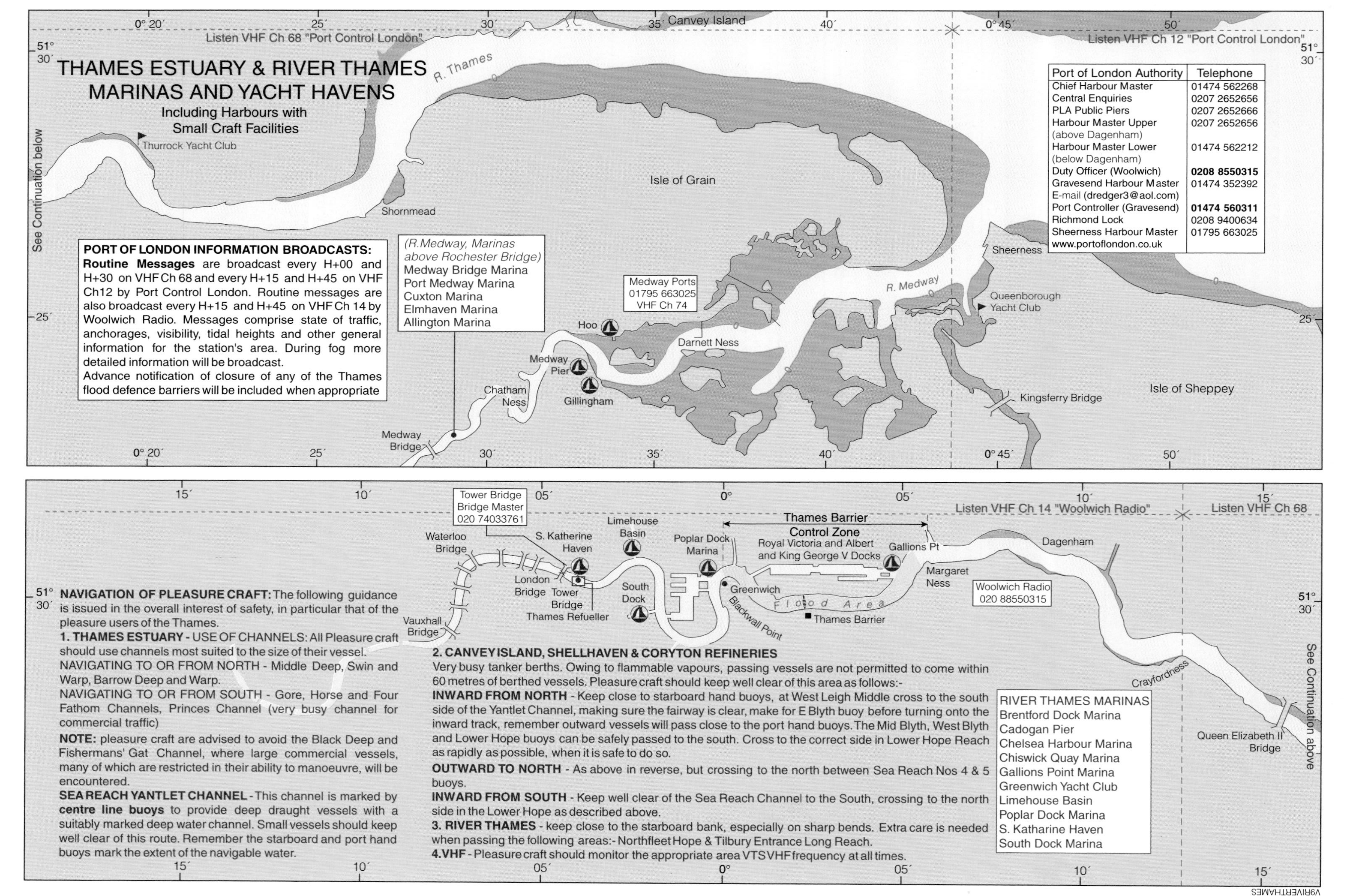

Port of London Authority	Telephone
Chief Harbour Master	01474 562268
Central Enquiries	0207 2652656
PLA Public Piers	0207 2652666
Harbour Master Upper (above Dagenham)	0207 2652656
Harbour Master Lower (below Dagenham)	01474 562212
Duty Officer (Woolwich)	**0208 8550315**
Gravesend Harbour Master	01474 352392
E-mail (dredger3@aol.com)	
Port Controller (Gravesend)	**01474 560311**
Richmond Lock	0208 9400634
Sheerness Harbour Master	01795 663025
www.portoflondon.co.uk	

PORT OF LONDON INFORMATION BROADCASTS:
Routine Messages are broadcast every H+00 and H+30 on VHF Ch 68 and every H+15 and H+45 on VHF Ch12 by Port Control London. Routine messages are also broadcast every H+15 and H+45 on VHF Ch 14 by Woolwich Radio. Messages comprise state of traffic, anchorages, visibility, tidal heights and other general information for the station's area. During fog more detailed information will be broadcast.
Advance notification of closure of any of the Thames flood defence barriers will be included when appropriate

(R.Medway, Marinas above Rochester Bridge)
Medway Bridge Marina
Port Medway Marina
Cuxton Marina
Elmhaven Marina
Allington Marina

NAVIGATION OF PLEASURE CRAFT: The following guidance is issued in the overall interest of safety, in particular that of the pleasure users of the Thames.

1. THAMES ESTUARY - USE OF CHANNELS: All Pleasure craft should use channels most suited to the size of their vessel.
NAVIGATING TO OR FROM NORTH - Middle Deep, Swin and Warp, Barrow Deep and Warp.
NAVIGATING TO OR FROM SOUTH - Gore, Horse and Four Fathom Channels, Princes Channel (very busy channel for commercial traffic)

NOTE: pleasure craft are advised to avoid the Black Deep and Fishermans' Gat Channel, where large commercial vessels, many of which are restricted in their ability to manoeuvre, will be encountered.

SEA REACH YANTLET CHANNEL - This channel is marked by **centre line buoys** to provide deep draught vessels with a suitably marked deep water channel. Small vessels should keep well clear of this route. Remember the starboard and port hand buoys mark the extent of the navigable water.

2. CANVEY ISLAND, SHELLHAVEN & CORYTON REFINERIES
Very busy tanker berths. Owing to flammable vapours, passing vessels are not permitted to come within 60 metres of berthed vessels. Pleasure craft should keep well clear of this area as follows:-

INWARD FROM NORTH - Keep close to starboard hand buoys, at West Leigh Middle cross to the south side of the Yantlet Channel, making sure the fairway is clear, make for E Blyth buoy before turning onto the inward track, remember outward vessels will pass close to the port hand buoys. The Mid Blyth, West Blyth and Lower Hope buoys can be safely passed to the south. Cross to the correct side in Lower Hope Reach as rapidly as possible, when it is safe to do so.

OUTWARD TO NORTH - As above in reverse, but crossing to the north between Sea Reach Nos 4 & 5 buoys.

INWARD FROM SOUTH - Keep well clear of the Sea Reach Channel to the South, crossing to the north side in the Lower Hope as described above.

3. RIVER THAMES - keep close to the starboard bank, especially on sharp bends. Extra care is needed when passing the following areas:- Northfleet Hope & Tilbury Entrance Long Reach.

4. VHF - Pleasure craft should monitor the appropriate area VTS VHF frequency at all times.

RIVER THAMES MARINAS
Brentford Dock Marina
Cadogan Pier
Chelsea Harbour Marina
Chiswick Quay Marina
Gallions Point Marina
Greenwich Yacht Club
Limehouse Basin
Poplar Dock Marina
S. Katharine Haven
South Dock Marina

V9RIVERTHAMES

LONDON AND THE RIVER THAMES (Continued) — 51°30'N 0°05'E

(3) **POLARIVER**
Details of a major incident above Crayfordness will be broadcast by the Port of London Authority through Woolwich Radio and will be codenamed POLARIVER.

BOW LOCK, RIVER THAMES — CALL: Bow Lock — 51°30'·8N 0°00'·6E

☎ +44(0)207 9875661	Fax
FREQUENCY: Ch 16 74	HOURS OPEN: 0500-2200 LT

KING GEORGE V DOCK LOCK — CALL: KG Control — 51°30'N 0°04'E

FREQUENCY: Ch 68

PROCEDURE: All vessels bound for the King George V, Royal Albert and Royal Victoria Docks should obtain final docking instructions when close to dock

Thames Refueller on VHF Ch 14 during the following: Mon-Sat: 0900-1600 LT
Sun: 0900-1300 LT

Fuel Barge Leonard Normal hours +44(0)207 4748714 and VHF Channel 14 Out of hours contact Tel./Fax. +44(0)207 5117750	Open 0900-1600 LT weekdays

THAMES LOCK — CALL: Thames Lock — 51°30'N 0°04'W

FREQUENCY: Ch 74	LOCATION: Brentford	HOURS OPEN: Summer (1 April-31 Oct): 0800-1800 LT Winter (1 Nov-31 Mar): 0800-1630 LT

THAMES BARRIER CONTROL ZONE — CALL: Woolwich Radio — VHF Channel 14

A **Control Zone** exists between **Margaretness** and **Blackwall Point** for regulating traffic through the Thames Flood Barrier. All vessels proceeding through this area to and from the berths within the area, are subject to the requirements detailed

The Thames Flood Barrier consists of nine piers numbered 1 to 9 from north to south and ten spans lettered A to K from south to north

Spans B to G are open to navigation subject to the restrictions

Spans C, D, E and **F** are 61 m wide with a depth of 5·8 m below Chart Datum

Spans B and **G** are 31·5 m wide with a depth of 1·2 m below Chart Datum and have depth boards on Piers 3 and 9

Spans A, H, J and **K** are permanently closed to navigation

Under normal circumstances, the northern spans E, F and G will be used for inward bound traffic and the southern spans B, C and D will be used for outward bound traffic

Depth over sills: Gates C, D, E & F = 5·8 m CD. Gates B & G = 1·25 m CD

Navigation through this Zone is regulated by the **Thames Barrier Navigation Centre**. This operations room has radar coverage from Erith to Greenwich and operates on VHF Channel **14** (Call sign: **Woolwich Radio**). Under certain circumstances, messages may be relayed by Port Control London at Gravesend (Channels 12 or 68)

Vessels intending to transit the Barrier must confirm that they have permission to proceed when passing Margaret Point inward or Blackwall Point outward

1 Traffic Regulations
All vessels fitted with VHF intending to navigate in the **Thames Barrier Control Zone** must inform **Woolwich Radio** on VHF Channel 14 of their ETA at the Barrier or other destination when:

(a) Passing Crayfordness point inward bound

(b) On leaving a berth which lies between Crayfordness Point and Margaretness inward bound

(c) When clearing Tower Bridge outward bound

(d) On leaving a berth or lock between Tower Bridge and Blackwall Point outward bound

2 **All** vessels bound to or from berths or locks within the Barrier Control Zone, whether bound through the Barrier or not, **must** contact **Woolwich Radio** at least 30 minutes before arriving or departing to obtain information on expected traffic movement. These vessels **must** maintain a listening watch on VHF **Channel 14** and obtain permission to proceed before entering the Barrier Control Zone or leaving a berth within the Zone

3 Vessels transiting the Barrier **must** use the spans indicated by the Traffic Signals displayed at the Barrier and/or allocated by **Woolwich Radio**. Information regarding spans open for navigation will be broadcast by **Woolwich Radio** on routine broadcasts

4 Small Vessels (under 20m in length)
All small vessels and craft such as yachts, dinghies, power boats, sculls, rowing boats and canoes **not** fitted with VHF are advised that in general they should navigate **inwards** through the Northern most span and **outwards** through the Southern most span which is open to navigation. It should be noted that the minimum depth of water in spans B and G is 1.2m below Chart Datum

Loud hailers are fitted at certain points to pass instructions. They may also transmit Morse Signal "K". On hearing Morse Signal (indicating Barrier Closure) contact **Woolwich Radio** if fitted with VHF RT. If not fitted, stop your vessel and listen to voice instructions

a. It is extremely dangerous to go through a Span marked Closed (for navigation), the gates may be in a semi-raised position
b. Do not navigate above Thames Refinery Jetty or below Gulf Oil Island Jetty unless intending to pass through the Barrier
c. ALL GATES CLOSED: No vessels to navigate within 200 metres of Barrier due to turbulence
d. Call **Woolwich Radio** (Barrier control) on Channel 14 at Margaretness and/or Blackwall Point for permission to pass through the Barrier. If no VHF Radio then pass through between Green Arrows. Use the side spans wherever possible, i.e. B or G. DO not "sail" through - use engine at all times

5 All such vessels are to comply with signals exhibited at the **Barrier Notice Boards** and instructions received from the **Barrier Audio Stations**

6 VHF Radio
All vessels over 50 gross tons (GT) and all self-propelled vessels under 50 GT regularly transiting the area, **must** have a VHF radio set capable of transmitting and receiving on Channels 12, 68 and 14. Barrier Traffic Control Messages will be broadcast by Port Control London on VHF Channel 12 and 68 and **Woolwich Radio** on VHF Channel 14

NAVIGATION THROUGH THE BARRIER	Woolwich Barrier Control Zone: Margaretness to Blackwall Point.
Notice Boards with lights at Thamesmead, Barking Power Station, Blackwall Stairs (north shore) and Blackwall Point (south shore): **Amber light means: *Proceed with extreme caution*** **Red light means: *Navigation within Zone prohibited*** **DIRECTIONAL LIGHTS ON THE BARRIER:** **Red S. Andrew's Crosses (lit) on Piers means: *Barrier or span closed*** **Green Arrows (lit) on Piers means: *Span open***	
RADAR BEACONS: Thames Barrier. Piers 4, 5, 6, 7 and 8: MORSE IDENT: **T**	
OTHER FLOOD BARRIERS (Head Clearances)	

Creek	Barrier	Clearance
Barking Creek	Tidal Barrier	Clearance 33·5m MHWS
Dartford Creek	Tidal Barrier	Clearance 12·2m MHWS
Easthaven Creek	Tidal Barrier	Clearance 3·3m MHWS
Fobbing Creek	Tidal Barrier	Clearance 9·3m MHWS
Benfleet Creek	Tidal Barrier	Clearance 1·6m MHWS.

Creek Barriers show
Fl R (Red flashing light) when closed

MHWS = Mean High Water Spring tide

THAMES BARRIER

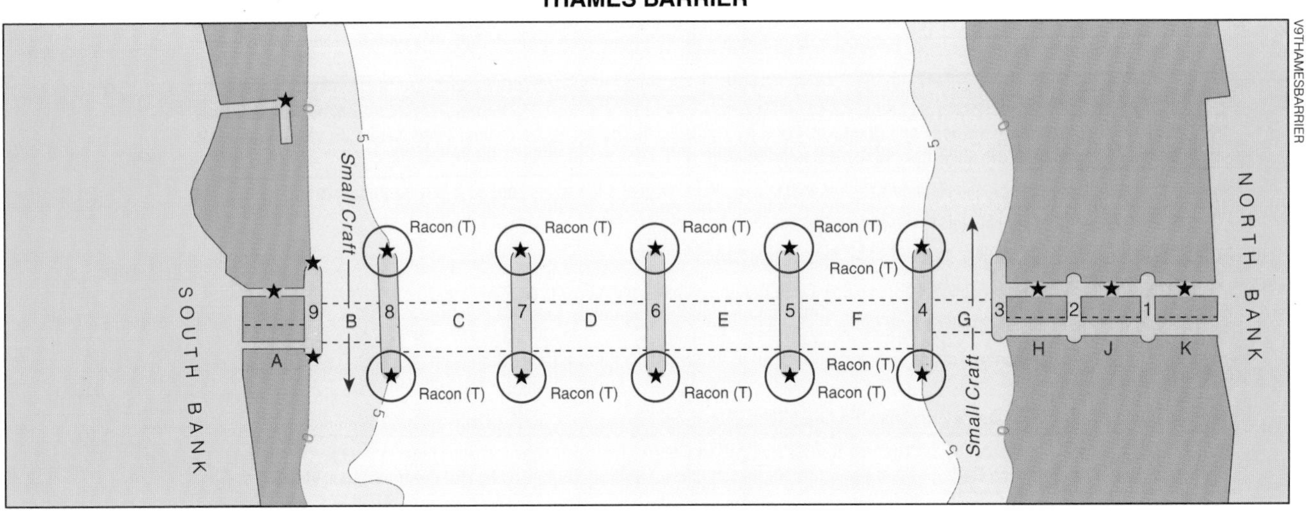

LOWESTOFT	Port: CALL: Lowestoft Harbour Control	52°29′N 1°45′E
Port Control: +44(0)1502 572286/7		Port Control: +44(0)1502 586375 Port House: +44(0)1502 500032
FREQUENCY: Ch 11 **14** 16	LOCATION: Pilot Control: Lowestoft Bascule Bridge	HOURS: H24
NOTES: 1. Vessels approaching, departing or transiting Lowestoft should make every reasonable effort to establish and maintain contact with the Lowestoft Harbour Control on VHF Ch 14 2. Yachts may use a bridge opening for commercial shipping provided that prior arrangement has been made with Lowestoft Harbour Control		

ROYAL NORFOLK & SUFFOLK YACHT CLUB	CALL: Yacht Club	52°28′·3N 1°45′·2E
+44(0)1502 566726 rnsyc@ctc-net.co.uk		+44(0)1502 517981
FREQUENCY: Ch **80**	LOCATION: Yacht Basin, SW Outer Harbour	HOURS: H24 ACCESS: HW ± 4h

MALDON, RIVER BLACKWATER		51°43′·75N 0°41′·40E
Hr Mr: +44(0)1621 852238 Heybridge Basin Lock Keeper: +44(0)1621 853506		+44(0)1621 852575
FREQUENCY: Ch 16	LOCATION: Hythe Quay, Maldon	HOURS OPEN: 0900-1700 LT ACCESS: HW ± 2h

MEDWAY PORTS

Call: Medway Radio

Tel: Hr Mr: +44(0)1795 561234
Sheerness Hr Mr: +44(0)1795 663025
Duty Office: +44(0)1795 596593
Medway Navigation Service: +44(0)1795 663025
Yacht Hr Mr: +44(0)1795 596548 & 596506

Fax: Hr Mr: +44(0)1795 660072

FREQUENCY: Ch 74; RADAR ASSISTANCE: Ch 22
ACCESS: HW ± 2h (Lock)

ALLINGTON MARINA, RIVER MEDWAY

Tel: +44(0)1622 752057
Lock: +44(0)1622 752864

Fax: +44(0)1622 763286

HOURS OPEN: 0800-2100 LT
ACCESS: HW -3h to +2h

MEDWAY BRIDGE MARINA

CALL: Medway Bridge Marina — 160 Berths 15 Visitor — 51°22′·6N 0°28′·9E

Tel: +44(0)1634 826134 & 843576

Fax: +44(0)1634 843820

FREQUENCY: Ch M 80
HOURS OPEN: 0900-1800 LT

MEDWAY PIER MARINE LTD

60 Berths Pontoon — 51°23′·8N 0°33′·5E

Tel: +44(0)1634 851113
Mistley Marine Mobile: 07850 208918

Depth 4 m, Maximum LOA: 14 m

FREQUENCY: Ch 80
LOCATION: Gillingham Pier
HOURS OF WATCH: 0700-2230 LT
ACCESS: HW ± 3·5h

NEPTUNE MARINA, IPSWICH

52°03′·1N 1°09′·9E

Tel: +44(0)1473 215204
enquiries@neptune-marina.com

Maximum LOA: 10 m

Fax: +44(0)1473 780366

FREQUENCY: Through Ipswich Port Radio or direct on Ch M or 80
HOURS OPEN: 0730-2230 LT
ACCESS: HW -2h to +¾h

NORTH FAMBRIDGE YACHT CENTRE, RIVER CROUCH

150 Berths Visitor Berths Available — 51°38′·15N 0°40′·70E

Tel: +44(0)1621 740370

Maximum LOA: 15·24 m
Deepwater swinging moorings 3 m at LW

FREQUENCY: Ch M 80
HOURS OPEN: 0900-1730 LT ACCESS: HW ± 5h

POPLAR DOCK MARINA, RIVER THAMES

51°30′·04N 0°00′·40W

Tel: +44(0)20 75151046

Fax: +44(0)20 75385537

FREQUENCY: Ch 13
HOURS: 0600 - 2200 LT

PORT MEDWAY MARINA

CALL: Port Medway — 51°22′·4N 0°27′·9E

Tel: +44(0)1634 720033

Fax: +44(0)1634 720315

FREQUENCY: Ch M 80
LOCATION: Cuxton
HOURS OPEN: 0800-1800 LT ACCESS: H24

QUEENBOROUGH, RIVER MEDWAY

CALL: Harbour Controller — 140 Berths — 51°25N 0°44E

Tel: +44(0)1795 662051
Mobile: 07850 703389 or 07850 716762

Depth 2 m, Maximum LOA 10 m
No alongside berths. Lighter for rafting off-shore

FREQUENCY: Ch M
Trot Boat at weekends Ch 08

HOURS OPEN: Mon-Fri: 0800-1600 LT
Sat: 1600-2330 LT,
Sun: 1000-1600 LT (including Bank Holidays)

RICE & COLE, SEA END BOATHOUSE, RIVER CROUCH

51°37′·30N 0°49′·65E

Tel: +44(0)1621 782063

Fax: +44(0)1621 782063

FREQUENCY: Ch M
LOCATION: Burnham-on-Crouch

ROYAL QUAYS (TYNE)	**Marina**	240 Berths	54°59′·77N 1°26′·98W

Tel: +44(0)191 2728282
rqmarina@quiknet.co.uk

Fax: +44(0)191 2728288
www.crestnicholsonmarinas.co.uk

FREQUENCY: Ch 80

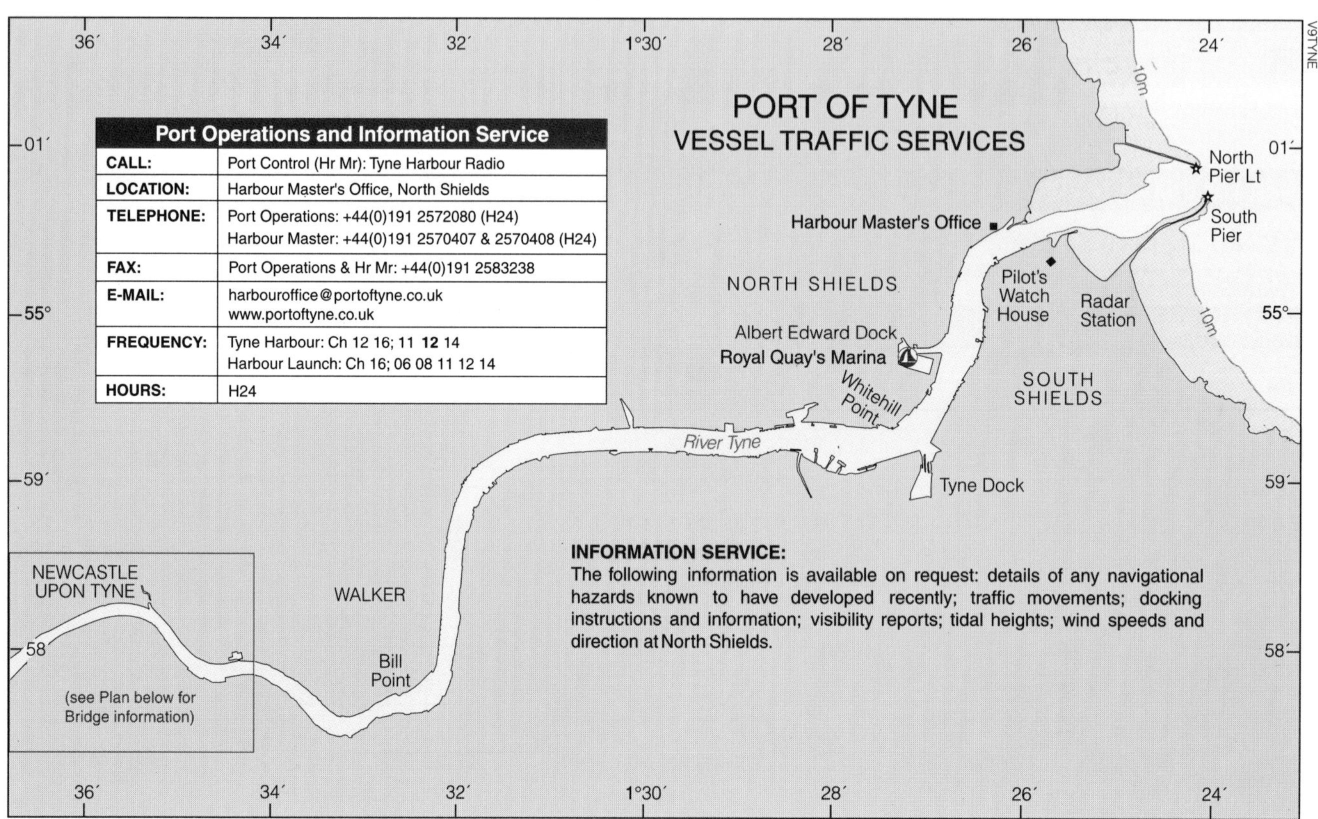

Port Operations and Information Service	
CALL:	Port Control (Hr Mr): Tyne Harbour Radio
LOCATION:	Harbour Master's Office, North Shields
TELEPHONE:	Port Operations: +44(0)191 2572080 (H24) Harbour Master: +44(0)191 2570407 & 2570408 (H24)
FAX:	Port Operations & Hr Mr: +44(0)191 2583238
E-MAIL:	harbouroffice@portoftyne.co.uk www.portoftyne.co.uk
FREQUENCY:	Tyne Harbour: Ch 12 16; 11 **12** 14 Harbour Launch: Ch 16; 06 08 11 12 14
HOURS:	H24

INFORMATION SERVICE:
The following information is available on request: details of any navigational hazards known to have developed recently; traffic movements; docking instructions and information; visibility reports; tidal heights; wind speeds and direction at North Shields.

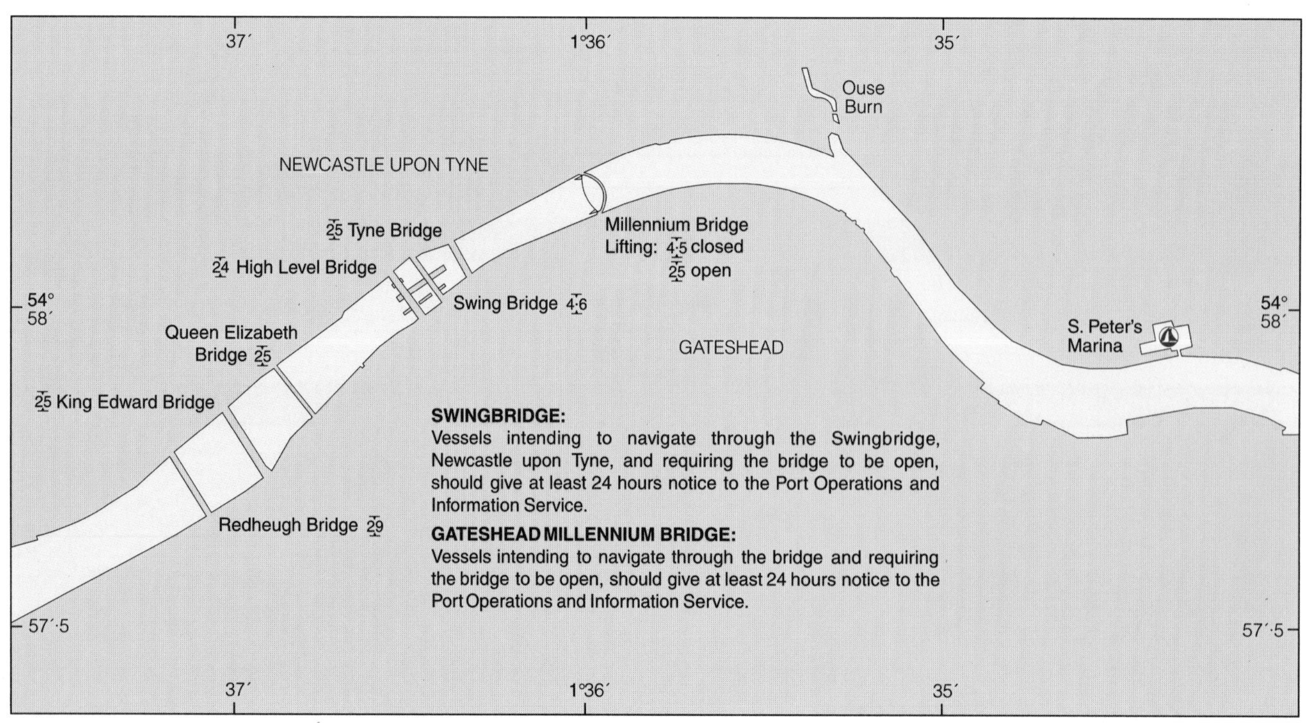

SWINGBRIDGE:
Vessels intending to navigate through the Swingbridge, Newcastle upon Tyne, and requiring the bridge to be open, should give at least 24 hours notice to the Port Operations and Information Service.

GATESHEAD MILLENNIUM BRIDGE:
Vessels intending to navigate through the bridge and requiring the bridge to be open, should give at least 24 hours notice to the Port Operations and Information Service.

SCARBOROUGH	Port: CALL: Scarborough Lighthouse	54°17'N 0°23'W
Tel: Hr Mr: +44(0)1723 373530		Fax: Hr Mr: +44(0)1723 350035
FREQUENCY: Port: Ch 12 16		HOURS: H24 ACCESS: HW ± 3h

SEAHAM	Port: CALL: Seaham Harbour	54°50'·24N 1°19'·28W
Tel: Hr Mr's Office: +44(0)191 5161703 Operations Office: +44(0)191 5161700 dph@portofseaham.com		Fax: Operations: +44(0)191 5161710
FREQUENCY: Port: Ch 06 **12** 16 Operations: Ch 12	LOCATION: Hr Mr's Office and Operations Office	HOURS: Hr Mr Office: HW -2½h to +1½h Operations Office: Mon-Fri: Office hours

SHOTLEY MARINA, HARWICH HARBOUR	350 Berths	51°57'·6N 1°16'·7E
Tel: +44(0)1473 788982 sales@shotley-marina.co.uk		Fax: +44(0)1473 788868 www.shotley-marina.co.uk
FREQUENCY: Ch 16 M 71 80	LOCATION: River Orwell, Harwich Harbour	HOURS OPEN: H24 ACCESS: H24 through the lock
PROCEDURE: Vessels are advised to monitor VHF Ch 80 (Ch M if vessels not fitted with VHF Ch 80) whilst approaching the marina, locking through and whilst underway within the marina basin		

S. KATHARINE HAVEN LTD, RIVER THAMES	Call: S. Katherines Dock	51°30'N 0°04'W
Tel: +44(0)207 4818350 (H24) +44(0)207 2645312 mary.pakan@\tayprop.co.uk		Fax: +44(0)207 7022252 www. stkaths.co.uk
FREQUENCY: Ch 80		HOURS: HX
ACCESS: Summer: (April - October) The lock operates HW -2h to +1½h, during 0600-2030 LT Winter: (November - March) The lock operates HW -2h to +1½h, during 0800-1800 LT November - March the lock is closed to traffic on Tuesdays and Wednesdays		

SOUTH DOCK MARINA, RIVER THAMES	CALL: South Dock Marina	51°29'·6N 0°02'·0W
Tel: +44(0)207 2522244		Fax: +44(0)207 2373806
FREQUENCY: Ch M 80	LOCATION: Rotherhithe	HOURS OPEN: H24 ACCESS: HW ± 2-2½h through the lock

SOUTH FERRIBY MARINA, RIVER HUMBER	CALL: South Ferriby Base 40 Berths 10 Visitor Berths	53°35'·12N 0°03'·97W
Tel: Lock: +44(0)1652 635219 Marina: +44(0)1652 635620	Depth 2·5 m, Maximum LOA: 12 m	Fax: +44(0)1482 224148 (Lock)
FREQUENCY: Ch **M** 80		HOURS OF WATCH: 0930-1730 LT HOURS OPEN: Mon-Fri: 0930-1730 LT Sat, Sun & Holidays: 1030-1700 LT ACCESS: HW ± 3h through the lock

S. PETER'S MARINA, RIVER TYNE		54°57'·9N 1°34'·3E
Tel: +44(0)191 2654472		Fax: +44(0)191 2762618
FREQUENCY: Ch M 80	LOCATION: Newcastle upon Tyne	HOURS OF WATCH: H24 ACCESS: HW -5h to +4h

SUFFOLK YACHT HARBOUR, RIVER ORWELL	CALL: Suffolk Yacht Harbour 500 Berths	51°59'·7N 1°16'·4E
Tel: +44(0)1473 659465 & 659240		Fax: +44(0)1473 659632
FREQUENCY: Ch **M** 80		HOURS OPEN: 0730-2130 LT ACCESS: H24

S. PETER'S MARINA

SUNDERLAND	**Port:** CALL: Sunderland Harbour Radio	54°55′N 1°21′W
☎ Hr Mr: +44(0)191 5672626 & 5532131 Signal Station: +44(0)191 5670161 & 5142752 (H24) info@portofsunderland.org.uk		Fax: Pilot Office: +44(0)191 5532120 www.portofsunderland.org.uk
FREQUENCY: Port: Ch 14 16	LOCATION: Pilot Office, Old North Pier	HOURS: H24
Marina	**Marina:** CALL: Sunderland Marina	
☎ +44(0)191 5144721		Fax: +44(0)191 5141847
FREQUENCY: Ch M		HOURS: H24 ACCESS: H24

SWALE MARINA, CONYER CREEK	130 Berths	51°21′·3N 0°49′·0E
☎ +44(0)1795 521562 enquiries@swalemarina.co.uk		Fax: +44(0)1795 520788 www.swalemarina.co.uk
	LOCATION: Head of the creek, W of village	ACCESS: HW ± 1·5h

TEES	**Port Operations and Information Service:** CALL: Tees Ports Control	54°36′·2N 1°09′·5W
☎ Hr Mr: +44(0)1642 277201 Port Operations: +44(0)1642 277205 & 277206 harbourmaster@thpal.co.uk		Fax: Hr Mr: +44(0)1642 277227 Port Operations: +44(0)1642 277207 www.thpal.co.uk
FREQUENCY: Ch 08 11 12 **14** 16 **22**	LOCATION: Hr Mr Office, Tees Dock	HOURS: H24
INFORMATION SERVICE: Vessels may obtain navigational advice and port operations information at any time by calling Tees Ports Control on VHF Ch 14 AREA: The Port Operations and Information Service which includes Harbour Surveillance Radar covers the River Tees, Tees and Hartlepool Bays and Approaches seawards for ranges up to 12 n miles		
River Tees Barrage	CALL: Tees Barrage Radio	
☎ +44(0)1642 633273		Fax:
FREQUENCY: Ch M	LOCATION: 54°33′·9N 1°17′·1W	HOURS: H24
PROCEDURE: Vessels wishing to pass the barrage should use the channel and lock located to the south of the barrage. Prior to entering the channel and lock, vessels should contact Tees Barrage Radio on VHF Ch M or by telephone to obtain clearance		

TIDEMILL YACHT HARBOUR LTD, RIVER DEBEN	CALL: Tidemill Yacht Harbour	52°05′·4N 1°19′·5E
☎ Marina: +44(0)1394 385745 Hr Mr (Mobile): 07803 476621 richard@tidemillyachtharbour.co.uk	Depth 2·5 m	Fax: +44(0)1480 380735 www.tidemillyachtharbour.co.uk
FREQUENCY: Ch M **80** NOTES: 1. Ch M used for berthing 2. Pilot available at Felixstowe Ferry 07803 476621 (VHF Ch 8)		HOURS OPEN: H24 ACCESS: HW -2h to +3h

TITCHMARSH MARINA, WALTON BACKWATERS	450 Berths & Visitors	51°51′·8N 1°15′·6E
Tel: Marina: +44(0)1255 672185 Hr Mr: +44(0)1255 851899		Fax: +44(0)1255 851091
FREQUENCY: Ch M 80		HOURS OF WATCH: Summer: 0830-1700 LT ACCESS: HW ± 5h

TOLLESBURY MARINA, RIVER BLACKWATER	240 Berths	51°45′·4N 0°51′·2E
Tel: +44(0)1621 869202 & 868471 marina@woodrolfe.demon.co.uk		Fax: +44(0)1621 868489 www.tolesbury-marina.co.uk
FREQUENCY: Ch M 80		HOURS OPEN: Mon-Fri: 0900-1700 LT Sat: 0930-1230 1430-1600 LT Sun: 1000-1230 1430-1600 LT ACCESS: HW ± 2h

WALTON YACHT BASIN, WALTON BACKWATERS	60 Berths	51°51′N 1°16′E
Tel: +44(0)1255 675873	Boatyard owned by Bedwell & Co	Fax:

WELLS-NEXT-THE-SEA	**Port:** CALL: Wells Harbour Radio	52°57′N 0°51′E
Tel: Hr Mr: +44(0)1328 711646 Mobile: 0775 507284 wellsharbour@talk21.com		Fax: +44(0)1328 710623
FREQUENCY: Ch 12 16		HOURS: HW ± 3h and when a vessel is expected

WEST MERSEA MARINE, RIVER COLNE		51°46′·6N 0°54′·1E
Tel: +44(0)1206 382244		Fax: +44(0)1206 384455
FREQUENCY: Ch M	LOCATION: Mersea Island	HOURS: HX

WEST WICK MARINA, RIVER CROUCH	180 Berths Visitor Berths Available	51°38′·58N 0°39′·90E
Tel: +44(0)1621 741268	Maximum LOA: 15·24 m	Fax:
FREQUENCY: Ch M 80	LOCATION: North Fambridge, Chelmsford	ACCESS: Not LW ± 1½ h

WHITBY	**Port & Marina** 180 Berths Visitor Berths Available	54°29′N 0°37′W
Tel: Hr Mr: +44(0)1947 602354 Marina: +44(0)1947 602354 & 600165 portofwhitby@btinternet.com	Bridge opened on request, but only on the hour and H+30 for 2h ± HW	Fax: Hr Mr: +44(0)1947 600380
FREQUENCY: Ch **11** 16 Bridge: Ch **11** 16		HOURS: H24 ACCESS: HW ± 2h

WHITSTABLE	CALL: Whitstable Harbour Radio	51°21·86N 01°01′·46E
Tel: Hr Mr: +44(0)1227 274086 whitstable.harbour@canterbury.gov.uk		Fax: +44(0)1227 265441 www.marinas.co.uk
FREQUENCY: Ch **09** 12		HOURS: 0830-1700 LT
NOTE: Limited leisure facilities, priority given to commercial shipping		

WHITTON MARINE, RIVER MEDWAY	90 Berths	51°24·5N 0°35′·7E
Tel: +44(0)1634 250593	Depth 2·1 m, Maximum LOA 30 m	Fax: +44(0)1634 250593
FREQUENCY: Ch M 80	LOCATION: Hoo S. Werburgh	HOURS: HX ACCESS: HW ± 2h

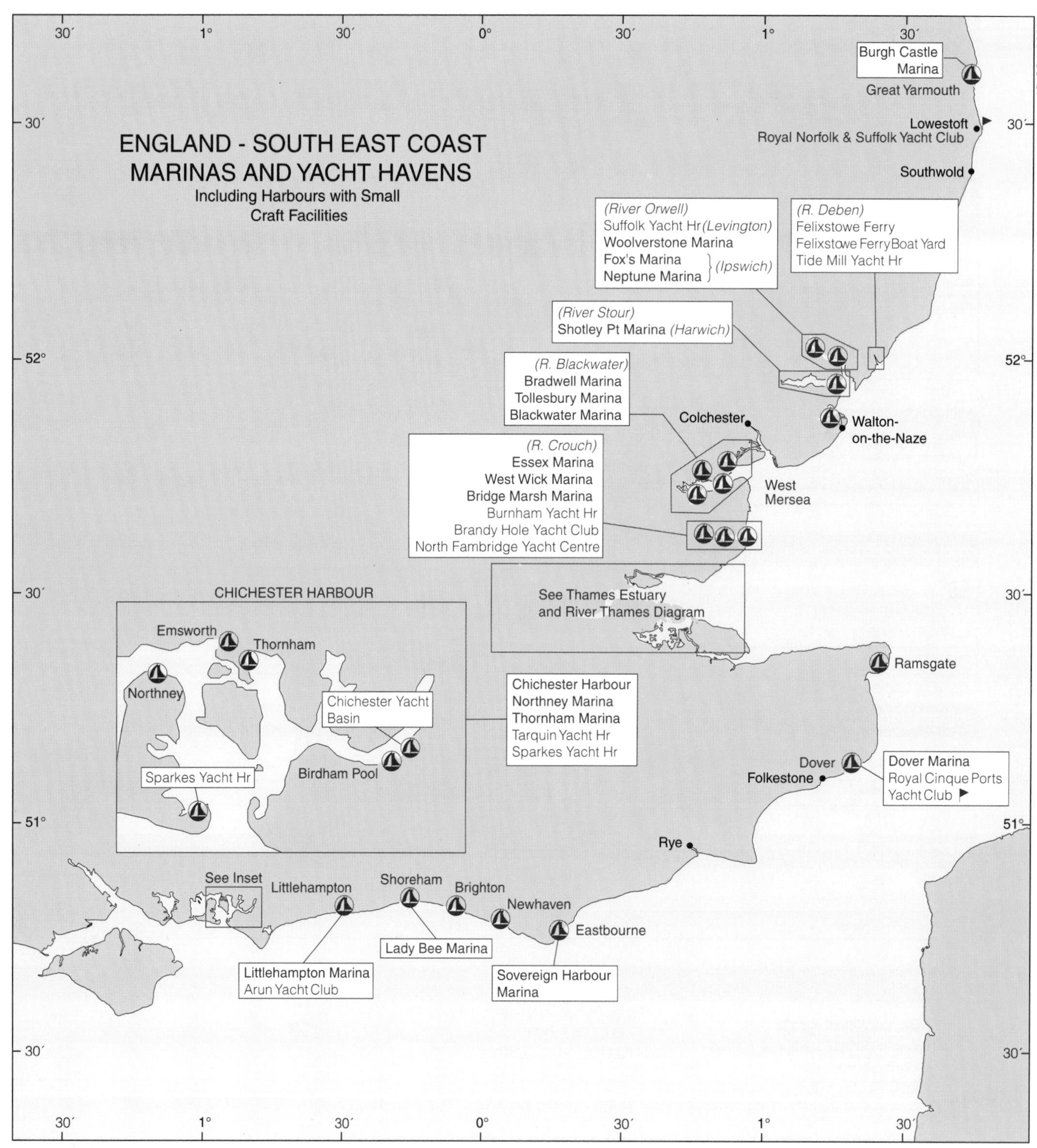

WISBECH	**Port**	**52°40'N 0°10'E**

Yacht Harbour Master: +44(0)1945 588059
Mobile: 07860 576685
Sutton Bridge Port +44(0)1406 350364

Port Office: +44(0)1945 588059
Sutton Bridge Port: +44(0)1406 350503

FREQUENCY: Port: Ch **09** 16 72
Sutton Bridge: Ch 09

HOURS: From HW -3h to HW when a vessel is expected

INFORMATION: Yacht berthing Ch 80 and 77, information broadcasts on Ch **09** - maintain listening watch on Ch 09 at all times

WOOLVERSTONE MARINA, RIVER STOUR	200 Berths 120 Swinging Moorings	52°00′·4N 1°11′·7E
☎ +44(0)1473 780206 woolverstone@mdlmarinas.co.uk	Maximum LOA 24 m	Fax +44(0)1473 780273 www.marinas.co.uk
FREQUENCY: Ch M **80**		HOURS OPEN: Mon-Fri: 0800-1900 LT Sat & Sun: 0800-2100 LT ACCESS: H24

UNITED KINGDOM, ENGLAND - SOUTH COAST INCLUDING THE CHANNEL ISLANDS

NAVTEX [T] [M]

T M	Oostende	518 kHz	51°11′N 2°48′E
DIAGRAMS: pages 159 and 161			
Weather Bulletins			
T: On receipt and at the next following broacast 0310 0710 1110 1510 1910 2310	Strong breeze warnings for Dover, Thames		
T: 0710 1910	Strong breeze warnings forecast for Dover and Thames		
Navigational Warnings			
T: 0310 0710 1110 1510 1910 2310	In English		
M: 0200 0600 1000 1400 1800 2200	In English for Area Juliett		

BRIXHAM (Coastguard MRSC) MMSI 002320013 — DSC VHF √

50°24′N 3°31′W — Operational area: Topsham to Dodman Point

Tel: +44(0)1803 882704 — Fax: +44(0)1803 882780

RT (MF) Transmits **2182** Receives **2182** — **VHF** Ch **10 23** 16 67 **73 84 86**

MARITIME SAFETY INFORMATION BROADCASTS		
	VHF Ch **10 23 73 84 86**	An announcement will be made on VHF Channel 16 indicating which VHF working channel will be used for the broadcast

Weather and Navigational warnings broadcast on receipt — DIAGRAMS: pages 158, 159, 161, 186 and 187

Weather Bulletins	
0050 0450 0850 1250 1650 2050	Gale warnings for Areas Plymouth and Portland. Local area strong wind warnings (Beaufort Force 6 / 7) and / or gale warnings. Inshore forecast for Region 8
0850 2050	Shipping forecast: gale warnings, synopsis, 24 hour forecast for Areas Plymouth and Portland
Navigational Warnings	
0050 0450 0850 1250 1650 2050	For Areas Delta (East of longitude for Land's End) and Golf. Local warnings as and when agreed with the Hydrographer, Lighthouse Authority or Harbour Authority. **Submarine / Gunnery Exercises (SUBFACTS / GUNFACTS — South Coast).** Broadcast after any storm warnings, weather messages and navigational warnings. Will cover any planned submarine activity for the following 24 hours

CHANNEL ISLANDS

National SAR Agency: SOUTH
Address: Harbour Office, P.O. Box 599, S. Helier, Jersey, JE4 9XF, UK
Tel: 44 (0)1534 885588 **Fax:** 44 (0)1534 885599

National SAR Agency: NORTH
Address: Harbour Office, New Jetty, S. Peter Port, Guernsey, GY1 2LW, UK
Tel: 44 (0)1534 720229 **Fax:** 44 (0)1534 714177

The Channel Islands area is split in two zones for the purpose of Search and Rescue, with Jersey Harbour Authority controlling Search and Rescue in the Southern Area and Guernsey Harbour Authority being the principal station for the Northern Area
In the Northern Area, in addition to Guernsey there is Alderney which is recognised as a Sub-Station
The area is recognised as extending up to 12 n miles from the Channel Islands coastline or the median line whichever is the nearer
Jersey Radio maintains a continuous listening watch on 2182 kHz, VHF Ch 16 and DSC Ch 70. S. Peter Port Radio maintains a continuous listening watch on 2182 kHz and VHF Ch 16. Alderney Radio maintains watch on VHF Ch 16 during daylight hours

	Telephone +44	**Fax** +44	**Others**
ALDERNEY RADIO	(0)1481 822620	(0)1481 822436	
JERSEY RADIO	(0)1534 741121	(0)1534 499089	
S. PETER PORT RADIO	(0)1481 720672 & 710277	(0)1481 714177	

BBC RADIO JERSEY

	1026	AM	Trinity
	88·8 MHz	FM	Les Platons
Weather Bulletins			
Mon-Fri: 0600 1900 LT Sat & Sun: 0700 1900 LT	**Wind Information:** Wind direction and force for local waters around Jersey		
Mon-Fri: 0635 1903 LT Sat, Sun: 0735 LT	Shipping forecast: including forecast, synopsis, visibility, reports from selected observation stations, wind direction and force, for local waters around Jersey		

BBC RADIO JERSEY (Continued)

Navigational Warnings	
Mon-Fri: 0600 1900 LT Sat & Sun: 0700 1300 LT	Tidal Information

GUERNSEY, S. PETER PORT (COMMUNICATION SERVICES) MMSI 002320064 DSC CH70

49°26'·2N 2°35'·77W

☎ +44(0)1481 720672 & 720085
+44(0)1481 710277 (Shore-Ship Link Call)

	Transmits	Receives	Hours of Watch
RT (MF)	1662·5[1]	1662·5[1]	
	1764	2049 2056	
	2182	2182	H24
VHF	Ch 16 20 62[1] 67[2]		H24

Direct calling on working channels required

1 Available for link calls
2 Available on request for yacht safety messages

S. PETER PORT RT (MF) 1764 VHF Ch 20 62

Weather Bulletins	
0133 0533 0933 1333 1733 2133	Weather Bulletins for Guernsey

JERSEY

	1659	RT (MF)	Broadcasts are announced on 2182 kHz and VHF Ch 16
	Ch 25 82	VHF	

Weather Bulletins	
On receipt 0307 0907 1507 2107	Storm Warnings: Near gale warnings for Channel Islands; S of 50°N, E of 3°W
0645[1] 0745[1] 0845[1] 1245 1845 2245 On request 1. Broadcasts given 1 hour earlier when DST is in force	Near gale warnings, synopsis, 24 hour forecast and outlook for a further 24 hours for Channel Islands; S of 50°N, E of 3°W Reports from meteorological observation stations
Navigational Warnings	
On receipt 0433 0833 1633 2033	For Channel Islands

JERSEY (COMMUNICATION SERVICES) MMSI 002320060 DSC Ch 70

49°11'N 2°14'W

☎ +44(0)1534 741121
Fax +44(0)1534 499089
commserv@itl.net

	Transmits	Receives	Hours of Watch
RT (MF)	1659	2045 2048 2084	
	2182	2182	H24
VHF	Ch 16 25[2] 67 82[1]		H24

1 Direct calling on working channels for UK registered vessels
2 Available for link calls

Please note that VHF Ch M (Marina Frequency) is not to be used in S. Helier

S. HELIER PIERHEADS VHF Ch 18

Continuous Broadcast Automatic wind information broadcast every 2 minutes, comprising 10 minute mean wind speed / gust / direction

DOVER (Coastguard MRCC) MMSI 002320010 — DSC VHF √

50°08'N 1°20'E

Operational area: Reculver Towers to Beachy Head

☎ +44(0)1304 210008
Fax +44(0)1304 202137

RT (MF) Transmits **2182** Receives **2182**

VHF Ch 06 10 11 **16 23** 67 73 **86**

Dover Coastguard operates the Channel Navigation Information Service (CNIS) in conjunction with Gris Nez Traffic. VHF Ch 11 is Dover Coastguard's primary working frequency for routine CNIS traffic. CNIS information broadcasts are made on VHF Ch 11 at H+40 (additional broadcast at H+55 when visibility is less than 2 n miles). Gris Nez broadcasts at H+10 and H+25 when visibility is less than 2 n miles

DOVER (Coastguard MRCC) MMSI 002320010 (Continued) — DSC VHF √

MARITIME SAFETY INFORMATION BROADCASTS

	VHF Ch **23** **86**	An announcement will be made on VHF Ch 16 indicating which VHF working channel will be used for the broadcast

Weather and Navigational warnings broadcast on receipt — DIAGRAMS: pages 158, 159 and 161

Weather Bulletins

0105 0505 0905 1305 1705 2105	Warnings: Gale warnings for Areas Thames, Dover and Wight. Local area strong wind warnings (Beaufort Force 6 / 7) and / or gale warnings. Inshore forecast for Region 6
0905 2105	Shipping forecast: gale warnings, synopsis, 24 hour forecast for Areas Thames, Dover and Wight

Navigational Warnings

0105 0505 0905 1305 1705 2105	For Areas India and Juliett. Local warnings as and when agreed with the Hydrographer, Lighthouse Authority or Harbour Authority

FALMOUTH (Coastguard MRCC) MMSI 002320014 — DSC VHF √ MF √

50°09′N 5°03′W — Operational area: Dodman Point to Marsland Mouth

Tel: +44(0)1326 317575 — Fax: +44(0)1326 318342

RT (MF)	Transmits	Receives	VHF Ch 06 10 **16** **23** 67 73 84 **86**
	2182	2182	
	2226	**2226**	
	2670	2670	

MARITIME SAFETY INFORMATION BROADCASTS

A	**2226**	RT (MF)		
B	VHF Ch **23** **86**	An announcement will be made on VHF Ch 16 indicating which VHF working channel will be used for the broadcast		

Weather and Navigational warnings broadcast on receipt — DIAGRAMS: pages 158, 159, 161, 186 and 187

Weather Bulletins

A: 0140 0540 0940 1340 1740 2140	Gale warnings for Areas Plymouth, Lundy, Fastnet and Sole
B: 0140 0540 0940 1340 1740 2140	Local area strong wind warnings (Beaufort Force 6 / 7) and / or gale warnings. Inshore forecast for Regions 8 and 9
A, B: 0940 2140	Shipping forecast: gale warnings, synopsis, 24 hour forecast for Areas Plymouth, Lundy, Fastnet and Sole

Navigational Warnings

A: 0140 0540 0940 1340 1740 2140	For Areas Delta, Foxtrot and Golf
B: 0140 0540 0940 1340 1740 2140	For Areas Delta, Foxtrot and Golf. Local warnings as and when agreed with the Hydrographer, Lighthouse Authority or Harbour Authority. **Submarine / Gunnery Exercises (SUBFACTS / GUNFACTS — South Coast).** Broadcast after any storm warnings, weather messages and navigational warnings. Will cover any planned submarine activity for the following 24 hours

OOSTENDE

A	2761	RT (MF)		
B	Ch 27	VHF		

DIAGRAMS: pages 159 and 161

Weather Bulletins

A, B: On receipt	Storm Warnings: Strong breeze warnings in English and Dutch for Dover & Thames
A, B: 0820 1720	Strong breeze warnings, forecast in English and Dutch for Dover & Thames

Navigational Warnings

A, B: On receipt **A:** 0233 0633 1033 1433 1833 2233	In English and Dutch

PORTLAND (Coastguard MRSC) MMSI 002320012 — DSC VHF √

50°36′N 2°27′W	Operational area: Chewton Bunney to Topsham
☎ +44(0)1305 760439	Fax +44(0)1305 760452
	VHF Ch 06 **10** 16 23 67 69* **73** 84 **86** *Ch 69 is a Vessel reporting frequency

MARITIME SAFETY INFORMATION BROADCASTS

	VHF Ch **10** **73** or **86**	An announcement will be made on VHF Ch 16 indicating which VHF working channel will be used for the broadcast

Weather and Navigational warnings broadcast on receipt — DIAGRAMS: pages 158, 159 and 161

Weather Bulletins

0220 0620 1020 1420 1820 2220	Gale warnings for Areas Plymouth, Portland and Wight. Local area strong wind warnings (Beaufort Force 6 / 7) and / or gale warnings. Inshore forecast for Region 7
1020 2220	Shipping forecast: gale warnings, synopsis, 24 hour forecast for Areas Plymouth, Portland and Wight

Navigational Warnings

0220 0620 1020 1420 1820 2220	For Areas Delta, Golf and Hotel. Local warnings as and when agreed with the Hydrographer, Lighthouse Authority or Harbour Authority

SOLENT (Coastguard MRSC) MMSI 002320011 — DSC VHF √

50°48′N 1°12′W	Operational area: Beachy Head to Chewton Bunney including Isle of Wight
☎ +44(0)23 92552100	Fax +44(0)23 92551763

RT (MF)	Transmits	Receives	
	1641	**1641**	**VHF** Ch 06 10 16 **23** 67 **73** 84 **86**
	2182	2182	
	2596	2596	

MARITIME SAFETY INFORMATION BROADCASTS

A	**1641**	RT (MF)		
B	VHF Ch **23** **86**	An announcement will be made on VHF Ch 16 indicating which VHF working channel will be used for the broadcast		

Weather and Navigational warnings broadcast on receipt — DIAGRAMS: pages 158, 159 and 161

Weather Bulletins

B: 0040 0440 0840 1240 1640 2040	Gale warnings for Areas Portland and Wight. Local area strong wind warnings (Beaufort Force 6 / 7) and / or gale warnings. Inshore forecast for Region 7
A: 0040 0440 0840 1240 1640 2040	Gale warnings for Areas Portland and Wight
A, B: 0840 2040	Shipping forecast: gale warnings, synopsis, 24 hour forecast for Areas Portland and Wight

Navigational Warnings

B: 0040 0440 0840 1240 1640 2040	For Areas Golf, Hotel and India. Local warnings as and when agreed with the Hydrographer, Lighthouse Authority or Harbour Authority
A: 0040 0440 0840 1240 1640 2040	For Areas Golf, Hotel and India

BEAUCETTE MARINA (GUERNSEY) — 49°30′·2N 2°30′·2W

☎ +44(0)1481 245000 Mobile: +44(0)07781 102302 beaucette@premiermarinas.com	Fax +44(0)1481 247071 www.premiermarinas.com
FREQUENCY: Ch 80	HOURS OF WATCH: 0830-2030 LT ACCESS: HW ± 3h

BEMBRIDGE MARINA, ISLE OF WIGHT — CALL: Bembridge Marina — 100 Pontoon Berths — 50°41′·6N 1°06′·4W

☎ Marine Office: +44(0)1983 872828	Depth: 2 m, Maximum LOA 18 m	Fax +44(0)1983 872922 www.harbours.co.uk
FREQUENCY: Marina: Ch 80 Harbour Launch: Ch M		ACCESS: HW -3h to 2½ h

BIRDHAM POOL, CHICHESTER — 50°48′·0N 0°49′·4W

☎ +44(0)1243 512310	Fax +44(0)1243 513163

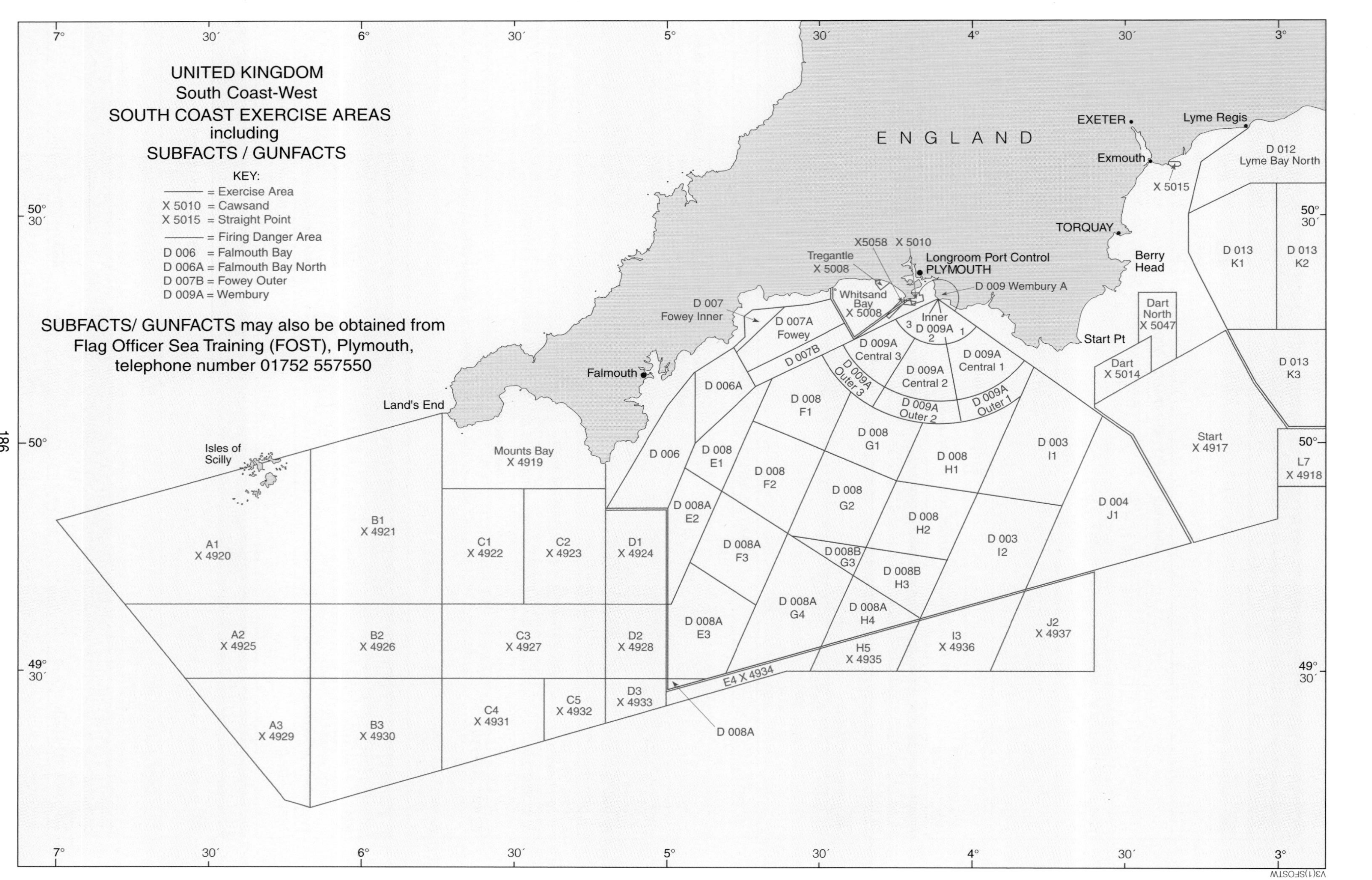
UNITED KINGDOM
South Coast-West
SOUTH COAST EXERCISE AREAS
including
SUBFACTS / GUNFACTS
KEY:
= Exercise Area
X 5010 = Cawsand
X 5015 = Straight Point
= Firing Danger Area
D 006 = Falmouth Bay
D 006A = Falmouth Bay North
D 007B = Fowey Outer
D 009A = Wembury
SUBFACTS/ GUNFACTS may also be obtained from Flag Officer Sea Training (FOST), Plymouth, telephone number 01752 557550
ENGLAND
EXETER
Lyme Regis
Exmouth
X 5015
TORQUAY
Berry Head
Start Pt
Longroom Port Control
PLYMOUTH
X5058 X 5010
Tregantle X 5008
Whitsand Bay X 5008
D 009 Wembury A
D 007 Fowey Inner
Falmouth
Land's End
Isles of Scilly
Mounts Bay X 4919
D 012 Lyme Bay North
D 013 K1
D 013 K2
D 013 K3
Dart North X 5047
Dart X 5014
Start X 4917
L7 X 4918
D 007A Fowey
D 007B
D 006A
D 006
Inner D 009A 1 2 3
D 009A Central 1
D 009A Central 2
D 009A Central 3
D 009A Outer 1
D 009A Outer 2
D 009A Outer 3
D 008 F1
D 008 G1
D 008 H1
D 003 I1
D 004 J1
D 008 E1
D 008 F2
D 008 G2
D 008 H2
D 003 I2
D 008A E2
D 008A F3
D 008B G3
D 008B H3
D 008A G4
D 008A H4
D 008A E3
H5 X 4935
I3 X 4936
J2 X 4937
E4 X 4934
D 008A
A1 X 4920
B1 X 4921
C1 X 4922
C2 X 4923
D1 X 4924
A2 X 4925
B2 X 4926
C3 X 4927
D2 X 4928
A3 X 4929
B3 X 4930
C4 X 4931
C5 X 4932
D3 X 4933
7° 30′ 6° 30′ 5° 30′ 4° 30′ 3°
50° 30′
50°
49° 30′
V3(1)SFOSTW

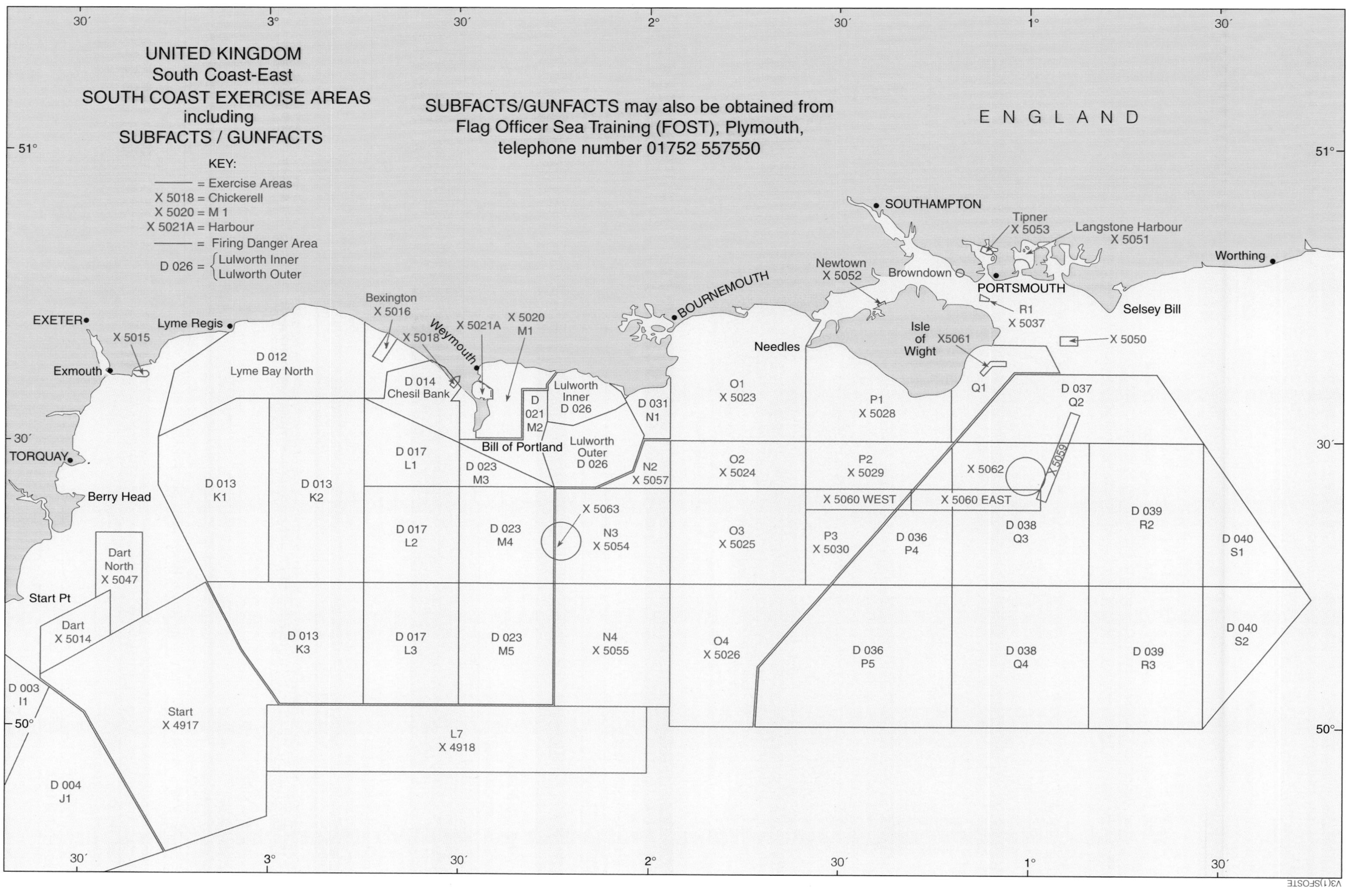
UNITED KINGDOM
South Coast-East
SOUTH COAST EXERCISE AREAS
including
SUBFACTS / GUNFACTS
SUBFACTS/GUNFACTS may also be obtained from
Flag Officer Sea Training (FOST), Plymouth,
telephone number 01752 557550
KEY:
= Exercise Areas
X 5018 = Chickerell
X 5020 = M 1
X 5021A = Harbour
= Firing Danger Area
D 026 = Lulworth Inner
Lulworth Outer
ENGLAND
EXETER
Exmouth
X 5015
Lyme Regis
TORQUAY
Berry Head
Start Pt
Bexington
X 5016
X 5018
Weymouth
X 5021A
X 5020
M1
Bill of Portland
BOURNEMOUTH
Needles
Newtown
X 5052
Browndown
SOUTHAMPTON
Tipner
X 5053
Langstone Harbour
X 5051
PORTSMOUTH
R1
X 5037
Isle of Wight
X5061
X 5050
Selsey Bill
Worthing
D 012
Lyme Bay North
D 014
Chesil Bank
D
021
M2
Lulworth
Inner
D 026
Lulworth
Outer
D 026
D 031
N1
N2
X 5057
O1
X 5023
O2
X 5024
O3
X 5025
O4
X 5026
P1
X 5028
P2
X 5029
P3
X 5030
Q1
D 037
Q2
X 5059
X 5062
X 5060 WEST
X 5060 EAST
D 036
P4
D 036
P5
D 038
Q3
D 038
Q4
D 039
R2
D 039
R3
D 040
S1
D 040
S2
D 013
K1
D 013
K2
D 013
K3
D 017
L1
D 017
L2
D 017
L3
D 023
M3
D 023
M4
D 023
M5
X 5063
N3
X 5054
N4
X 5055
Dart
North
X 5047
Dart
X 5014
D 003
I1
D 004
J1
Start
X 4917
L7
X 4918
30´
3°
2°
1°
51°
50°
V3(1)SFOSTE

BRAYE (ALDERNEY HARBOUR)	Port: CALL: Alderney Radio 64 Berths (Mooring Buoys)	49°43'80N 2°11'·45W
☎ Hr Mr's Office: +44(0)1481 822620 alderneyharbourmaster@gtonline.net		Fax Hr Mr's Office: +44(0)1481 823699 www.alderney.gov.uk
FREQUENCY: Ch 16 **74** NOTE: 1. A water taxi service is available by calling Mainbrayce Taxi on VHF Ch 37 80 (01481 822772) Outside these hours vessels should call S. Peter Port who will advise the officer on-call 2. A Vessel Traffic Service (VTS) with Port Radar and VHF is available when the Harbour Office is open. This service is available to small craft needing assistance during fog or limited visibility		HOURS: May: 0800-1800 LT June-Sept: 0800-2000 LT Oct-Apr: Mon-Fri: 0800-1700 LT

ALDERNEY HARBOUR

BRIDPORT	Port: CALL: Bridport Harbour Radio	50°42'N 2°46'W
☎ Hr Mr: +44(0)1308 423222		Fax Hr Mr: +44(0)1308 251481
FREQUENCY: Ch 11 16		HOURS: Summer: 0730-1700 LT

BRIGHTON MARINA	CALL: Brighton Marina 1500 Berths 200 Visitor Berths	50°48'·5N 0°06'·0W
☎ +44(0)1273 819919 brighton@premiermarinas.com		Fax +44(0)1273 675082 www.premiermarinas.com
FREQUENCY: Ch 16 M **80**		HOURS OPEN: H24, ACCESS: 0800-1800 LT

BRIXHAM MARINA	CALL: Brixham Marina	50°24'·0N 3°30'·5W
☎ +44(0)1803 882929 Port: +44(0)1803 853321 brixham@mdlmarinas.co.uk		Fax +44(0)1803 882737 www.marinas.co.uk
FREQUENCY: Ch 80 Port: Ch 14 16		HOURS OPEN: H24, ACCESS: H24

BUCKLER'S HARD YACHT HARBOUR		50°48'·1N 1°25'·3W
☎ +44(0)1590 616200 & 616234 beaulieu@tcp.co.uk		Fax +44(0)1590 616211 www.beaulieu.co.uk
FREQUENCY: Ch M 80	LOCATION: Beaulieu River	
PROCEDURE: Visiting yachts should report to the Harbour Master within 24h of arrival		

CATTEWATER HARBOUR, PLYMOUTH	CALL: Cattewater Harbour	50°22'N 4°07'W
☎ Office hours: +44(0)1752 665934 info@plymouthport.co.uk		Fax +44(0)1752 253624
FREQUENCY: Ch 14 16		HOURS: Mon-Fri: 0900-1700 LT

CATTEWATER HARBOUR FROM W

CHARLESTOWN, S. AUSTELL BAY	Port: CALL: Charlestown	50°20′N 4°45′W
Tel: Hr Mr: +44(0)1726 73021 Hr Office: +44(0)1726 67526 & 70241 info@square-sail.com		Fax: Hr Office: +44(0)1726 61839 www.square-sail.com
FREQUENCY: Ch 14 16		HOURS: HW -2h to +1h

CHICHESTER	Port: CALL: Chichester Harbour Radio or Chichester Harbour Patrol (for Harbour Launch)	50°48′N 0°56′W
Tel: Hr Mr Office: +44(0)1243 512301 Emsworth Hr Office: +44(0)1243 376422 mooringsofficer@conservancy.co.uk	Visiting yachts requiring moorings are advised to make arrangements in advance Requests for overnight swinging moorings should be made when in the vicinity of Chichester Bar Beacon	Fax: Hr Mr Office: +44(0)1243 513026 www.conservancy.co.uk
FREQUENCY: Port: Ch **14** 16	LOCATION: Harbour Office, Itchenor	HOURS: 1 Oct-31 Mar: Mon-Fri: 0900-1300 1400-1700 LT 1 Apr-30 Sept: 0900-1300 1400-1700 LT Sat: 0900-1300 LT
PROCEDURE: (1) Ferry available 0900-1800 Mobile: 07970 378350 or VHF Ch 08 (Hx) (2) Link to Chichester Bar Beacon Weather Station on www.chimet.co.uk gives depth of water, wind direction, barometric pressure, etc		

CHICHESTER MARINA	CALL: Chichester Marina 1100 Berths Visitors Berths Available	50°48′·2N 0°49′·2W
Tel: +44(0)1243 512731 chichester@premiermarinas.com		Fax: +44(0)1243 513472 www.premiermarinas.com
FREQUENCY: Marina & Lock Control: Ch **80**	LOCATION: Birdham	HOURS OF WATCH: Apr-Sept: Mon-Thur: 0700-2100 LT Fri-Sun: 0700-0000 LT Oct-Mar: 0800-1700 LT HOURS OPEN: 0900-1730 LT ACCESS: HW ± 5h through the lock

COBBS QUAY MARINA, POOLE	CALL: Cobbs Quay Marina/CQ Marina 850 Berths	50°43′·3N 2°00′·1W
Tel: +44(0)1202 674299 Mobile: 07740 806036 cobbsquay@mdlmarinas.co.uk		Fax: +44(0)1202 665217 www.marinas.co.uk
FREQUENCY: Ch **80**	LOCATION: Hamworthy	HOURS OPEN: 0730-1930 LT ACCESS: HW ± 4h (according to opening of Poole Bridge)

COWES, ISLE OF WIGHT

Port: CALL: Cowes Harbour Radio — 50°46'N 1°18'W

Tel: Hr Mr: +44(0)1983 293952
Mobile: +44(0)7050 344820
Folly Waterbus: 07974 864627
Water Taxi Mobile: 07050 344818

Fax: Hr Mr: +44(0)1983 290018

chc@cowes.co.uk — www.cowes.co.uk

FREQUENCY: Port: Ch **69**
Oil Pollution Control: Ch 10
Water Taxi: Ch 77

LOCATION: Harbour Office (50°45'·71N 1°17'·75W)

HOURS: Port: Mon-Fri: 0800-1700 LT

NOTES:
1. All private/recreational vessels of 30 metres LOA and above, in addition to all commercial vessels, should give notice on VHF Channel 69 to "All ships in Cowes Harbour" on entry and when getting underway upon departure. Additionally, these vessels should contact " Cowes Chain Ferry" on VHF Channel 69 before passing
2. Private/recreational vessels less than 30 metres LOA are NOT required to announce their movements on VHF Channel 69 **but are strongly advised** to monitor this channel for information purposes
3. Harbour launches will listen on VHF Channel 69

Chain Ferry: CALL: Cowes Chain Ferry

Tel: +44(0)1983 293041

Fax:

FREQUENCY: Ch 69

HOURS: Mon - Sat: 0435 - 2359 LT
Sun: 0635 - 2359 LT

PROCEDURE: The Chain Ferry gives way to all traffic. All commercial vessels and, in addition, all private/recreational vessels of 30m LOA and above are required to advise the Chain Ferry of their intention to pass through the ferry area. The ferry will acknowledge the call

COWES YACHT HAVEN LTD

CALL: Cowes Yacht Haven — 260 Berths — 50°45'·6N 1°17'·6W

Maximum LOA: 50 m

Tel: +44(0)1983 295724 & 299975

Fax: +44(0)1983 200332

info@cowesyachthaven.demon.co.uk — www.cowesyachthaven.demon.co.uk

FREQUENCY: Ch 80

HOURS & ACCESS: H24

DARTMOUTH FROM S

DARTMOUTH

Port: CALL: Port: Dartnav — 50°21'N 3°34'W

Tel: Port: +44(0)1803 832337
Emergency only: Outside office hours: +44(0)1803 835220
Mobile: 07970 346571
Britannia Royal Naval College: +44(0)1803 83 2141

Fax: Port: +44(0)1803 833631

dhna@dartharbour.org.uk — www.dartharbour.org.uk

FREQUENCY: Hr Mr: Ch 11 16
Yacht Taxi: Ch 69
Britannia Royal Naval College: Ch 71

LOCATION: Harbour Office (50°21'·0N 3°34'·6W)

HOURS: Port: Mon-Fri: 0900-1700 LT
Sat: 0900-1200 LT

DART MARINA	CALL: Dart Marina	50°21′·4N 3°34′·6W
☎ +44(0)1803 833351 marinas@philip-group.demon.co.uk		Fax +44(0)1803 832307 www.ybw.com/web/philipleisure/
FREQUENCY: Ch 80	LOCATION: Sandquay	HOURS OPEN: 0730-2000 LT, ACCESS: H24
DARTHAVEN MARINA LTD	CALL: Darthaven Marina	50°21′·0N 3°34′·3W
☎ Marina: +44(0)1803 752545 & 752242 Mobile: 0411 404259		Fax +44(0)1803 752722 www.darthaven.co.uk
FREQUENCY: Ch M 80	LOCATION: Kingswear	HOURS OPEN: 0830-1730 LT, ACCESS: H24
DARTSIDE QUAY	CALL: Dartside Quay 400 Berths	50°23′·5N 3°34′·5W
☎ +44(0)1803 845445 dartsidequay@mdlmarinas.co.uk		Fax +44(0)1803 843558 www.marinas.co.uk
FREQUENCY: Ch 80	LOCATION: Galmpton Creek	ACCESS: HW ± 3h
NOSS-ON-DART MARINA	CALL: Noss Marina	50°21′·9N 3°34′·6W
☎ +44(0)1803 833351		Fax +44(0)1803 835150
FREQUENCY: Ch M 80	LOCATION: Kingswear	HOURS OPEN: 0730-1800 LT, ACCESS: H24
DOLPHIN SHIPYARD, RIVER DART		50°23′·5N 3°35′·4W
☎ +44(0)1803 842424		Fax
	LOCATION: Galmpton Creek	

DOVER	**Port:** CALL: Dover Port Control	51°07′N 1°18′E
AREA: Dover Harbour and the area within 1 n mile to seaward of the breakwaters		
☎ Hr Office: +44(0)1304 240400 (H24) pr@doverport.co.uk		Fax Hr Office: +44(0)1304 240465 www.doverport.co.uk
FREQUENCY: Port Control: Ch 12 16 **74**	LOCATION: Dover VTS Station, Eastern Arm Head	HOURS: H24
PROCEDURE: (1) **Vessels passing Dover Harbour** and the area within 1 n mile to seaward of the breakwaters should contact Dover Port Control on VHF Ch 74 to advise their ETA at a range of 3 n miles from the port and should monitor VHF Ch 74 for harbour movement broadcasts (2) International port traffic signals are in operation day and night on light panels near Port Control at the Eastern Entrance and on the seaward end of the Admiralty Pier at the Western Entrance **IT IS IMPORTANT THAT SPECIFIC PERMISSION TO ENTER OR LEAVE THE EASTERN OR WESTERN ENTRANCE MUST BE OBTAINED FROM DOVER PORT CONTROL ON VHF**		
DOVER MARINA	400 Berths	51°07′·2N 1°18′·8E
☎ Marina: +44(0)1304 241663 Fuel: +44(0)1304 201073 marina@doverport.co.uk		Fax +44(0)1304 242549 www.doverport.co.uk
FREQUENCY: Marina: Ch 80 (should only be used within the Tidal Harbour and Marina)		HOURS OF WATCH: H24 ACCESS: HW ± 1½ h through the lock
NOTE: Diesel available from Dover Boat Co. close by Granville dock gates (Call: Dover Motor Boats on VHF Ch 74). Water Taxis on VHF Ch 74		

EAST COWES MARINA, ISLE OF WIGHT	150 Visitor Berths	50°45′·1N 1°17′·4W
☎ +44(0)1983 293983 sales@eastcowesmarina.co.uk		Fax +44(0)1983 299276 www.eastcowesmarina.co.uk
FREQUENCY: Ch 80		HOURS: Winter: 0800-1700LT Summer: 0800-2000 LT ACCESS: H24

EMSWORTH YACHT HARBOUR LTD, CHICHESTER HARBOUR	CALL: Emsworth Yacht Harbour	50°50′·4N 0°55′·8W
☎ +44(0)1243 377727 info@emsworth-marina.co.uk		Fax +44(0)1243 373432 www.emsworth-marina.co.uk
FREQUENCY: Ch M 80	LOCATION: Emsworth	HOURS OPEN: 0800-1700 LT, ACCESS: HW ± 2½ h

EXMOUTH	Marina	172 Berths 5 Visitor Moorings	50°37′·00N 3°25′·37W
☎ Exmouth Hr Mr: +44(0)1395 269314 Exeter Hr Mr: +44(0)1392 274306 Retreat Boatyard, Topsham: +44(0)1392 874720 Water Taxi: 07970918418		Maximum LOA: 13 m	Fax: Exeter Hr Mr: +44(0)1392 250234 Marina (Exmouth): +44(0)1392 267537
FREQUENCY: Ch **14** 16 (Marina) Ch 6 **12** 16 (Exeter)			HOURS: Mon-Fri: 0730-1630 LT
INFORMATION: Footbridge opens on request from 0800-1700 LT then on the hour during the evening - remaining open over night			

FALMOUTH	Port: CALL: Falmouth Harbour Radio	50°09′N 5°04′W
☎ Commercial Services: +44(0)1326 211376 Leisure Services: (Yacht Haven): +44(0)1326 312285 & 314379 Water Taxi "Aqua Cab" Mobile: 07970 242258		Fax: Leisure Services: +44(0)1326 211352
FREQUENCY: Port Operations Working: Ch 12 16 Pollution Control: Ch 10 Hr Launch "Killigrew": Ch 12	LOCATION: Harbour Office, Custom House Quay	HOURS: Mon-Fri: 0800-1700 LT Outside these times: Hr Mr may be contacted through Falmouth Pilot Radio
ACCIDENT PROCEDURES: Maritime Emergency Plan — Fal Estuary: Implementation of the Emergency Plan will be announced on VHF Ch 16 and all available information provided. All vessels should maintain a listening watch on VHF Ch 12 for further instructions. VHF Ch 11 is reserved as an Emergency Operational frequency and no other transmissions should be made on this channel		

FALMOUTH MARINA	CALL: Falmouth Marina	337 Berths	50°09′·8N 5°05′·0W
☎ +44(0)1326 316620 falmouth@premiermarinas.com			Fax: +44(0)1326 313939 www.premiermarinas.com
FREQUENCY: Ch M 80			HOURS OPEN: H24, ACCESS: H24

BURSLEDON FROM SE

FOULKES & SON BOATYARD

FAREHAM MARINA	CALL: Fareham Marina	50°50′·8N 1°10′·7W
☎ +44(0)1329 822445 & 234297		Fax:
FREQUENCY: Ch M 80		HOURS OPEN: 0900-1730 LT, ACCESS: HW ± 3h

FAREHAM YACHT HARBOUR	CALL: Portsmouth Marine	50°50′·8N 1°10′·7W
☎ Boatyard: +44(0)1329 232854 Office: +44(0)1329 288221		Fax: Office: +44(0)1329 822780
FREQUENCY: Ch M 80		HOURS OPEN: 0900-1730 LT, ACCESS: HW ± 3h

FOLKESTONE	**Port:** CALL: Folkestone Port Control 70 Berths Buoy Drying	51°04′·56N 01°11′·78E
☎ Harbour Master: +44(0)1303 220544 Port Office: +44(0)1303 715354 (H24)	Depth: 5·3 m, Maximum LOA: 90 m	Fax: Port Office: +44(0)1303 715392
FREQUENCY: Port Control: Ch **15** 16		HOURS: H24, ACCESS: HW ± 3h

FOULKES & SON RIVERSIDE BOATYARD, SOUTHAMPTON WATER		50°53′·2N 1°17′·9W
☎ +44(0)2380 406349		Fax: +44(0)2380 406349
FREQUENCY: Ch 08	LOCATION: Bursledon	

FOWEY	**Port:** CALL: Fowey Harbour Radio	50°20′N 4°39′W
☎ Hr Mr: +44(0)1726 832471 & 832472 Fuel: +44(0)1726 833055 Water Taxi: +44(0)1726 870417 Refueller: +44(0)1726 833055 fhc@foweyharbour.co.uk		Fax: +44(0)1726 833738 www.foweyharbour.co.uk
FREQUENCY: Fowey Harbour Radio: Ch 16 12 Fowey Harbour Patrol: Ch 12 Water Taxi: Ch 06 Refueller: Ch 10	LOCATION: Hr Mr Office, Albert Quay	HOURS: 0900-1700 LT

GOREY, JERSEY	**Port:** CALL: Gorey Harbour Office	49°12′N 2°01′W
☎ +44(0)1534 853616 Mobile: +44(0)07797 719336		Fax: +44(0)1534 856927
FREQUENCY: Ch 74	LOCATION: Gorey Pier	HOURS: HW ± 3h

GOSPORT MARINA (CAMPER & NICHOLSONS)	CALL: Camper Base	50°47′·8N 1°07′·0W
☎ +44(0)2392 524811 mail@gosport-marina.com		Fax: +44(0)2392 589541 www.cnmarinas.com
FREQUENCY: Ch M **80**		HOURS OPEN: H24, ACCESS: H24

GUNWHARF MARINA, PORTSMOUTH		50°47′·66N 1°06′·40W
☎ +44(0)2392 836732 info@gunwharf-quays.com	ETA giving 24 hours notice required	Fax: +44(0)2392 836738 www.gunwharf-quays.com
FREQUENCY: Ch 80		
PROCEDURE: All vessels under 20 m entering or leaving Gunwharf Quays are required to contact Queen's Harbour Master on Ch 11 before crossing the Main Channel. Yachts must pass to the north of Ballast Buoy when entering or leaving the berths		

HAMBLE RIVER	**Harbour Office:** CALL: Hamble Harbour Radio	50°51′·2N 01°18′·3W
☎ +44(0)1489 576387 office@hamble-river.demon.co.uk		Fax: +44(0)1489 576387 www.hants.gov.uk/hambleharbour
FREQUENCY: Hr Mr: Ch 68 Water Taxi Service on VHF Ch 77 Vessels over 20m LOA should call Hamble Harbour Radio before entering the river or getting underway and are to maintain a listening watch on the VHF Ch 68 whilst underway within the Harbour limits		HOURS OPEN: Summer: 0600-2200 LT Winter: 0730-1830 LT

HAMBLE POINT MARINA	CALL: Hamble Marina	50°51′·1N 1°18′·6W
☎ +44(0)2380 452464 hamblepoint@mdlmarinas.co.uk		Fax: +44(0)2380 456440 www.marinas.co.uk
FREQUENCY: Ch 80		HOURS OPEN: H24, ACCESS: H24
PORT HAMBLE MARINA	CALL: Port Hamble	50°51′·6N 1°18′·6W
☎ +44(0)2380 452741 porthamble@mdlmarinas.co.uk		Fax: +44(0)2380 455206 www.marinas.co.uk
FREQUENCY: Ch 80		HOURS OPEN: H24, ACCESS: H24

HAMBLE RIVER ENTRANCE FROM SW

HAMBLE YACHT SERVICES	CALL: HYS	50°51′·8N 1°18′·5W
☎ +44(0)2380 454111		Fax +44(0)2380 455682
FREQUENCY: Ch 80		HOURS OPEN: 0800-1700 LT, ACCESS: H24

HASLAR MARINA, PORTSMOUTH	CALL: Haslar Marina	50°47′·4N 1°07′·5W
☎ +44(0)2392 601201		Fax +44(0)2392 602201
FREQUENCY: Ch 11 M **80**	LOCATION: Gosport	HOURS OPEN: H24, ACCESS: H24

HYTHE MARINA VILLAGE, SOUTHAMPTON WATER	CALL: Hythe Marina 210 Berths	50°52′·4N 1°24′·0W
☎ +44(0)2380 207073 & 849263 hythe@mdlmarinas.co.uk		Fax +44(0)2380 842424 www.marinas.co.uk
FREQUENCY: Ch **80**		ACCESS: H24 through the lock

ISLAND HARBOUR MARINA, ISLE OF WIGHT	150 Visitor Berths	50°43′·5N 1°16′·6W
☎ +44(0)1983 822999 pafharbour@aol.com		Fax +44(0)1983 526020
FREQUENCY: Ch **80**		HOURS OPEN: 0830-1730 LT ACCESS: HW ± 4h through the lock

ITCHEN MARINA, SOUTHAMPTON		50°54′·1N 1°23′·3W
☎ +44(0)2380 631500		Fax +44(0)2380 335606
FREQUENCY: Ch 12	LOCATION: American Wharf	HOURS OF WATCH: HX

KEMPS QUAY, SOUTHAMPTON WATER	**Marina** 200 Berths	50°54′·9N 1°22′·6W
☎ +44(0)2380 632323		Fax +44(0)2380 226002
FREQUENCY: Ch M 80 (Via Chandler)		ACCESS: HW ± 3½ h

LAKEYARD, POOLE	**Marina** 60 Deep Water Berths 90 Moorings Visitors Berths	50°42′·7N 2°01′·1W
+44(0)1202 674531	Maximum Depth: 1·7 m, Maximum LOA: 15 m	+44(0)1202 677518 www.lakeyard.co.uk
FREQUENCY: Ch M 80	LOCATION: Wareham Channel	HOURS OPEN: 0900-1730 LT

LANGSTONE HARBOUR	**Port:** CALL: Langstone Harbour Radio	50°49′N 1°01′W
Hr Office: +44(0)2392 463419 (Office hours: 0900-1700 LT) jardine@langstoneharbour.org.uk		Hr Office: +44(0)2392 467144 www.langstoneharbour.org.uk
FREQUENCY: Ch 12 16	LOCATION: Harbour Office, Ferry Point, Hayling Island	HOURS: May-Oct: 0800-1700 LT Nov-Apr. Closed

LITTLEHAMPTON		50°48′N 0°32′W
Hr Mr Office: Office hours: +44(0)1903 721215 harbour@littlehampton.org.uk		+44(0)1903 739472 www.littlehampton.org.uk
FREQUENCY: Ch **71**		HOURS: HX
LITTLEHAMPTON MARINA		50°48′·6N 0°33′·3W
+44(0)1903 713553		+44(0)1903 732264
FREQUENCY: Ch M 80		HOURS OPEN: 0800-1800 LT, ACCESS: H24
ARUN YACHT CLUB		50°48′·35N 0°32′·60W
+44(0)1903 714533	Limited visitor moorings	+44(0)1903 716016
FREQUENCY: Ch M	LOCATION: Littlehampton	ACCESS: HW ± 3h

LOOE HARBOUR		50°21′·04N 4°27′·03W
+44(0)1503 262839		
FREQUENCY: Ch 16		HOURS OPEN: Mon-Fri: 0900-1700 LT

LYME REGIS	**Port:** CALL: Lyme Regis Harbour	50°43′N 2°56′W
+44(0)1297 442137		+44(0)1297 442137
FREQUENCY: Ch 14 16		HOURS: Summer: 0800-2000 LT Winter: 1000-1500 LT ACCESS HW ± 2½ h

LYMINGTON MARINA	CALL: Lymington Marina	50°45′·4N 1°31′·8W
+44(0)1590 673312 ext 237		+44(0)1590 679811
FREQUENCY: Ch 80		HOURS OPEN: Summer: 0800-2200 LT Winter: 0800-2000 LT ACCESS: H24

LYMINGTON YACHT HAVEN	CALL: Lymington Yacht Haven	50°45′·0N 1°31′·5W
Yacht Haven: +44(0)1590 677071 Hr Mr: +44(0)1590 672014 lymington@aol.com		Hr Mr: +44(0)1590 671823 +44(0)1590 678186 www.yachthavens.com
FREQUENCY: Ch 80		HOURS OPEN: 0800-2100 LT (Summer) 0800-1800 LT (Winter) ACCESS: H24

MALPAS MARINE, TRURO		50°14′·7N 5°01′·4W
+44(0)1872 271260		
FREQUENCY: Ch M		HOURS OPEN: HJ, ACCESS: HW ± 3h

LYMINGTON RIVER FROM SE

MAYFLOWER INTERNATIONAL MARINA, PLYMOUTH	CALL: Mayflower Marina	50°21'·8N 4°10'·0W
☎ +44(0)1752 556633 & 567106 mayflower@mayflowermarina.co.uk		Fax +44(0)1752 606896 www.mayflowermarina.co.uk
FREQUENCY: Ch M **80**		HOURS OPEN: H24, ACCESS: H24

MERCURY YACHT HARBOUR, RIVER HAMBLE	CALL: Mercury Yacht Harbour	50°52'·2N 1°18'·6W
☎ +44(0)2380 455994 mercury@mdlmarinas.co.uk		Fax +44(0)2380 457369 www.marinas.co.uk
FREQUENCY: Ch 80		HOURS OPEN: H24, ACCESS: H24

MEVAGISSEY	**Port:** CALL: Mevagissey Harbour Radio	50°16'N 4°47'W
☎ Office: +44(0)1726 843305 After Office Hours: +44(0)1726 842496 meva.harbour@talk21.com		Fax +44(0)1726 842535 www.mevagisseyharbour.co.uk
FREQUENCY: Ch 14 16	LOCATION: Harbour Office, East Quay	HOURS: Summer: 0900-2100 LT Winter: 0900-1700 LT

MILLBAY MARINA VILLAGE, PLYMOUTH	CALL: Millbay Marina	50°21'·8N 4°09'·1W
☎ +44(0)1752 226785		Fax +44(0)1752 226785
FREQUENCY: Ch M 80		HOURS OF WATCH: 0800-1700 LT, ACCESS: H24

MYLOR YACHT HARBOUR, FALMOUTH BAY	CALL: Mylor Yacht Harbour	50°10'·72N 5°03'·13W
☎ +44(0)1326 372121 enquires@mylor.com		Fax +44(0)1326 372120 www.mylor.com
FREQUENCY: Ch M 80		HOURS OPEN: H24, ACCESS: H24

NEWHAVEN	**Port:** CALL: Newhaven Radio	50°47'N 0°04'E
☎ Hr Mr: +44(0)1273 612872		Fax Hr Mr: +44(0)1273 612878
FREQUENCY: Ch 12	LOCATION: Signal Station, West Pier	HOURS: H24

MYLOR YACHT HARBOUR

NEWHAVEN (Continued)	**Port:** CALL: Newhaven Radio	50°47′N 0°04′E
	Swingbridge: CALL: Bridge Control	
☎ +44(0)1273 612926		Fax:
FREQUENCY: Ch 12		

PROCEDURE:
(1) Commercial vessels navigating the River Ouse, to and from the North Quay berths, have the right of way in all circumstances (especially when passing through the swingbridge). All small craft should keep clear
(2) At times of the swingbridge openings, no small craft should attempt to pass through the swingbridge without the permission from the Bridge Control Operator
(3) Vessels not equipped with VHF should keep clear until commercial vessels have passed by. Only then may they proceed in accordance with the Bridge Control Tower Light Signals

NEWHAVEN MARINA LTD	CALL: Newhaven Marina — 320 Berths	50°47′·2N 0°03′·2E
☎ +44(0)1273 513881 john.stirling@seacontainers.com		Fax: +44(0)1273 510493 www.seacontainers.com
FREQUENCY: Ch M 80		HOURS OPEN: 0800-1700 LT, ACCESS: HW±4h

NEWLYN	**Port:** CALL: Newlyn Harbour	50°06′N 5°33′W
☎ Hr Mr: Office hours: +44(0)1736 362523 Outside office hours: +44(0)1736 361017 Berthing Master: +44(0)1736 763362		Fax: Hr Mr: Office hours: +44(0)1736 351614
FREQUENCY: Ch 09 12 16	LOCATION: Harbour Office, North Pier	HOURS: Mon-Fri: 0800-1700 LT Sat: 0800-1200 LT

NEWPORT, ISLE OF WIGHT	**Port and Yacht Harbour**	50°42′N 1°17′W
☎ Hr Mr: +44(0)1983 525994 Marina: +44(0)1983 526020		Fax:
FREQUENCY: Hr Mr: Ch 16 69 Marina: Ch M 80		HOURS: 0800-1600 LT when office is manned

NEWTON FERRERS HARBOUR, RIVER YEALM (NEWTON CREEK)		50°18′·60N 4°05′·70W
☎ Hr Mr: +44(0)1752 872533 Yealm YC: +44(0)1752 872291		Fax:
FREQUENCY: Ch 10		HOURS: Hr Mr: 0930-1200 LT (Summer only)

NORTHNEY MARINA, LANGSTONE HARBOUR	CALL: Northney Marina	50°50'N 0°58'W
Tel: +44(0)2392 466321 northneymarinas@mdlmarinas.co.uk		Fax: +44(0)2392 461467 www.marinas.uk
FREQUENCY: Ch 80		HOURS OPEN: 0800-1700 LT, ACCESS: H24

OCEAN VILLAGE MARINA, SOUTHAMPTON WATER	CALL: Ocean Village Marina 450 Berths	50°53'·7N 1°23'·3W
Tel: +44(0)2380 229385 oceanvillage@mdlmarinas.co.uk		Fax: +44(0)2380 233515 www.marinas.co.uk
FREQUENCY: Ch 80 NOTE: Fuel obtainable as follows: (1) Call: Wyefuel on Ch 08 or telephone +44(0)2380 631500 (2) Call: Mr Diesel on Ch 08		HOURS OPEN: H24, ACCESS: H24

PENZANCE	Port 250 Berths 50 Visitors	50°07'N 5°32'W
Tel: Hr Mr: Office hours: +44(0)1736 366113 Outside office hours: +44(0)1736 365029 Mobile: 07779 264335	Depth: 4·3 m	Fax: FAX: Hr Office: +44(0)1736 366114
FREQUENCY: Ch 09 12 16	LOCATION: Hr Mr Office: Seaward end of the North Arm (pier) below docking signal flagstaff	HOURS: Mon-Fri: 0800-1730 LT Sat: 0830-1230 LT ACCESS: HW -2h to +1h

PLYMOUTH (LONG ROOM PORT CONTROL)		50°22'N 4°09'W
Tel: +44(0)1752 836528 & 836490		Fax: +44(0)1752 836401
FREQUENCY: Ch **14** 16		
PLYMOUTH YACHT HAVEN	**CALL: Plymouth Yacht Haven 450 Berths**	**50°21'·5N 4°07'·2W**
Tel: +44(0)1752 404231 Mobile: 07721 498422 (1900-0800 LT) plymhaven@aol.com	Depth: 2·25 m	Fax: +44(0)1752 484177 www.yachthavens.com
FREQUENCY: Ch **M** 80		HOURS OPEN: H24, ACCESS: H24

POOLE HARBOUR	Yacht Services 100 Berths for Visitors	50°42'N 2°00'W
Tel: Harbour Control Office: +44(0)1202 440230 Dolphin Quay: +44(0)1202 649488 Hr Mr: +44(0)1202 440200 & 440233 (direct) Bridge: +44(0)1202 674115 harbourmaster@phc.co.uk	Maximum draft at Dolphin Quay 2·5 m	Fax: Office: +44(0)1202 440231 Dolphin Quay: +44(0)1202 649488 www.phc.co.uk
FREQUENCY: Ch 14 16 H24 Bridge: Ch 14 Dolphin Quay: Ch 80 Poole Hr Water Taxis on VHF Ch 06 or telephone: +44(0)1860 346313 Fuel: Poole Bay Fuels: VHF Ch 80 (Mon-Fri: 0900-1730, weekends in season: 0830-1800 LT telephone 01202 842877)		
PROCEDURE: Vessels should listen to Poole Harbour Control on VHF Ch 14. A traffic light system is operated **POOLE BRIDGE** (50°41'·3N 1°56'·5W) **OPENING TIMES:** The bridge will lift once during a 15 minute period, starting at the following times: Mon-Fri: 0930, 1030, 1230, 1430, 1630, 1830 and 2130 LT Sat, Sun and Bank Holidays: As for Mon-Fri, plus 0730 LT In addition the bridge will open at 2345 for any vessel on request		
NOTES: Vessels which are not in the immediate vicinity of the bridge at the time of opening should wait until the next opening. The control system only allows one cycle of traffic in each direction at a time. Town Quay - used when Dolphin Quay is full or for larger vessels (15 metres)		

POOLE YACHT CLUB HAVEN	CALL: Pike Delta	50°42'·5N 1°59'·8W
Tel: +44(0)1202 672687		Fax: www.pooleyc.co.uk
FREQUENCY: Ch M 80		HOURS OPEN: May-Sept: 0800-2200 LT ACCESS: H24

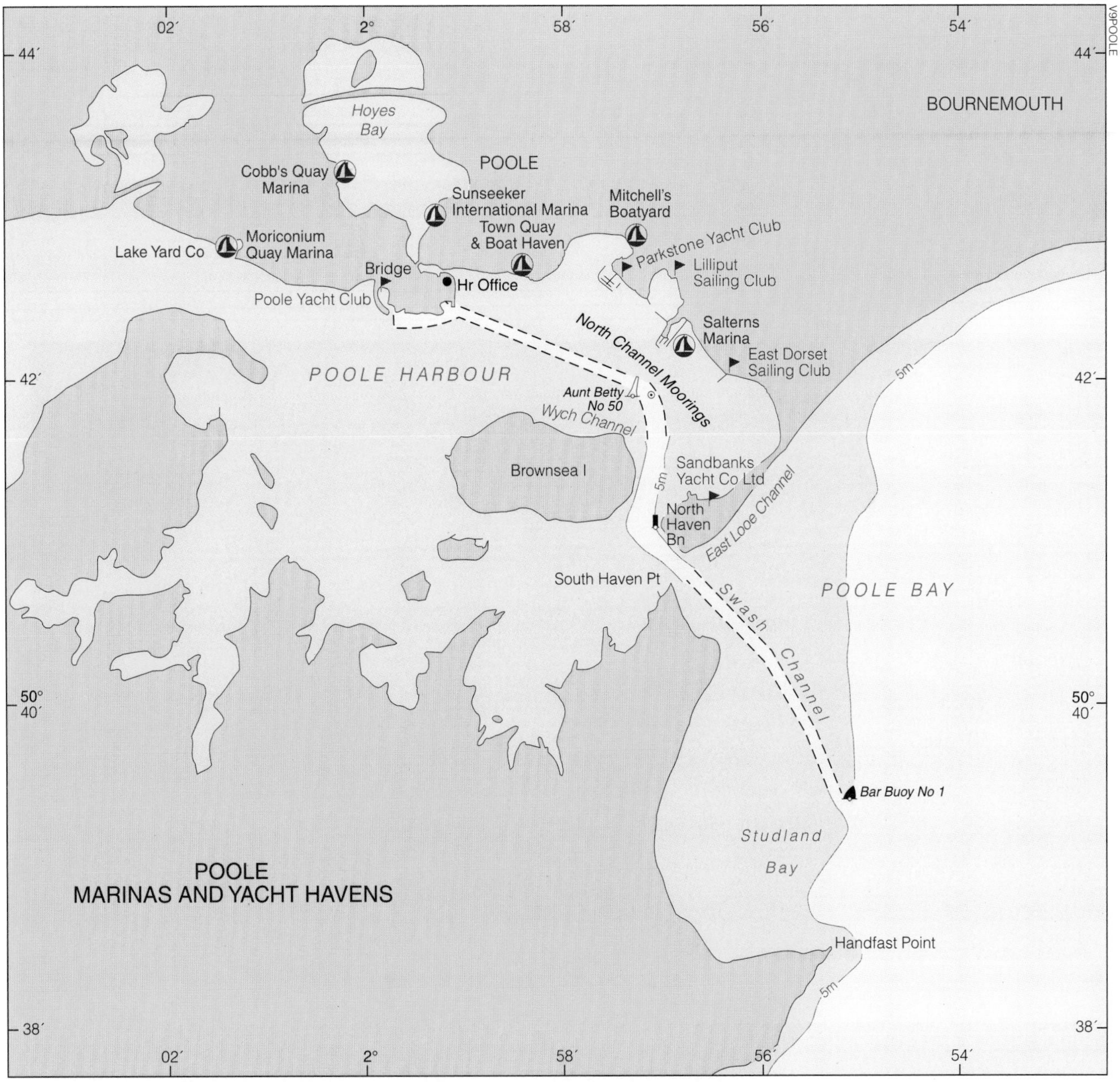

V9POOLE

02′ 2° 58′ 56′ 54′
44′ 42′ 50° 40′ 38′

BOURNEMOUTH
Hoyes Bay
POOLE
Cobb's Quay Marina
Sunseeker International Marina
Mitchell's Boatyard
Town Quay & Boat Haven
Moriconium Quay Marina
Lake Yard Co
Parkstone Yacht Club
Lilliput Sailing Club
Bridge
Hr Office
Poole Yacht Club
Salterns Marina
North Channel Moorings
East Dorset Sailing Club
POOLE HARBOUR
Aunt Betty No 50
Wych Channel
Brownsea I
Sandbanks Yacht Co Ltd
5m
North Haven Bn
East Looe Channel
South Haven Pt
Swash Channel
POOLE BAY
Bar Buoy No 1
Studland Bay
Handfast Point

POOLE
MARINAS AND YACHT HAVENS

POOLE HARBOUR **TOWN QUAY**

PORT PENDENNIS MARINA	CALL: Port Pendennis	50°09′·0N 5°03′·6W
☎ +44(0)1326 311113 & 211211 marina@portpendennis.com		Fax +44(0)1326 311116 www.portpendennis.com
FREQUENCY: Ch M 80		HOURS OPEN: H24

PORT SOLENT MARINA	CALL: Port Solent 808 Berths	50°50′·5N 1°06′·0W
☎ +44(0)2392 210765 portsolent@premiermarinas.com		Fax +44(0)2392 324241 www.premiermarinas.com
FREQUENCY: Ch **80**		HOURS OPEN: H24, ACCESS: H24 through the lock

PORT SOLENT MARINA FROM W

QUEEN ANNE'S BATTERY MARINA, PLYMOUTH	CALL: Queen Anne's Battery Marina 260 Berths	50°21′·9N 4°07′·9W
☎ +44(0)1752 671142 qab@mdlmarinas.co.uk		Fax +44(0)1752 266297 www.marinas.co.uk
FREQUENCY: Ch 80		HOURS OPEN: H24, ACCESS: H24

RAMSGATE	**Marina:** CALL: Ramsgate Marina	51°20′N 1°25′E
☎ Ramsgate Marina: +44(0)1843 572100 Sandwich Marina: +44(0)1304 613690 marina@ramsgatemarina.co.uk		Fax Harbour Office: +44(0)1843 590941 Port Control: +44(0)1843 850181 www.ramsgatemarina.co.uk
FREQUENCY: Ch 14 80 Emergency secondary Port Working: Ch 68		HOURS: Port Control: H24 Ramsgate Marina: 0600-2200 LT

PROCEDURE:
(1) All leisure craft in the port approaches or intending to enter the port should listen on VHF Ch 14 (Ramsgate Port Control) until clear inside the Royal Harbour
(2) Leisure craft intending to leave the Royal Harbour should commence listening on VHF Ch 14 prior to leaving and maintain this watch until clear of the approaches
(3) Access to the Inner (Tidal) Marina is approximately HW ± 2h through the lock and is controlled by International Traffic Signal Lights on the lock entrance

RETREAT BOATYARD, TOPSHAM		50°41′·33N 3°28′·60W
☎ +44(0)1392 874720		Fax +44(0)1392 876182
FREQUENCY: Ch M		ACCESS: HW ± 3½ h

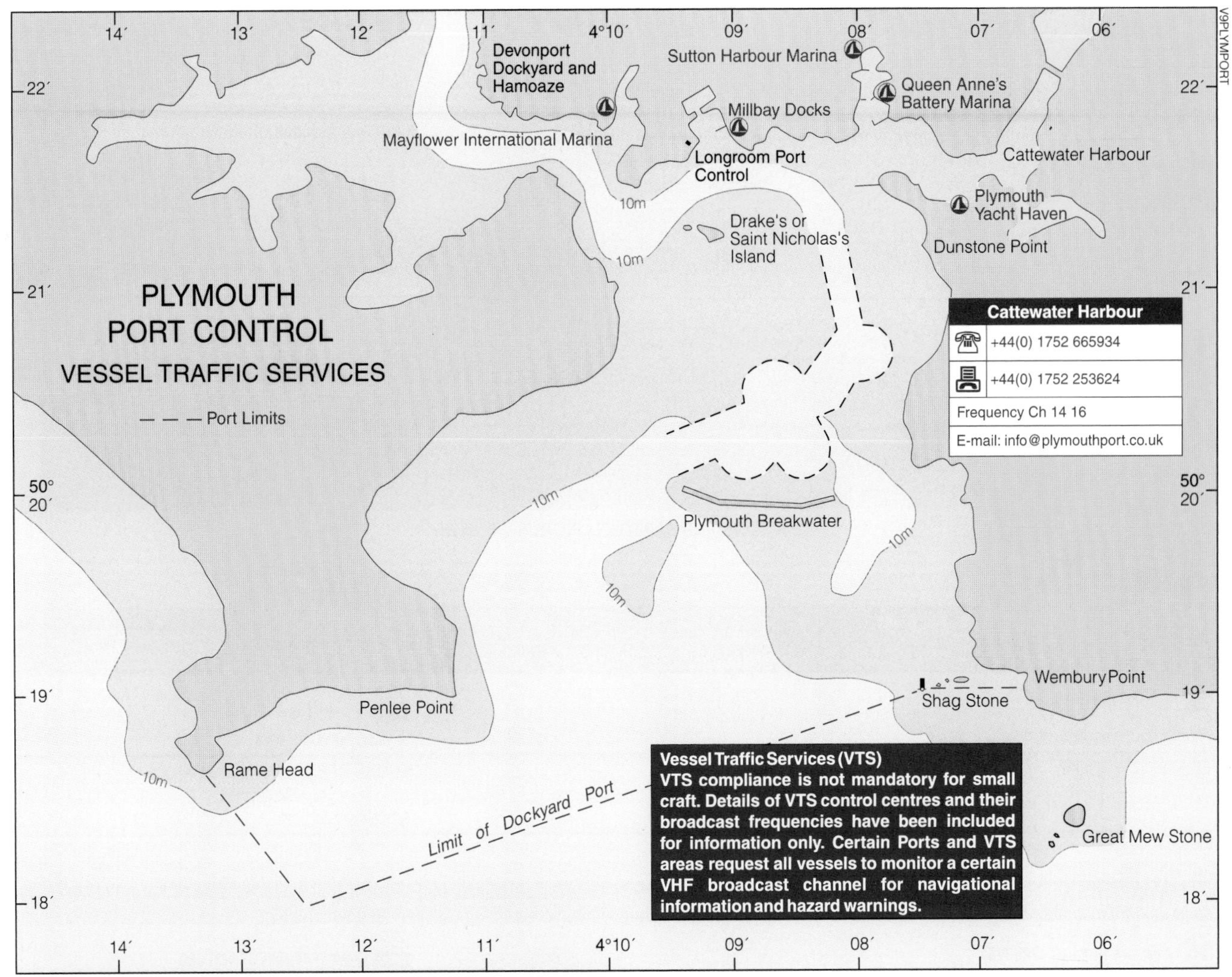

Port Operations and Information Service PLYMOUTH PORT CONTROL	
AREA:	The Dockyard Port of Plymouth: all tidal waters N of a line from Rame Head to a point 175° 1·25 n miles distant from Rame church, thence to the Shag Stone and thence due E to the shore
CALL:	Longroom Port Control
TELEPHONE:	Port Control: +44(0) 1752 836528 & 836490 & 663225 Harbour Control Officer: +44(0) 1752 836930 & 836427
FAX:	+44(0) 1752 836401
FREQUENCY:	Ch 14 16
HOURS:	H24

INFORMATION SERVICE:
Vessels reporting will be advised of shipping movements in the ports and approaches. Tidal and wind speed information is also available on request.

FOG WARNINGS: Information on fog conditions available on VHF Ch 13, 14 or 16 from Longroom Port Control or Flag.

NOTES:
(1) Vessels may obtain information on Traffic Signals displayed at Drake's Island and Flagstaff from either Longroom Port Control or Flag.
(2) Port Control Traffic Light System: there are no restrictions imposed when the signals are unlit unless notified on VHF Ch 13, 14 or 16.
(3) Submarines regularly operate in Plymouth Sound and Approaches with equipment deployed astern, extending out to 800m. Vessels should not therefore pass within 200m of any submarine, or cross astern of a submarine within 800m. If in doubt, vessels should contact the submarine direct on VHF Ch 13 or 16 to seek advice. If radio contact with the submarine cannot be established, vessels should call Longroom Port Control.

RIBS MARINA, LITTLE AVON MARINA, CHRISTCHURCH	CALL: Little Avon	50°43′·5N 1°46′·3W
Tel: +44(0)1202 477327		Fax: +44(0)1202 471456
FREQUENCY: Ch M 80		HOURS OPEN: 0800-1700 LT, ACCESS: HW ± 2h

CHRISTCHURCH HARBOUR (THE RUN) FROM NE

RYDE LEISURE HARBOUR, ISLE OF WIGHT	75 Visitor Berths	50°43′·9N 1°09′·2W
☎ +44(0)1983 613879 rydeharbour@amserve.net		Fax +44(0)1983 812034 www.rydeharbour.com
FREQUENCY: Ch 80		HOURS OPEN: Summer: 0900-2000 LT Winter: HX ACCESS: HW ± 2h

RYE, RIVER ROTHER	**Port:** CALL: Rye Harbour Radio	50°56′N 0°47′E
☎ Port: +44(0)1797 225225		Fax Port: +44(0)1797 227429
FREQUENCY: Ch 14 16		HOURS: Port: 0900-1700 LT or when a vessel is expected

SALCOMBE	**Port:** CALL: Salcombe Harbour	50°14′N 3°46′W
☎ Harbour Office: +44(0)1548 843791 salcombe-harbour@south-hams-dc.gov.uk		Fax Harbour Office: +44(0)1548 842033 www.salterns.co.uk
FREQUENCY: Hr Mr & Hr Mr Launches: Ch 14 Yacht Taxi Service: Ch 12	LOCATION: Harbour Office, Whitestrand, Salcombe	HOURS: Harbour Office: Mon-Thur: 0900-1300 1400-1645 LT Fri: 0900-1300 1400-1615 LT
PROCEDURE: Vessels should send ETA during office hours. Assistance with mooring can be obtained from the Hr Mr launches (marked "Harbour Master")		
	Yacht Services	
FUEL BARGE: A fuel barge is moored in approx position 50°14′·22N 3°45′·52W. Service can be obtained by: calling "Fuel barge" on VHF Ch 06 or Mobile 07801 798862		
WINTERS MARINE LTD, SALCOMBE	CALL: Lincombe Yard	50°15′·03N 3°45′·90W
☎ +44(0)1548 843580 lincombeboatyard@eclipse.co.uk	Winter storage and repair facilities	Fax +44(0)1548 843006 www.harbours.co.uk
FREQUENCY: Ch 72	LOCATION: Lincolmbe	ACCESS: HW ± 5h

SALTERNS MARINA, POOLE	CALL: Salterns Marina 300 Berths 75 Moorings	50°42′·3N 1°57′·0W
☎ +44(0)1202 707321 & 709971 marina@salterns.co.uk	Depth: 2·5 m, Maximum LOA: 20 m Free launch service	Fax +44(0)1202 707398 www.salterns.co.uk
FREQUENCY: Ch **M** 80	LOCATION: Lilliput	HOURS OPEN: H24, ACCESS: H24

SHAMROCK QUAY AND SAXON WHARF, SOUTHAMPTON WATER	CALL: Shamrock Quay 250 Berths	50°54'·5N 1°22'·7W
Tel: +44(0)2380 229461 shamrockquay@mdlmarinas.co.uk saxonwharf@mdlmarinas.co.uk	Saxon Wharf superyacht and large craft facility	Fax: +44(0)2380 333384 www.marinas.co.uk
FREQUENCY: Ch **80**		HOURS OPEN: 0830-2130 LT, ACCESS: H24

S. HELIER FROM S

S. HELIER, JERSEY	**Port Control:** CALL: S. Helier Port Control	49°11'N 2°06'W
Tel: Hr Office: +44(0)1534 885588 Harbour Office: jerseyharbours@jersey-harbours.com Hr Mr: harbourmaster@jersey-harbours.com Moorings: moorings@jersey-harbours.com Information: jsyhbr@itl.net		Fax: Hr Office: 0700-2300 LT: +44(0)1534 885599 Shipping and Boat Registration: +44(0)1534 885598 www.jersey.gov.uk www.jersey-harbours.com
FREQUENCY: Port Control: Ch 14	LOCATION: Pier Head Control, Victoria Pier	HOURS: H24, ACCESS: HW ± 3h
NOTE: Marinas situated within the commercial port of S. Helier. Traffic through the area, particularly at peak shipping times, has to be closely controlled. Visiting craft are therefore advised to keep a listening watch on VHF Ch 14 when approaching S. Helier		
S. HELIER MARINA	200 Visitor Berths	49°10'·9N 21°06'·6W
Tel: +44(0)1534 885508		Fax: +44(0)1534 879549
		ACCESS: HW ± 3h
LA COLLETTE YACHT BASIN	60 Visitor Berths	49°10'·5N 21°06'·7W
Tel: +44(0)1534 885529	Jersey's deep water yacht harbour with access H24	Fax:
ELIZABETH MARINA	564 Berths	49°10'·9N 21°07'·1W
Tel: +44(0)1534 885530	Maximum LOA: 20 m	Fax: +44(0)1534 885593
		ACCESS: HW ± 3h

SHEPARDS WHARF BOATYARD, COWES	75 Berths	50°45'·6N 01°17'·6W
Tel: +44(0)1983 297821 mail@shepards.co.uk	Visitors' moorings and yacht service centre	Fax: +44(0)1983 294814 www.shepards.co.uk

SHOREHAM	**Port:** CALL: Shoreham Harbour Radio	50°50′N 0°15′W
Tel: Port Control: +44(0)1273 592366 Hr Office: +44(0)1273 598100 shorport@pavilion.co.uk		Fax: Hr Office: +44(0)1273 592492 www.portshoreham.co.uk
FREQUENCY: Ch 14 16	LOCATION: Locks	HOURS: H24
LADY BEE MARINA	CALL: Shoreham Harbour Radio	50°49′·8N 0°14′·0W
Tel: +44(0)1273 593801		Fax: +44(0)1273 870349
FREQUENCY: Ch 14	LOCATION: Shoreham Harbour	HOURS OF WATCH: Mon-Sat: 0800-1830 LT Sun: 0900-1300 LT ACCESS: H24 through the lock

SOUTHDOWN MARINA, TORPOINT		50°21′·15N 4°11′·82W
Tel: +44(0)1752 823084		Fax: +44(0)1752 823084
FREQUENCY: Ch M 80		HOURS OPEN: 0900-1700 LT, ACCESS: HW±6h

SOVEREIGN HARBOUR MARINA LTD, EASTBOURNE	CALL: Sovereign Harbour 800 Berths 150 Visitor Berths	50°47′·37N 0°20′·81E
Tel: +44(0)1323 470099 sovereignharbour@carillionplc.com	Depth: 2 m, Maximum LOA: 22 m	Fax: +44(0)1323 470077 www.sovereignharbour.co.uk
FREQUENCY: Ch **15** 16 **17** Locks & Bridges work VHF Ch 17 (H24). Before making approach obtain clearance by VHF: CALL: Sovereign Lock Control whilst approaching lock through tidal harbour Water Taxi 07763 111246 or Ch 17		HOURS OPEN: H24, ACCESS: H24 through the lock

SOUTHSEA MARINA	CALL: Southsea Marina	50°47′·4N 1°02′·0W
Tel: +44(0)2392 822719 southseamarina@attglobal.net		Fax: +44(0)2392 822220 www.southsea-marina.com
FREQUENCY: Ch **80**		HOURS OPEN: H24 ACCESS: Marina: HW Portsmouth ±3h Working Pontoon outside marina: H24

SPARKES YACHT HARBOUR, HAYLING ISLAND	CALL: Sparkes Yacht Harbour	50°47′N 1°56′W
Tel: +44(0)2392 463572 Mobile: 07770 365610 info@sparkes.co.uk		Fax: +44(0)2392 465741 www.sparkes.co.uk
FREQUENCY: Ch M 80	LOCATION: Hayling Island	HOURS OPEN: 0900-1800 LT, ACCESS: H24

S. MARY'S HARBOUR, ISLES OF SCILLY	**Port:** CALL: S. Mary's Harbour	49°55′N 6°19′W
Tel: Hr Mr: +44(0)1720 422768 Emergency Hr Mr: +44(0)1720 423343 Tresco Hr Mr: +44(0)1720 422792 Mobile: 07778 601237 Fuel (Sibley's): +44(0)1720 422431		Fax: +44(0)1720 422768
FREQUENCY: Ch 14 16		HOURS: Mon-Fri: 0800-1700 LT Sat: (season) 0800-1700 LT

S. MAWES	**Port**	50°10′N 5°01′W
Tel: +44(0)1326 270553		Fax:
FREQUENCY: Ch **12** 16		

THE SOLENT, SOUTHAMPTON AND PORTSMOUTH
VESSEL TRAFFIC SERVICES AND MARINAS

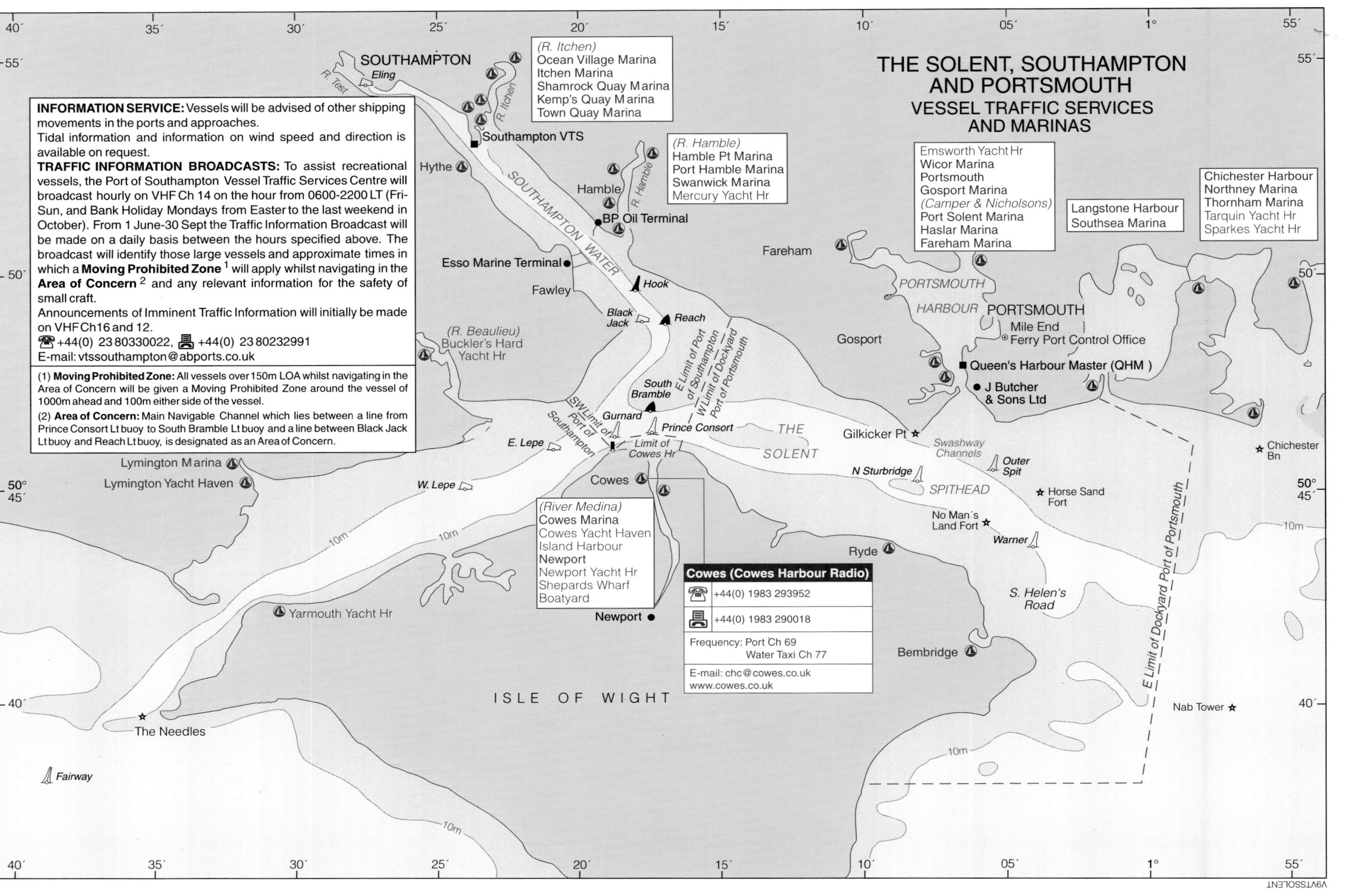

SOUTHAMPTON, PORTSMOUTH AND THE SOLENT

Port Operations and Information Service: CALL: Southampton VTS

DESCRIPTION: The service covers the Solent and Southampton Water, includes the ports of Southampton and Portsmouth, and involves the monitoring and co-ordination of shipping movements

Vessel Traffic Services (VTS) Centre, Southampton

TRAFFIC INFORMATION BROADCASTS AND RELEVANT INFORMATION RELATING TO RESTRICTED AREAS IN THE SOLENT: Southampton VTS broadcasts on VHF Ch 12 for small craft every even hour, 0600 to 2200 LT, Friday to Sunday and Bank Holiday Mondays from Easter to 30 September

AREA: Co-ordination of movement of all vessels of 20m LOA or over in the Solent and Southampton Water excluding Port of Portsmouth N of a line joining Gilkicker Pt and Horse Sand Fort Lt

Tel: VTS Officer & Hr Mr: 0800-1800 LT: +44(0)2380 330022 ext 2440 & 2441 (VTS Centre)
Other times: +44(0)2380 339733

Fax: VTS Officer & Hr Mr: +44(0)2380 232991

WEBSITE: www.abports.co.uk

FREQUENCY: Port Operations: Ch **12** 14
Harbour Radar Info & selected Harbour Operations: Ch 18 20 22
Marine Pollution: Ch 10 Southampton Patrol: Ch **69**

HOURS: H24

NOTE: Duty Patrol Officer maintains continuous patrol in the Southampton Port Waters

Queen's Harbour Master, Portsmouth — CALL: Queen's Harbour Master or QHM — 50°47′·95N 1°06′·52W

Tel: QHM: +44(0)2392 723124 & 723794
Harbour Control Officer: +44(0)2392 723694

Fax: QHM: +44(0)2392 722831

FREQUENCY: Harbour Working Channel: Ch 11
Dockyard Craft: Ch 73
Queen's Harbour Patrol: Ch 11

LOCATION: Harbour Control in Semaphore Tr

HOURS: H24

NOTE: VHF Ch 11 should be used by all vessels underway in Portsmouth, N of Outer Spit buoy. QHM may instruct vessels to use VHF Ch 13 instead of VHF Ch 11; vessels wanting to use VHF Ch 13 should first obtain permission from QHM on VHF Ch 11

WARSASH MARINE

Tel: +44(0)1489 583813
info@warsashmarine.com

Fax: +44(0)1489 583813
www.warsashmarine.com

FREQUENCY: Ch **80** — LOCATION: Stone Pier Yard, Warsash, Southampton — HOURS OPEN: HX

S. PETER PORT, GUERNSEY

Port Control: CALL: Port Control — 49°27′N 2°32′W

Tel: Marina: +44(0)1481 725987
Duty Dockmaster: +44(0)1481 712422
Port Control: +44(0)1481 720481
Hr Office: 0900-1700: +44(0)1481 720229
Sark Hr Mr: +44(0)1481 822323
Harbour Taxi Mobile: 07781 108767

guernsey.harbour.gov.gg

Fax: Hr Office: +44(0)1481 714177

www.guernsey.net

FREQUENCY: Port Control: Ch 12 Marina: Ch M 80
Monday - Friday Office Hours Water Taxi: Ch 10

LOCATION: Port Control, White Rock

HOURS: H24 (Access is HW ± 3h)

Moorings for Visiting Yachts

All visiting vessels must clear inwards at the main harbour of S. Peter Port, regardless of whichever marina they moor in. Mooring in the QEII Marina is by prior arrangement only

In the Victoria Marina: Moorings alongside pontoons are available for boats up to a maximum of 42ft (12·8 m) LOA and a maximum draft of 6ft (1·8 m). The sill height is 4·2 m above chart datum, with access to the marina approximately 2½ hours either side of high water. Entry is controlled by the marina staff. Control lights are positioned on both pierheads at the entrance to Victoria Marina.

If the moorings within the Marinas are full, yachts may be directed to moor on pontoons laid east of the Marina Entrance. When the tide is low, a waiting pontoon is provided adjacent to the entrance

VICTORIA MARINA, GUERNSEY

49°27′N 2°32′W

Tel: +44(0)1481 725987

Depth: 2 m, Maximum LOA: 13 m Draught

Fax:

FREQUENCY: Ch 80
Water taxi on VHF Ch 10 (0700-2000)

HOURS OF WATCH: July & August only: HX
ACCESS: HW ± 2·5 hours via control lights

SUTTON HARBOUR MARINA, PLYMOUTH

CALL: Sutton Harbour Radio — 50°22′N 4°08′W

Tel: +44(0)1752 204186

Fax: +44(0)1752 223521

FREQUENCY: Sutton Lock: Ch 12 16 Marina: Ch M 80

HOURS: H24, ACCESS: H24 through the lock

S. PETER PORT FROM SE

SWANWICK MARINA, RIVER HAMBLE	CALL: Swanwick Marina	50°52′·9N 1°17′·9W
☎ +44(0)1489 885000 After Hours: +44(0)1489 885262 sales@moody.co.uk		Fax: +44(0)1489 885509 www.moody.co.uk
FREQUENCY: Ch 80		HOURS OPEN: H24, ACCESS: H24

TEIGNMOUTH	**Port** 1 Visitors Berth	50°32′·74N 3°30′·02W
☎ Harbour Master: +44(0)1626 773165 Emergencies Only: 07796 178456 Harbour Master: teignmouthharbourmaster@eclipse.co.uk		Fax: Harbour Master: +44(0)1626 775162
FREQUENCY: Harbour Master: Ch 12 16		HOURS: Mon-Fri: 0800-1700 LT Sat 0900-1200 LT

THORNHAM MARINA, CHICHESTER HARBOUR	77 Berths 6 Visitor	50°50′·4N 0°55′W
☎ +44(0)1243 375335		Fax: +44(0)1243 371522

TORBAY HARBOUR	**Port:** CALL: Torquay Port	50°27′N 3°32′W
☎ Paignton +44(0)1803 557812 Torquay: +44(0)1803 292429 Brixham: +44(0)1803 853321 & 851854 Salcombe: +44(0)1548 843791 Torbay Hr Mr Mobile: 07714 432288 marine.services@torbay.gov.uk	Torbay Harbour includes Torbay and the harbours of Brixham, Paignton and Torquay	Fax: Paignton: +44(0)1803 520057 Torquay: +44(0)1803 299257 Brixham: +44(0)1803 852434 www.tor-bay-harbour.co.uk
FREQUENCY: Ch 09 **14** 16 NOTE: Leisure craft should monitor VHF Ch 09 or 14. Torbay Harbour patrol craft and Brixham Pilot Vessels may give directions to leisure craft for their safety		HOURS: 1 Oct-30 April: Mon-Fri: 0900-1700 LT 1 May-30 Sept: 0800-1800 LT

TORPOINT YACHT HARBOUR		50°22′·0N 4°11′·5W
☎ +44(0)1752 813658		Fax:
FREQUENCY: Ch M 80		HOURS: H24, ACCESS: H24

TORQUAY MARINA	CALL: Torquay Marina 500 Berths	50°27'·5N 3°31'·7W
Tel: +44(0)1803 200210 Torquay Fuel: +44(0)1803 294509 Mobile: 07785 226839 torquaymarina@mdlmarinas.co.uk		Fax: +44(0)1803 200225 www.marinas.co.uk
FREQUENCY: Marina: Ch 80 Fuel: Ch M		HOURS OPEN: H24, ACCESS: H24

TORQUAY HARBOUR FROM SW

TOWN QUAY MARINA, SOUTHAMPTON WATER	CALL: Town Quay Marina	50°53'·7N 1°24'·2W
Tel: +44(0)2380 234397		Fax: +44(0)2380 235302
FREQUENCY: Ch 80		HOURS OPEN: H24, ACCESS: H24
NOTE: Entrance to the marina is a "dog leg" between floating breakwaters which appear continuous from the sea		

TRURO	**Port:** CALL: Carrick Three	50°15'N 5°05'W
Tel: +44(0)1872 224231, 22400 & 272130 harbouroffice@carrick.gov.uk		Fax: +44(0)1872 225346 www.portoftruro.gov.uk
FREQUENCY: Ch **12**		

UNIVERSAL SHIPYARDS, SARISBURY GREEN, RIVER HAMBLE	CALL: Universal	50°52'·5N 1°18'·1W
Tel: +44(0)1489 574272		Fax: +44(0)1489 577357
FREQUENCY: Ch M 80		HOURS OPEN: 0900-1700 LT, ACCESS: H24

WEYMOUTH	**Port:** CALL: Weymouth Harbour Radio	50°36'N 2°27'W
Tel: Hr Mr: +44(0)1305 206423 Hr Office: +44(0)1305 206422		Fax: Hr Mr: +44(0)1305 767927 www.weymouth.gov.uk
FREQUENCY: Ch **12** 16		HOURS: 0800-1700 LT
	Marina	
Tel: +44(0)1305 767576 FUEL (RAYBAR): Mobile: 07860 912401		Fax: +44(0)1305 767575
FREQUENCY: Ch 80 Fuel: Ch 60		HOURS: Summer: 0730-2130 LT Winter: 0830-1730 LT

WEYMOUTH INNER HARBOUR FROM S

WEYMOUTH (Continued)	**Port:** CALL: Weymouth Harbour Radio	50°36'N 2°27'W
	Town Bridge: CALL: Weymouth Town Bridge	
☎ +44(0)1305 206423 & 789357		📠
FREQUENCY: Ch 12		
PROCEDURE: Vessels requiring bridge lifts should be within sight of the Town Bridge Operator by the scheduled time and listen on VHF Ch 12 for Town Bridge information at least 5 mins before scheduled opening time. Town Bridge Opening Times: 0800 1000 1200 1400 1600 & 1800 LT (Apr: 1930, May: 2030, June & July: 2130, Aug: 2030, Sept: 1930 LT) During Oct-Mar: 1h notice required for all bridge lifts		

YARMOUTH HARBOUR ENTRANCE FROM NE

WICOR MARINA, PORTSMOUTH		50°50'·4N 1°08'·7W
Tel: +44(0)1329 237112		Fax: +44(0)1329 825660
FREQUENCY: Ch 80		HOURS OPEN: 0900-1730 LT (Mon-Sat) ACCESS: HW ± 3h

YARMOUTH HARBOUR, ISLE OF WIGHT	**Port:** CALL: Yarmouth Harbour 250 Visitors Berths 38 Visitor Moorings in Yarmouth Roads	50°42'N 1°30'W
Tel: Hr Mr: +44(0)1983 760321 Mobile (HN): 07774 202326 hm@yar-iow-harbour.demon.co.uk	Leisure craft are advised to check for berth availability prior to arrival	Fax: Hr Mr: +44(0)1983 761192 www.yarmouth-harbour.co.uk www.harbours.co.uk
FREQUENCY: Ch 68 Yar Bridge: Ch 68 Water Taxi: Ch 15		HOURS: H24

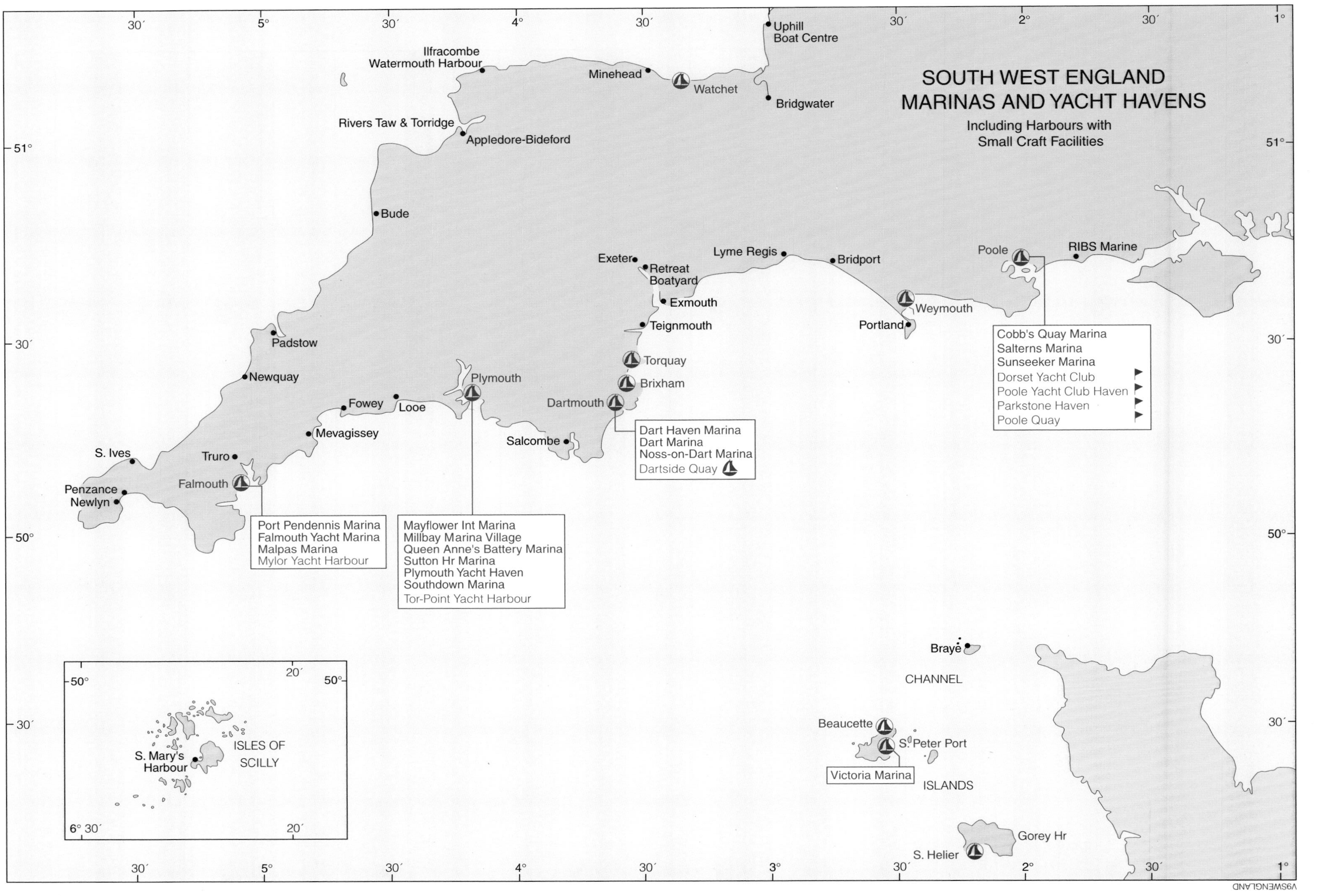
SOUTH WEST ENGLAND
MARINAS AND YACHT HAVENS
Including Harbours with
Small Craft Facilities
Uphill
Boat Centre
Ilfracombe
Watermouth Harbour
Minehead
Watchet
Bridgwater
Rivers Taw & Torridge
Appledore-Bideford
Bude
Exeter
Retreat
Boatyard
Exmouth
Teignmouth
Lyme Regis
Bridport
Poole
RIBS Marine
Weymouth
Portland
Cobb's Quay Marina
Salterns Marina
Sunseeker Marina
Dorset Yacht Club
Poole Yacht Club Haven
Parkstone Haven
Poole Quay
Padstow
Newquay
Torquay
Brixham
Dartmouth
Plymouth
Fowey
Looe
Mevagissey
Salcombe
Dart Haven Marina
Dart Marina
Noss-on-Dart Marina
Dartside Quay
S. Ives
Truro
Falmouth
Penzance
Newlyn
Port Pendennis Marina
Falmouth Yacht Marina
Malpas Marina
Mylor Yacht Harbour
Mayflower Int Marina
Millbay Marina Village
Queen Anne's Battery Marina
Sutton Hr Marina
Plymouth Yacht Haven
Southdown Marina
Tor-Point Yacht Harbour
Braye
CHANNEL
ISLANDS
Beaucette
S. Peter Port
Victoria Marina
Gorey Hr
S. Helier
ISLES OF
SCILLY
S. Mary's
Harbour
V9SWENGLAND

UNITED KINGDOM, ENGLAND - WEST COAST

LIVERPOOL (Coastguard MRSC) **MMSI 002320019**			**DSC VHF √**
53°30′N 3°03′W			Operational area: Queensferry to the Mull of Galloway
☎ +44(0)151 9313341			Fax +44(0)151 9313347
RT (MF)	Transmits **2182**	Receives **2182**	**VHF** Ch 06 **10** 16 **23** 67 **73** 84 **86**
MARITIME SAFETY INFORMATION BROADCASTS			
	VHF Ch **10 23 73 86**	An announcement will be made on VHF Channel 16 indicating which VHF working channel will be used for the broadcast	
Weather and Navigational warnings broadcast on receipt			DIAGRAMS: pages 158, 159, 160 and 161
Weather Bulletins			
0210 0610 1010 1410 1810 2210	Gale warnings for Areas Irish Sea and Malin. Local area strong wind warnings (Beaufort Force 6 / 7) and / or gale warnings. Inshore forecast for Region 11		
1010 2210	Shipping forecast: gale warnings, synopsis, 24 hour forecast for Areas Irish Sea and Malin		
Navigational Warnings			
0210 0610 1010 1410 1810 2210	For Areas Charlie and Echo. Local warnings as and when agreed with the Hydrographer, Lighthouse Authority or Harbour Authority		

APPLEDORE—BIDEFORD	**Port:** CALL: PV: "Two Rivers"	51°02′N 4°12′W
☎ Hr Mr: Bideford: +44(0)1237 428816 Mobile: 0797 7287404		Fax
FREQUENCY: Ch 12 16	LOCATION: PV based at Appledore	HOURS: PV: 2h before HW at Bideford

AVONMOUTH SIGNAL STATION	CALL: Avonmouth Radio	51°30′N 2°43′W
☎ +44(0)117 9820000 ext 4761 & 4494 or 9822257 signal.station@bristolport.co.uk		Fax +44(0)117 9235320 www.bristolport.co.uk
FREQUENCY: Vessel Traffic Services: Ch 12 Port Operations: Ch 14	LOCATION: South Pier, Royal Edward Dock	HOURS: H24
RADAR SURVEILLANCE: Steep Holm to Second Severn Crossing		

BRISTOL CITY DOCKS	CALL: City Docks Radio	51°27′N 2°37′W
☎ Dockmaster: +44(0)117 927 3633 Harbour Master: +44(0)117 903 1484 harbour_office@bristol-city.gov.uk		Fax www.bristol-city.gov.uk
AREA: River Avon from Black Rock to City Docks entrance lock		
FREQUENCY: Dockmaster: Ch 11 **14**	LOCATION: The Watch House, south side of entrance lock	HOURS: HW -3h to +1h
BRISTOL HARBOUR	CALL: Bristol Harbour	51°27′N 2°37′W
☎ +44(0)117 9031484 Prince Street Bridge: +44(0)117 9299338 harbour_office@bristol-city.gov.uk		Fax +44(0)117 9031487
FREQUENCY: Hr Mr: Ch 16 73 Locks: Ch 73 Prince Street Bridge: Ch 73	LOCATION: Underfall Yard	HOURS: Mon-Thurs: 0800-1700 LT Fri: 0800-1630 LT Other times: 0800 LT-Sunset
BRISTOL MARINA		51°26′·9N 2°36′·6W
☎ +44(0)1179 213198		Fax +44(0)1179 297672
FREQUENCY: Ch M 80		HOURS OPEN: Office Hours ACCESS: HW -3h to HW

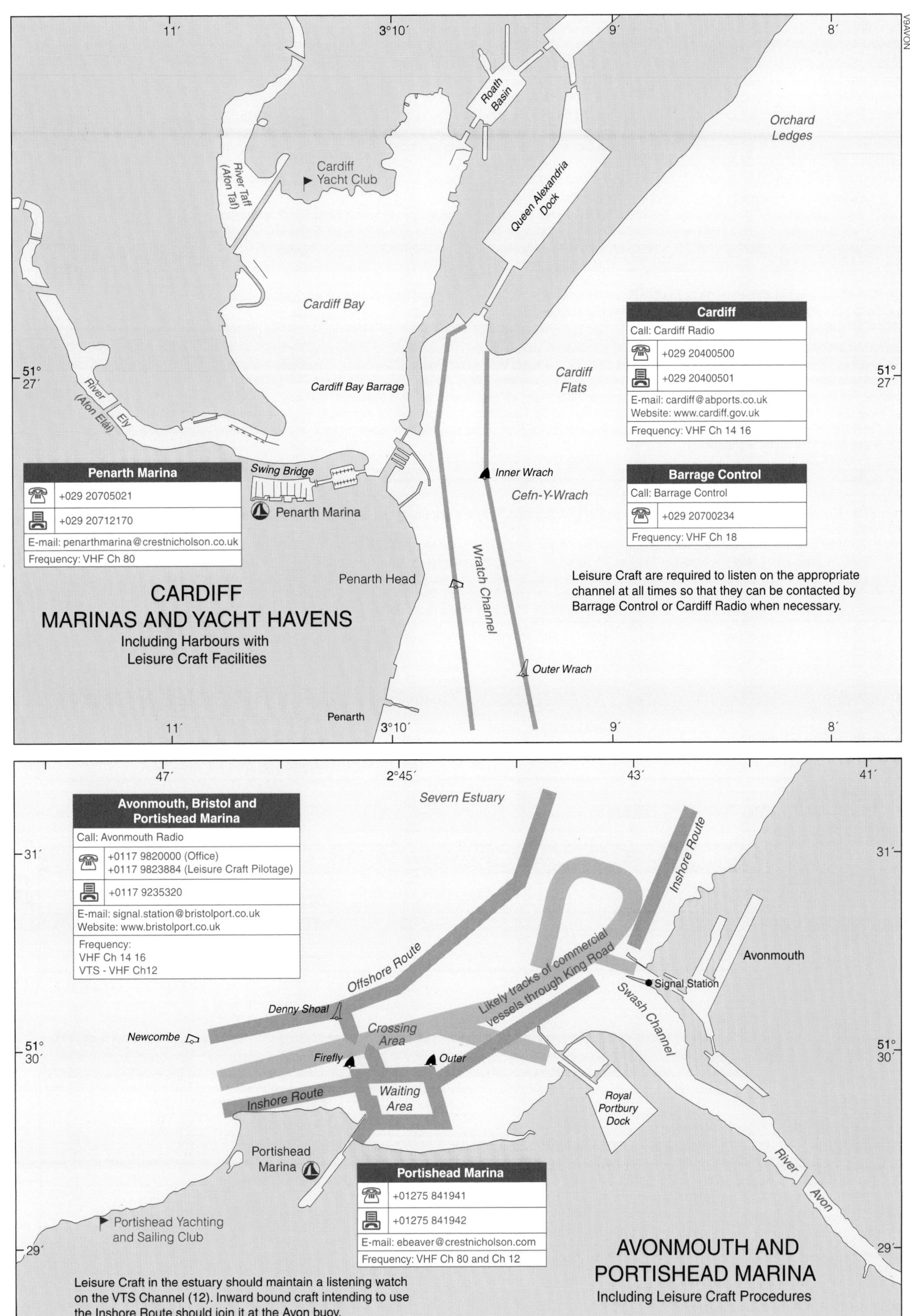

V9AVON
11´
3°10´
9´
8´
Roath Basin
Orchard Ledges
River Taff (Afon Taf)
Cardiff Yacht Club
Queen Alexandria Dock
Cardiff Bay
Cardiff Bay Barrage
Cardiff Flats
River Ely (Afon Elái)
51° 27´
Cardiff
Call: Cardiff Radio
+029 20400500
+029 20400501
E-mail: cardiff@abports.co.uk
Website: www.cardiff.gov.uk
Frequency: VHF Ch 14 16
Penarth Marina
+029 20705021
+029 20712170
E-mail: penarthmarina@crestnicholson.co.uk
Frequency: VHF Ch 80
Swing Bridge
Penarth Marina
Inner Wrach
Cefn-Y-Wrach
Barrage Control
Call: Barrage Control
+029 20700234
Frequency: VHF Ch 18
Penarth Head
Wratch Channel
Leisure Craft are required to listen on the appropriate channel at all times so that they can be contacted by Barrage Control or Cardiff Radio when necessary.
CARDIFF
MARINAS AND YACHT HAVENS
Including Harbours with Leisure Craft Facilities
Outer Wrach
Penarth
47´
2°45´
43´
41´
Severn Estuary
Avonmouth, Bristol and Portishead Marina
Call: Avonmouth Radio
+0117 9820000 (Office)
+0117 9823884 (Leisure Craft Pilotage)
+0117 9235320
E-mail: signal.station@bristolport.co.uk
Website: www.bristolport.co.uk
Frequency:
VHF Ch 14 16
VTS - VHF Ch12
31´
Inshore Route
Avonmouth
Offshore Route
Likely tracks of commercial vessels through King Road
Signal Station
Swash Channel
Denny Shoal
Newcombe
Crossing Area
51° 30´
Firefly
Outer
Inshore Route
Waiting Area
Royal Portbury Dock
Portishead Marina
Portishead Marina
+01275 841941
+01275 841942
E-mail: ebeaver@crestnicholson.com
Frequency: VHF Ch 80 and Ch 12
River Avon
Portishead Yachting and Sailing Club
29´
AVONMOUTH AND PORTISHEAD MARINA
Including Leisure Craft Procedures
Leisure Craft in the estuary should maintain a listening watch on the VTS Channel (12). Inward bound craft intending to use the Inshore Route should join it at the Avon buoy.

THE PASSAGE - BRISTOL TO SHARPNESS

Vessels leaving Bristol City Docks should obtain details of traffic in the River Avon from the Dockmaster City Docks, or by VHF radio from the Avonmouth Signal Station before proceeding from the Cumberland Basin Locks. Thereafter they are required to report their position to Avonmouth Radio on passing Sea Mills and Shirehampton. It is advisable to check with Avonmouth Radio on the traffic in King Road when rounding Nelson Point. The majority of shipping entering Avonmouth or Royal Portbury Docks on the flood tide will proceed North of the entrance before swinging to enter against the flood. **They are restricted in their ability to manoeuvre. Vessels should only cross the traffic stream when advised by Avonmouth Signal station that it is safe to do so.** Seek advice from Avonmouth Signal Station as to the best position (allowing for weather and the vessel's construction) to anchor. Portishead can be dangerous with winds from North West, through North, to East.
Plan your passage to arrive off Sharpness NO EARLIER than 1 hour before High Water and NO LATER than High Water Sharpness. This is for two reasons:

i) Outbound traffic passes through the locks at Sharpness before inbound.
ii) If you make the passage up the River Severn too early there will be very little water above the Severn Road Bridge, and there is a danger that you will touch the bottom at times. In severe cases vessels can be literally rolled over on the sand banks between the Road Bridge and Sharpness. More often you will be "bumped" further and further onto the bank and you could well lose your propeller and/or rudder, endangering your vessel and all aboard.

CALL "SHARPNESS RADIO" ON VHF CHANNEL 17 or by Mobile Phone as soon as possible after leaving Avonmouth. Keep Sharpness pierhead advised of your position and ETA.
Movement of commercial shipping into and out of Sharpness dictates what can and cannot be achieved on any specific tide. At times small craft may be required to pass through the lock chamber with commercial shipping.

THE PASSAGE - SHARPNESS TO BRISTOL

Small craft locking out of Sharpness will normally enter the Dock 2 to 2½ hours before High Water at Sharpness. **Sharpness bridges have to be booked in advance.** Contact **Sharpness Pierhead (Tel: 01453 511968)** 6 hours before to 2 hours after HW, or the Dock Office (Tel: 01453 811862) in normal working hours for bridge bookings. The bridges will be swung as required, at the beginning and end of the tidal window, to allow passage to and from the dock for leisure traffic on that tide. If you miss the allotted opening at the beginning of the tidal window it may not be possible to open again before High Water. All movements within the Dock are controlled by the Harbour Master or his staff. On entering the Dock follow the instructions given by the duty Harbour Master or Lockgateman regarding your movements within the Dock. **If you have VHF monitor channel 17.**

On leaving Sharpness follow the charted channel to Avonmouth. You will need to anchor off Avonmouth over the low water before proceeding up the River Avon on the flood. Contact "**Avonmouth Radio**" **on channel 12 VHF** or by phone on 0117 982257 on clearing the Shoots Channel. Information will be passed regarding vessel movement and advice will be given on the best position to wait prior to entering the River Avon. **Please note that the entrance to the River Avon is flanked by two busy docks. The vessels using these docks are large and deep draughted. They are extremely restricted in their ability to manoeuvre and small craft must keep clear.**
Vessels bound for Bristol entering the River Avon should make their destination known to Avonmouth Signal Station by passing a message to the effect by VHF Radio or Mobile Phone. **Vessels are required to report to Avonmouth Radio on passing Shirehampton and Sea Mills.**
The last inward locking at City Docks is scheduled for 15 minutes before High Water. However, it is sometimes possible for special arrangements to be made with the Dock Master for him to keep the outer lock gates open until 15 minutes after High Water. The Dock Master at City Docks, may be called on **LOW POWER ONLY VHF Ch 14** after passing Black Rock inward. Using call sign "**City Docks Radio.**" Watch is from 3 hours before High Water (Avonmouth) until 1 hour after.

BUDE	**Port**	50°49'·93N 04°33'·37W
☎ Hr Mr: +44(0)1288 353111	Limited facilities for yachts	Fax +44(0)1288 353111
FREQUENCY: Ch 12 16		HOURS: HX: ACCESS: HW ± 2h

DOUGLAS BOATYARD (RIVER RIBBLE)	CALL: Douglas Boatyard	53°45'·6N 2°44'·5W
☎ +44(0)1772 812462		Fax +44(0)1772 731881
FREQUENCY: Ch 16		HOURS OPEN: Mon-Fri: 0830-1800 Sat & Sun: 1400-1800 ACCESS: HW Liverpool ± 2h

DOUGLAS, ISLE OF MAN	**Port Operations and Information Service:** CALL: Douglas Harbour Control	54°09'N 4°28'W
☎ +44(0)1624 686627 & 686628 enquiries@harbours.dot.gov.im		Fax +44(0)1624 626403 www.gov.im
FREQUENCY: Calling & Port Ops: Ch 12 16	LOCATION: Sea Terminal building, root of Victoria Pier	HOURS: H24

AREA: Douglas Harbour Control Area comprises the area within 3 n miles of the port

PROCEDURE: These procedures apply to all vessels including leisure craft

(1) Vessels Inward-Bound other than scheduled services should send ETA at least 24h in advance. Amendments are accepted by telephone, telex or fax H24
(2) Pilotage is not compulsory but is available on request through the Harbour Master. Minimum advance notice 6h, except in emergency
(3) Additional Reports: Vessels entering or leaving should report when 1 n mile from harbour entrance
(4) Vessels entering the Harbour Control Area, manoeuvring within or leaving the harbour area (including the buoyed channel), should first obtain clearance on VHF Ch 12 and then maintain a continuous listening watch on VHF Ch 12

NAVIGATIONAL WARNINGS: Broadcast on VHF Ch 12 at 0133 0533 0733 0933 1333 1733 2133 and covering all Isle of Man ports and coastal waters

RADAR SURVEILLANCE: Maintained from radar on Douglas Head

ISLE OF MAN PORTS			
	Position	**Telephone/Fax**	**Information**
CASTLETOWN	54°04'N 4°40'W	TEL: +44(0)1624 823549	**Port:** CALL: Castletown Harbour
LAXEY HARBOUR	54°13'·45N 4°23'·20W	TEL: +44(0)1624 861663	VHF 12 16
PEEL	54°14'N 4°40'W	TEL: +44(0)1624 842338	**Port:** CALL: Peel Harbour
PORT ERIN HARBOUR	54°05'·11N 4°45'·79W	TEL: +44(0)1624 833206	VHF 12 16
PORT S. MARY	54°04'N 4°44'W	TEL: +44(0)1624 833205	**Port:** CALL: Port S. Mary Harbour
RAMSEY	54°19'N 4°21'W	TEL: +44(0)1624 812245 FAX: +44(0)1624 812245	**Port:** CALL: Ramsey Harbour

FLEETWOOD - HARBOUR VILLAGE MARINA

CALL: Fleetwood Dock — 53°55'·0N 3°00'·5W

Tel: Marina: +44(0)1253 872323
Harbour Control: +44(0)1253 770523
fleetwood@abports.co.uk

Fax: Dock Office: +44(0)1253 777549
www.abports.co.uk

FREQUENCY: Ch 11 12 16

HOURS OPEN: 0900-1700 LT
ACCESS: HW ± 2h through the lock

FLEETWOOD - HARBOUR VILLAGE MARINA FROM SW

GLASSON BASIN YACHT CO LTD, FLEETWOOD

53°59'·75N 2°50'·65W

Tel: +44(0)1524 751491

Fax: +44(0)1524 752626

FREQUENCY: Ch 08 16 — LOCATION: Glasson Dock — ACCESS: HW -1h to HW

HAYLE HARBOUR

Port — 50°11'N 5°26'W

Tel: +44(0)1736 754043
off@hayle-harbour.fsbusiness.co.uk

Fax: +44(0)1736 756632
www.hayleharbour.co.uk

FREQUENCY: Ch 14 16 **18**

HOURS: 0900-1700 LT

ILFRACOMBE

Port: CALL: Ilfracombe Harbour — 51°13'N 4°07'W

Tel: +44(0)1271 862108
Mobile: 07775 532606
harbour_master@northdevon

Fax: +44(0)1271 862108

FREQUENCY: Ch 12 16

HOURS: Apr-Oct: 0815-1700 LT (when manned)
Nov-Mar: HX
ACCESS: HW ± 2h

Port Operations and Information Service LIVERPOOL	
CALL:	Mersey Radio
LOCATION:	Port Operations Control: Maritime Centre (53° 28´·03N 3° 01´·13W) Port Radar: Royal Seaforth Dock (53° 27´·95N 3° 02´·44W)
TELEPHONE:	Port Operations Control: +44(0)151 9496136 (H24) Port Auth: +44(0)151 9496000
FAX:	Port Operations Control: +44(0)151 9496150
FREQUENCY:	Calling and Safety: Ch 16 Port Operations: Calling and Navigation: Ch 12 Port Operations and Routine Broadcasts: Ch 09 Port Operations and Radar Information: Ch 18
HOURS:	VHF Ch 12 & 16: H24

A general situation and movement statement, giving traffic movements, local navigational warnings and weather reports is broadcast on VHF Ch 09 at 3h and 2h before HW.

Vessels requesting radar assistance will be directed to communicate with Mersey Radio on VHF Ch 18. The vessel will be advised of its position relative to buoys or other reference points close by.

Taylors Bank
Queen's Channel
Formby Bank
Crosby Channel (marked and lit)
Great Burbo Bank
Great Burbo Flats
Liverpool
Q1
Q2
3°15´
10´
5´
33´
53° 30´
27´

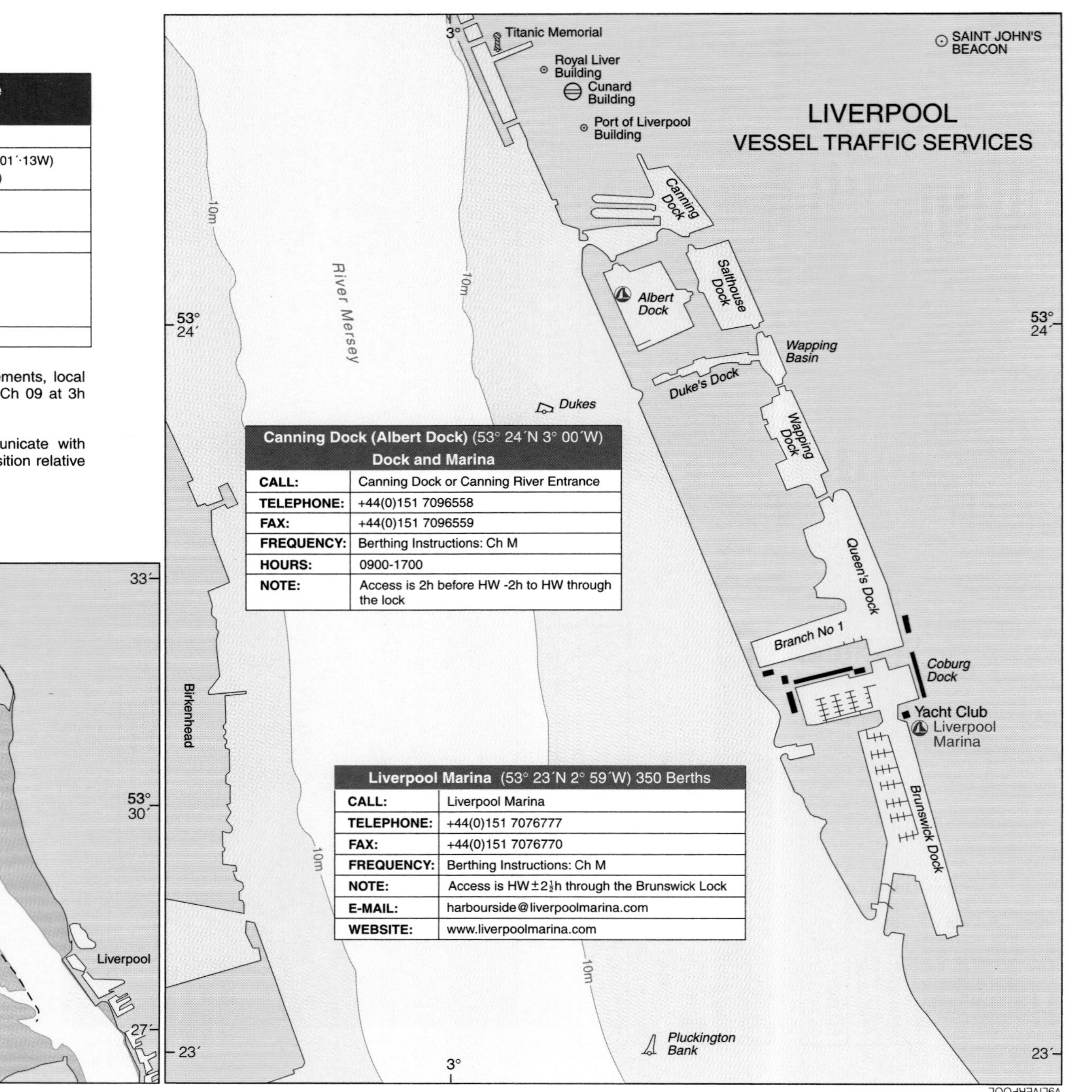

Canning Dock (Albert Dock) (53° 24´N 3° 00´W) Dock and Marina	
CALL:	Canning Dock or Canning River Entrance
TELEPHONE:	+44(0)151 7096558
FAX:	+44(0)151 7096559
FREQUENCY:	Berthing Instructions: Ch M
HOURS:	0900-1700
NOTE:	Access is 2h before HW -2h to HW through the lock

Liverpool Marina (53° 23´N 2° 59´W) 350 Berths	
CALL:	Liverpool Marina
TELEPHONE:	+44(0)151 7076777
FAX:	+44(0)151 7076770
FREQUENCY:	Berthing Instructions: Ch M
NOTE:	Access is HW±2½h through the Brunswick Lock
E-MAIL:	harbourside@liverpoolmarina.com
WEBSITE:	www.liverpoolmarina.com

V9LIVERPOOL

GLASSON BASIN YACHT HARBOUR FROM SE

LIVERPOOL MARINA	CALL: Liverpool Marina 350 Berths	53°23′N 2°59′W
☎ Hr Mr: +44(0)151 7085228 Marina Office: +44(0)151 7076777 harbourside@liverpoolmarina.co.uk	Access Depth: 3 m	Fax: +44(0)151 7098731 Marina: +44(0)151 7076770 www.liverpoolmarina.com
FREQUENCY: Ch **M**		HOURS: 0845-1730 LT LOCK HOURS: 0600-2200 LT (summer) ACCESS: via Brunswick Dock Lock HW ± 2½ h

LIVERPOOL MARINA FROM S

MARYPORT MARINA	CALL: Maryport Marina	54°43′·0N 3°30′·3W
☎ +44(0)1900 814431 & 818447 Mobile: 07880 607082 maryport_marina@lineone.net		Fax: +44(0)1900 810212 www.maryport-marina.co.uk
FREQUENCY: Ch 16 M **80**		HOURS OPEN: H24 ACCESS: HW ± 2½ h through the lock

MARYPORT MARINA

MINEHEAD	**Port**	51°12'·79N 03°28'·27W
Tel: +44(0)1643 702566	Depth: 2·5 m, Maximum LOA: 60 m	Fax: +44(0)1643 702566
FREQUENCY: Ch 12 14 16		HOURS: HX

PADSTOW	**Port:** CALL: Padstow Harbour	50°32'·51N 04°56'·17W
Tel: Hr Mr: +44(0)1841 532844 & 532239 padstowharbour@compuserve.com		Fax: Port: +44(0)1841 533346 www.padstow-harbour.co.uk
FREQUENCY: Ch **12** 16		HOURS: Mon-Fri: 0800-1700 LT Other times: HW ± 3h

PORTISHEAD MARINA	CALL: Portishead Quays Marina 150 Berths 400 Planned	51°30'N 2°45'W
Tel: Marina & Lock: +44(0)1275 841941 berthin-cnm@pearce.co.uk ebeaver@crestnicholson.com		Fax: Marina and Lock: +44(0)1275 841942 www.crestnicholsonmarinas.co.uk
FREQUENCY: Lock & Marina: Ch 12* 80 *Channel 12 to be used outside marina		HOURS: H24 ACCESS: HW ± 4½ h Mean Neaps HW ± 3¾ h Mean Springs

PRESTON MARINA	CALL: Riversway Control	53°45'·6N 2°44'·5W
Tel: +44(0)1772 733595 malcolm_miller@prestonmarina.co.uk		Fax: +44(0)1772 731881 www.prestonmarina.co.uk
FREQUENCY: Ch 14 16		HOURS OPEN: 0900-1700 LT ACCESS: HW Liverpool ± 1½ h through the lock

SHARPNESS	**Port:** CALL: Sharpness Pierhead	51°43'N 2°29'W
Tel: Hr Mr: +44(0)1453 811862 Pierhead: +44(0)1453 511968 Sharpness Marine: +44(0)1453 811476 ght.sharpness@virgin.net		Fax: +44(0)1453 811863 www.gloucesterharbourtrustees.org.uk
FREQUENCY: Calling & Working: Ch 13 Port Operations: Ch 09 Gloucester & Sharpness Canal Operations: Ch 74		HOURS: HW -6h to +2h
FOG SIGNALS: At the entrance to Sharpness Dock and Sharpness Point, Fog Signals are available on request through the Pierhead Duty Watchkeeper on VHF Ch 13 or by telephone +44(0) 1453511968 during navigable hours		

PRESTON MARINA AND LOCKS

S. IVES	Port	50°13′N 5°29′W
☎ Hr Mr: +44(0)1736 795018		Fax: Hr Mr: +44(0)1736 795018
FREQUENCY: Ch 12 16		HOURS: HX

WATCHET	Marina 220 Berths 70 Visitor Berths	51°11′N 3°19′·64W
☎ Marina & Hr Mr: +44(0)1984 631264 Watchet Boat Owners Association: +44(0)1984 634242 watchethm@deandyball.co.uk		Fax: +44(0)1984 639285 www.watchet-harbour-marina.com wwww.boa.co.uk
FREQUENCY: Ch 80	Marina Lock: Access regulated by lights	HOURS: 0830-1730 LT ACCESS: ±1½h HW

WHITEHAVEN ENTRANCE FROM NW

WHITEHAVEN	Marina	150 Berths	54°33′N 3°36′W
☎ Hr Mr: +44(0)1946 692436 Office: +44(0)1946 692435 Sea Lock: +44(0)1946 694672 office@whitehaven-harbour.co.uk			Fax: +44(0)1946 691135 Sea Lock: +44(0)1946 591998 www.whitehaven-harbour.co.uk
FREQUENCY: Port: Ch 12 16 NOTE: Contact Sea Lock on Ch 12 to obtain permission to enter			HOURS: H24 ACCESS: (Sea Lock) H24

WORKINGTON	Port: Workington Harbour Radio	54°39′N 3°34′W
☎ Dock Office & Hr Mr: +44(0)1900 602301		Fax: Dock Office & Hr Mr: +44(0)1900 604696
FREQUENCY: Port: Ch 11 14 16	LOCATION: Lock Gates	HOURS: HW -2½ h to +2h

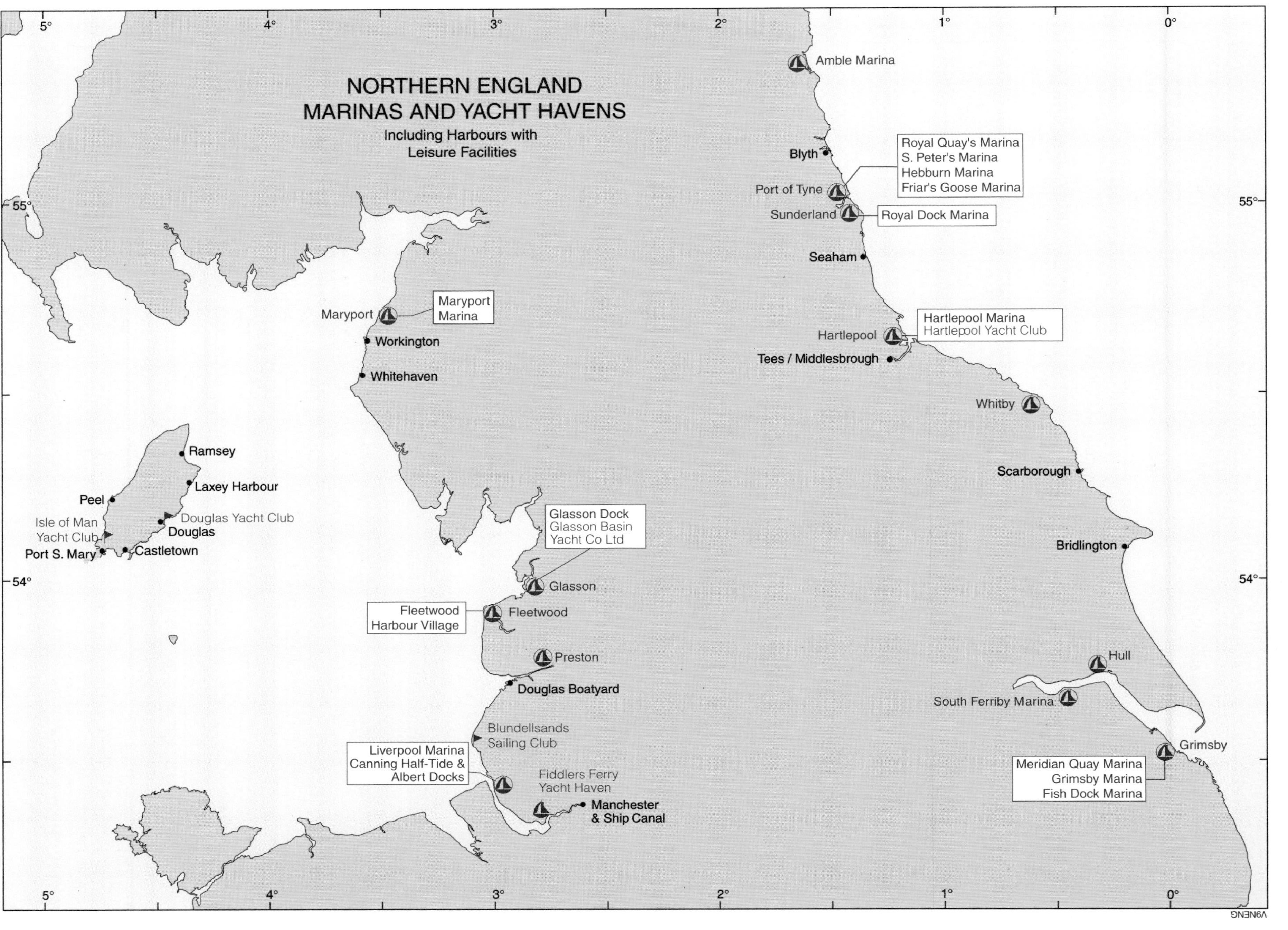
NORTHERN ENGLAND
MARINAS AND YACHT HAVENS
Including Harbours with
Leisure Facilities
5°
4°
3°
2°
1°
0°
55°
54°
Amble Marina
Blyth
Royal Quay's Marina
S. Peter's Marina
Hebburn Marina
Friar's Goose Marina
Port of Tyne
Sunderland
Royal Dock Marina
Seaham
Hartlepool
Hartlepool Marina
Hartlepool Yacht Club
Tees / Middlesbrough
Whitby
Scarborough
Bridlington
Hull
South Ferriby Marina
Grimsby
Meridian Quay Marina
Grimsby Marina
Fish Dock Marina
Maryport
Maryport
Marina
Workington
Whitehaven
Ramsey
Laxey Harbour
Peel
Douglas Yacht Club
Isle of Man
Yacht Club
Douglas
Port S. Mary
Castletown
Glasson Dock
Glasson Basin
Yacht Co Ltd
Glasson
Fleetwood
Harbour Village
Fleetwood
Preston
Douglas Boatyard
Blundellsands
Sailing Club
Liverpool Marina
Canning Half-Tide &
Albert Docks
Fiddlers Ferry
Yacht Haven
Manchester
& Ship Canal
V9NENG

UNITED KINGDOM, NORTHERN IRELAND

BELFAST (Coastguard MRCC) MMSI 002320021 — DSC VHF √

54°40′N 5°40′W		Operational area: Northern Ireland
☎ +44(0)2891 463933		Fax +44(0)2891 465886
RT(MF) 2182		**VHF** Ch 06 10 **16** 23 67 **73 84 86**
MARITIME SAFETY INFORMATION BROADCASTS		
	Ch **73 84 86**	An announcement will be made on VHF Channel 16 indicating which VHF working channel will be used for the broadcast
Weather and Navigational warnings broadcast on receipt		DIAGRAMS: pages 157, 159, 161 and 225
Weather Bulletins		
0305 0705 1105 1505 1905 2305	Gale warnings for Areas Irish Sea and Malin. Local area strong wind warnings (Beaufort Force 6 / 7) and gale warnings. Inshore forecast for Region 12	
0705 1905	Shipping forecast: gale warnings, synopsis, 24 hour forecast for Areas Irish Sea and Malin	
Navigational Warnings		
0305 0705 1105 1505 1905 2305	For Areas Charlie and Echo. Local warnings as and when agreed with the Hydrographer, Lighthouse Authority or Harbour Authority . **Submarine / Gunnery Exercises (SUBFACTS / GUNFACTS — Clyde).** Broadcast after any storm warnings, weather bulletins and navigational warnings; SUBFACTS will cover any planned submarine activity for the following 24 hours and will refer to areas 36-41, 43, 45, 46 & 49-81 shown on diagram on page 225, followed by any GUNFACTS (if in force)	

ARDGLASS (PHENNICK COVE MARINA) — Port and Marina — 80 Berths — 54°15′·63N 5°35′·96W

☎ Hr Mr: +44(0)2844 841291 Marina: +44(0)2844 842332	Fax Marina: +44(0)2844 842332
FREQUENCY: Hr Mr: Ch 12 14 16 Marina: M 80	HOURS: Mon-Fri: 0900-1700 LT

BALLYCASTLE — Marina — 55°12′·50N 6°14′·30W

☎ Hr Mr: +44(0)2820 768525 Mobile: 07803 505084	Fax
FREQUENCY: Ch 80	HOURS: Office Hours ACCESS: H24

BANGOR — Marina — 560 Berths — 54°40′·0N 5°40′·2W

☎ +44(0)2891 453297 bangormarina@dnet.co.uk	Fax +44(0)2891 453450 www.crestnicholsonmarinas.co.uk
FREQUENCY: Marina: Ch 16 80 Harbour: Ch 11	HOURS: H24

BELFAST — Traffic and Port Information Service: CALL: Belfast Harbour Radio — 54°36′N 5°56′W

☎ Port Control: +44(0)2890 553504 (H24) Hr Mr's Office: +44(0)2890 553015 info@belfast-harbour.co.uk		Fax Hr Mr's Office: +44(0)2890 553017 www.belfast-harbour.co.uk
FREQUENCY: Belfast Harbour Radio: Ch **12** 16	LOCATION: Port Operations Centre, Milewater Basin	HOURS: Ch 12: H24
RADAR SURVEILLANCE: Belfast harbour and the greater part of Belfast Lough is under Radar Surveillance from the Port Operations Centre, Milewater Basin		

CARRICKFERGUS MARINA — 54°42′·7N 5°48′·8W

☎ +44(0)2893 366666	Fax +44(0)2893 350505
FREQUENCY: Ch M	HOURS OPEN: H24 ACCESS: H24

COLERAINE — Marina & Port — 45 Berths 15 Visitors — 55°08′·6N 6°40′·4W

☎ Hr Office: +44(0)2870 342012 Marina: +44(0)2870 344768	Fax +44(0)2870 352000
FREQUENCY: Ch M **12** 16	HOURS: Mon-Fri: 0900-1700 LT ACCESS: H24

COPELANDS MARINA, DONAGHADEE — 54°38′·4N 5°31′·7W

☎ +44(0)2891 882184 Mobile: 07802 363382	Fax Hr Mr: +44(0)2891 882184
FREQUENCY: Ch 11 16 80	HOURS: HJ ACCESS: HW ± 4h

GLENARM HARBOUR	Marina 50 Berths	54°58′·33N 5°57′·02W
Tel: +44(0)2828 260088 Mobile: 0770 3606763	Depth: 4 - 7 m, Maximum LOA: 24 m	Fax: +44(0)2828 260088

KILKEEL	Port	54°03′N 6°00′W
Tel: +44(0)2841 762287		Fax:
FREQUENCY: Ch **12** 14 16		HOURS: Mon-Fri: 0800-1530 LT Sat: 0800-1200 LT

KILLYLEAGH	Port	54°03′N 6°00′W
Tel: +44(0)2844 828375	Marina Planned	Fax:
FREQUENCY: Ch 12 16		HOURS: HX

LARNE	Port: CALL: Larne Harbour	54°51′N 5°48′W
Tel: Hr Mr: +44(0)2828 872177 Port Control: +44(0)2828 872179 info@portoflarne.co.uk		Fax: Harbour Office: +44(0)2828 872209 Port Control: +44(0)2828 872220 www.portoflarne.co.uk
FREQUENCY: Hr Mr: Ch 14 16		HOURS: Ch 16: H24

LONDONDERRY	Port: CALL: Londonderry Harbour Radio	54°59′N 7°19′W
Tel: Hr Office: +44(0)2871 860555 & 861113 Hr Mr Mobile: 07801 032387 Harbour Radio: +44(0)2827 860313 bill@londonderry-port.co.uk		Fax: Hr Office: +44(0)2871 861656 www.londonderry-port.co.uk
FREQUENCY: Port: Ch **14** 16		HOURS: H24

PORTAFERRY MARINA	30 Berths	54°22′·67N 5°32′·85W
Tel: Marina: +44(0)2842 729598 Mobile: 07703209780	Depth: 2·5 m	Fax: +44(0)2842 729784
FREQUENCY: Ch M 80		

PORTRUSH	Port: CALL: Portrush Harbour	55°12′·34N 6°39′·49W
Tel: Hr Mr: +44(0)2870 822307		Fax:
FREQUENCY: Ch 12 16		HOURS: Mon-Fri: 0900-1700 LT Sat-Sun: 0900-1700 LT (June - Sept only)

SEATONS MARINA, RIVER BANN		55°09′·2N 6°41′·7W
Tel: +44(0)2870 832086 Mobile: 07733100915 ssp@seatonsmarina.co.uk	Depth: 2·5 m, LOA: 14 m	Fax: www.seatonsmarina.co.uk
FREQUENCY: Ch M		HOURS OPEN: H24 ACCESS: H24

STRANGFORD HARBOUR	Port	54°22′N 5°33′W
Tel: Port: +44(0)2844 881637		Fax: Port: +44(0)2844 881249
FREQUENCY: Port: Ch 12 14 16 M		HOURS: Mon-Fri: 0900-1700 LT

WARRENPOINT	Port	54°06′N 6°16′W
Tel: +44(0)2841 752878 info@warrenpointharbour.co.uk		Fax: +44(0)2841 773962 warrenpointharbour.co.uk
FREQUENCY: Ch **12** 16		HOURS: H24

UNITED KINGDOM, SCOTLAND

ABERDEEN (Coastguard MRCC) MMSI 002320004 — DSC VHF √ MF √

57°08′N 2°05′W	Operational area: Cape Wrath to Doonie Point (Approximately 50 North) including the Pentland Firth		
☎ +44(0)1224 592334		Fax +44(0)1224 575920	
RT (MF)	Transmits 2182 **2226** 2596 2691	Receives 2182 **2226** 2596 2691	**VHF** Ch 06 10 16 **23** 67 73 **84 86**

MARITIME SAFETY INFORMATION BROADCASTS

A	**2226**	RT (MF)
B	VHF Ch **23 84 86**	An announcement will be made on VHF Channel 16 indicating which VHF working channel will be used for the broadcast

Weather and Navigational warnings broadcast on receipt — DIAGRAMS: pages 157, 159, 160, 161 and 225

Weather Bulletins

A: 0320 0720 1120 1520 1920 2120	Gale warnings for Areas Fair Isle, Cromarty, Forth and Forties
B: 0320 0720 1120 1520 1920 2320	Gale warnings for Areas Fair Isle, Cromarty, Forth and Forties. Local area strong wind warnings. Inshore forecast for Region 1
A, B: 0720 1920	Shipping forecast: gale warnings, synopsis, 24 hour forecast for Areas Fair Isle, Cromarty, Forth and Forties

Navigational Warnings

A: 0320 0720 1120 1520 1920 2320	For Areas Mike and November
B: 0320 0720 1120 1520 1920 2320	For Areas Mike and November. Local warnings as and when agreed with the Hydrographer, Lighthouse Authority or Harbour Authority

CLYDE (Coastguard MRCC) MMSI 002320022 — DSC VHF √ MF √

55°58′N 4°48′W	Operational area: Mull of Galloway to Ardnamurchan Point including Arran, Bute, Coll, Colonsay, Cumbrae, Gigha, Islay, Jura, Mull and Tiree		
☎ +44(0)1475 729988		Fax +44(0)1475 786955	
RT (MF)	Transmits **1883** 2182	Receives **1883** 2182	**VHF** Ch 06 **10** 16 **23** 67 **73 84 86**

MARITIME SAFETY INFORMATION BROADCASTS

A	**1883**	RT (MF)
B	VHF Ch **10 23 73 84 86**	An announcement will be made on VHF Channel 16 indicating which VHF working channel will be used for the broadcast

Weather and Navigational warnings broadcast on receipt — DIAGRAMS: pages 157, 159, 160, 161 and 225

Weather Bulletins

A: 0020 0420 0820 1220 1620 2020	Gale warnings for Areas Hebrides and Malin
B: 0020 0420 0820 1220 1620 2020	Local area strong wind warnings. Inshore forecast for Regions 13 and 14
A: 0820 2020	Shipping forecast: gale warnings, synopsis, 24 hour forecast for Areas Bailey, Hebrides, Rockall and Malin
B: 0820 2020	Shipping forecast: gale warnings, synopsis, 24 hour forecast for Areas Hebrides and Malin

Navigational Warnings

A: 0020 0420 0820 1220 1620 2020	For Areas Bravo and Charlie Information on military firing practice exercises, when required
B: 0020 0420 0820 1220 1620 2020 On request	For Areas Bravo and Charlie Local warnings as and when agreed with the Hydrographer, Lighthouse Authority or Harbour Authority. **Submarine / Gunnery Exercises (SUBFACTS / GUNFACTS — Clyde).** Broadcast after any storm warnings, weather bulletins and navigational warnings; SUBFACTS will cover any planned submarine activity for the following 24 hours and will refer to all areas shown on diagram on page 225, followed by any GUNFACTS (if in force) NOTE: On notification from the Ministry of Defence of NATO Exercises, SUBFACTS / GUNFACTS may also be broadcast through RT (MF)

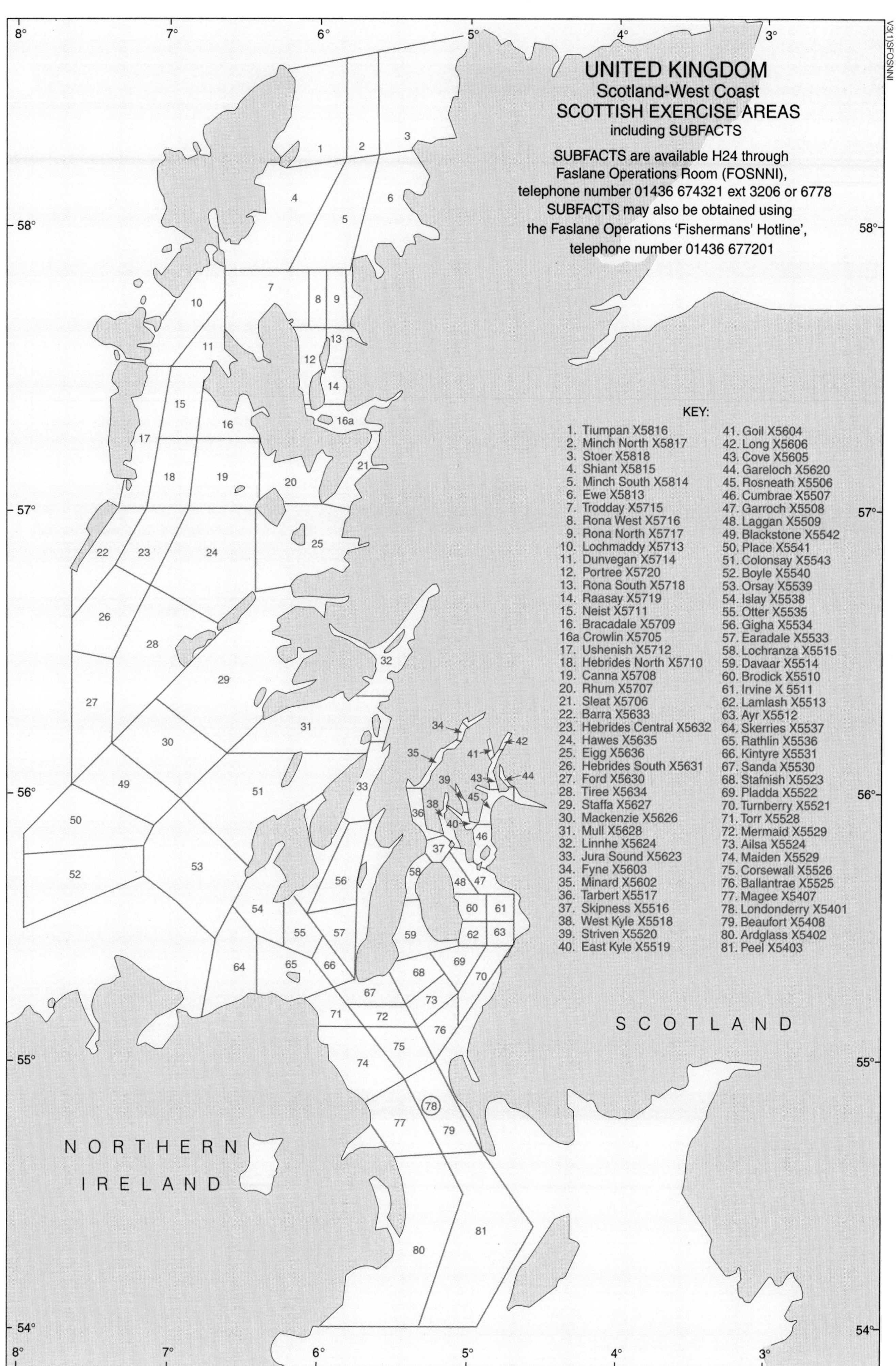

UNITED KINGDOM
Scotland-West Coast
SCOTTISH EXERCISE AREAS
including SUBFACTS
SUBFACTS are available H24 through
Faslane Operations Room (FOSNNI),
telephone number 01436 674321 ext 3206 or 6778
SUBFACTS may also be obtained using
the Faslane Operations 'Fishermans' Hotline',
telephone number 01436 677201
KEY:
1. Tiumpan X5816
2. Minch North X5817
3. Stoer X5818
4. Shiant X5815
5. Minch South X5814
6. Ewe X5813
7. Trodday X5715
8. Rona West X5716
9. Rona North X5717
10. Lochmaddy X5713
11. Dunvegan X5714
12. Portree X5720
13. Rona South X5718
14. Raasay X5719
15. Neist X5711
16. Bracadale X5709
16a Crowlin X5705
17. Ushenish X5712
18. Hebrides North X5710
19. Canna X5708
20. Rhum X5707
21. Sleat X5706
22. Barra X5633
23. Hebrides Central X5632
24. Hawes X5635
25. Eigg X5636
26. Hebrides South X5631
27. Ford X5630
28. Tiree X5634
29. Staffa X5627
30. Mackenzie X5626
31. Mull X5628
32. Linnhe X5624
33. Jura Sound X5623
34. Fyne X5603
35. Minard X5602
36. Tarbert X5517
37. Skipness X5516
38. West Kyle X5518
39. Striven X5520
40. East Kyle X5519
41. Goil X5604
42. Long X5606
43. Cove X5605
44. Gareloch X5620
45. Rosneath X5506
46. Cumbrae X5507
47. Garroch X5508
48. Laggan X5509
49. Blackstone X5542
50. Place X5541
51. Colonsay X5543
52. Boyle X5540
53. Orsay X5539
54. Islay X5538
55. Otter X5535
56. Gigha X5534
57. Earadale X5533
58. Lochranza X5515
59. Davaar X5514
60. Brodick X5510
61. Irvine X 5511
62. Lamlash X5513
63. Ayr X5512
64. Skerries X5537
65. Rathlin X5536
66. Kintyre X5531
67. Sanda X5530
68. Stafnish X5523
69. Pladda X5522
70. Turnberry X5521
71. Torr X5528
72. Mermaid X5529
73. Ailsa X5524
74. Maiden X5529
75. Corsewall X5526
76. Ballantrae X5525
77. Magee X5407
78. Londonderry X5401
79. Beaufort X5408
80. Ardglass X5402
81. Peel X5403
SCOTLAND
NORTHERN IRELAND
8° 7° 6° 5° 4° 3°
58° 57° 56° 55° 54°
V3(1)SFOSNNI

FORTH (Coastguard MRSC) MMSI 002320005 — DSC VHF √

56°17′N 2°35′W — Operational area: Doonie Point to English Border

+44(0)1333 450666 — +44(0)1333 450725

VHF Ch 6 10 16 **23** 67 73 **84 86**

MARITIME SAFETY INFORMATION BROADCASTS		
	VHF Ch **23 86**	An announcement will be made on VHF Channel 16 indicating which VHF working channel will be used for the broadcast

Weather and Navigational warnings broadcast on receipt — DIAGRAMS: pages 157, 159, 160, 161 and 225

Weather Bulletins	
0205 0605 1005 1405 1805 2205	Gale warnings for Areas Forth, Tyne Dogger and Forties. Local area strong wind warnings. Inshore forecast for Region 2
1005 2205	Shipping forecast: gale warnings, synopsis, 24 hour forecast for Areas Forth, Tyne, Dogger and Forties
Navigational Warnings	
0205 0605 1005 1405 1805 2205	For Areas Lima and Mike. Local warnings as and when agreed with the Hydrographer, Lighthouse Authority or Harbour Authority

SHETLAND (Coastguard MRSC) MMSI 002320001 — DSC VHF √ MF √

60°09′N 1°08′W — Operational area: Shetland Islands, Fair Isle and Orkney Islands

+44(0)1595 692976 — +44(0)1595 694810

RT (MF)	Transmits	Receives
	1770	**1770**
	2182	2182

VHF Ch 06 **10** 16 **23** 67 **73 84** 86

MARITIME SAFETY INFORMATION BROADCASTS				
A	**1770**	RT (MF)		
B	VHF Ch **10 23 73 84**	An announcement will be made on VHF Channel 16 indicating which VHF working channel will be used for the broadcast		

Weather and Navigational warnings broadcast on receipt — DIAGRAMS: pages 157, 159, 160, 161 and 225

Weather Bulletins	
A: 0105 0505 0905 1305 1705 2105	Gale warnings for Areas Faeroes, Fair Isle and Viking. An inshore forecast covering the local area up to 60 nautical miles from Lerwick
B: 0105 0505 0905 1305 1705 2105	Gale warnings for Areas Faeroes, Fair Isle and Viking. Local area strong wind warnings. An inshore forecast covering the local area up to 60 nautical miles from Lerwick
A, B: 0905 2105	Shipping forecast: gale warnings, synopsis, 24 hour forecast for Areas Faeroes, Fair Isle and Viking
Navigational Warnings	
A: 0105 0505 0905 1305 1705 2105	For Area November
B: 0105 0505 0905 1305 1705 2105	For Area November. Local warnings as and when agreed with the Hydrographer, Lighthouse Authority or Harbour Authority

STORNOWAY (Coastguard MRSC) MMSI 002320024 — DSC VHF √ MF √

58°12′N 6°22′W — Operational area: Ardnamurchan Point to Cape Wrath, Barra Head to Butt of Lewis (Western Isles) and S. Kilda

+44(0)1851 702013 — +44(0)1851 704387

RT (MF)	Transmits	Receives
	1743	**1743**
	2182	2182

VHF Ch 06 **10** 16 23 **67 73 84** 86

MARITIME SAFETY INFORMATION BROADCASTS				
A	**1743**	RT (MF)		
B	VHF Ch **10 67 73 84**	An announcement will be made on VHF Channel 16 indicating which VHF working channel will be used for the broadcast		

Weather and Navigational warnings broadcast on receipt — DIAGRAMS: pages 157, 159, 160, 161 and 225

STORNOWAY (Coastguard MRSC) MMSI 002320024 (Continued)	DSC VHF √ MF √
Weather Bulletins	
A: 0110 0510 0910 1310 1710 2110	Gale warnings for Areas Bailey, Faeroes, Fair Isle, Hebrides, Malin and Rockall
B: 0110 0510 0910 1310 1710 2110	Local area strong wind warnings. Inshore forecast for Region 15
A, B: 0910 2110	Shipping forecast: gale warnings, synopsis, 24 hour forecast for Areas Bailey, Faeroes, Fair Isle, Hebrides, Malin and Rockall
Navigational Warnings	
A: 0110 0510 0910 1310 1710 2110	For Areas Alfa, Bravo, November Information on military firing practice exercises, when required
B: 0110 0510 0910 1310 1710 2110	For Areas Alfa, Bravo, November. Local warnings as and when agreed with the Hydrographer, Lighthouse Authority or Harbour Authority Information on military firing practice exercises, when required
A, B: 0110 0510 0910 1310 1710 2110	**Submarine / Gunnery Exercises (SUBFACTS / GUNFACTS — Clyde).** Broadcast after any storm warnings, weather bulletins and navigational warnings; SUBFACTS will cover any planned submarine activity for the following 24 hours and will refer to Areas 1-28 shown on diagram on page **225**, followed by GUNFACTS (if in force) NOTE: On notification from the Ministry of Defence of NATO Exercises, SUBFACTS / GUNFACTS may also be broadcast through RT(MF)

BBC RADIO SCOTLAND			
	93·1 MHz	FM	Ben Gullipen / Kirkconnel
	94·3 MHz		Black Hill
	810	AM	Burghead
	92·8 MHz	FM	Campbeltown
	93·7 MHz		Crieff
	93·9 MHz		Darvel
	92·7 MHz		Forfar
	93·3 MHz		Girvan
	92·7 MHz		Lethanhill
	92·7 MHz		Millburn Muir
	93·6 MHz		Pitlochry
	810	AM	Redmoss
	94·0 MHz	FM	Rosemount
	93·6 MHz		Rosneath
	92·9 MHz		Rothesay
	93·7 MHz		South Knapdale
	93·2 MHz		Strachur
	810	AM	Westerglen
	93·5 MHz	FM	West Kilbride
Weather Bulletins			
Sat: 0700 (after news bulletin) 1825 LT	Detailed conditions forecast, synopsis and outlook together with any storm warnings in force, for coastal (and inland) areas		

ABERDEEN	Port: CALL: Aberdeen Port Control	57°09′N 2°03′W
☎ Hr Office: +44(0)1224 597000		Fax: Port Control: +44(0)1224 584301
FREQUENCY: Port: Ch 06 11 **12** 13 16	LOCATION: Port Control: Signal Station, North Pier	HOURS: H24

ANSTRUTHER HARBOUR	22 Berths 8 Visitors	56°13′·2N 2°41′·8W
☎ Hr Mr: +44(0)1333 310836		Fax: Hr Mr: +44(0)1333 310836
FREQUENCY: Ch **11** 16		HOURS: Hr Mr: 0900-1700 LT

ARDFERN YACHT CENTRE LTD	CALL: Ardfern Yacht Centre 25 Visitors Berths	56°10′·97N 5°31′·8W
☎ +44(0)1852 500247, 500636 & 0700 ARDFERN office@ardfernyacht.co.uk		Fax: +44(0)1852 500624 www.ardfernyacht.co.uk
FREQUENCY: Ch M 80	LOCATION: Loch Craignish	HOURS OPEN: 0830-1730 LT, ACCESS: H24

ARDORAN MARINE, LERAGS, OBAN		56°21′·7N 5°29′·5W
☎ +44(0)1631 566123 colin@ardoran.co.uk		Fax +44(0)1631 566611 www.ardoran.co.uk
FREQUENCY: Ch 16	LOCATION: Lerags, Loch Feochan	ACCESS: Not LW ± 2h
OBAN YACHTS & MARINE SERVICES LTD	CALL: Oban Yachts	56°25′·10N 5°29′·75W
☎ +44(0)1631 565333 sales@obanyachts.co.uk		Fax +44(0)1631 565888 www.obanyachts.co.uk
FREQUENCY: Ch 16 80	LOCATION: Ardantrive Bay, Kerrera	HOURS OPEN: 0800-1700 LT ACCESS: H24

ARDROSSAN	Port	55°38′N 4°49′W
☎ +44(0)1294 463972		Fax +44(0)1294 601289
FREQUENCY: Ch 12 14 16		HOURS: H24 ACCESS: H24
CLYDE	Marina 500 Berths	55°38′·4N 4°49′·1W
☎ +44(0)1294 607077 clydmarina@aol.com	Depth: 5 m, Maximum LOA: 120 feet	Fax +44(0)1294 607076 www.clydemarina.com
FREQUENCY: Ch 16 80	LOCATION: Ardrossan Harbour	ACCESS: H24

ARDROSSAN

ARINAGOUR PIER, ISLE OF COLL	Port	56°37′N 6°31′W
☎ Piermaster: +44(0)1879 230347 Home: +44(0)1879 230359		Fax +44(0)1879 230447
FREQUENCY: Ch 31 (Tx: 157·550 kHz Rx: 162·150 kHz)		HOURS: HX

ARISAIG	CALL: Arisaig Marine 50 Berths	56°54′·6N 5°51′·0W
☎ +44(0)1687 450224 info@arisaig.co.uk		Fax +44(0)1687 450678 www.arisaig.co.uk
FREQUENCY: Ch 16 M		HOURS OPEN: 0900-1900 LT ACCESS: HW -3h to +2h

AYR, FIRTH OF CLYDE	Port	55°28′N 4°38′W
☎ +44(0)1292 281687		Fax +44(0)1292 287787
FREQUENCY: Ch 14 16		HOURS: H24

BALINTORE, MORAY FIRTH		57°45'N 3°55'W
Hr Mr: +44(0)1862 832833 king@balintore.screaming.net		
FREQUENCY: Ch 16 71		HOURS: HX

BALTASOUND HARBOUR, UNST, SHETLAND		60°45'N 0°50'W
FREQUENCY: Ch 16 20		HOURS: Office hours or as required

BANFF	Port	57°40'·24N 02°31'·18W
Hr Mr: +44(0)1261 815544 (part-time)		
FREQUENCY: Ch 14 16		ACCESS: HW ± 4h.
NOTE: 1. The Harbour is tidal but movement during neaps is not a problem for vessels with a shallow draught 2. Also controls Portsoy 57°41'·36N 2°41'·50W		

BUCKIE	Port	57°41'N 2°57'W
Port: +44(0)1542 831700		Port: +44(0)1542 834742
FREQUENCY: Ch 12 16	LOCATION: Harbour Office near Pier 3	HOURS: Ch 16: H24

BURGHEAD	Port	57°42'N 3°30'W
Hr Mr: +44(0)1343 835337		
FREQUENCY: Ch 12 **14** 16		HOURS: HX

CALEDONIAN CANAL	British Waterways	www.britishwaterways.co.uk
CORPACH SEA LOCK	CALL: Corpach Lock	56°50'N 5°08'W
Canal Office: +44(0)1463 233140 Pilots: +44(0)1397 772304 Lockkeeper: +44(0)1397 772249 Fort William Pier: +44(0)1397 703881		Lockkeeper: +44(0)1397 772484 Canal Office: +44(0)1463 710942 www.scottishcanals.co.uk
FREQUENCY: Ch 16 **74**	LOCATION: Fort William	HOURS: Summer: 0700-2200 LT Spring/Autumn: 0830-1650 LT Winter: 0930-1530 LT
PROCEDURE: Pilotage is not compulsory, but is available on request for Corpach and Caledonian Canal passage		
CLACKNAHARRY SEA LOCK	**Lock:** CALL: Clachnaharry Sea Lock	57°29'·4N 4°15'·5W
Clachnaharry Sea Lock: +44(0)1463 713896 Canal Office & Seaport Marina: +44(0)1463 233140 Muirtown Bridge & Lock: +44(0)1463 236573		Canal Office & Seaport Marina: +44(0)1463 710942
FREQUENCY: Ch 16 **74**	Location (Marina): Muirtown Wharf Inverness	
NOTE: Seaport Marina operated by British Waterways		
INVERNESS	**Port & Yacht Haven:** CALL: Inverness Harbour Office	57°29'N 4°14'W
+44(0)1463 715715 hm@invernessharbour.co.uk		+44(0)1463 715705 www.invernessharbour.co.uk
FREQUENCY: Ch **12** 16		HOURS: Mon-Fri: 0900-1700 LT
CALEY MARINA AND YACHT SERVICE CENTRE	50 Berths (including visitors berths)	57°29'·4N 4°15'·5W
+44(0)1463 236539 info@caleymarina.com		+44(0)1463 238323 www.caleymarina.com
	LOCATION: NE entrance to Caledonian Canal Muirtown Inverness	HOURS: 0830-1730 LT ACCESS: HW ± 4h

CAMPBELTOWN		55°02'N 3°41'W
Hr Mr: +44(0)1586 552552 Yacht Pontoon Berthing Master: +44(0)1586 552131		Hr Mr: +44(0)1586 552552
FREQUENCY: Hr Mr: Ch 13 16		HOURS: Hr Mr (Ch 16): Mon-Fri: 0900-1700 LT

CRAIGNURE PIER, ISLAND OF MULL	Port	56°28′N 5°42′W
☎ Piermaster: +44(0)1680 812343 Home: +44(0)1680 812342 craignure@calmac.co.uk		Fax: +44(0)1680 801433
FREQUENCY: Ch 31 (Tx: 157·550 kHz Rx: 162·150 kHz)		HOURS: HX

CRAOBH MARINA	CALL: Craobh Marina	56°12′·7N 5°33′·4W
☎ +44(0)1852 500222 craobh@kipmarina.co.uk		Fax: +44(0)1852 500252 www.kipmarina.co.uk
FREQUENCY: Ch M 80	LOCATION: Craobh Haven	HOURS OPEN: Oct-April: 0830-1700 LT May, June & Sept: 0830-1800 LT July & Aug: 0830-1900 LT ACCESS: H24

CRINAN CANAL	British Waterways	
ARDRISHAIG (EASTERN END)	CALL: Ardrishaig Sea Lock	56°00′·7N 5°26′·7W
☎ Canal Office: +44(0)1546 603210 & 603797 Sea Lock: +44(0)1546 602458		Fax: Canal Office: +44(0)1546 603941 www.britishwaterways.co.uk
FREQUENCY: Ch 16 **74**	CANAL OFFICE: ACCESS:	Monday - Friday: 0830 - 1700* LT (*1630 Friday) Summer: 0830-1730 LT (Later times during peak Summer months) Spring/Autumn: Mon-Sat: 0830-1630 LT Winter: Mon-Fri: 0830-1530 LT
CRINAN (WESTERN END)	CALL: Crinan Sea Lock	56°05′·5N 5°33′·5W
☎ Canal Office: +44(0)1546 603210 Sea Lock: +44(0)1546 830285 Crinan Boats: +44(0)1546 830232 tiedup@crinanboatyard.co.uk		Fax: Crinan Boats: +44(0)1546 830281 www.crinanboatyard.co.uk
FREQUENCY: Boatyard: Ch 12 16 M Sea Lock: Ch 16 **74**	LOCATION: Sound of Jura	HOURS: HX

CRINAN CANAL, ARDRISHAIG (EASTERN END)

CROMARTY FIRTH (INCLUDING INVERGORDON)	**Port:** CALL: Cromarty Firth Port Control	57°41′N 4°10′W
☎ +44(0)1349 852308 shipping@cfpa.co.uk		Fax: +44(0)1349 854172 www.cfpa.co.uk
FREQUENCY: Port: Ch **11** 16 13		HOURS: H24

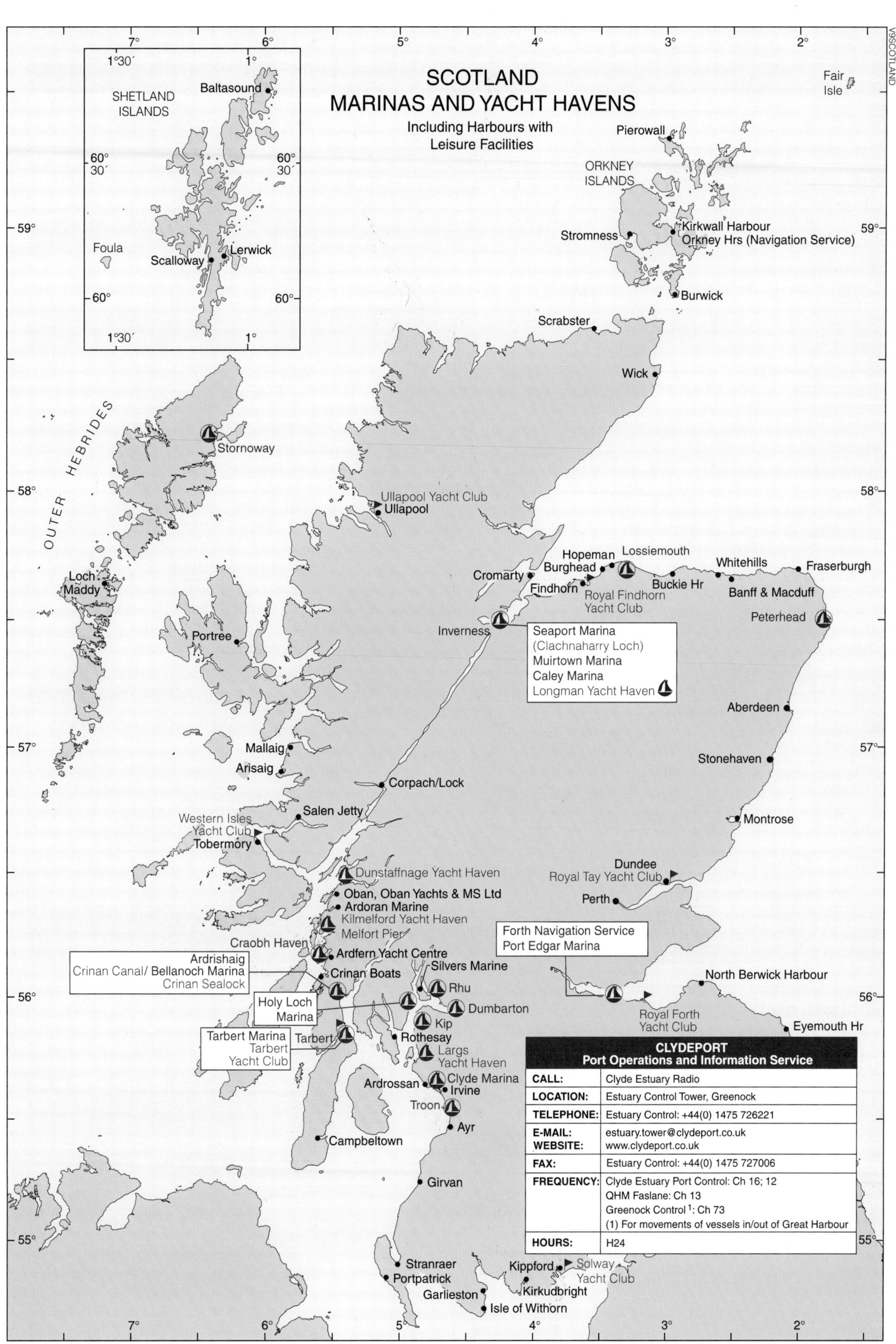

CLYDEPORT Port Operations and Information Service	
CALL:	Clyde Estuary Radio
LOCATION:	Estuary Control Tower, Greenock
TELEPHONE:	Estuary Control: +44(0) 1475 726221
E-MAIL: WEBSITE:	estuary.tower@clydeport.co.uk www.clydeport.co.uk
FAX:	Estuary Control: +44(0) 1475 727006
FREQUENCY:	Clyde Estuary Port Control: Ch 16; 12 QHM Faslane: Ch 13 Greenock Control [1]: Ch 73 (1) For movements of vessels in/out of Great Harbour
HOURS:	H24

DUNDEE	**Port:** CALL: Dundee Harbour Radio	56°28′N 2°57′W
☎ +44(0)1382 224121 or direct dial +44(0)1382 878140		Fax: Port: +44(0)1382 200834 Port Control: +44(0)1382 459448
FREQUENCY: Port: Ch 12 16		HOURS: H24
INFORMATION SERVICE: Local navigational warnings, weather forecasts, tidal information and visibility reports are available on request NOTE: Dundee has an operational surveillance radar which allows Port Control to monitor shipping in the estuary		

DUNSTAFFNAGE MARINA	CALL: Alba	56°27′·0N 5°25′·9W
☎ +44(0)1631 566555		Fax: +44(0)1631 567422
FREQUENCY: Ch M 80	LOCATION: Dunbeg, 4 miles N of Oban	HOURS OPEN: 0900-1700 LT

EYEMOUTH HARBOUR	**Port**	55°52′·5N 2°05′·0W
☎ +44(0)1890 750223	Yachts normally berth at outer end of E Pier	Fax:
FREQUENCY: Ch 12 16		HOURS OF WATCH: Office Hours

FORTH AND CLYDE CANAL	**British Waterways (BW)**	
BOWLING HARBOUR	**Marina:** CALL: Bowling Basin	55°55′·8N 4°29′·0W
☎ Estuary Control: +44(0)1475 726221 Sea Lock (Bowling Basin): +44(0)1389 877969 Auchinstarry Basin: +44(0)1236 823507 British Waterways Office: +44(0)141 332 6936		Fax: Bowling Harbour: +44(0)1389 879533 BW Office: +44(0)141 332 6936 www.britishwaterways.co.uk
FREQUENCY: Estuary Control: Ch **12** Bowling Basin Ch 16 **74** (During Lock operating hours)	LOCATION: River Clyde	HOURS: April - September: 0800-2000 LT October - March: 0800-1600 LT ACCESS: Sea Lock operates HW ± 2h
NOTES: 1. Vessels intending to proceed to or from Bowling Harbour via the River Clyde are required to contact Estuary Control and **monitor Ch12** 2. Essential to contact Lockkeeper **in advance** to receive instructions on Ch 74		

CARRON SEA LOCK	**Lowlands Canal** CALL: Carron Sea Lock	56°02′N 3°41′W
☎ Lockkeeper Mobile: 07810 794468 Emergency (Out of Hours): 0800 479 9947 Auchinstarry Basin: +44(0) 1236 823507 British Waterways Office: +44(0)1324 671217		Fax: Lowlands Canal Office: +44(0)1324 671225 www.scottishcanals.co.uk
FREQUENCY: Lockkeeper: Ch 74	LOCATION: Firth of Forth	ACCESS: HW -4h to +1h 30 min Lock Operates: 0800-2000 LT
NOTES: 1. Passage through the Sea Lock will require advance booking 2. It is mandatory to call Lockkeeper prior to entering River Carron 3. Vessels should monitor Grangemouth Locks on Ch 14, but do not need to report - except for safety reasons		

FORTH PORTS PLC — FORTH NAVIGATION SERVICE	CALL: Forth Navigation	
	AREA: The River and Firth of Forth west of a line joining North Carr Bn to Great Car (South Car) Bn	
☎ +44(0)131 5558877 fns@forthports.co.uk		Fax: +44(0)131 5535428
FREQUENCY: Ch 12 20 **71**	LOCATION: Port Operations Building, Leith	HOURS: H24
NOTE: VHF Ch 71 should be used to call Forth Navigation and for subsequent reporting. VHF Ch 20 or Ch 12 will be requested if necessary		

FRASERBURGH	**Port** No facilities for liesure craft	57°42′N 2°00′W
☎ Port: +44(0)1346 515926 enquiries@fraserburgh-harbour.co.uk		Fax: +44(0)1346 516641 www.fraserburgh-harbour.co.uk
FREQUENCY: Ch 12 16	LOCATION: Harbour Control Tower on West Pier	HOURS: H24

GAIRLOCH HARBOUR	**Port**	57°43′N 5°41′W
☎ Hr Mr: +44(0)1445 712140 Mobile: 077696 71966 raymond.gault@highland.gov.uk		Fax: +44(0)1445 712140
FREQUENCY: Ch 12 16	LOCATION: Gairloch Pier	HOURS: 0900-1400, 1900-2300 LT

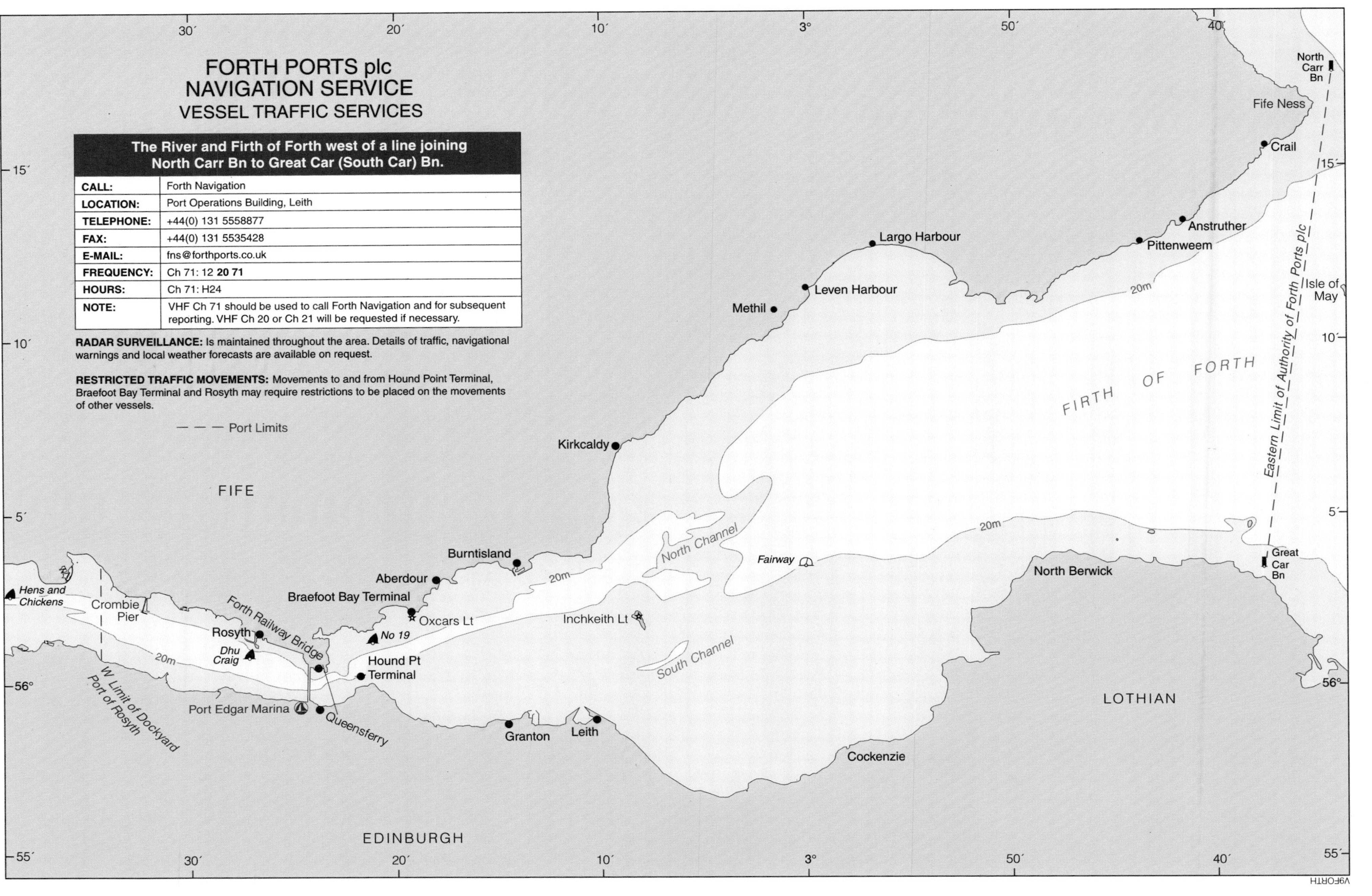

FORTH PORTS plc
NAVIGATION SERVICE
VESSEL TRAFFIC SERVICES

The River and Firth of Forth west of a line joining North Carr Bn to Great Car (South Car) Bn.	
CALL:	Forth Navigation
LOCATION:	Port Operations Building, Leith
TELEPHONE:	+44(0) 131 5558877
FAX:	+44(0) 131 5535428
E-MAIL:	fns@forthports.co.uk
FREQUENCY:	Ch 71: 12 **20 71**
HOURS:	Ch 71: H24
NOTE:	VHF Ch 71 should be used to call Forth Navigation and for subsequent reporting. VHF Ch 20 or Ch 21 will be requested if necessary.

RADAR SURVEILLANCE: Is maintained throughout the area. Details of traffic, navigational warnings and local weather forecasts are available on request.

RESTRICTED TRAFFIC MOVEMENTS: Movements to and from Hound Point Terminal, Braefoot Bay Terminal and Rosyth may require restrictions to be placed on the movements of other vessels.

GARLIESTON	Port	54°47′·35N 4°21′·75W
☎ +44(0)1988 600274		Fax +44(0)1988 600274

GIRVAN	Port	55°15′N 4°51′W
☎ +44(0)1465 713648		Fax +44(0)1465 714454
FREQUENCY: Ch 12 16		HOURS: Mon-Fri, 0900-1700 LT

GOTT BAY PIER, TIREE	Port	56°31′N 6°48′W
☎ +44(0)1879 220337		Fax +44(0)1879 220880
FREQUENCY: Ch 31 (Tx: 157·550 kHz Rx: 162·150 kHz)		HOURS: HX

GRANTON, FIRTH OF FORTH	Port & Marina CALL: Boswell	55°59′N 3°13′W
☎ Hr Mr (via Leith): +44(0)0131 5558866 Marina (Royal Forth YC): +44(0)0131 5523006 Forth Corinthian YC: +44(0)0131 5525939 info@royalforth.mariner.co.uk		Fax +44(0)0131 8560
FREQUENCY: Ch M 80		ACCESS: HW ±3h 30 min
NOTES: 1. Harbour owned by Forth Ports plc, refer to Forth Navigation Service 2. Marina owned and operated by Edinburgh Marina Ltd which is jointly owned by RFYC and FCYC		

HOLY LOCH MARINA	100 Berths 400 Planned	55°58′·3N 4°55′·8W
☎ +44(0)1369 701800 berths@holylochmarina.co.uk info@holylochmarina.co.uk	Depth: 3 m	Fax +44(0)1369 704749 www.holylochmarina.co.uk
FREQUENCY: Ch M 80		HOURS: 0800-2200 LT

HOPEMAN	Port: CALL: Burghead Radio	57°42′N 3°26′W
☎ Hr Mr: +44(0)1343 835337 (part-time)		Fax +44(0)1343 835337
FREQUENCY: Ch 14		HOURS: 0700-1700 LT
NOTE: West-facing entrance channel offers 3-4m at HW, but as the harbour effectively dries out at LW, it is advisable to check with the Harbour Master about arrival times and access		

IRVINE	Port	55°36′N 4°42′W
☎ Hr Mr: +44(0)1294 487286		Fax Hr Mr: +44(0)1294 487896
FREQUENCY: Hr Mr Office: Ch **12** 16	LOCATION: Hr Mr Office situated at Upper Wharf	HOURS: Mon-Fri: 0800-1600 LT
IRVINE HARBOUR BRIDGE		55°36′·17N 4°42′·00W
☎ Hr Mr: +44(0)1294 487286 Bridge Operator: +44(0)8708 403123 Harbourside Office: +44(0)1294 278132	At MHWS there is an air draft of 5 metres under the central span of the bridge	Fax
FREQUENCY: Ch 12 (Bridge Operator)		HOURS OPEN: Hx
NOTE: Vessels requiring the bridge to be opened to enter or leave the harbour should contact the bridge operator		

ISLE OF WITHORN	Port	54°41′·90N 4°21′·80W
☎ +44(0)1988 500246		Fax

KILMELFORD YACHT HAVEN	CALL: Kilmelford Yacht Haven 55 Moorings 6 Visitors Berths	56°15′·4N 5°29′·5W
☎ +44(0)1852 200248 & 200279 info@kilmelfordyachthaven.co.uk		Fax +44(0)1852 200343 www.kilmelfordyachthaven.co.uk
FREQUENCY: Ch **M** 80	LOCATION: Loch Melfort	HOURS OPEN: Mon-Sat: 0830-1700 LT ACCESS: H24

KINLOCHBERVIE	Port — Pontoon Berths Available	58°28′N 5°04′W
Tel: +44(0)1971 521235		Fax: +44(0)1971 521718
FREQUENCY: Ch 14 16		HOURS: HX

KIP MARINA	700 Berths 40 Visitors	55°54′·6N 4°52′·5W
Tel: +44(0)1475 521485 enquire@kipmarina.co.uk	Depth: 3 m, Maximum LOA: 24 m Repair facilities	Fax: +44(0)1475 521298 www.kipmarina.co.uk
FREQUENCY: Ch 16 M 80	LOCATION: Yacht Harbour, Inverkip	HOURS OPEN: H24 ACCESS: H24

KIPPFORD. SOLWAY YACHT CLUB	Yacht Club — Visitor Berths Available	54°52′·35N 4°21′·75W
Tel: Yacht Club: +44(0)1556 620312 Slipway: +44(0)1556 620249		Fax: +44(0)1556 620312
FREQUENCY: Ch 16 **M**		HOURS: HX

KIRKCUDBRIGHT TOWN QUAY AND PONTOONS FROM SE

KIRKCUDBRIGHT	Marina	54°50′N 4°03′W
Tel: Hr Mr: +44(0)1557 331135		Fax: +44(0)1557 331135
FREQUENCY: Port: Ch 12 16		HOURS: 0800 - 1700 LT

KIRKWALL, ORKNEY	**Port:** CALL Kirkwall Harbour Radio	58°59′N 2°57′W
Tel: Harbour Office: +44(0)1856 873636		Fax: Harbour Office: +44(0)1856 873012
FREQUENCY: Harbour Office: Ch **12** 16		HOURS: Harbour Office: Mon-Fri: 0800-1700 LT

PROCEDURE:
1) Any vessel over 20 metres LOA or certified to carry more than 12 passengers, when navigating within 1000 metres of Kirkwall Pier, is required to report its position and intended movement to Kirkwall Harbour Radio
2) Any vessel over 20 metres LOA or certified to carry more than 12 passengers, prior to arriving or departing Kirkwall Pier must report its movement and position to Kirkwall Harbour Radio

NOTE: If unable to raise Kirkwall Harbour Radio, vessels are required to report to Orkney Harbour Radio on VHF Ch 11 or 16

KYLE OF LOCHALSH	Port — 8 Visitors Berths	57°17′N 5°44′W
Tel: +44(0)1599 534167		Fax: +44(0)1599 534589
FREQUENCY: Hr Mr: Ch 11 16		HOURS: HX

KYLE OF LOCHALSH (Continued)	Port 8 Visitors Berths	57°17′N 5°44′W
	Skye Bridge Crossing: CALL: Skye Bridge Control	
Tel: +44(0)1599 534844		Fax: +44(0)1599 534969
FREQUENCY: Ch 12		HOURS: HX

LARGS YACHT HAVEN	CALL: Largs Yacht Haven 600 Berths	55°46′·5N 4°51′·5W
Tel: +44(0)1475 675333 largsyh@aol.com		Fax: +44(0)1475 672245 www.yachthavens.com
FREQUENCY: Ch M 80		HOURS OPEN: H24 ACCESS: H24

LARGS YACHT HAVEN

LEITH	**Port:** CALL: Leith Harbour Radio	55°59′N 3°10′W
Tel: Hr Mr: +44(0)131 5558877		Fax: Hr Mr: +44(0)131 5535428
FREQUENCY: Port Operations: Ch 12 16	Commercial port (see Granton)	HOURS: H24

LERWICK, SHETLAND	**Port:** CALL: Lerwick Harbour	60°09′N 1°08′W
Tel: Lerwick Harbour Trust: +44(0)1595 692991 info@lerwickharbour.co.uk		Fax: Port Control: +44(0)1595 695911 Lerwick Harbour Trust: +44(0)1595 693452 www.shetland.news.co.uk/websites/lht
FREQUENCY: Port: Ch 11 **12** 16	LOCATION: N end of Albert Wharf	HOURS: H24

LOCHINVER HARBOUR	Port	58°09′N 5°15′W
Tel: Hr Mr: +44(0)1571 844247 & 844265		Fax: +44(0)1571 844247
FREQUENCY: Ch 12 16	LOCATION: Harbour Office, Lochinver Fishmarket	HOURS: HX

LOCH MADDY	Port	57°49′N 8°35′W
Tel: Port Manager: +44(0)1876 500337 Hr Mr: Benbecula: +44(0)1870 602425 calum-macleod@cne-siar.gov.uk		Fax: Port Manager: +44(0)1870 500412 Hr Mr: Benbecula: +44(0)1870 602988 www.cne-siar.gov.uk
FREQUENCY: Port: Ch 12 16		HOURS: HX

LOSSIEMOUTH	Port and Marina	57°41′N 2°57′W
Tel: Port: +44(0)1343 813066		Fax: +44(0)1343 813066
FREQUENCY: Ch 12		HOURS: 0800-2400 LT

MACDUFF		57°40'N 2°30'W
☎ +44(0)1261 832236 Watchman: +44(0)1261 833962		Fax: +44(0)1261 833612
FREQUENCY: Ch 12 16		HOURS: H24 Mon-Fri only

MALLAIG	**Port:** CALL: Mallaig Harbour Radio	57°00'N 5°50'W
☎ Hr Office: Office hours: +44(0)1687 462154 Outside office hours: +44(0)1687 462411 harbourauthority@mallaig.dialnet.com		Fax: +44(0)1687 462172
FREQUENCY: Ch 09 16		HOURS: Office hours

MELFORT PIER & HARBOUR	CALL: Melfort Pier 8 Moorings	56°16'·2N 5°30'·1W
☎ +44(0)1852 200333		Fax: +44(0)1852 200329
FREQUENCY: Ch 12 16	LOCATION: Fearnach Bay, Loch Melfort	ACCESS: H24

METHIL DOCKS	**Port:** CALL: Methil Dock Radio	56°11'N 3°00'W
☎ Hr Mr: +44(0)1333 426725		Fax: Hr Mr: +44(0)1333 424873
FREQUENCY: Port Operations: Ch 14 16		HOURS: HW -3h to +1h

MONTROSE	**Port:** CALL: Montrose Port Control	56°42'N 2°28'W
☎ +44(0)1674 672302		Fax: +44(0)1674 675530
FREQUENCY: Ch 12 16	LOCATION: Hr Office: South Quay, Ferryden	HOURS: H24

NORTH QUEENSFERRY NAVAL SIGNAL STATION	CALL: Queensferry	56°00'N 3°23'W
☎ +44(0)1383 419676		Fax:
FREQUENCY: Ch 16 71 74	LOCATION: Battery Pt	HOURS: H24

OBAN	**Port Coastguard Broadcasts**	56°25'N 5°28'W
SUBMARINE EXERCISES: All vessels and submarines operating within the 12 n mile limit between Ardnamurchan Pt (56°44'N 6°13'W) and Lat 54°N should attempt to establish contact with other vessels and submarines in the vicinity on VHF Ch 16 06 Information relating to these activities is broadcast by the Coastguard		
Port-North Pier	CALL: North Pier	56°24'·9N 5°28'·4W
☎ Pier Master: +44(0)1631 562892 (Strathclyde Regional Council)		Fax:
FREQUENCY: Ch 12 16		HOURS: 0900-1700 LT
Port-Railway Pier	CALL: CAL-MAC	56°24'·74N 5°28'·50W
☎ Pier Master: +44(0)1631 562286 (Caledonian Macbrayne Ltd)		Fax: Pier Master: +44(0)1631 566588
FREQUENCY: Ch 12 16		HOURS: 0700-0100 LT

ORKNEY HARBOURS NAVIGATION SERVICE	**Port:** CALL: Orkney Harbour Radio	58°57'·70N 2°58'·10W
☎ +44(0)1856 873636		Fax: +44(0)1856 873012
FREQUENCY: Ch 09 11 12 16	LOCATION: Orkney Harbour Authority Building, Scapa	HOURS: H24
WEATHER MESSAGES: Broadcast on VHF Ch 11 at 0915 and 1715, comprising 12h forecast and outlook for a further 12h for the Orkney Islands, Scapa Flow and Pentland Firth. A listening watch is kept on Ch 16		

PERTH	**Port:** CALL: Perth Harbour	56°23'N 3°26'W
☎ Hr Office: +44(0)1738 624056 & 636245		Fax: +44(0)1738 622263
FREQUENCY: Ch 09 16		HOURS: HX

PETERHEAD MARINA	Port and Marina	57°30′·17N 1°46′·36W
Peterhead Harbour: +44(0)1779 483600 & 483630 (H24) postmaster@peterhead-harbours.co.uk		Peterhead Harbour: +44(0)1779 475715
FREQUENCY: Port: Ch 14 16	LOCATION: Marina located SW corner of harbour	HOURS: H24
Peterhead Bay: Office hours: +44(0)1779 474020 (Marina): Outside office hours: +44(0)1779 474281 info@peterhead-bay.co.uk		Peterhead Bay: +44(0)1779 475712 (Marina) www.peterhead-bay.co.uk

PIEROWALL (WESTRAY PIER), ORKNEY		59°19′N 2°59′W
Hr Office: +44(0)1857 677273		
FREQUENCY: Ch 14 16		HOURS: HX

PORT EDGAR MARINA		55°59′·7N 3°24′·6W
Port: +44(0)1313 313330 North Yacht Marina: +44(0)1324 665071		+44(0)1313 314878 North Queensferry: +44(0)1324 483635 www.portedgar.co.uk
FREQUENCY: Ch M **80**	LOCATION: South Queensferry	HOURS OF WATCH: Apr-Sept: 0900-1930 LT Oct-Mar: 0900-1630 LT ACCESS: H24

PORT EDGAR MARINA

PORTPATRICK	Port	54°50′·42N 5°07′·11W
Hr Mr: +44(0)1776 810355		

PORTREE HARBOUR, ISLAND OF SKYE	Port	57°43′N 5°41′W
Hr Mr: +44(0)1478 612926 Highland Harbours: +44(0)1571 844800		Hr Mr: +44(0)1478 612926
FREQUENCY: Ch 12 16	LOCATION: Pier Head	HOURS: HX

RHU MARINA		56°00′·7N 4°46′·4W
Hr Mr: +44(0)1436 820652 Office: +44(0)1436 820238 any@rhumarina.force9.co.uk		+44(0)1436 821039 rhumarina.co.uk
FREQUENCY: Ch M 80		HOURS OPEN: 0800-0000 LT ACCESS: H24

RHU MARINA

ROTHESAY, BUTE	Port	55°50'N 5°03'W
☎ Hr Mr: +44(0)1700 503842 Bute Berthing Co: +44(0)1700 500630 Moorings: +44(0)1700 504750		📠
FREQUENCY: Ch 12 16		HOURS: 1 May-30 Sept: 0600-2100 LT 1 Oct-30 April: 0600-1900 LT

SALEN JETTY		56°42'·75N 5°46'·60W
☎ +44(0)1967 431 333		📠
FREQUENCY: Ch 16	LOCATION: Loch Sunart	HOURS: HX

SANDPOINT MARINA (DUNBARTON)		55°60'·00N 4°34'·19W
☎ +44(0)1389 762396		📠 +44(0)1389 732605
FREQUENCY: Ch M		HOURS: HX

SCALLOWAY, SHETLAND	**Port:** CALL: Scalloway Harbour Radio	60°08'·2N 1°16'·59W
☎ Hr Mr & Port Control: +44(0)1806 242551 (H24) Pier Master: +44(0)1595 880574 (answerphone outside office hours) scalloway.harbour@sic.shetland.gov.uk		📠 Hr Mr & Port Control: +44(0)1595 242118 shetland.gov.uk
FREQUENCY: Hr Radio: Ch 09 **12** 16		HOURS: Hr Radio: Mon-Fri: 0600-1800 LT Sat: 0600-1230 LT

SCRABSTER, THURSO	Pilots and Port	58°37'N 3°32'W
☎ +44(0)1847 892779 & 894618 harbour@scrabster.co.uk		📠 +44(0)1847 892353 www.scrabster.co.uk
FREQUENCY: Port: Ch 12 16		HOURS: H24

SILVERS MARINE	CALL: Silvers Marine	56°00'·8N 4°47'·9W
☎ +44(0)1436 831222		📠 +44(0)1436 831879
FREQUENCY: Ch M	LOCATION: Rosneath	HOURS OPEN: 0800-1630 LT

S. KILDA	Port: CALL: Kilda Radio	57°49'N 8°35'W
☎ Office Hours: +44(0)1870 604406 Outside Office Hours: +44(0)1870 604612		Fax +44(0)1870 604601
FREQUENCY: Ch 16		HOURS: HJ
NOTE: Kilda Radio is operated in conjunction with Hebrides Range Control. For full details see Firing Practice and Exercise Areas		

STONEHAVEN	Port	56°57'·57N 02°12'·02W
☎ Hr Mr: +44(0)1569 762741 Mobile: 07882 702831	Drying harbour - 140 regular moorings with limited visitor deepwater berths	Fax
FREQUENCY: Ch 11		HOURS: H24

STORNOWAY, LEWIS	Port	58°12'N 6°22'W
☎ Hr Mr: +44(0)1851 702688 sphc@sol.co.uk		Fax +44(0)1851 705714 www.hebrides.com
FREQUENCY: Ch 12 16		HOURS: H24

STRANRAER	Port	54°55'N 5°02'W
☎ +44(0)1557 331135		Fax +44(0)1557 330853
FREQUENCY: Port: Ch 12 16		HOURS: HW ± 3h

STROMNESS, ORKNEY	Port: CALL Stromness Harbour Radio	58°58'N 3°18'W
☎ Harbour Office: +44(0)1856 850744		Fax
FREQUENCY: Harbour Office: Ch **12** 16		HOURS: Harbour Office: Mon-Fri: 0900-1700 LT
PROCEDURE: 1) Any vessel over 20 metres LOA or certified to carry more than 12 passengers, when navigating within 1000 metres of Stromness Pier, is required to report its position and intended movement to Stromness Harbour Radio. 2) Any vessel over 20 metres LOA or certified to carry more than 12 passengers, prior to arriving or departing Stromness Pier must report its movement and position to Stromness Harbour Radio		
NOTE: If unable to raise Stromness Harbour Radio, vessels are required to report to Orkney Harbour Radio on VHF Ch 11 or 16		

TARBERT, JURA	CALL: Tarbert Harbour	55°52'·0N 5°24'·5W
☎ +44(0)1880 820344		Fax +44(0)1880 820719 www.talbertlochfine.com
FREQUENCY: Ch 14 16	LOCATION: Westside of Loch Fyne, 7 miles N of Skipness Point	HOURS OPEN: Office Hours ACCESS: H24

TOBERMORY, MULL		56°37'·4N 6°04'·0W
☎ Piermaster: +44(0)1688 302017 Hr Mr: +44(0)1688 302277		Fax www.tobermory.org
FREQUENCY: Ch 12 16		HOURS OF WATCH: Office hours, listens only

TROON YACHT HAVEN	Marina and Yacht Service Centre 300 Berths	55°33'N 4°40'W
☎ Hr Mr: +44(0)1292 281687 Marina: +44(0)1292 315553 troonyh@aol.com		Fax +44(0)1292 287787 +44(0)1292 312836 www.yachthavens.com
FREQUENCY: Ch 14 16 Marina: Ch M **80**		HOURS: OPEN: H24 ACCESS: H24

UIG, ISLE OF SKYE	Port	57°35'N 6°22'W
☎ Highland Harbours: +44(0)1571 844800		Fax
FREQUENCY: Ch 08 16	LOCATION: Harbour Master's Office, Uig Pier	HOURS: HX

TROON YACHT HAVEN

ULLAPOOL	Port	57°54′N 5°10′W
☎ +44(0)1854 612091 & 612724 info@ullapool-harbour.demon.co.uk		Fax +44(0)1854 612678
FREQUENCY: Ch 12 14 16		HOURS: During fishing season: H24 Outside fishing season: Office hours

WHITEHILLS	Marina 44 Berths	57°40′·82N 2°34′·78W
☎ +44(0)1261 861291 enquiries@whitehillsharbour.co.uk		Fax
FREQUENCY: Ch **14** 16		HOURS: HX

WICK	Port	58°26′N 3°05′W
☎ +44(0)1955 602030 troonyh@aol.com		Fax +44(0)1955 605936 www.wickharbour.co.uk
FREQUENCY: Ch 14 16	LOCATION: Hr Office, Hr Terrace	HOURS: HX

UNITED KINGDOM, WALES

HOLYHEAD (Coastguard MRSC) MMSI 002320018 — DSC VHF √ MF √

53°19′N 4°38′W — Operational area: Frigo to Queensferry (River Dee)

Tel: +44(0)1407 762051 — Fax: +44(0)1407 764373

RT (MF)	Transmits	Receives	VHF Ch 06 10 **16** 23 67 **73 84** 86
	1880	**1880**	
	2182	2182	

MARITIME SAFETY INFORMATION BROADCASTS

A	1880	RT (MF)		
B	VHF Ch **73 84**	An annoucement will be made on VHF Channel 16 indicating which VHF working channel will be used for the broadcast		

Weather and Navigational warnings broadcast on receipt — DIAGRAMS: pages 158, 159 and 161

Weather Bulletins

A: 0235 0635 1035 1435 1835 2235	Gale warnings for Area Irish Sea
B: 0235 0635 1035 1435 1835 2235	Gale warnings for Area Irish Sea. Local area strong wind warnings (Beaufort Force 6 / 7) and / or gale warnings. Inshore forecast for Region 11
A, B: 0635 1835	Shipping forecast: gale warnings, synopsis, 24 hour forecast for Area Irish Sea

Navigational Warnings

A: 0235 0635 1035 1435 1835 2235	For Area Echo
B: 0235 0635 1035 1435 1835 2235	For Area Echo. Local warnings as and when agreed with the Hydrographer, Lighthouse Authority or Harbour Authority

MILFORD HAVEN (Coastguard MRSC) MMSI 002320017 — DSC VHF √ MF √

51°41′N 5°10′W — Operational area: River Towy to Frigo

Tel: +44(0)1646 690909 — Fax: +44(0)1646 692176

RT (MF)	Transmits	Receives	VHF Ch 06 10 **16** 23 67 73 **84 86**
	1767	**1767**	
	2182	2182	

MARITIME SAFETY INFORMATION BROADCASTS

A	1767	RT (MF)		
B	VHF Ch **84 86**	An annoucement will be made on VHF Channel 16 indicating which VHF working channel will be used for the broadcast		

Weather and Navigational warnings broadcast on receipt — DIAGRAMS: pages 158, 159 and 161

Weather Bulletins

A: 0335 0735 1135 1535 1935 2335	Gale warnings for Areas Lundy, Irish Sea and Fastnet
B: 0335 0735 1135 1535 1935 2335	Gale warnings for Areas Lundy, Irish Sea and Fastnet. Local area strong wind warnings (Beaufort Force 6 / 7) and / or gale warnings. Inshore forecast for Regions 9 and 10
A, B: 0735 1935	Shipping forecast: gale warnings, synopsis, 24 hour forecast for Areas Lundy, Irish Sea and Fastnet

Navigational Warnings

A: 0335 0735 1135 1535 1935 2335	For Areas Echo and Foxtrot
B: 0335 0735 1135 1535 1935 2335	For Areas Echo and Foxtrot. Local warnings as and when agreed with the Hydrographer, Lighthouse Authority or Harbour Authority

SWANSEA (Coastguard MRCC) MMSI 002320016 — DSC VHF √

51°34′N 3°58′W — Operational area: Marsland Mouth to River Towy

Tel: +44(0)1792 366534 — Fax: +44(0)1792 369005

VHF Ch 06 **10 16 23 73 84 86**

MARITIME SAFETY INFORMATION BROADCASTS

	VHF Ch **10 23 73 84 86**	An annoucement will be made on VHF Channel 16 indicating which VHF working channel will be used for the broadcast

Weather and Navigational warnings broadcast on receipt — DIAGRAMS: pages 158, 159 and 161

SWANSEA (Coastguard MRCC) **MMSI 002320016 (Continued)**	**DSC VHF √**
	Weather Bulletins
0005 0405 0805 1205 1605 2005	Gale warnings for Areas Lundy, Irish Sea and Fastnet. Local area strong wind warnings (Beaufort Force 6 / 7) and / or gale warnings. Inshore forecast for Region 9
0805 2005	Shipping forecast: gale warnings, synopsis, 24 hour forecast for Areas Lundy, Irish Sea and Fastnet
	Navigational Warnings
0005 0405 0805 1205 1605 2005	For Area Foxtrot Local warnings as and when agreed with the Hydrographer, Lighthouse Authority or Harbour Authority

BBC RADIO CYMRU / WALES				
A	657	AM	NE Wales	Broadcasts as BBC Radio Wales
B	882		(All) Wales	
C	1125		Mid Wales	
D	92·4-94·6 MHz	FM		Broadcasts as BBC Radio Cymru, from over 40 transmission sites
E	96·8 MHz			
F	103·5-105 MHz			
	Weather Bulletins			
A-C: Mon-Fri: 0658 0758 0903 LT Sat: 0903 LT Sun: 0859 LT	General forecast, synopsis for that day, in English, live from National Weather Centre for Wales			
A-C: 1259 LT	General forecast, synopsis for that afternoon and night, in English, live from National Weather Centre for Wales			
A-C: Mon-Fri: 1734 LT Sat, Sun: 1759 LT	General forecast, synopsis for that night and following day, in English, live from National Weather Centre for Wales			
D-F: Mon-Fri: 0601 0728 0758 0824 1759 LT	General forecast, synopsis, in Welsh			

ABERYSTWYTH FROM SE

ABERAERON	CALL: Aberaeron Harbour	52°14′·5N 4°15′·7W
☎ +44(0)1545 571645	Aberaeron Harbour is served by the New Quay Hr Mr	Fax +44(0)1545 571645
FREQUENCY: Ch 14 16		HOURS OPEN: 0900-1700 LT ACCESS: HW ± 3h

ABERDOVEY	**Port:** CALL: Aberdovey Harbour	52°33′N 4°03′W
☎ +44(0)1654 767626 pauledwards@gwynedd.gov.uk		Fax +44(0)1654 767626
FREQUENCY: Ch 12 16		HOURS: 0900-1700 LT or as required by tides ACCESS: HW ± 3h

ABERYSTWYTH	CALL: Aberystwyth Marina 104 Berths 10-15 Visitor Berths	52°24′·4N 4°05′·4W
Tel: Hr Mr: +44(0)1970 611433 Marina: +44(0)1970 611422 abermarina@aol.com	Depth: 1·32 m	Fax: +44(0)1970 624122 www.abermarina.co.uk
FREQUENCY: Marina: Ch 16 80		ACCESS: HW ± 3h

BANGOR AND MENAI STRAIT (PORT PENRHYN)		53°15′·7N 4°05′·3W
Tel: Beaumaris & Menai Hr Mr: +44(0)1248 712312 Penrhyn Hr Mr: +44(0)1248 352525 Menai Hr Mr Mobile: 07778 253178 Plas Menai: +44(0)1248 670964 harbourmaster@portpenrhyn.co.uk		Fax: Penrhyn Hr Mr: +44(0)1248 352525 www.portpenrhyn.co.uk
FREQUENCY: Ch 12 16 69 (Sports Council for Wales: Ch M 80)		HOURS: H24 Movement is restricted to HW ± 1h

BARMOUTH	CALL: Barmouth Harbour 12 Berths	52°43′N 4°03′W
Tel: Port: +44(0)1341 280671 Mobile: 07879 433146 keithallday@gwynedd.gov.uk		Fax: Port: +44(0)1341 280671
FREQUENCY: Ch **12** 16	LOCATION: Hr Mr Office on the quay	HOURS: May-Sept: 0900-2200 LT Oct-April: 0900-1700 LT Weekdays only

BARRY DOCKS	**Port:** CALL: Barry Radio	51°24′N 3°16′W
Tel: Hr Mr: +44(0)1446 700754 Port Office: +44(0)1446 700311	TIDAL INFORMATION: Available on request	Fax: Port Office: +44(0)1446 700100
FREQUENCY: Ch 10 **11** 16		HOURS: HW -4h to +3h

CAERNARFON	**Port and Marina:** CALL: Caernarfon Harbour 46 Berths	53°09′N 4°17′W
Tel: Hr Office: +44((0)1286 672118 Dockmaster: +44((0)1286 672346 cht@caernarfon-hbr.demon.co.uk	Landerne Pier available whilst waiting for access to marina in Victoria Dock	Fax: Hr Office: +44((0)1286 678729 Dockmaster: +44((0)1286 672346 www.caernarfon-hbr.demon.co.uk
FREQUENCY: Port: Ch 14 16 Marina: Ch 80	LOCATION: Victoria Dock	HOURS OPEN: Summer: 0700-2300 LT Winter: Office Hours ACCESS: HW ± 3h

CAERNARFON - VICTORIA DOCK MARINA

CARDIFF	**Port:** CALL: Cardiff Radio	51°29′N 3°10′W
Tel: Hr Mr: +44(0)2920 400500 cardiff@abports.co.uk		Fax: +44(0)2920 400501
FREQUENCY: Ch **14** 16	DIAGRAM: See page 213	HOURS: HW -4h to +3h

CARDIFF (Continued)	**Port:** CALL: Cardiff Radio	51°29′N 3°10′W
Barrage Control:	CALL: Barrage Control	
☎ +44(0)2920 700234		Fax:
FREQUENCY: Ch 18		HOURS: H24

PROCEDURE:

(1) Vessels should maintain a continuous listening watch on VHF Ch 14. Vessels wishing to pass through the barrage must first contact "Barrage Control" preferably by VHF radio on Channel 18. Outbound vessels will be locked through the Barrage on the hour and half hour. Inbound vessels should call "Barrage Control" in advance of their arrival at the Outer Harbour. Vessels should not enter the Outer Harbour unless instructed to do so, either by light signals displayed at the Outer Harbour entrance, or by VHF radio

Access to the Marina once you have passed through the Barrage Locks, is via double sector lock gates:

Traffic Light Signals	
Double Red	Keep clear of lock, DANGER
Single Red	Keep clear, lock in use
Green	Proceed only on instruction from marina staff

(2) Barrage Control maintains contact with Cardiff Port Radio on VHF Ch 14 so that vessel movements can be co-ordinated

CARDIFF FROM SW

CONWY	**Port:** CALL: Conwy Harbour	53°17′·5N 3°50′·3W
☎ Hr Mr: +44(0)1492 596253 conwy.harbour@conwy.gov.uk tony.mead@conwy.gov.uk		Fax: +44(0)1492 585222
FREQUENCY: Ch 12 **14** 16		HOURS: 1 Apr-30 Sept: 0900-1800 LT 1 Oct-31 Mar: Mon-Fri: 0900-1800 LT ACCESS: HW -3h to +2h

CONWY MARINA	CALL: Conwy Marina 500 Berths Visitor Berths Available on Request	53°17′·5N 3°50′·3W
☎ +44(0)1492 593000 stovell.cnm@pearce.co.uk conwymarina.cnm@pearce.co.uk	Depth: 3 m, Maximum LOA: 25 m New Marina at Deganwy Quay Planned	Fax: +44(0)1492 572111 www.crestnicholsonmarinas.co.uk
FREQUENCY: Ch 80		HOURS OPEN: H24 ACCESS: HW ±3½h (Tidal Sensor)

DINORWIC MARINA	CALL: Dinorwic Marina 230 Berths	53°11′·0N 4°12′·5W
☎ Marina: +44(0)1248 671500 Mobile (Lock): 07768 794361 rod.parry@virgin.net		Fax: +44(0)1248 671252
FREQUENCY: Ch 80		HOURS OPEN: HW±3 h

FISHGUARD	**Port**	
☎ +44(0)1348 404406 Outside Office Hours: +44(0)1348 404487 & 404401		Fax: +44(0)1348 404406
FREQUENCY: Ch 14 16		HOURS: Office Hours

HOLYHEAD	Port: CALL: Holyhead Port Control	53°19′N 4°41′W
☎ +44(0)1407 766700		Fax +44(0)1407 606622
FREQUENCY: Ch 14 16	LOCATION: Admiralty Pier	HOURS: H24

HOLYHEAD MARINA	CALL: Holyhead Marina 500 Berths	53°19′·08N 4°37′·10W
☎ +44(0)1407 764242 info@holyhead-marina.co.uk		Fax +44(0)1407 769152 www.holyhead-marina.co.uk
FREQUENCY: Ch M 80		ACCESS: H24

LAWRENNY YACHT STATION	Swinging Moorings	51°43′N 4°53′W
☎ +44(0)1646 651212 Mobile: 07778 819273	Depth: 1·5 m	Fax
FREQUENCY: Ch M	LOCATION: Lawrenny Quay, River Cleddau	

MILFORD MARINA	Marina: CALL: Milford Marina 300 Berths Visitor Berths Available	51°43′N 5°02′W
☎ Marina: +44(0)1646 696312 Port Control: +44(0)1646 696137 marina@milford-docks.co.uk		Fax Marina: +44(0)1646 696314 Port: +44(0)1646 623401 www.milford-docks.co.uk
FREQUENCY: Lock: Ch 14 Marina: Ch M Port Operations: Ch 12		ACCESS: freeflow HW -2h
NOTE: Milford Haven P.A. broadcasts Forecasts on Ch 12 & 14 at 0900 1500 UTC		

MILFORD MARINA FROM S

MONKSTONE CRUISING & SAILING CLUB		51°37′·8N 3°49′·97W
☎ +44(0)1792 812229		Fax
FREQUENCY: Ch M	LOCATION: Neath	ACCESS: HW ± 2½ h through the lock

NEWPORT	Port	51°33′·5N 2°59′W
☎ +44(0)1633 244411		Fax +44(0)1633 221285
FREQUENCY: Ch 09 16 69 **71**	LOCATION: South Lock	HOURS: HW ± 4h

NEW QUAY	CALL: New Quay Harbour	52°12′·9N 4°21′·3W
☎ +44(0)1545 560368		Fax
FREQUENCY: Ch **14** 16		HOURS OPEN: 0900-1700 LT ACCESS: HW ± 3h

NEYLAND YACHT HAVEN	CALL: Neyland Yacht Haven 370 Berths 20 Visitor Berths	51°42′·6N 4°56′·5W
☎ +44(0)1646 601601 neylandh@aol.com	Depth: 2 m, Maximum LOA: 20 m	Fax +44(0)1646 600713 www.yachthavens.com
FREQUENCY: Ch M 80		HOURS OPEN: H24 ACCESS: H24

NEYLAND YACHT HAVEN FROM S

PENARTH MARINA	CALL: Penarth Marina 350 Berths	51°26′·7N 3°10′·2W
☎ +44(0)2920 705021 penarthmarina.cnm@pearce.co.uk	Depth: 3 m, Maximum LOA: 25 m	Fax +44(0)2920 712170 www.crestnicholsonmarinas.co.uk
FREQUENCY: Ch 80	LOCATION: Portway Village	HOURS OPEN: H24 ACCESS: HW ± 4h through the lock
PROCEDURE: Commercial vessels have right of way within the area of the Cardiff Harbour Authority. Leisure craft should call the marina on VHF Ch 80 or Barrage Control on VHF Ch 18 (Refer to Cardiff)		

CARDIFF BARRAGE AND PENARTH MARINA

PORTHCAWL	CALL: Porthcawl Harbour	51°28'·5N 3°42'·0W
☎ Hr Mr (Seasonal): +44(0)1656 782756		Fax:
FREQUENCY: Hr Mr (Seasonal): Ch 80		HOURS OPEN: 0900-2100 LT ACCESS: HW ± 3h

PORTHMADOG	Port: CALL: Porthmadog Harbour	52°55'N 4°08'W
☎ +44(0)1766 512927 dafyddp@gwynedd.gov.uk		Fax:
FREQUENCY: Port: Ch **12** 14 16	LOCATION: Harbour Master's Office	HOURS: 0900-1700 LT ACCESS: HW ± 1½ h

PORTHMADOG FROM N

PWLLHELI MARINA (HAFEN PWLLHELI)	CALL: Hafen Pwllheli 400 Pontoon Berths	52°53'N 4°25'W
☎ Hr Mr: +44(0)1758 704081 Marina: +44(0)1758 701219 Mobile: 07879 433145 kenf@gwynedd.gov.uk		Fax: Marina: +44(0)1758 701443 www.hafanpwllheli.co.uk
FREQUENCY: Hr Mr: Ch 12 16 Marina: Ch 80		HOURS: Hr Mr: 0900-1715 LT ACCESS: HW ± 5h
ABERSOCH LAND & SEA LTD	CALL: Abersoch Land Sea	52°49'·5N 4°30'·0W
☎ Hr Mr: +44(0)1758 704081 Boatyard: +44(0)1758 713434		Fax: Boatyard: +44(0)1758 713150
FREQUENCY: Boatyard: Ch M		HOURS OPEN: 0800-1700 LT

SAUNDERSFOOT	CALL: Saundersfoot Harbour	51°42'·5N 4°42'·2W
☎ +44(0)1834 812094		Fax: +44(0)1834 812094
FREQUENCY: Ch 11 16		HOURS OPEN: Summer: 0800-2100 LT Winter: Mon-Fri: 0800-1800 LT ACCESS: HW ± 2½ h

PWLLHELI MARINA FROM NE

SWANSEA MARINA FROM W

SWANSEA	**Port:** CALL: Swansea Docks Radio	51°37′N 3°56′W
☎ Hr Office: +44(0)1792 633000 King's Dock Locks: +44(0)1792 633382 swahm@abports.co.uk		Fax Hr Office: +44(0)1792 633355 King's Dock Locks: +44(0)1792 459802
FREQUENCY: Port: Ch 14 Tawe Lock: Ch 18	LOCATION: King's Dock Locks	HOURS: H24

SWANSEA MARINA	50 Visitor Berths	51°37′·0N 3°56′·2W
Tel: +44(0)1792 470310 swanmar@cableol.co.uk		Fax: +44(0)1792 463948 www.swansea.gov.uk
FREQUENCY: Ch 18 **80** Call Tawe Lock on VHF Ch 18 for barrage		HOURS OPEN: Summer: 0700-2200 LT Winter: Mon-Fri: 0700-1900 LT Sat & Sun: 0700-2200 LT ACCESS: Lock: 0700-2200 LT, not LW ± 1h at LWS

TENBY		51°40′N 4°42′W
Tel: Hr Mr: +44(0)1834 842717 Mobile: Outside office hours: 07977 609947 tenby.harbour@pembrokeshire.gov.uk		Fax: +44(0)1834 842717 www.tenbyharbour.co.uk
FREQUENCY: Ch 16 80		ACCESS: HW ± 2½h

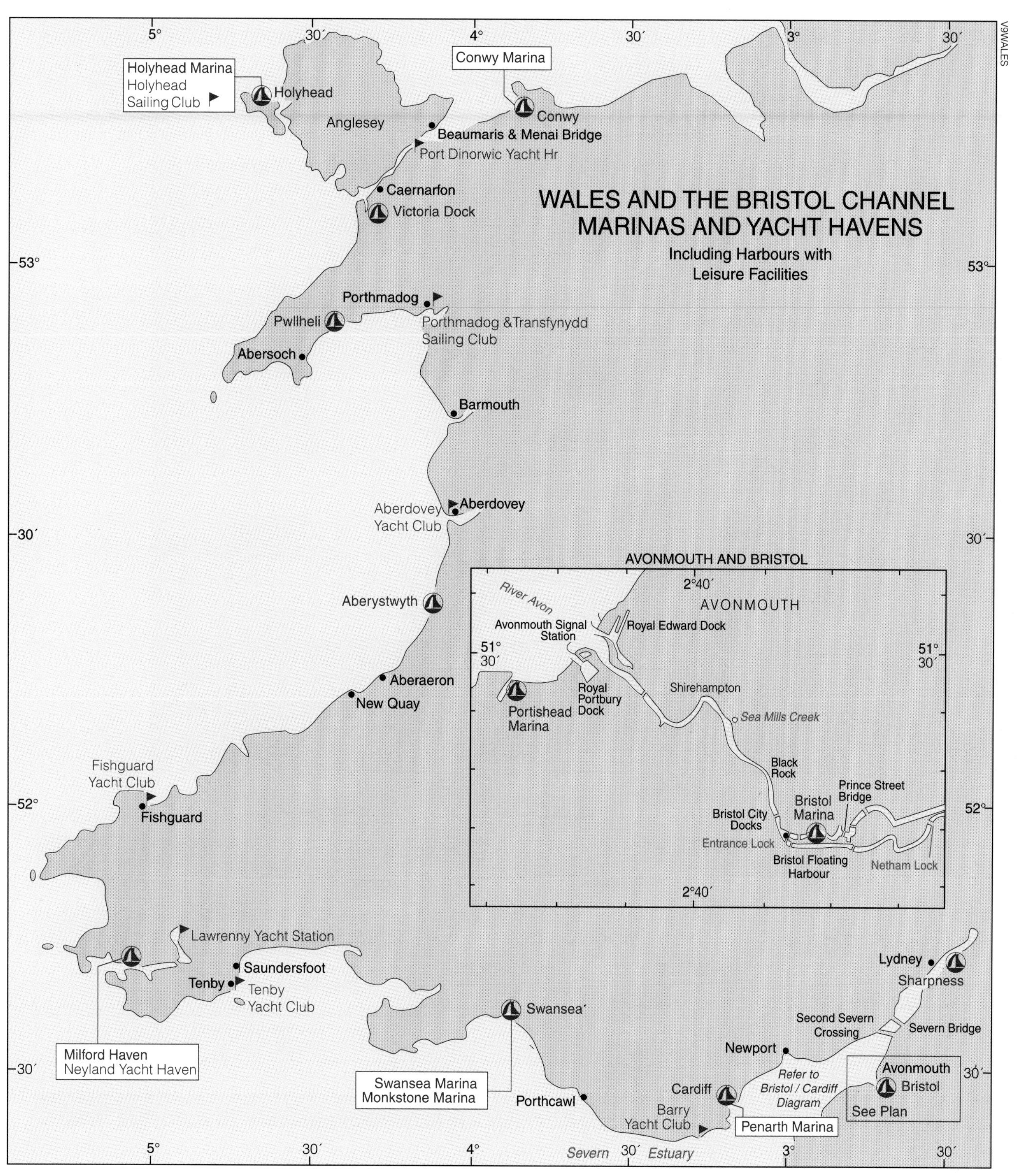
WALES AND THE BRISTOL CHANNEL
MARINAS AND YACHT HAVENS
Including Harbours with
Leisure Facilities
Holyhead Marina
Holyhead
Sailing Club
Holyhead
Anglesey
Conwy Marina
Conwy
Beaumaris & Menai Bridge
Port Dinorwic Yacht Hr
Caernarfon
Victoria Dock
Porthmadog
Pwllheli
Porthmadog &Transfynydd
Sailing Club
Abersoch
Barmouth
Aberdovey
Yacht Club
Aberdovey
Aberystwyth
Aberaeron
New Quay
Fishguard
Yacht Club
Fishguard
Lawrenny Yacht Station
Saundersfoot
Tenby
Tenby
Yacht Club
Milford Haven
Neyland Yacht Haven
Swansea
Swansea Marina
Monkstone Marina
Porthcawl
Cardiff
Barry
Yacht Club
Penarth Marina
Refer to
Bristol / Cardiff
Diagram
Newport
Second Severn
Crossing
Severn Bridge
Lydney
Sharpness
Avonmouth
Bristol
See Plan
Severn
Estuary
AVONMOUTH AND BRISTOL
River Avon
AVONMOUTH
Avonmouth Signal
Station
Royal Edward Dock
Royal
Portbury
Dock
Portishead
Marina
Shirehampton
Sea Mills Creek
Black
Rock
Prince Street
Bridge
Bristol
Marina
Bristol City
Docks
Entrance Lock
Bristol Floating
Harbour
Netham Lock
V9WALES

MARITIME SAFETY INFORMATION, MARINA AND PORT COMMUNICATIONS MEDITERRANEAN

ALBANIA

DURRËS	**Pilots and Port:** CALL: Pilots: Durrës Piloti Hr Mr: Durrës Capitaineria	41°19′N 19°27′E
☎ Pilots: +355(0)52 22844 Hr Mr: +355(0)52 22268 (H24)		Fax Pilots: +355(0)52 22844
FREQUENCY: Pilots: Ch 11 Hr Mr: Ch 16; 15		HOURS: Pilots: 0600-2200 LT Hr Mr: H24

SARANDË	**Pilots and Port**	39°53′N 20°00E
FREQUENCY: Port Captain: Ch 12 Agent: Ch 11		
PROCEDURE: (1) Pilotage is compulsory and is available HJ only (2) Vessels Inward-Bound must wait for a pilot in position 39°51′·83N 20°01′·17E (3) Leisure Craft should call SARANDË Port Captain on VHF Ch 12 when entering Albanian territorial waters. It is advisable for small craft to use an agent to obtain water and fuel (VHF Ch 11)		

SHËNGJIN	**Pilots and Port:** CALL: Shëngjin Harbour	41°49′N 19°35′E
FREQUENCY: Ch 16 71		HOURS: H24

VLORË (VALONA)	**Pilots and Port:** CALL: Harbour Port Control	40°27′N 19°30′E
FREQUENCY: Port: Ch 11 12 14 16		HOURS: 0800-1800 LT

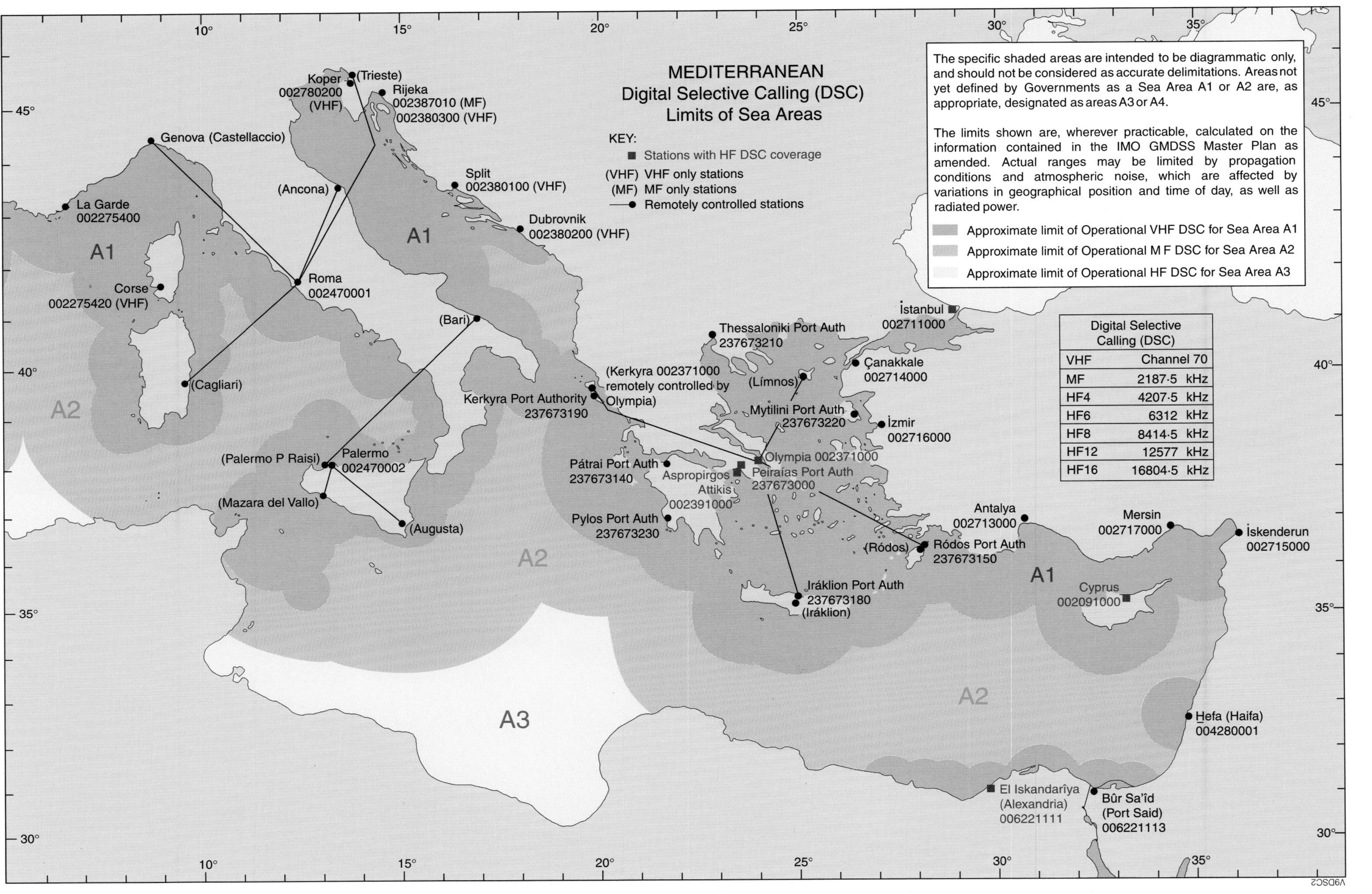
MEDITERRANEAN
Digital Selective Calling (DSC)
Limits of Sea Areas
KEY:
Stations with HF DSC coverage
(VHF) VHF only stations
(MF) MF only stations
Remotely controlled stations
The specific shaded areas are intended to be diagrammatic only, and should not be considered as accurate delimitations. Areas not yet defined by Governments as a Sea Area A1 or A2 are, as appropriate, designated as areas A3 or A4.
The limits shown are, wherever practicable, calculated on the information contained in the IMO GMDSS Master Plan as amended. Actual ranges may be limited by propagation conditions and atmospheric noise, which are affected by variations in geographical position and time of day, as well as radiated power.
Approximate limit of Operational VHF DSC for Sea Area A1
Approximate limit of Operational M F DSC for Sea Area A2
Approximate limit of Operational HF DSC for Sea Area A3
Digital Selective Calling (DSC)
VHF Channel 70
MF 2187·5 kHz
HF4 4207·5 kHz
HF6 6312 kHz
HF8 8414·5 kHz
HF12 12577 kHz
HF16 16804·5 kHz
Koper 002780200 (VHF)
(Trieste)
Rijeka 002387010 (MF) 002380300 (VHF)
Genova (Castellaccio)
La Garde 002275400
Corse 002275420 (VHF)
Roma 002470001
(Ancona)
Split 002380100 (VHF)
Dubrovnik 002380200 (VHF)
(Cagliari)
(Bari)
(Palermo P Raisi)
Palermo 002470002
(Mazara del Vallo)
(Augusta)
Kerkyra Port Authority 237673190
(Kerkyra 002371000 remotely controlled by Olympia)
Pátrai Port Auth 237673140
Pylos Port Auth 237673230
Aspropirgos Attikis 002391000
Thessaloniki Port Auth 237673210
(Límnos)
Mytilini Port Auth 237673220
Olympia 002371000
Peiraías Port Auth 237673000
Iráklion Port Auth 237673180
(Iráklion)
İstanbul 002711000
Çanakkale 002714000
İzmir 002716000
Antalya 002713000
(Ródos)
Ródos Port Auth 237673150
Mersin 002717000
İskenderun 002715000
Cyprus 002091000
Hefa (Haifa) 004280001
El Iskandarîya (Alexandria) 006221111
Bûr Sa'îd (Port Said) 006221113
A1
A2
A3
10°
15°
20°
25°
30°
35°
40°
45°
V9DSC2

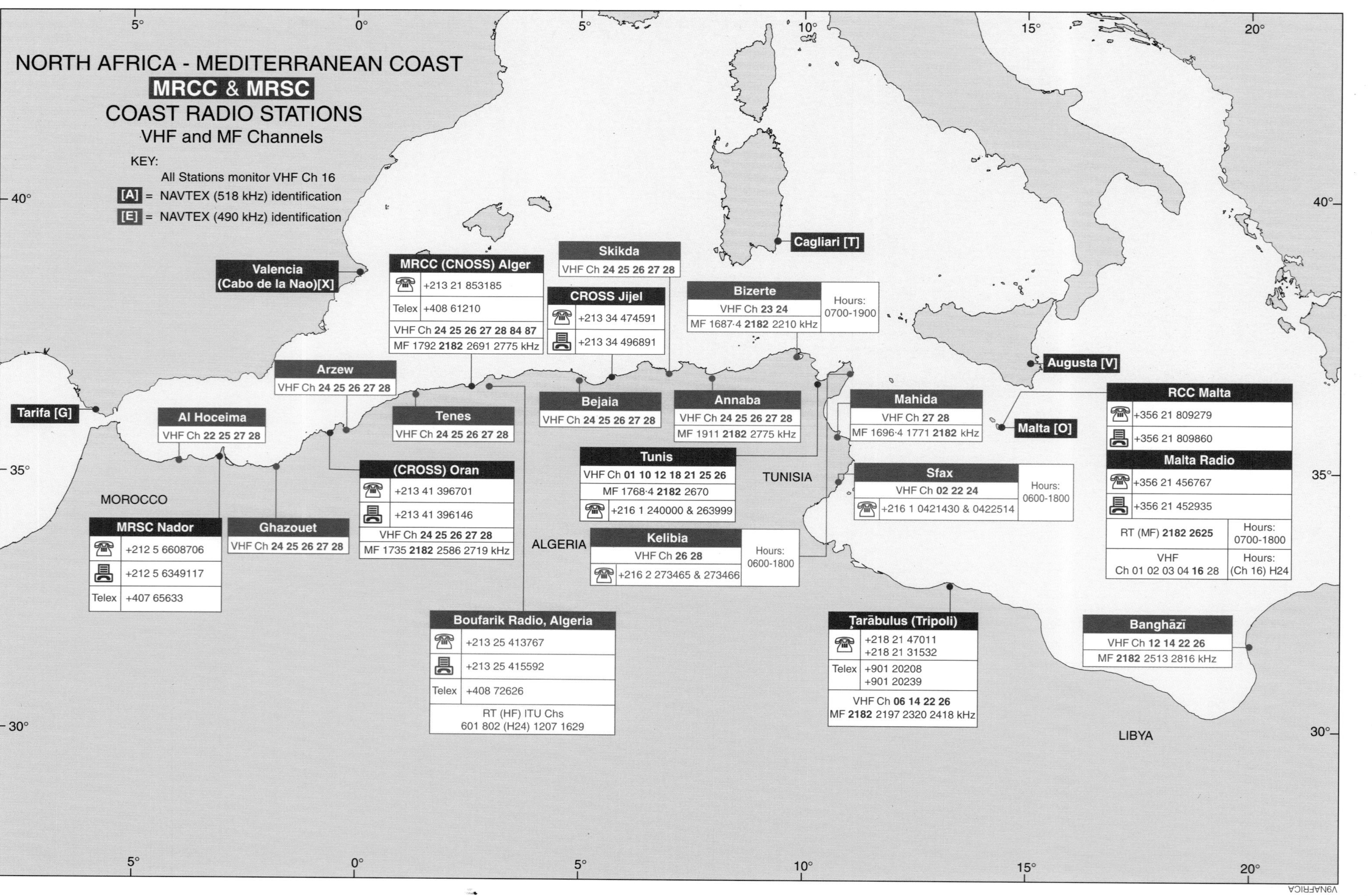
NORTH AFRICA - MEDITERRANEAN COAST
MRCC & MRSC
COAST RADIO STATIONS
VHF and MF Channels
KEY:
All Stations monitor VHF Ch 16
[A] = NAVTEX (518 kHz) identification
[E] = NAVTEX (490 kHz) identification
Tarifa [G]
Valencia (Cabo de la Nao)[X]
MRSC Nador
+212 5 6608706
+212 5 6349117
Telex +407 65633
Al Hoceima
VHF Ch 22 25 27 28
Ghazouet
VHF Ch 24 25 26 27 28
Arzew
VHF Ch 24 25 26 27 28
(CROSS) Oran
+213 41 396701
+213 41 396146
VHF Ch 24 25 26 27 28
MF 1735 2182 2586 2719 kHz
Tenes
VHF Ch 24 25 26 27 28
MRCC (CNOSS) Alger
+213 21 853185
Telex +408 61210
VHF Ch 24 25 26 27 28 84 87
MF 1792 2182 2691 2775 kHz
Boufarik Radio, Algeria
+213 25 413767
+213 25 415592
Telex +408 72626
RT (HF) ITU Chs
601 802 (H24) 1207 1629
Skikda
VHF Ch 24 25 26 27 28
CROSS Jijel
+213 34 474591
+213 34 496891
Bejaia
VHF Ch 24 25 26 27 28
Annaba
VHF Ch 24 25 26 27 28
MF 1911 2182 2775 kHz
Bizerte
VHF Ch 23 24
MF 1687·4 2182 2210 kHz
Hours: 0700-1900
Tunis
VHF Ch 01 10 12 18 21 25 26
MF 1768·4 2182 2670
+216 1 240000 & 263999
Kelibia
VHF Ch 26 28
+216 2 273465 & 273466
Hours: 0600-1800
Mahida
VHF Ch 27 28
MF 1696·4 1771 2182 kHz
Sfax
VHF Ch 02 22 24
+216 1 0421430 & 0422514
Hours: 0600-1800
Cagliari [T]
Augusta [V]
Malta [O]
RCC Malta
+356 21 809279
+356 21 809860
Malta Radio
+356 21 456767
+356 21 452935
RT (MF) 2182 2625
Hours: 0700-1800
VHF
Ch 01 02 03 04 16 28
Hours: (Ch 16) H24
Ṭarābulus (Tripoli)
+218 21 47011
+218 21 31532
Telex +901 20208
+901 20239
VHF Ch 06 14 22 26
MF 2182 2197 2320 2418 kHz
Banghāzī
VHF Ch 12 14 22 26
MF 2182 2513 2816 kHz
MOROCCO
ALGERIA
TUNISIA
LIBYA
5°
0°
5°
10°
15°
20°
40°
35°
30°
V9NAFRICA

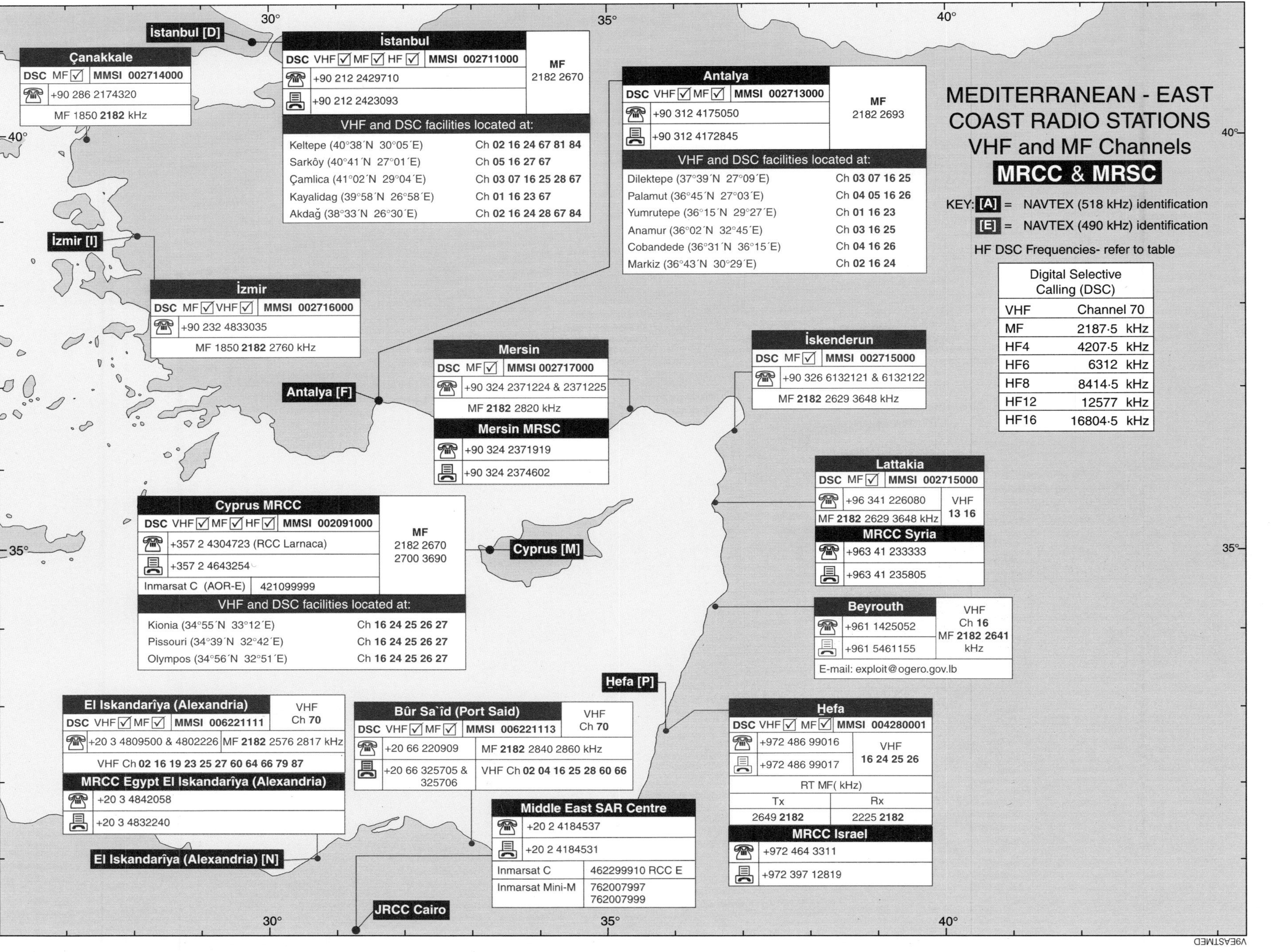

MEDITERRANEAN - EAST
COAST RADIO STATIONS
VHF and MF Channels
MRCC & MRSC
KEY: [A] = NAVTEX (518 kHz) identification
[E] = NAVTEX (490 kHz) identification
HF DSC Frequencies- refer to table
Digital Selective Calling (DSC)
VHF Channel 70
MF 2187·5 kHz
HF4 4207·5 kHz
HF6 6312 kHz
HF8 8414·5 kHz
HF12 12577 kHz
HF16 16804·5 kHz
İstanbul [D]
Çanakkale
DSC MF ☑ MMSI 002714000
+90 286 2174320
MF 1850 2182 kHz
İstanbul
DSC VHF ☑ MF ☑ HF ☑ MMSI 002711000
+90 212 2429710
+90 212 2423093
MF 2182 2670
VHF and DSC facilities located at:
Keltepe (40°38′N 30°05′E) Ch 02 16 24 67 81 84
Sarkôy (40°41′N 27°01′E) Ch 05 16 27 67
Çamlica (41°02′N 29°04′E) Ch 03 07 16 25 28 67
Kayalidag (39°58′N 26°58′E) Ch 01 16 23 67
Akdağ (38°33′N 26°30′E) Ch 02 16 24 28 67 84
Antalya
DSC VHF ☑ MF ☑ MMSI 002713000
+90 312 4175050
+90 312 4172845
MF 2182 2693
VHF and DSC facilities located at:
Dilektepe (37°39′N 27°09′E) Ch 03 07 16 25
Palamut (36°45′N 27°03′E) Ch 04 05 16 26
Yumrutepe (36°15′N 29°27′E) Ch 01 16 23
Anamur (36°02′N 32°45′E) Ch 03 16 25
Cobandede (36°31′N 36°15′E) Ch 04 16 26
Markiz (36°43′N 30°29′E) Ch 02 16 24
İzmir [I]
İzmir
DSC MF ☑ VHF ☑ MMSI 002716000
+90 232 4833035
MF 1850 2182 2760 kHz
Antalya [F]
Mersin
DSC MF ☑ MMSI 002717000
+90 324 2371224 & 2371225
MF 2182 2820 kHz
Mersin MRSC
+90 324 2371919
+90 324 2374602
İskenderun
DSC MF ☑ MMSI 002715000
+90 326 6132121 & 6132122
MF 2182 2629 3648 kHz
Lattakia
DSC MF ☑ MMSI 002715000
+96 341 226080
MF 2182 2629 3648 kHz
VHF 13 16
MRCC Syria
+963 41 233333
+963 41 235805
Cyprus MRCC
DSC VHF ☑ MF ☑ HF ☑ MMSI 002091000
+357 2 4304723 (RCC Larnaca)
+357 2 4643254
Inmarsat C (AOR-E) 421099999
MF 2182 2670 2700 3690
VHF and DSC facilities located at:
Kionia (34°55′N 33°12′E) Ch 16 24 25 26 27
Pissouri (34°39′N 32°42′E) Ch 16 24 25 26 27
Olympos (34°56′N 32°51′E) Ch 16 24 25 26 27
Cyprus [M]
Beyrouth
+961 1425052
+961 5461155
VHF Ch 16
MF 2182 2641 kHz
E-mail: exploit@ogero.gov.lb
Hefa [P]
El Iskandarîya (Alexandria)
DSC VHF ☑ MF ☑ MMSI 006221111
VHF Ch 70
+20 3 4809500 & 4802226 MF 2182 2576 2817 kHz
VHF Ch 02 16 19 23 25 27 60 64 66 79 87
MRCC Egypt El Iskandarîya (Alexandria)
+20 3 4842058
+20 3 4832240
Bûr Sa`îd (Port Said)
DSC VHF ☑ MF ☑ MMSI 006221113
VHF Ch 70
+20 66 220909 MF 2182 2840 2860 kHz
+20 66 325705 & 325706 VHF Ch 02 04 16 25 28 60 66
Middle East SAR Centre
+20 2 4184537
+20 2 4184531
Inmarsat C 462299910 RCC E
Inmarsat Mini-M 762007997 762007999
Hefa
DSC VHF ☑ MF ☑ MMSI 004280001
+972 486 99016
+972 486 99017
VHF 16 24 25 26
RT MF(kHz)
Tx 2649 2182
Rx 2225 2182
MRCC Israel
+972 464 3311
+972 397 12819
El Iskandarîya (Alexandria) [N]
JRCC Cairo
30°
35°
40°
V9EASTMED

HF R/T (SSB) RADIO STATIONS

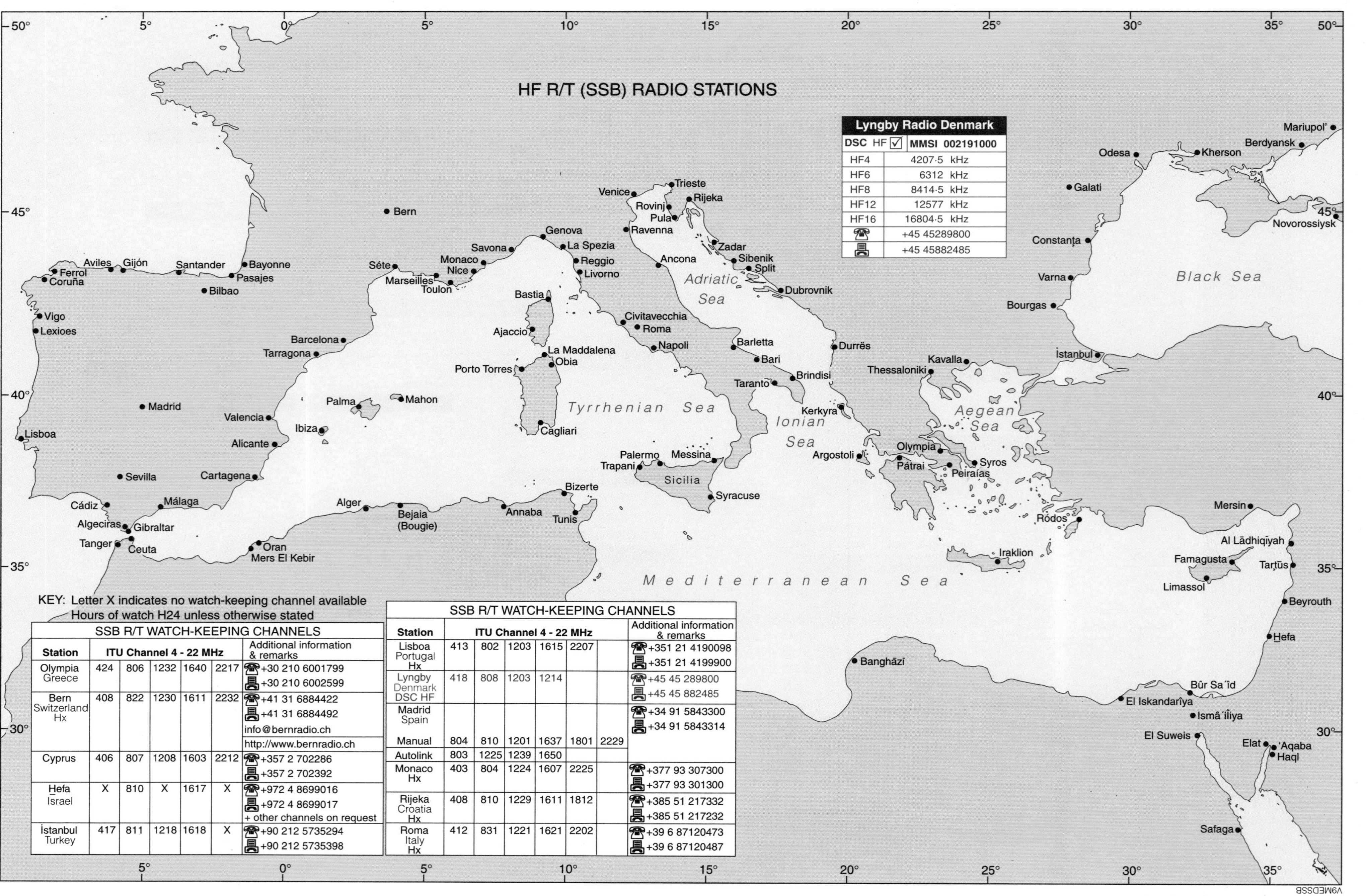

Lyngby Radio Denmark	
DSC HF ✓	MMSI 002191000
HF4	4207·5 kHz
HF6	6312 kHz
HF8	8414·5 kHz
HF12	12577 kHz
HF16	16804·5 kHz
(Tel)	+45 45289800
(Fax)	+45 45882485

KEY: Letter X indicates no watch-keeping channel available
Hours of watch H24 unless otherwise stated

SSB R/T WATCH-KEEPING CHANNELS

Station	ITU Channel 4 - 22 MHz					Additional information & remarks
Olympia Greece	424	806	1232	1640	2217	+30 210 6001799 +30 210 6002599
Bern Switzerland Hx	408	822	1230	1611	2232	+41 31 6884422 +41 31 6884492 info@bernradio.ch http://www.bernradio.ch
Cyprus	406	807	1208	1603	2212	+357 2 702286 +357 2 702392
Hefa Israel	X	810	X	1617	X	+972 4 8699016 +972 4 8699017 + other channels on request
İstanbul Turkey	417	811	1218	1618	X	+90 212 5735294 +90 212 5735398

SSB R/T WATCH-KEEPING CHANNELS

Station	ITU Channel 4 - 22 MHz						Additional information & remarks
Lisboa Portugal Hx	413	802	1203	1615	2207		+351 21 4190098 +351 21 4199900
Lyngby Denmark DSC HF	418	808	1203	1214			+45 45 289800 +45 45 882485
Madrid Spain							+34 91 5843300 +34 91 5843314
Manual	804	810	1201	1637	1801	2229	
Autolink	803	1225	1239	1650			
Monaco Hx	403	804	1224	1607	2225		+377 93 307300 +377 93 301300
Rijeka Croatia Hx	408	810	1229	1611	1812		+385 51 217332 +385 51 217232
Roma Italy Hx	412	831	1221	1621	2202		+39 6 87120473 +39 6 87120487

V9MEDSSB

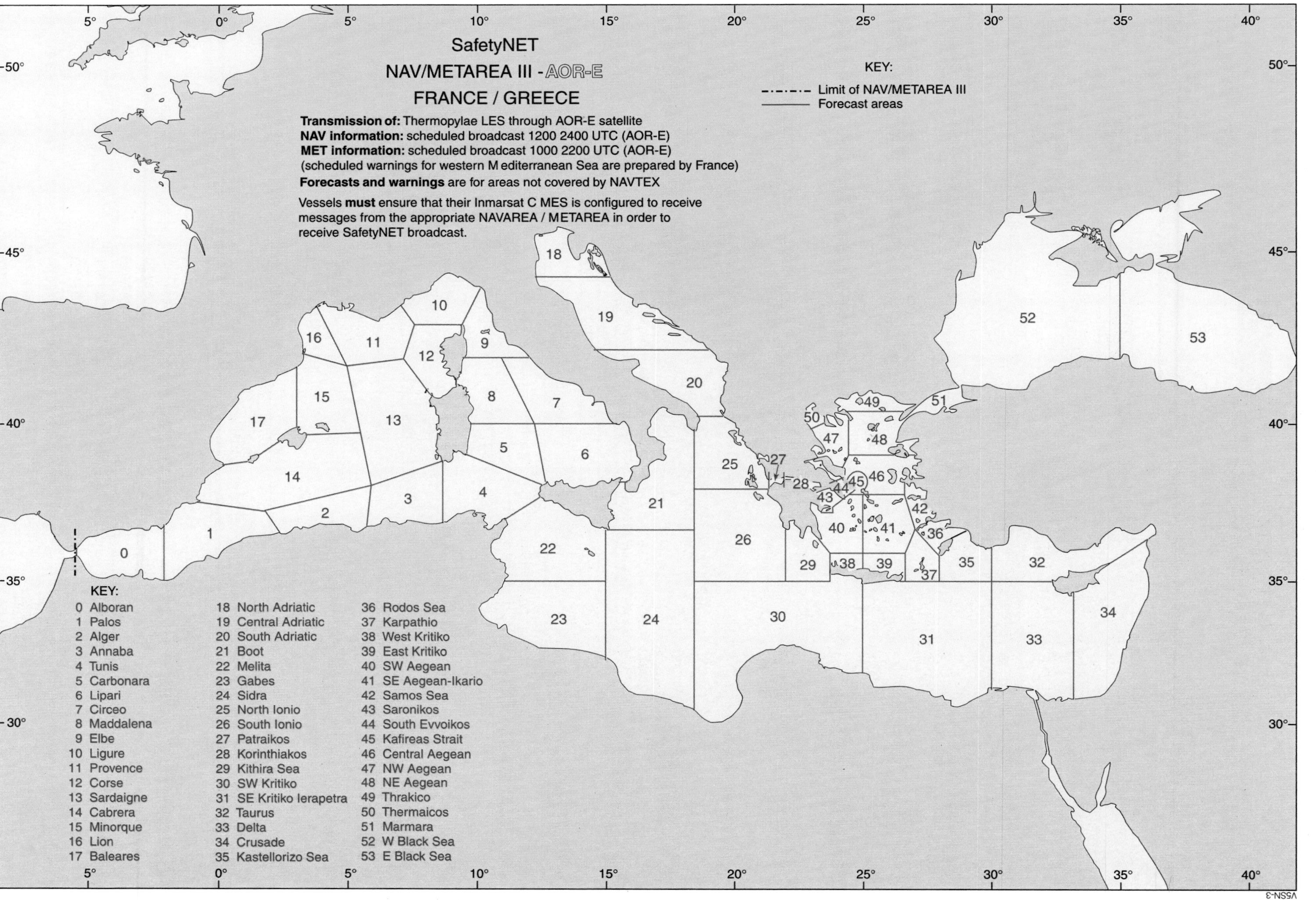
SafetyNET
NAV/METAREA III - AOR-E
FRANCE / GREECE
Transmission of: Thermopylae LES through AOR-E satellite
NAV information: scheduled broadcast 1200 2400 UTC (AOR-E)
MET information: scheduled broadcast 1000 2200 UTC (AOR-E)
(scheduled warnings for western Mediterranean Sea are prepared by France)
Forecasts and warnings are for areas not covered by NAVTEX
Vessels **must** ensure that their Inmarsat C MES is configured to receive messages from the appropriate NAVAREA / METAREA in order to receive SafetyNET broadcast.
KEY:
Limit of NAV/METAREA III
Forecast areas
KEY:
0 Alboran
1 Palos
2 Alger
3 Annaba
4 Tunis
5 Carbonara
6 Lipari
7 Circeo
8 Maddalena
9 Elbe
10 Ligure
11 Provence
12 Corse
13 Sardaigne
14 Cabrera
15 Minorque
16 Lion
17 Baleares
18 North Adriatic
19 Central Adriatic
20 South Adriatic
21 Boot
22 Melita
23 Gabes
24 Sidra
25 North Ionio
26 South Ionio
27 Patraikos
28 Korinthiakos
29 Kithira Sea
30 SW Kritiko
31 SE Kritiko Ierapetra
32 Taurus
33 Delta
34 Crusade
35 Kastellorizo Sea
36 Rodos Sea
37 Karpathio
38 West Kritiko
39 East Kritiko
40 SW Aegean
41 SE Aegean-Ikario
42 Samos Sea
43 Saronikos
44 South Evvoikos
45 Kafireas Strait
46 Central Aegean
47 NW Aegean
48 NE Aegean
49 Thrakico
50 Thermaicos
51 Marmara
52 W Black Sea
53 E Black Sea
V5SN-3

ALGERIA

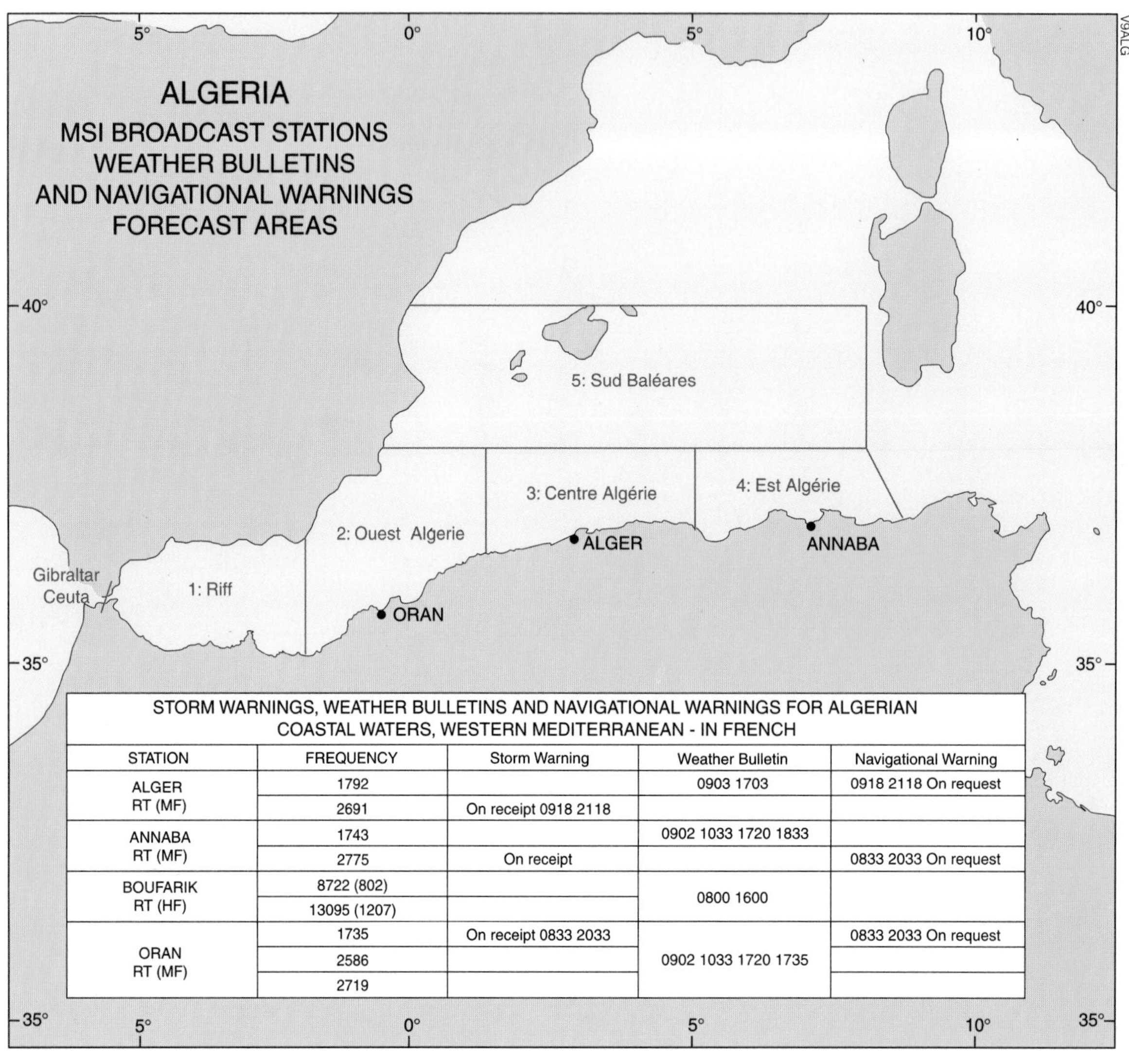

STORM WARNINGS, WEATHER BULLETINS AND NAVIGATIONAL WARNINGS FOR ALGERIAN COASTAL WATERS, WESTERN MEDITERRANEAN - IN FRENCH

STATION	FREQUENCY	Storm Warning	Weather Bulletin	Navigational Warning
ALGER RT (MF)	1792		0903 1703	0918 2118 On request
	2691	On receipt 0918 2118		
ANNABA RT (MF)	1743		0902 1033 1720 1833	
	2775	On receipt		0833 2033 On request
BOUFARIK RT (HF)	8722 (802)		0800 1600	
	13095 (1207)			
ORAN RT (MF)	1735	On receipt 0833 2033	0902 1033 1720 1735	0833 2033 On request
	2586			
	2719			

National SAR Agency: Naval Forces Command MRCC Alger
The Coast Guard, is responsible for co-ordinating Search and Rescue operations. A network of Coast Radio Stations maintains a continuous listening watch on international distress frequencies.

	Telephone +213	**Fax** +213	**Others**
MRCC (CNOSS) ALGER	2185 3185		**Telex** +408 61210
ALGER RADIO	2120 1567	2120 3309	**Telex** +408 63601
ANNABA RADIO	3883 6997	3880 4231	**Telex** +408 81803
ARZEW RADIO	4147 7222		**Telex** +408 12020
BEJAIA RADIO	3423 5766		**Telex** +408 83985
GHAZAOUET RADIO	4332 4900		**Telex** +408 18951
ORAN RADIO	4138 3322	4143 2939	**Telex** +408 87821
SKIKDA RADIO	3875 5106		**Telex** +408 87018
TENES RADIO	2777 6341		**Telex** +408 78888

RADIODIFFUSION-TELEVISION ALGERIENNE			
A	746	Tlemcen	AM
B	890 11715	Alger	
C	1304	Constantine	
D	1304	Oran	
E	6080	Alger	
F	11835		
Weather Bulletins			
A-D, F: 1300	Storm warnings, forecast, supplementary forecast for coastal shipping in French for N Africa & W Mediterranean		
B-E: 2000	Storm warnings, forecast in French for N Africa & W Mediterranean		

ANNABA (BÔNE)	Port	36°54′N 7°46′E
Hr Mr: +213(0)8 834591		
FREQUENCY: Ch 10 11 12 13 **14** 16		HOURS: H24

ARZEW	Port	35°51′N 0°18′W
+213(0)6 377527, 377491 & 377970		
FREQUENCY: Port Captain (Hr Mr): Ch 14 16 El Djedid Captain: Ch 12 16		HOURS: H24

BEJAIA (BOUGIE)	Port	36°45′N 5°05′E
Port Office: +213(0)5 921804, 921805 & 923503		
FREQUENCY: Port Control: Ch 16		HOURS: 0800-1200 1400-1800 LT

GHAZAOUET	Pilots and Port	35°06′N 1°52′W
+213(0)7 321220 & 221345		
FREQUENCY: Ch 10 12 14 16 18		HOURS: 0500-2100 LT
PROCEDURE: (1) Pilotage is compulsory and is available 0500-2100 LT. (2) Vessels should maintain continuous listening watch on VHF Ch 14 or 16 whilst awaiting the pilot.		

MOSTAGANEM	Port	35°56′N 0°05′E
+213(0)6 265938 & 268185		
FREQUENCY: Ch 11 12 14 16		HOURS: H24

ORAN	Pilots and Port	35°42′N 0°38′W
+213(0)6 334363		
FREQUENCY: Ch 12 14 16		HOURS: H24

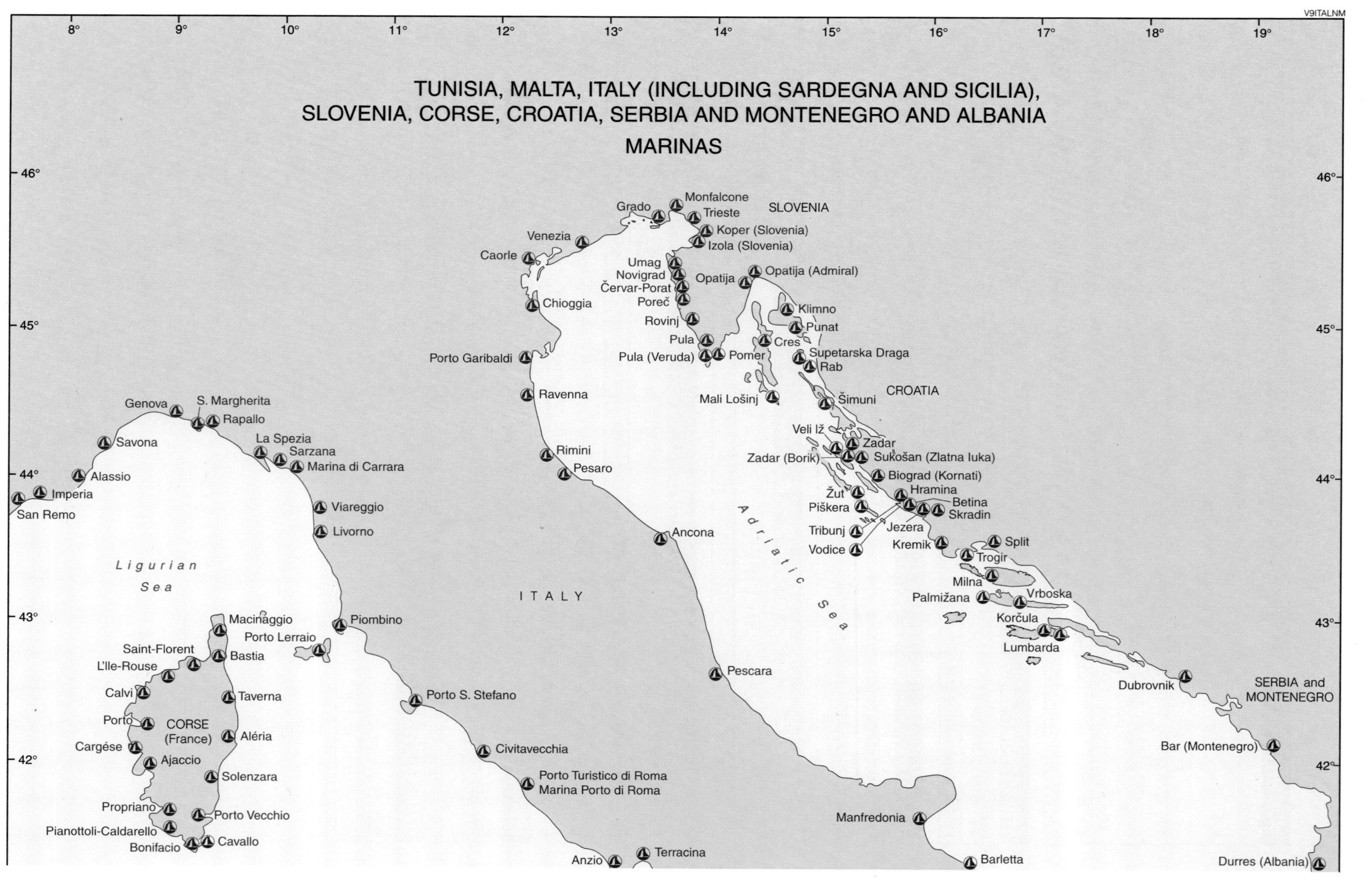
V9ITALNM
TUNISIA, MALTA, ITALY (INCLUDING SARDEGNA AND SICILIA), SLOVENIA, CORSE, CROATIA, SERBIA AND MONTENEGRO AND ALBANIA
MARINAS
8°
9°
10°
11°
12°
13°
14°
15°
16°
17°
18°
19°
46°
45°
44°
43°
42°
SLOVENIA
CROATIA
SERBIA and MONTENEGRO
ITALY
CORSE (France)
Ligurian Sea
Adriatic Sea
Grado
Monfalcone
Trieste
Koper (Slovenia)
Izola (Slovenia)
Venezia
Caorle
Umag
Novigrad
Červar-Porat
Poreč
Opatija
Opatija (Admiral)
Chioggia
Rovinj
Klimno
Punat
Pula
Cres
Porto Garibaldi
Pula (Veruda)
Pomer
Supetarska Draga
Rab
Ravenna
Mali Lošinj
Šimuni
Genova
S. Margherita
Rapallo
Savona
La Spezia
Sarzana
Marina di Carrara
Alassio
Imperia
San Remo
Rimini
Pesaro
Veli Iž
Zadar
Zadar (Borik)
Sukošan (Zlatna luka)
Biograd (Kornati)
Žut
Hramina
Piškera
Betina
Skradin
Viareggio
Livorno
Ancona
Tribunj
Jezera
Vodice
Kremik
Split
Trogir
Milna
Palmižana
Vrboska
Macinaggio
Piombino
Porto Lerraio
Korčula
Lumbarda
Saint-Florent
Bastia
L'Ile-Rouse
Pescara
Dubrovnik
Calvi
Taverna
Porto S. Stefano
Porto
Aléria
Cargése
Ajaccio
Civitavecchia
Bar (Montenegro)
Solenzara
Porto Turistico di Roma
Marina Porto di Roma
Propriano
Porto Vecchio
Manfredonia
Pianottoli-Caldarello
Cavallo
Bonifacio
Anzio
Terracina
Barletta
Durres (Albania)

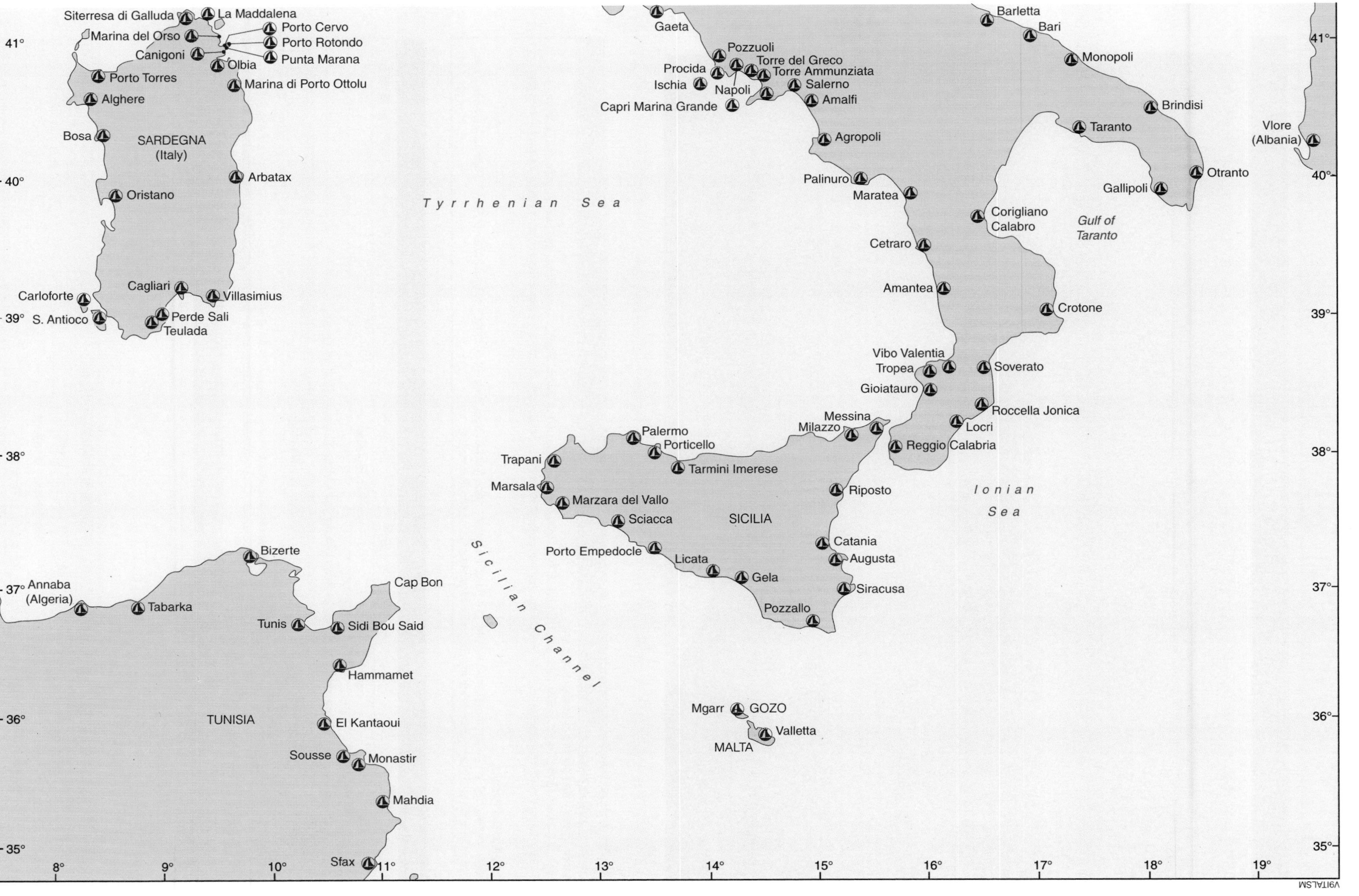

Siterresa di Galluda
La Maddalena
Marina del Orso
Porto Cervo
Porto Rotondo
Canigoni
Punta Marana
Olbia
Porto Torres
Marina di Porto Ottolu
Alghere
Bosa
SARDEGNA
(Italy)
Arbatax
Oristano
Tyrrhenian Sea
Cagliari
Villasimius
Carloforte
S. Antioco
Perde Sali
Teulada
Gaeta
Pozzuoli
Torre del Greco
Procida
Torre Ammunziata
Ischia
Napoli
Salerno
Amalfi
Capri Marina Grande
Agropoli
Palinuro
Maratea
Cetraro
Amantea
Vibo Valentia
Tropea
Gioiatauro
Barletta
Bari
Monopoli
Brindisi
Taranto
Vlore
(Albania)
Otranto
Gallipoli
Corigliano
Calabro
Gulf of
Taranto
Crotone
Soverato
Roccella Jonica
Locri
Messina
Milazzo
Reggio Calabria
Palermo
Porticello
Trapani
Tarmini Imerese
Marsala
Marzara del Vallo
Sciacca
SICILIA
Riposto
Ionian Sea
Porto Empedocle
Licata
Gela
Catania
Augusta
Siracusa
Pozzallo
Sicilian Channel
Bizerte
Annaba
(Algeria)
Tabarka
Cap Bon
Tunis
Sidi Bou Said
Hammamet
TUNISIA
El Kantaoui
Sousse
Monastir
Mahdia
Sfax
Mgarr
GOZO
Valletta
MALTA
41°
40°
39°
38°
37°
36°
35°
8°
9°
10°
11°
12°
13°
14°
15°
16°
17°
18°
19°
V9ITALSM

CROATIA

KORNATI ISLANDS

GENERAL INFORMATION

Customs offices - for entering of foreign boats are:
Throughout the year: Umag, Porec, Rovinj, Pula, Rasa-Brsica, Rijeka, Mali Losinj, Senj, Maslenica, Zadar, Sibenik, Split, Ploce, Metkovic, Korcula and Dubrovnik. Additionally during the summer season 1 April to 30 October: Kanegra, Novigrad, Bozava, Sali, Soline, Primosten, Ravni Zakan, Hvar, Komiza, Vela Luka and Ubli (Lastovo) Vis

Registration and Permits.
All boats whose length exceeds 3 metres must register at a Harbour Master's office (Lucka Kapentanija) or its branch office (Lucka ispostava). Harbour Master's offices operate on VHF Ch 10. Cruising permits are mandatory for all yachts cruising Croatina waters

NAVTEX [Q]

Q	Split	518 kHz	43°11′N 16°26′E
	Weather Bulletins		
Q: 0240 0640 1040 1440 1840 2240	Gale warnings, synopsis, 24 hour forecast for Adriatic Sea and Strait of Otranto		
	Navigational Warnings		
Q: 0240 0640 1040 1440 1840 2240	In Croatian and English for coastal waters of Croatia		

DUBROVNIK

	Ch 85	VHF	Hum	42°45′N 16°52′E
	Ch 07		Srdj (Dubrovnik)	42°39′N 18°07′E
	Ch 04		Uljenje (Poluotok Pelješac)	42°54′N 17°29′E
	Weather Bulletins			
0625 1320 2120	Weather bulletins for Adriatic Sea in Croatian and English			
	Navigational Warnings			
0625 1320 2120	In Croatian and English for coastal waters of Croatia			

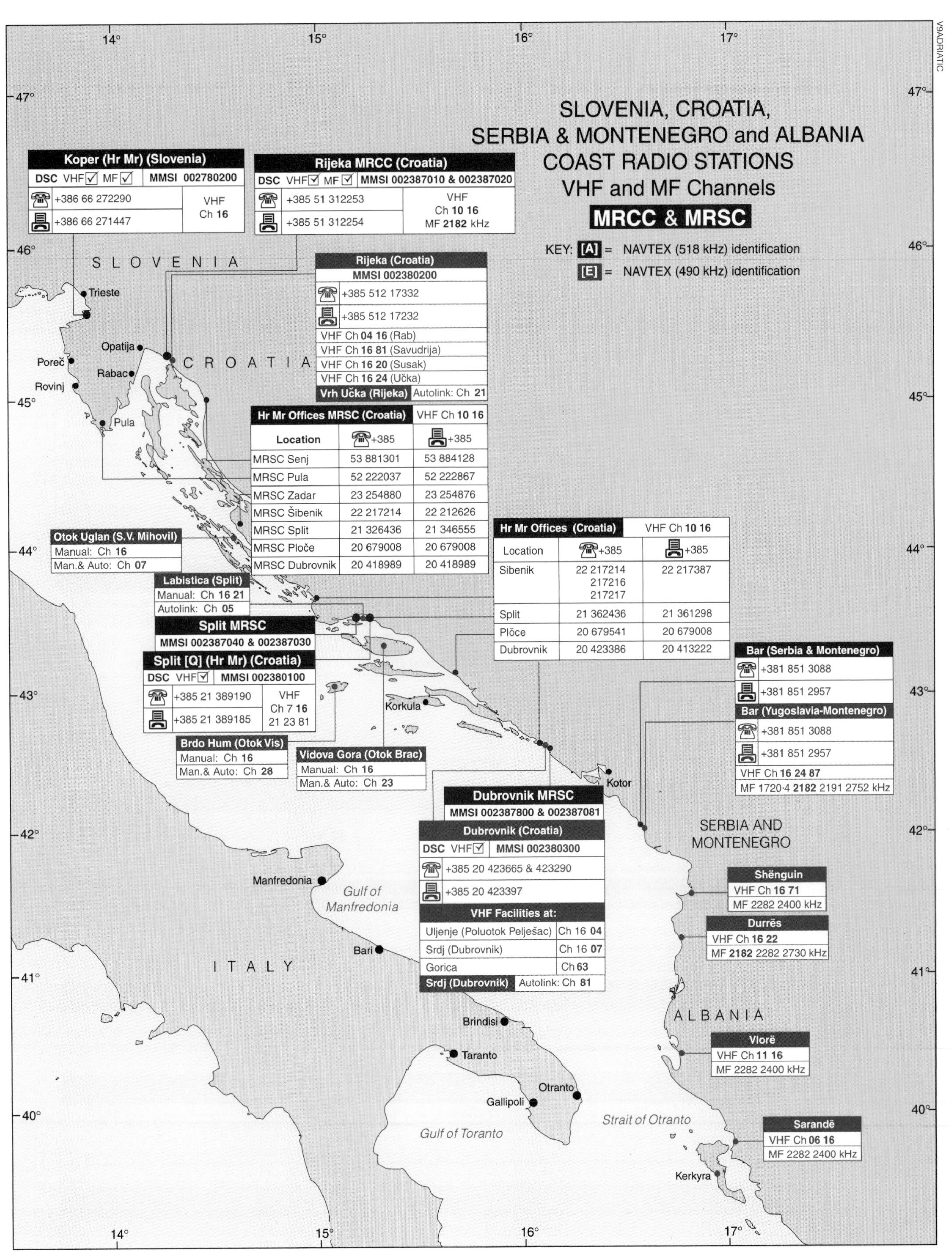
SLOVENIA, CROATIA,
SERBIA & MONTENEGRO and ALBANIA
COAST RADIO STATIONS
VHF and MF Channels
MRCC & MRSC
KEY: [A] = NAVTEX (518 kHz) identification
[E] = NAVTEX (490 kHz) identification
Koper (Hr Mr) (Slovenia)
DSC VHF☑ MF☑ MMSI 002780200
+386 66 272290
+386 66 271447
VHF Ch 16
Rijeka MRCC (Croatia)
DSC VHF☑ MF☑ MMSI 002387010 & 002387020
+385 51 312253
+385 51 312254
VHF Ch 10 16 MF 2182 kHz
Rijeka (Croatia)
MMSI 002380200
+385 512 17332
+385 512 17232
VHF Ch 04 16 (Rab)
VHF Ch 16 81 (Savudrija)
VHF Ch 16 20 (Susak)
VHF Ch 16 24 (Učka)
Vrh Učka (Rijeka) Autolink: Ch 21
Hr Mr Offices MRSC (Croatia) VHF Ch 10 16
Location +385 +385
MRSC Senj 53 881301 53 884128
MRSC Pula 52 222037 52 222867
MRSC Zadar 23 254880 23 254876
MRSC Šibenik 22 217214 22 212626
MRSC Split 21 326436 21 346555
MRSC Ploče 20 679008 20 679008
MRSC Dubrovnik 20 418989 20 418989
Hr Mr Offices (Croatia) VHF Ch 10 16
Location +385 +385
Sibenik 22 217214 217216 217217 22 217387
Split 21 362436 21 361298
Ploče 20 679541 20 679008
Dubrovnik 20 423386 20 413222
Otok Uglan (S.V. Mihovil)
Manual: Ch 16
Man.& Auto: Ch 07
Labistica (Split)
Manual: Ch 16 21
Autolink: Ch 05
Split MRSC
MMSI 002387040 & 002387030
Split [Q] (Hr Mr) (Croatia)
DSC VHF☑ MMSI 002380100
+385 21 389190
+385 21 389185
VHF Ch 7 16 21 23 81
Brdo Hum (Otok Vis)
Manual: Ch 16
Man.& Auto: Ch 28
Vidova Gora (Otok Brac)
Manual: Ch 16
Man.& Auto: Ch 23
Dubrovnik MRSC
MMSI 002387800 & 002387081
Dubrovnik (Croatia)
DSC VHF☑ MMSI 002380300
+385 20 423665 & 423290
+385 20 423397
VHF Facilities at:
Uljenje (Poluotok Pelješac) Ch 16 04
Srdj (Dubrovnik) Ch 16 07
Gorica Ch 63
Srdj (Dubrovnik) Autolink: Ch 81
Bar (Serbia & Montenegro)
+381 851 3088
+381 851 2957
Bar (Yugoslavia-Montenegro)
+381 851 3088
+381 851 2957
VHF Ch 16 24 87
MF 1720·4 2182 2191 2752 kHz
Shënguin
VHF Ch 16 71
MF 2282 2400 kHz
Durrës
VHF Ch 16 22
MF 2182 2282 2730 kHz
Vlorë
VHF Ch 11 16
MF 2282 2400 kHz
Sarandë
VHF Ch 06 16
MF 2282 2400 kHz
SLOVENIA
CROATIA
ITALY
SERBIA AND MONTENEGRO
ALBANIA
Trieste
Opatija
Poreč
Rabac
Rovinj
Pula
Korkula
Kotor
Manfredonia
Gulf of Manfredonia
Bari
Brindisi
Taranto
Otranto
Gallipoli
Gulf of Toranto
Strait of Otranto
Kerkyra
14°
15°
16°
17°
47°
46°
45°
44°
43°
42°
41°
40°
V9ADRIATIC

RIJEKA				
	Ch 04	VHF	Kamenjak (Otok Rab)	44°46′N 14°47′E
	Ch 81		Savudrija	45°29′N 13°29′E
	Ch 20		Susak	44°31′N 14°18′E
	Ch 24		Vrh Učka	45°17′N 14°13′E
Weather Bulletins				
0535 1435 1935	Weather bulletins for Adriatic Sea in Croatian and English			
Navigational Warnings				
0535 1435 1935	In Croatian and English for coastal waters of Croatia			

SPLIT				
	Ch 81	VHF	Brdo Hum (Otok Vis)	43°01′N 16°07′E
	Ch 28		Celavac	44°16′N 15°47′E
	Ch 21		Labistica (Split)	43°35′N 16°13′E
	Ch 07		Sveti Mihovil (Otok Ugljan)	44°04′N 15°10′E
	Ch 23		Vidova Gora (Otak Brač)	43°17′N 16°37′E
	Ch 21		Vrh Učka (Rijeka)	43°35′N 16°13′E
Weather Bulletins				
0545 1245 1945	Weather bulletins for Adriatic Sea in Croatian and English			
Navigational Warnings				
0545 1245 1945	In Croatian and English for coastal waters of Croatia			

CONTINUOUS VHF WEATHER BROADCAST

Taped-voice weather information in Croatian, English, Italian and German for the coastal waters of Croatia is broadcast continuously from the Harbour Master's Offices shown on the table below. Broadcasts are made throughout the year and are repeated approximately every 10 minutes, the tape is updated at 0700 1300 and 1900 LT. Information broadcast includes a brief situation report, 24 hour short forecast and a barometric pressure report.

VHF coverage area	Harbour Master Office	VHF Channel
North Adriatic — west coast of Istra	Pula	73
North Adriatic — east part	Rijeka	69
Central Adriatic — east part	Split	67
South Adriatic — east part	Dubrovnik	73

BAKAR	Port	45°18′N 14°32′E
Hr Office: +385(0)51 761214		
FREQUENCY: Ch 10 16		HOURS: HX

BAŠKA, OTOK KRK	Port	44°58′N 14°45′E
Hr Office: +385(0)51 856821		
FREQUENCY: Hr Office: Ch 10 16		HOURS: HX

BIOGRAD	Port	43°57′N 15°26′E
Hr Office: +385(0)23 383210		Hr Office: +385(0)23 383210
FREQUENCY: Hr Office: Ch 10 16		HOURS: HX

KORNATI	Marina 600 Berths 150 Visitor Berths	44°50′·4N 13°50′·3E
+385(0)23 383800 & 383920 marina-kornati@zd.hinet.hr	Depth: 5 m Maximum LOA: 20 - 30 m	+385(0)23 384500 www.marinakornati.com
FREQUENCY: Ch 17	LOCATION: Biograd	HOURS: HX

MARINA ŠANGULIN	Marina 150 Berths	43°56′·4N 15°26′·8E
Hr Office: +385(0)23 385150 & 385020 info@sangulin.hr	Depth: 4·5 m	Hr Office: +385(0)23 384944 www.sangulin.hr
FREQUENCY: Ch 17		HOURS: HX

BIOGRAD (KORNATI BIOGRAD MARINA) FROM S

BOŽAVA, DUGI OTOK	Port	44°08'N 14°55'E
Tel: Hr Office: +385(0)23 377601		Fax:
FREQUENCY: Hr Office: Ch 10 16		HOURS: HX

CRES, ACI CRES	Marina and Port 450 Berths	44°57'·0N 14°24'·0E
Tel: ACI Marina: +385(0)51 571622 Hr Office: +385(0)51 571111 m.cres@aci-club.hr	Maximum LOA: 24 m	Fax: ACI Marina: +385(0)51 571125 Hr Office: +385(0)51 571111
FREQUENCY: Marina: Ch 17 Hr Office: Ch 10 16	LOCATION: Otok Cres	HOURS: H24

CRIKVENICA	Port	45°10'N 14°42'E
Tel: Hr Office: +385(0)51 242321		Fax: Hr Office: +385(0)51 242 321
FREQUENCY: Hr Office: Ch 10 16		HOURS: HX

DALMACIJA	Marina 1200 Berths 32 Visitor Berths	44°03'·2N 15°18'·2E
Tel: +385(0)23 393731 info@marinadalmacija.hr	Depth: 4 m, Maximum LOA: 15 m	Fax: +385(0)23 393588 www.marinadalmacija.hr
FREQUENCY: Ch 17		HOURS: HX

DRVENIK VELI MARINA, ZIRONA	Marina 15 Berths 140 Planned	43°27'·17N 16°09'·00E
Tel: +385(0)21 362722 info@marinadalmacija.hr	Maximum LOA: 25 m	Fax: www.marinadalmacija.hr
FREQUENCY: Ch 17		HOURS: HX

DUBROVNIK	Marinas and Port 450 Berths	42°40'·3N 18°07'·6E
Tel: ACI Marina: +385(0)204 55020 & 455021 Hr Mr: +385(0)204 11438 Porat Dubrovnik Marina: +385(0)204 17999 m.dubrovnik@aci-club.hr	Maximum LOA: 40 m	Fax: ACI Marina: +385(0)204 55022 Hr Mr: +385(0)204 11472 Porat Dubrovnik Marina: +385(0)204 17944 www.aci-club.hr
FREQUENCY: Marina: Ch 17 Hr Mr: Ch 10 16		HOURS: H24

GAŽENICA	Port	44°05'N 15°16'E
Tel: Hr Office: +385(0)23 312065 ext 29		Fax:
FREQUENCY: Hr Office: Ch 10 16		HOURS: HX

MARINA DALMACIJA

HVAR (PAKLENI OTOCI) ACI PALMIŽANA	Marina and Port 164 Berths	43°09'·8N 16°23'·8E
☎ ACI Marina: +385(0)21 744995 Hr Office: +385(0)21 741007 Mobile: 099 470039 m.palmizana@aci-club.hr	Maximum LOA: 25 m	Fax ACI Marina: +385(0)21 744985 Hr Office: +385(0)21 742099
FREQUENCY: Marina: Ch 17 Hr Office: Ch 10 16	LOCATION: Otok Hvar	HOURS: H24

IST, OTOK IST	Marina and Port	44°16'N 14°46'E
☎ Marina: +385(0)23 372419 Hr Office: +385(0)23 372449		Fax Marina: +385(0)23 372464 Hr Office: +385(0)23 372449
FREQUENCY: Marina: Ch 17 Hr Office: Ch 10 16		HOURS: HX

JABLANAC	Port	44°42'N 14°55'E
☎ Hr Office: +385(0)53 887049		Fax
FREQUENCY: Hr Office: Ch 10 16		HOURS: HX

JELSA, OTOK HVAR	Port	43°10'N 16°42'E
☎ Hr Office: +385(0)21 761055		Fax Hr Office: +385(0)21 761055
FREQUENCY: Hr Office: Ch 10 16		HOURS: HX

JEZERA (O. MURTER) ACI JEZERA	Marina 200 Berths	43°47'·1N 15°39'·2E
☎ Hr Office: +385(0)22 439315 m.jezera@aci-club.hr		Fax Hr Office: +385(0)22 439294 www.aci-club.hr
FREQUENCY: Ch 17		HOURS: H24

JEZERA (O. ŽUT) ACI ŽUT	Marina 120 Berths	43°53'·2N 15°18'·0E
☎ +385(0)22 7860278 Mobile: 099 470028 m.zut@aci-club.hr	Depth: 2·58 m, Maximum LOA: 25 m	Fax +385(0)22 7860279 www.aci-club.hr
FREQUENCY: Ch 17		HOURS: H24

JEZERA (PANITULA VELA) ACI PÍŠKERA	150 Berths	43°45'·5N 15°21'·2E
Hr Office: +385(0)22 34341 Mobile: 099 470009 m.piskera@aci-club.hr	Depth: 3·5 m, Maximum LOA: 30 m	Hr Office: +385(0)22 34341 www.aci-club.hr
FREQUENCY: Ch 17	LOCATION: Kornati Islands	HOURS: H24

KARLOBAG	Port	44°32'N 15°04'E
Hr Office: +385(0)53 694030		
FREQUENCY: Hr Office: Ch 10 16		HOURS: HX

KOMIŽA, OTOK VIS	Port	43°03'N 16°05'E
Hr Office: +385(0)21 713085		Hr Office: +385(0)21 713085
FREQUENCY: Ch 10 16		HOURS: HX

KORČULA (O.KORČULA) ACI KORČULA	Marina and Port 135 Berths	42°57'·5N 17°08'·4E
ACI Marina: +385(0)20 711661 Hr Office: +385(0)20 711178 m.korcula@aci-club.hr	Maximum LOA: 35 m	ACI Marina +385(0)20 711748 www.aci-club.hr
FREQUENCY: Marina: Ch 17 Hr Office: Ch 09 12 **16**		HOURS: H24

KRALJEVICA	Port	45°16'N 14°34'E
Hr Office: +385(0)51 281330		
FREQUENCY: Hr Office: Ch 10 16		HOURS: HX

KRK, OTOK KRK	Port	45°01'N 14°35'E
Hr Office: +385(0)51 221380		
FREQUENCY: Hr Office: Ch 10 16		HOURS: HX

LUMBARDA (O.KORČULA)	Marina 170 Berths	42°55'·5N 17°10'·6E
+385(0)20 712730 & 712623	Depth: 5 - 7 m, Maximum LOA: 35 m	+385(0)20 712755
FREQUENCY: Ch 17		HOURS: HX

OTOK KORČULA - LUMBARDA MARINA FROM N

MAKARSKA	Port	43°17'N 17°01'E
Hr Office: +385(0)21 611977		Hr Office: +385(0)21 611977
FREQUENCY: Hr Office: Ch 10 16		HOURS: HX

MALI LOŠINJ, OTOK LOŠINJ	Marina and Port 150 Berths	44°32′·6N 14°28′·0E
Tel: Marina: +385(0)51 231626 Hr Office: +385(0)51 231438	Depth: 10 m, Maximum LOA: 25 m	Fax: Marina: +385(0)51 231461 Hr Office: +385(0)51 231438 www.yc-marina.hr
FREQUENCY: Marina: Ch 17 Hr Office: Ch 10 16		HOURS: HX

MALINSKA, OTOK KRK	Port	45°07′N 14°31′E
Tel: Hr Office: +385(0)51 859 346		Fax:
FREQUENCY: Hr Office: Ch 10 16		HOURS: HX

MARINA VELI IŽ	50 Berths	44°00′·03N 15°06′·08E
Tel: +385(0)23 277006 tankerkomerc@tankerkomerc.tel.hr		Fax: +385(0)23 277186 www.tankerkomerc.tel.hr
FREQUENCY: Hr Office: Ch 17	LOCATION: Island of Iż	

METKOVIĆ	Port	43°03′N 17°39′E
Tel: Hr Office: +385(0)20 681681 & 679008		Fax: Hr Office: +385(0)20 681681
FREQUENCY: Hr Office: Ch 10 16		HOURS: HX

MILNA, OTOK BRAČ	Marina and Port 170 Berths	43°19′·5N 16°27′·3E
Tel: Marina: +385(0)21 636306 & 636366 Hr Office: +385(0)21 636205 m.milna@aci-club.hr	Maximum LOA: 35 m	Fax: Marina: +385(0)21 636272 Hr Office: +385(0)21 636205
FREQUENCY: Hr Office: Ch 10 16		HOURS: H24

MOŠĆENIČKA DRAGA	Port	45°13′N 14°15′E
Tel: Hr Office: +385(0)51 737501		Fax:
FREQUENCY: Hr Office: Ch 10 16		HOURS: HX

MURTER HRAMINA	Marina 450 Berths	43°49′·7N 15°35′·7E
Tel: Marina: +385(0)22 434411 Hr Mr: +385(0)22 435190 info@marina-hramina.hr	Maximum LOA: 50 m	Fax: +385(0)22 435242 www.marina-hramina.hr
FREQUENCY: Ch 17 Hr Office: Ch 10 16	LOCATION: Otok Murter	HOURS: HX

MARINA BETINA	Marina 190 Berths	43°49′·6N 15°36′·4E
Tel: +385(0)22 434497 marina-betina@si.tel.hr	Maximum LOA: 50 m	Fax: +385(0)22 434497 www.marina-betina.hr
FREQUENCY: Ch 17	LOCATION: Murter	HOURS: HX

NEZERINE LOSINJ	Port	44°40′N 14°24′E
Tel: +385(0)51 237033		Fax: +385(0)51 237033
FREQUENCY: Ch 17		HOURS: HX

NOVALJA, OTOK PAG	Port	44°33′N 14°53′E
Tel: Hr Office: +385(0)53 661301		Fax:
FREQUENCY: Hr Office: Ch 10 16		HOURS: HX

NOVIGRAD (ISTRIA)	Marina	45°19′·1N 13°34′·0E
Tel: Marina: +385(0)52 757077 Hr Office: +385(0)52 757035 marketing@laguna-novigrad.hr	Depth: 1·5 m	Fax: Marina: +385(0)52 757314 Hr Office: +385(0)52 757035
FREQUENCY: Ch 17	LOCATION: Modrač	HOURS: HX

NOVIGRAD HARBOUR AND MARINA FROM W

NOVI VINODOLSKI	Port	45°07'N 14°48'E
☎ Hr Office: +385(0)51 244345 & 791053 Mobile: 099 485132		Fax
FREQUENCY: Hr Office: Ch 10 16		HOURS: HX

OMIŠALJ, OTOK KRK	Port	45°13'N 14°33'E
☎ Hr Office: +385(0)51 842053		Fax
FREQUENCY: Ch 10 16		HOURS: HX

OMIŠ	Port	43°26'N 16°41'E
☎ Hr Office: +385(0)21 861025		Fax Hr Office: +385(0)21 861025
FREQUENCY: Hr Office: Ch 10 16		HOURS: HX

OPATIJA	Marina and Port ACI Opatija 304 Berths, Admiral 160 Berths	45°19'·6N 14°18'·4E
☎ ACI Opatija Marina: +385(0)51 704004 Admiral Marina: +385(0)51 271389 Hr Office: +385(0)51 711249 m.opatija@aci-club.hr & marina-admiral@irh.tel.hr	Maximum LOA: 30 m	Fax ACI Opatija Marina: +385(0)51 704024 Admiral Marina: +385(0)51 271708 Hr Office: +385(0)51 711249
FREQUENCY: Hr Office: Ch 10 16		HOURS: H24

OREBIC MARINA	Marina 240 Berths	42°58'·5N 17°11'·0E
☎ +385(0)20 713241		Fax +385(0)20 713277
FREQUENCY: Hr Office: Ch 10 16		HOURS: HX

PAG, OTOK PAG	Marina and Port 175 Berths	44°27'·9N 14°57'·5E
☎ ACI Šimuni: +385(0)23 697457 Hr Office: +385(0)53 611023 m.simuni@aci-club.hr		Fax ACI Šimuni: +385(0)23 697462
FREQUENCY: Marina: Ch 17 Hr Office: Ch 10 16		HOURS: H24.

PLOČE	Port	43°03'N 17°26'E
☎ Hr Mr: +385(0)20 679008		Fax Hr Mr: +385(0)20 679008
FREQUENCY: Hr Mr: Ch 10 16		HOURS: 0600-2200 LT

OTOK PAG - ŠIMUNI HARBOUR FROM SW

PARENTIUM MARINA FROM SW

PODGORA MARINA	Marina 220 Berths	43°15′N 17°05′E
☎ +385(0)21 625222		Fax +385(0)21 625311
FREQUENCY: Ch 17		HOURS: HX

POREČ	Marinas and Port Marina Poreč: 100 Berths Parentium: 200 Berths	45°12′N 13°35′E
☎ Marina Poreč: +385(0)52 451913 Parentium: +385(0)52 452210 Hr Office: +385(0)52 431663 Marina Poreč: marina.porec@pu.tel.hr Parentium: marina.parentium@plavalaguna.hr	Draught 5 m, Maximum LOA: 20 m	Fax Marina Poreč: +385(0)52 451050 Parentium: +385(0)52 452212 Hr Office: +385(0)52 431663 www.plavalaguna.hr
FREQUENCY: Marina: Ch 17 Hr Office: Ch 10 16		HOURS: HX

POREČ ČERVAR-PORAT	Marina 200 Berths	45°16′·30N 13°36′·04E
☎ +385(0)52 436661 marina.cervar@plavalaguna.hr	Maximum LOA: 30 m	Fax +385(0)52 436320 www.plavalaguna.hr
FREQUENCY: Ch 17		HOURS: HX

POREČ HARBOUR FROM NW

ČERVAR- PORAT MARINA FROM N

PREKO, OTOK UGLJAN	Port	44°05′N 15°11′E
☎ Hr Office: +385(0)23 86119		Fax: Hr Office: +385(0)23 86119
FREQUENCY: Ch 10 16		HOURS: HX

PRIMOŠTEN	Marina and Port 265 Berths	43°34′·3N 15°56′·7E
☎ Marina Kremik: +385(0)22 570068 Hr Office: +385(0)22 70266	Maximum LOA: 22 m	Fax: Marina Kremik: +385(0)22 570078
FREQUENCY: Marina: Ch 17 Hr Office: Ch 10 16		HOURS: HX

PULA	Marina and Port ACI Pomer: 220 Berths ACI Pula: 198 Berths	44°52′·6N 13°50′·0E
☎ ACI Pomer: +385(0)52 573162 & 573400 ACI Pula: +385(0)52 219142 Hr Mr: +385(0)52 22037 & 27646 Mobile: +385(0)99 483961 m.pomer@aci-club.hr & m.pula@aci-club.hr	ACI Pomer: Maximum LOA: 15 m ACI Pula: Maximum LOA: 36 m	Fax ACI Pomer: +385(0)52 573266 ACI Pula: +385(0)52 211850 Hr Mr: +385(0)52 27646 & 22110 www.aci-club.hr
FREQUENCY: Marina: Ch 17 Hr Mr: Ch 10 16		HOURS: H24

VERUDA-TEHNOMONT	Marina 630 Berths	44°50′·4N 13°50′·3E
☎ +385(0)52 224034 & 211033 marveruda@pu.tel.hr	Maximum LOA: 25 m	Fax +385(0)52 211194 www.marveruda.com
FREQUENCY: Ch 17	LOCATION: Pula	HOURS: HX

MARINA VERUDA

PUNAT	Marina & Port 830 Berths 100 Visitor Berths	45°02′·0N 14°38′·0E
☎ Punat: +385(0)51 654111 & 654120 Mobile: 099 481883 Marina Klimno: +385(0)51 864782 Hr Office: +385(0)51 854065 marina-punat@ri.tel.hr	Depth: 2·5 - 3 m, Maximum LOA: 25 m	Fax Punat: +385(0)51 654110 Marina Klimno: +385(0)51 848141 Hr Office: +385(0)51 854065 www.marina-punat.hr
FREQUENCY: Marina: Ch 17 Hr Office: Ch 10 16	LOCATION: Marina Klimno: Soline Bay North Eastern part of Krk (45°09′·4N 14°37′·4E)	HOURS: HX

RABAC	Port	45°04′N 14°10′E
☎ Hr Office: +385(0)52 872085		Fax Hr Office: +385(0)52 872085
FREQUENCY: Hr Office: Ch 10 16		HOURS: HX

RAB, OTOK RAB	Marinas and Port ACI Rab: 150 Berths ACI Supetarska Draga: 276 Berths	44°45′·4N 14°46′·0E
☎ ACI Rab: +385(0)51 724023 ACI Supetarska Draga: +385(0)51 776268 Hr Office: +385(0)51 724103 m.rab@aci-club.hr & m.supdraga@aci-club.hr	ACI Rab: Maximum LOA: 18 m ACI Supetarska Draga: Maximum LOA: 22 m	Fax ACI Rab: +385(0)51 724229 ACI Supetarska Draga: +385(0)51 776222 Hr Office: +385(0)51 724103 www.aci-club.hr
FREQUENCY: Marina: Ch 17 Hr Office: Ch 10 16		HOURS: H24

MARINA PUNAT

OTOK RAB - RAB HARBOUR FROM S

RAŠA (INCLUDING TRGET)	Port	45°00'N 14°05'E
Hr Office: +385(0)52 875127		Hr Office: +385(0)52 875127
FREQUENCY: Pilots: Ch 09 12 Hr Office: Ch 10 16		HOURS: Hr Office: HX
NOTE: Vessels sheltering from bad weather should maintain a listening watch on VHF Ch 09 or 12.		

RIJEKA	Port	45°19′N 14°27′E
☎ Hr Mr: +385(0)51 214031 Mobile: 0994 81281 & 422529		Fax: Hr Mr: +385(0)51 211660 & 212696
FREQUENCY: Hr Mr: Ch 10 16		HOURS: HX

ROGAČ, OTOK ŠOLTA	Port	43°24′N 16°18′E
☎ Hr Office: +385(0)21 654139		Fax: Hr Office: +385(0)21 654139
FREQUENCY: Hr Office: Ch 10 16		HOURS: HX

ROGOZNICA	Port	43°32′N 15°58′E
☎ Hr Office: +385(0)22 59045		Fax:
FREQUENCY: Hr Office: Ch 10 16		HOURS: HX
MARINA FRAPA	**Marina** 400 Berths 75 Visitor Berths	**43°31′·0N 15°58′·0E**
☎ +385(0)22 559900 & 559931 marina-frapai@si.hinet.hr	Depth: 3 - 8 m, Maximum LOA: 25 m	Fax: +385(0)22 559932 www.marinafrapa.com
FREQUENCY: Ch 17	LOCATION: Rogoznica	HOURS: HX

ROVINJ HARBOURS FROM NW

ROVINJ	Marinas and Port	45°04′·6N 13°38′·4E
☎ Hr Office: +385(0)52 811132		Fax: Hr Office: +385(0)52 811132
FREQUENCY: Hr Office: Ch 10 16 Marina: Ch 17		HOURS: HX
ROVINJ ACI ROVINJ	**Marina** 380 Berths	**45°04′·6N 13°38′·4E**
☎ +385(0)52 813133 m.rovinj@aci-club.hr	Maximum LOA: 25 m	Fax: +385(0)52 813133 www.aci-club.hr
		HOURS: H24
MARINA VALALTA	**Marina** 180 Berths	**45°07′N 13°37′E**
☎ +385(0)52 811033		Fax: +385(0)52 816025
MARINA VRSAR	**Marina** 180 Berths	**44°09′·2N 13°36′·1E**
☎ +385(0)52 441052		Fax: +385(0)52 441062

SALI, OTOK DUGI	Port	44°57′N 15°10′E
☎ Hr Office: +385(0)23 377021		Fax: Hr Office: +385(0)23 377021
FREQUENCY: Hr Office: Ch 10 16		HOURS: HX

MARINA VALALTA AND ENTRANCE TO LIMISKI KANALFROM WSW

SENJ	Port	44°59′N 14°54′E
☎ Hr Office: +385(0)53 881301		📠
FREQUENCY: Hr Office: Ch 10 16		HOURS: HX

ŠIBENIK	Marina and Port — Marina Kremik 265 Berths	43°44′N 15°54′E
☎ Marina Kremik: +385(0)22 570068 Hr Mr: +385(0)22 217216 & 217217 Mobile: 099 473066 & 473112		📠 Marina Kremik: +385(0)22 571142 Hr Mr: +385(0)22 217378
FREQUENCY: Marina: Ch 17 Hr Mr: Ch 10 16 **71**	LOCATION: Marina Kremik: 43°34′·4N 15°50′·6E	HOURS: H24

APPROACH: Through Dvainka passage, minimum depth 23 m. All vessels over 50 GT must apply for permission to enter the Sv. Ante channel by using international code signal Z by flag during daylight hours and a white light above a red one, visible 2 miles all round, or a sound signal (letter Z of morse code) during night-time hours. Vessels may enter channel only when authorised by a signal of two black balls vertically disposed by day, or two green lights vertically displayed by night made by the signaling station at Jadria, VHF Channel 71.

OTOK KRK - KRK HARBOUR FROM W

SILBA, OTOK SILBA	Port	44°23′N 14°41′E
☎ Hr Office: +385(0)23 370047		📠 Hr Office: +385(0)23 370047
FREQUENCY: Hr Office: Ch 10 16		HOURS: HX

ŠILO, OTOK KRK	Port	45°09′N 14°40′E
Hr Office: +385(0)51 852110		
FREQUENCY: Hr Office: Ch 10 16		HOURS: HX

SPLIT	Marina and Port 360 Berths	43°30′N 16°26′E
ACI Split: +385(0)21 398548 Hr Mr: +385(0)21 362436 Mobile: +358(0)99 471294 m.split@aci-club.hr	Maximum LOA: 60 m	ACI Split: +385(0)21 398556 Hr Mr: +385(0)21 361298 www.aci-club.hr
FREQUENCY: Marina: Ch 17 Hr Mr: Ch 10 16 74		HOURS: H24

SPLIT HARBOUR VIEWED FROM SW

SKRADIN, ACI SKRADIN	Marina 200 Berths	43°49′·0N 15°55′·6E
+385(0)22 771365 m.skradin@aci-club.hr		+385(0)22 771163 www.aci-club.hr
FREQUENCY: Ch 17		HOURS: H24

STARIGRAD, OTOK HVAR	Port	43°11′N 16°35′E
Hr Office: +385(0)21 765060		Hr Office: +385(0)21 765060
FREQUENCY: Hr Office: Ch 10 16		HOURS: HX

STARIGRAD-PAKLENICA	Port	44°17′N 15°26′E
Hr Office: +385(0)23 79062		
FREQUENCY: Hr Office: Ch 10 16		HOURS: HX

SUĆURAJ, OTOK HVAR	Port	43°07′N 17°11′E
Hr Office: +385(0)21 77228		Hr Office: +385(0)21 77228
FREQUENCY: Hr Office: Ch 10 16		HOURS: HX

RIJEKA KRKA - MARINA SKRADIN FROM SE

SUMARTIN, OTOK BRAČ	Marina and Port 170 Berths	43°19′·6N 16°27′·0E
Tel: Marina Milna: +385(0)21 636306 & 636366 Hr Office: +385(0)21 648222 m.marina@aci-club.hr		Fax: Marina Milna: +385(0)21 636272 Hr Office: +385(0)21 648222 www.aci-club.hr
FREQUENCY: Marina: Ch 17 Hr Office: Ch 10 16	LOCATION: Otok Brač	HOURS: HX

SUPERTAR, OTOK BRAČ	Port	43°23′N 16°33′E
Tel: Hr Office: +385(0)21 631116		Fax: Hr Office: +385(0)21 631116
FREQUENCY: Hr Office: Ch 10 16		HOURS: HX

SUSAK, OTOK SUSAK	Port	44°31′N 14°19′E
Tel: Hr Office: +385(0)51 239001		Fax: Hr Office: +385(0)51 239001
FREQUENCY: Hr Office: Ch 10 16		HOURS: HX

SVETI JURAJ	Port	44°56′N 14°55′E
Tel: Hr Office: +385(0)53 883006		Fax:
FREQUENCY: Hr Office: Ch 10 16		HOURS: HX

TISNO, OTOK MURTER	Port	43°48′N 15°39′E
Tel: Hr Office: +385(0)22 439313		Fax:
FREQUENCY: Hr Office: Ch 10 16		HOURS: HX

TRIBUNJ	Marina 350 Berths	43°45′N 15°45′E
Tel: +385(0)22 447140		Fax: +385(0)22 447141
FREQUENCY: Ch 17		HOURS: HX

TROGIR	Marina and Port	43°30′·8N 16°15′·0E
Tel: ACI Trogir: +385(0)21 881544 Hr Office: +385(0)21 881508 m.trogir@aci-club.hr	Maximum LOA: 20 m	Fax: ACI Trogir: +385(0)21 881258 Hr Office: +385(0)21 881508 www.aci-club.hr
FREQUENCY: Hr Office: Ch 10 16		HOURS: H24

TUCEPI MARINA	Marina 50 Berths	43°11′·5N 17°03′·4E
Tel: +385(0)21 601111		Fax: +385(0)21 601113
FREQUENCY: Ch 17		HOURS: HX

OTOK ZLARIN - TRIBUNJ MARINA FROM SW

UBLI, OTOK LASTOVO	Port	42°45′N 16°49′E
Hr Office: +385(0)20 805006		Fax:
FREQUENCY: Hr Office: Ch 10 16		HOURS: HX

UMAG	Marina and Port 518 Berths	45°26′·2N 13°31′·5E
ACI Umag: +385(0)52 741066 Hr Office: +385(0)52 741662 m.umag@aci-club.hr	Maximum LOA 40 m	Fax: ACI Umag: +385(0)52 741166 Hr Office: +385(0)52 741662 www.aci-club.hr
FREQUENCY: Marina: Ch 17 Hr Office: Ch 10 16		HOURS: Marina: H24 Hr Office: HX

UMAG HARBOUR AND MARINA FROM NW

VELA LUKA, OTOK KORČULA	Port	42°58′N 16°43′E
Hr Office: +385(0)20 812023		Fax:
FREQUENCY: Hr Office: Ch 10 16		HOURS: HX

VELI IŽ (O. IÝ)	Marina 58 Berths	444°03′·1N 15°06′·9E
+385(0)23 277006 & 277186 tankerkomerc@tankerkomerc.tel.hr	Maximum LOA: 20 m	Fax: +385(0)23 277186
FREQUENCY: Hr Office: Ch 10 16		HOURS: HX

VIS, OTOK VIS	Port	43°04′N 16°11′E
Hr Office: +385(0)21 711111		Fax: Hr Office: +385(0)21 711111
FREQUENCY: Hr Office: Ch 10 16		HOURS: HX

OTOK KORČULA - KORČULA VIEWED FROM N

VODICE	Marina and Port	415 Berths	43°45′·0N 15°47′·0E
ACI Vodice: +385(0)22 443086 & 443221 Hr Office: +385(0)22 443055 m.vodice@aci-club.hr			ACI Vodice: +385(0)22 442470 www.aci-club.hr
FREQUENCY: Marina: Ch 17 Hr Office: Ch 10 16			HOURS: H24

VRBOSKA (O. HVAR) ACI VRBOSKA	Marina	85 Berths	443°11′·0N 16°40′·0E
+385(0)21 774018 m.vodice@aci-club.hr	Maximum LOA: 28 m		+385(0)21 774144 www.aci-club.hr
FREQUENCY: Ch 17			HOURS: H24

OTOK ZLARIN - VODICE MARINA FROM SW

<table>
<tr><th>ZADAR</th><th>Marinas and Port
Boric: 220 Berths Zadar: 300 Berths</th><th>44°07'·1N 15°14'·0E</th></tr>
<tr><td>Tel: Boric: +385(0)23 444018 & 443020
Zadar: +385(0)23 204862
Hr Mr: +385(0)23 211103
Mobile: +385(0)99 470116 & 472080
Boric: prodaja@hoteliborik.hr
Zadar: tankeromerc@tankerkomerc.tel.hr</td><td>Boric: Depth: 1·54 m, Maximum LOA: 20 m
Zadar: Maximum LOA: 40 m</td><td>Fax: Boric: +385(0)23 436313
Zadar: +385(0)23 333917
Hr Mr: +385(0)23 437825
www.hoteliborik.hr
www.tankerkomerc.tel.hr</td></tr>
<tr><td colspan="2">FREQUENCY: Hr Mr: Ch 10 16</td><td>HOURS: H24</td></tr>
</table>

CYPRUS

NAVTEX [M]

M	Cyprus	518 kHz	35°03′N 33°17′E
DIAGRAM page 255			
Weather Bulletins			
M: On receipt 0200 0600 1000 1400 1800 2200	Forecast for Eastern Mediterranean. Gale warnings		
Navigational Warnings			
M: On receipt 0200 0600 1000 1400 1800 2200	For Eastern Mediterranean		

CYPRUS RT (MF) 2700 kHz

Navigational Warnings	
On receipt 0733 1533	For Eastern Mediterranean

BRITISH FORCES BROADCASTING SERVICES ONE (BFBS ONE)

A	89·7 MHz	FM	Nicosia
B	92·1 MHz	FM	Akrotiri
C	99·6 MHz	FM	Dhekelia
Weather Bulletins			
A-C: Mon-Fri: 0640 1015 Sat: 0635 Sun: 0710 0910 (All local times)	Inshore forecast in English for area between Cape Aspro and Cape Greco including sea state, wind speed and direction, visibility and temperatures. Forecast valid until 1900 LT on day of broadcast		

AKROTIRI

Port — 34°34′N 33°02′E

Tel: +357 25 276960

Fax:

FREQUENCY: Ch 16 73

HOURS: Mon: 0700-1630 LT
Tues-Fri: 0700-1330 LT
Sat: 1400-1600 LT
Sun: 1400-1900 LT

FAMAGUSTA

Port — 35°07′N 33°57′E

Tel: Hr Mr Office: +90(0)392 366626

Fax: Hr Mr Office: +90(0)392 50466

FREQUENCY: Ch 16

KYRENIA

Port and Marina — 35°20′N 33°19′E

Tel: Harbour Master: +90(0)392 8154988
Marina: +90(0)392 8153587

P.E.

Fax:

FREQUENCY: 2182 Khz RT
Ch 16

HOURS: Office hours

LARNACA

Pilots, Port and Marina — 34°55′N 33°38′E

Tel: Port Manager: +357 24 635405
Port Auth: +357 22 450100

cpa@cpa.gov.cy

P.E.

Fax: Port Manager: +357 24 635630
Port Auth: +357 22 365420

FREQUENCY: Pilots: Ch 14 16
Port: Ch 16

HOURS: 0730-1430 LT

Marina: CALL: Larnaca Marina — 34°55′·1N 33°38′·6E
450 Berths Limited Visitors Berths

Tel: +357 24 653110 & 653113

larnaca.marina@cybnet.com.cy

Depth: 1·5 - 5 m - Maximum draught 3·5 m,
Maximum LOA: 40 m

Fax: +357 24 624110

www.windowoncyprus.com/larnaca_marina.htm

FREQUENCY: Ch 08 16

HOURS: H24

LIMASSOL	Port and Marina	34°39′N 33°11′E
Port Authority: +357 25 819200 Port Manager: +357 25 365246 Limassol.port@cpa.gov.cy	P.E.	Port Manager: +357 25 575597
FREQUENCY: Ch 10 16		HOURS: 0600-1400 LT (then duty pilot on portable VHF)
St. Raphael Marina	**Marina:** CALL: St Raphael Limassol Marina 237 Berths Limited Visitors Berths	34°42′·8N 33°01′E
+357 25 636100 raphael@spidernet.com.cy	Depth: 3 - 5 m, Maximum LOA: 30 m	+357 25 636394 www.raphael.co.cy
FREQUENCY: Ch 09 16		

PAPHOS	Marina 1000 Berth Marina Under Construction, to be completed by 2004	34°45′N 32°24′E
	P.E	
FREQUENCY:		

VASILIKOS	Port	34°43′N 33°10′E
Port Auth: +357 22 7650005 & 7650010		Port Auth: +357 24 332651
FREQUENCY: Pilots: Ch 12 16		

EGYPT

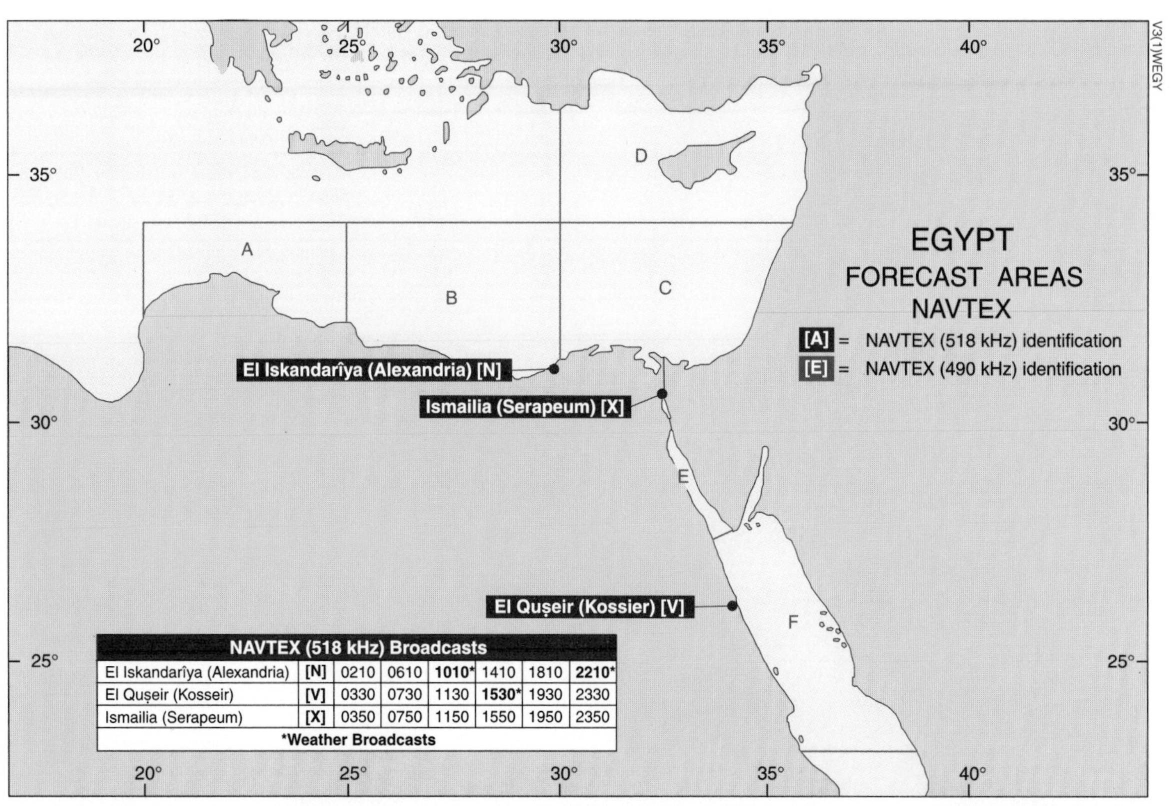

NAVTEX (518 kHz) Broadcasts							
El Iskandarîya (Alexandria)	[N]	0210	0610	**1010***	1410	1810	**2210***
El Quşeir (Kosseir)	[V]	0330	0730	1130	**1530***	1930	2330
Ismailia (Serapeum)	[X]	0350	0750	1150	1550	1950	2350
***Weather Broadcasts**							

EL ISKANDARÎYA (ALEXANDRIA) INCLUDING EL DIKHEILA

Port: CALL: Alexandria Port Control — 31°12′N 29°53′E

☎ Hr Mr: +20(0)3 4800546, 4800100 & 4800201

Fax: Hr Mr: +20(0)3 4807245
Pilots: +20(0)3 4805840

FREQUENCY: Port: Ch 11 13 16 67 | LOCATION: Arsenal Basin | HOURS: H24

PORT SAID YACHT CLUB MARINA

Marina: Feix Marina — 31°15′N 32°17′E

☎ Marina: +20(0)66 333132, 337165 & 348772
Mobile: 0122 119365

flx@intouch.com

Fax: Marina: +20(0)66 333510 & 348772

FREQUENCY: Ch 03 16 | HOURS: H24

INFORMATION: Contact Felix Maritime via VHF on arrival outside Port Said.

QUANÂT EL SUWEIS (SUEZ CANAL)

Vessel Traffic Management System — 31°15′·4N 32°18′·9E

☎ +20(0)64 330000 & 330009

Fax: +20(0)64 320784 & 320785

FREQUENCY: Ch 12 **14** 16 | LOCATION: Bûr Fu'âd (Port Fouad) Yacht Centre

NOTE: Suez Canal Mooring at the marina jetties at Ismailia is forbiden

FRANCE, CORSE

CORSE **MMSI 002275420**	**Centre Régional Opérationnel de Surveillance et du Sauvetage (Sous-CROSS):** CALL: CROSS Corse	41°55'N 8°46'E
DESCRIPTION: Provides a marine navigation and surveillance service		AREA: The coastal waters of Corse
☎ +33(0)4 95201363		Fax +33(0)4 95225191
FREQUENCY: Distress & Safety: 2182 kHz (MF) Ch 16 70 SAR Co-ordination: Ch 15 67 **68** 73 CROSS (Calling & Working): Ch **13** 79		HOURS: 2182 kHz & Ch 16: H24 When the station is closed, service is provided by La Garde CROSS.
INFORMATION BROADCASTS: Navigational information, when required, is broadcast on VHF Ch 79 following an announcement on VHF Ch 16 at 0845 and 1845 LT for the coastal waters of Corse		

BASTIA

AJACCIO	**Port:** CALL: Ajaccio Port Sémaphore de la Parata (La Parata Signal Station)	41°55'·1N 8°45'·7E
☎ Hr Mr: +33(0)4 95216834	**Port & Marinas**	Fax +33(0)4 95511784
FREQUENCY: Hr Mr: Ch 06 **12** 16		HOURS: Sémaphore de la Parata; HJ
	Marina (Port de L'Amirante) 830 Berths 160 Visitor Berths	41°55'·8N 8°44'·6E
☎ Hr Mr: +33(0)4 95223198	Depth: 0·5 - 1·5 m, Maximum LOA: 35 m	Fax Hr Mr: +33(0)4 95209808
FREQUENCY: Ch 09	LOCATION: Public Port	HOURS: Summer 0800-2100 LT Winter 0800-1200 1400-1800 LT
	Marina (Port Tino Rossi) 260 Berths 80 Visitor Berths	41°55'·2N 8°44'·6E
☎ Hr Mr: +33(0)4 95515543 & 4 95512272	Depth: 4 - 10 m, Maximum LOA: 60 m	Fax Hr Mr: +33(0)4 95219328
FREQUENCY: Ch 09	LOCATION: Port Tino Rossi (Public Port)	HOURS: Summer 0800-2100 LT Winter 0800-1200 1400-1800 LT

BASTIA	**Port & Marinas**	42°42′N 9°27′E
☎ Hr Mr: +33(0)4 95310715		Fax Hr Mr: +33(0)4 95316150
FREQUENCY: Ch 09 12 15 16		HOURS: Hr Mr: 0700-2000 LT
	Marina (Vieux-Port) 267 Berths	42°41′·7N 9°27′·2E
☎ Hr Mr: +33(0)4 95313110	Depth: 1 - 6 m, Maximum LOA: 12 - 40 m	Fax
FREQUENCY: Ch 09	LOCATION: Public Port	HOURS: Season: 0800-1200 1600-2000 LT Out of season: 0800-1200 1400-1700 LT
	Marina (Toga) 357 Berths 150 Visitor Berths	42°42′·5N 9°27′4E
☎ Hr Mr: +33(0)4 95349070	Depth: 2·5 - 6 m, Maximum LOA: 25 - 30 m	Fax Hr Mr: +33(0)4 95349071
FREQUENCY: Ch 09		HOURS: Summer 0800-2200 LT Winter 1400-1200 1400-1800 LT

BONIFACIO	**Port & Marina** 450 Berths 220 Visitor Berths	41°23′·1N 09°08′·8E
☎ +33(0)4 95730008 Marina Hr Mr: +33(0)4 95731007	Depth: 2 - 12 m, Maximum LOA: 60 m	Fax Marina Hr Mr: +33(0)4 95731873
FREQUENCY: Sémaphore de Pertusato: Ch 16 Marina: Ch 09		HOURS: H24 HOURS: Summer 0700-2100 LT Winter 0800-1200 1500-1800 LT

CALVI	**Port:** CALL: Sémaphore de î'le-Rousse	42°34′N 8°46′E
☎ Hr Mr: Office hours: +33(0)4 95650521 Outside office hours: +33(0)4 95650371		Fax
FREQUENCY: Ch 16		HOURS: HJ
	Marina 450 Berths 200 Visitor Berths	
☎ Port Office: +33(0)4 95651060 marie.calvi@wanadoo.fr	Depth: 1·5 - 4 m, Maximum LOA: 40 - 55 m	Fax Port Office: +33(0)4 95651513 (Indicate: for Port de Plaisance) www.villedecalvi.fr
FREQUENCY: Ch 09		HOURS: Season (1 July-31 Aug): 0700-2100 LT Out of season: 0830-1200 1400-1800 LT

CALVI

CARGÈSE	**Marina** 170 Berths 35 Visitor Berths	42°07′·9N 8°35′·9E
☎ Hr Mr: +33(0)4 95254724	Depth: 2 - 5 m, Maximum LOA: 15 m	Fax Hr Mr: +33(0)4 95264866 (Indicate: for the Port de Plaisance)
FREQUENCY: Ch 09		HOURS: Season (1 May-15 Oct): 0800-1200 1400-2100 LT

CAVALLO	**Marina** 240 Berths 35 Visitor Berths	41°21′·8N 9°15′·9E
☎ +33(0)4 95700374	Depth: 2·5 - 5 m, Maximum LOA: 20 m	Fax +33(0)4 95700374
FREQUENCY: Ch 67		HOURS: H24 15th June to 15th September

ÎLE-ROUSSE	**Port** 250 Berths 86 Visitor Berths	42°38′N 8°56′E
☎ Port: +33(0)4 95602651 Club Nautique: +33(0)4 95602255	Maximum LOA: 35 m	Fax Port: +33(0)4 95602651
FREQUENCY: Ch 09		HOURS: HX

MACINAGGIO

MACINAGGIO	Marina 580 Berths 250 Visitor Berths	41°58′·0N 9°27′·4E
Port Office: +33(0)4 95354257	Depth: 1 - 3·5 m, Maximum LOA: 30 m	Port Office: +33(0)4 95354700
FREQUENCY: Ch 09		HOURS: Season: 0630-2100 LT Out of season: (except Sun): 0800-1200 1400-1800 LT

PIANOTTOLI-CALDARELLO

PIANOTTOLI-CALDARELLO	Marina 200 Berths 120 Visitor Berths	41°29′·6N 9°04′·4E
Hr Mr: +33(0)4 95718357	Depth: 1 - 8 m, Maximum LOA: 40 m	Hr Mr: +33(0)4 95718021 (Indicate: for Capitainerie)
FREQUENCY: Ch 09		HOURS: Summer 0800-2100 LT Winter 0900-1200 1400-1700 LT

PORTO

PORTO	Marina 150 Berths 30 Visitor Berths	42°16′·1N 8°41′·5E
Town Hall: +33(0)4 95261005	Depth: 1 - 1·8 m	
FREQUENCY: Ch 09		HOURS: Season (15 May-1 Oct): 0830-1830 LT

PORTO-VECCHIO

PORTO-VECCHIO	Marina 450 Berths 150 Visitor Berths	41°35′·7N 9°21′·9E
Hr Mr: +33(0)4 95700603 Marina: +33(0)4 95701793	Depth: 1·5 - 3 m, Maximum LOA: 40 m	Hr Mr: +33(0)4 95703359 Marina: +33(0)4 95702768
FREQUENCY: Ch 09		HOURS: Summer 0900-2100 LT Winter 0830-1200 1400-1800 LT

PROPRIANO

PROPRIANO	Port and Marina 380 Berths 200 Visitor Berths	41°40′·7N 8°54′·4E
Hr Mr: +33(0)4 95761040	Depth: 2 - 5 m, Maximum LOA: 32 m	Hr Mr: +33(0)4 95762060 (Indicate: for Capitainerie du Port de Commerce)
FREQUENCY: Ch 09 16		HOURS: Summer 0600-1200 1400-2000 LT Winter 0800-1200 1400-1800 LT

SAINT-FLORENT

SAINT-FLORENT	Marina 790 Berths 270 Visitor Berths	42°41′N 9°18′E
Port Office: +33(0)4 95370079	Depth: Outer Port 5 - 6 m, Basin 2·5 - 3 m, Maximum LOA: 45 m	Port Office: +33(0) 95371137 (Indicate: for Port de Plaisance)
FREQUENCY: Ch 09		HOURS: Summer 0700-2100 LT Winter 0900-1200 1500-1800 LT

SOLENZARA

SOLENZARA	Marina 450 Berths 150 Visitor Berths	41°51′·6N 9°24′·3E
Hr Mr: +33(0)4 95574642	Depth: 1·5 - 3 m, Maximum LOA: 25 m	Hr Mr: +33(0)4 95574446
FREQUENCY: Ch 09		HOURS: Season: 0700-2100 LT Out of season: Mon-Fri: 0800-1200 1400-1800 LT

TAVERNA, PORT DE CAMPOLORO

TAVERNA, PORT DE CAMPOLORO	Marina 464 Berths 100 Visitor Berths	42°20′·5N 9°32′·5E
Port Office: +33(0)4 95380761	Depth: 1·5 - 3 m, Maximum LOA: 25 m	Port Office: +33(0)4 95384734
FREQUENCY: Ch 09		HOURS: H24

FRANCE, MEDITERRANEAN COAST

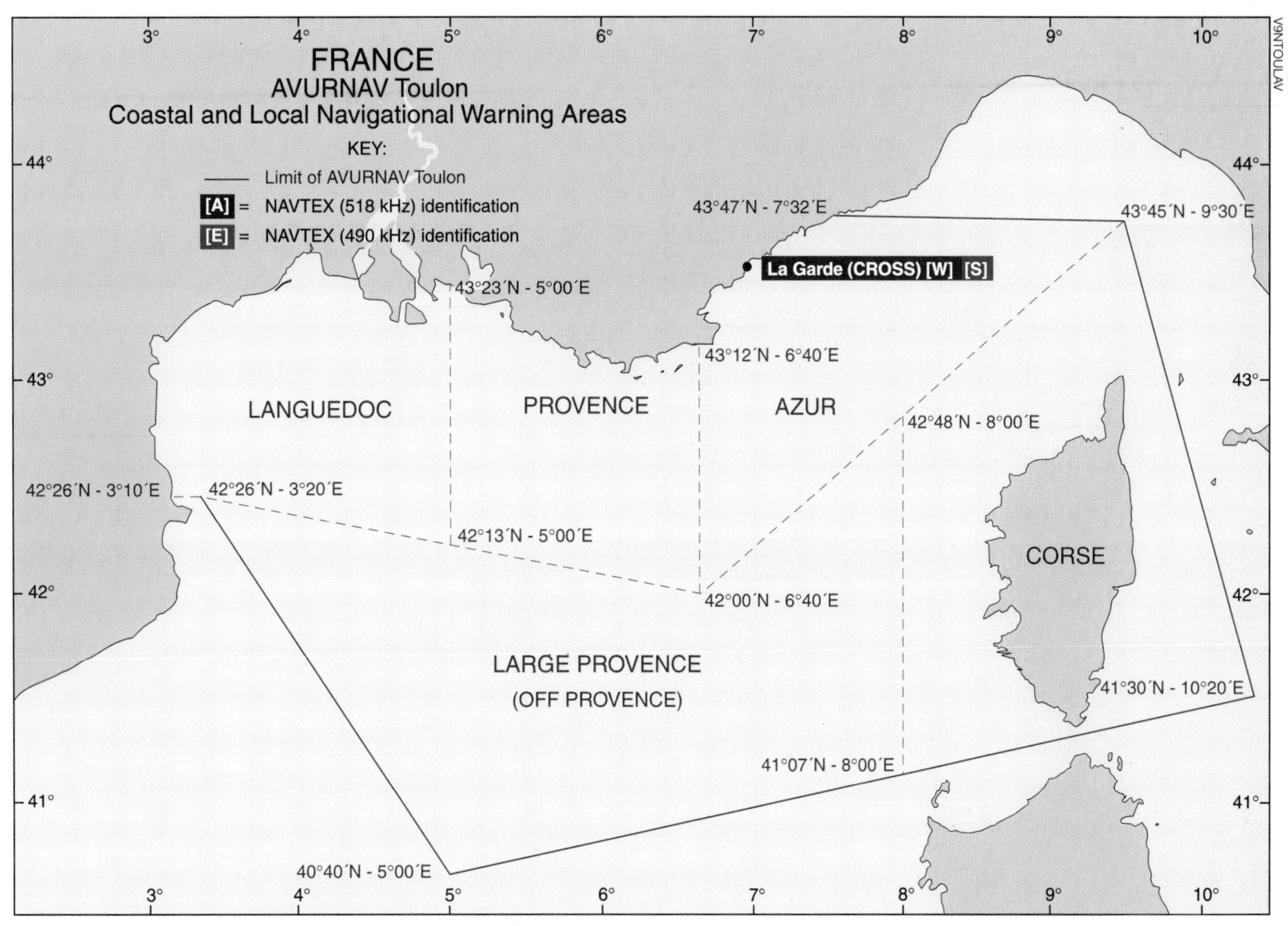

CENTRES RÉGIONAUX OPÉRATIONNELS DE SURVEILLANCE ET DE SAUVETAGE (CROSS)

CROSS provides a permanent, full time, all-weather operational presence along the coast of France and co-operates with foreign MRCC's and MRSC's as required
CROSS La Garde is linked with the COSPAS-SARSAT Mission Control Centre at Toulon in order to respond to satellite aided search and rescue operations
CROSS co-ordinates the following five main tasks:
(1) Surveillance of marine traffic, especially within the 12 n miles limit
(2) Maritime Search and Rescue
(3) Fishery Surveillance out to 200 n miles
(4) Monitoring of Pollution (tracks vessels carrying dangerous cargoes such as oil, gas and chemicals)
(5) Collection and organization of data for future use

The purpose of Marine Traffic Surveillance is to enhance navigational safety which includes the policing of International Maritime Organization (IMO)—agreed Traffic Separation Schemes (TSS) and Inshore Traffic Zones (ITZ)

INFORMATION BROADCASTS: CROSS broadcasts information bulletins comprising of navigational and traffic information of immediate interest and information on movements of vessels which appear to be navigating within a TSS or ITZ contrary to the requirements of Rule 10 of the International Collision Regulations

NAVTEX [W]			
W	La Garde (Fort Ste Marguerite)	518 kHz	43°06′N 5°59′E
NAVTEX [S]			
S	La Garde (Fort Ste Marguerite)	490 kHz	43°06′N 5°59′E
DIAGRAMS: pages 99 and 287			
Weather Bulletins			
W: On receipt 0340 0740 1140 1540 1940 2340	Storm warnings for Areas 514 (Eastern part), 515, 516, 521, 522, 523 and 531-534		
W: 1140 2340	Storm warnings, synopsis and development, 24 hour forecast for areas 514 (Eastern part), 515, 516, 521, 522, 523 and 531-534		
S: 0300 0700 1100 1500 1900 2300	Storm warnings for Areas 514 (Eastern part), 515, 516, 521, 522, 523 and 531-534. In French		
S: 0700 1900	Storm warnings, synopsis and development, 24 hour forecast for areas 514 (Eastern part), 515, 516, 521, 522, 523 and 531-534. In French		

NAVTEX [W] (Continued)

NAVTEX [S] (Continued)

Navigational Warnings	
W: 0340 0740 1140 1540 1940 2340	AVURNAV Toulon
S: 0300 0700 1100 1500 1900 2300	AVURNAV Toulon. In French

LA GARDE

MMSI 002275400
MMSI 002275410

Centre Régional Opérationnel de Surveillance et du Sauvetage (CROSS): CALL: CROSS La Garde

43°06′N 5°59′W

DESCRIPTION: Provides a marine navigation and surveillance service

AREA: From the French-Spanish border to the French-Italian border

Tel: +33(0)4 94617110

Fax: +33(0)4 94271149

FREQUENCY: Distress & Safety: 1696 2182 2677 kHz (MF) Ch 16 70
SAR Co-ordination: Ch 67 **68** 69 73
CROSS (Calling & Working): Ch 80 Information Broadcasts: Ch 80

HOURS: H24

LA GARDE (CROSS) (MRCC)

A	1696 2677	RT (MF)	La Garde	43°06′N 5°59′E
B	Ch 79	VHF	Pic de Neoulos	42°29′N 2°56′E
C			Agde	43°18′N 3°30′E
D	Ch 80		Phare du Planier	43°12′N 5°14′E
E			Mont Coudon	43°10′N 6°00′E
F			Pic de l'Ours	43°28′N 6°54′E
Corse				
G	Ch 79	VHF	Ersa	42°58′N 9°23′E
H			Serra Di Pigno	42°41′N 9°24′E
I			Conça	41°44′N 9°23′E
J			Serragia	41°31′N 8°58′E
K			La Punta	41°57′N 8°42′E
L			Piana	42°14′N 8°37′E

NOTE: All transmissions on RT(MF) are preceded by an announcement on 2182 kHz indicating the working frequency to be used for the broadcast.
All transmissions on VHF are preceded by an announcement on Ch 16, then broadcast sequentially on the working channel.
Scheduled broadcasts may be suspended whilst SAR action is in progress.

DIAGRAMS: pages 99 and 287

Weather Bulletins	
A: On receipt 0103 0503 0903 1303 1703 2103	Storm warnings and BMS for Mediterranean Areas 514-516, 521-523 and 531-534. In French repeated in English
A: 0650 1433 1850 LT	Storm warnings in force. Synopsis and 24 hour forecast for Areas 514-516, 521-523 and 531-534. Further 24 hour outlook. In French
B-L: On receipt Every H+03	Coastal BMS
B: 0703 1233 1903 LT **C:** 0715 1245 1915 LT	Storm warnings and BMS in force. 24 hour forecast and reports from Signal Stations. For Area: Languedoc Roussillon (Spanish frontier to Port-Camargue) extending 20 n miles from the coast. In French
D: 0733 1303 1933 LT **E:** 0745 1315 1945 LT	Storm warnings and BMS in force. 24 hour forecast and reports from Signal Stations. For Area: Provence (Port-Camargue to Saint-Raphaël) extending 20 n miles from the coast. In French
F: 0803 1333 2003 LT	Storm warnings and BMS in force. 24 hour forecast and reports from Signal Stations. For Area: Cote d'Azur (Saint-Raphaël to Menton) extending 20 n miles from the coast. In French
G: 0733 1233 1933 LT **H:** 0745 1245 1945 LT **I:** 0803 1303 2003 LT **J:** 0815 1315 2015 LT **K:** 0833 1333 2033 LT **L:** 0845 1345 2045 LT	Storm warnings and BMS in force. 24 hour forecast and reports from Signal Stations. For Area: coast of Corse extending 20 n miles from the coast. In French
Navigational Warnings	
A: 0833 1603 LT	Warnings for Golfe du Lion

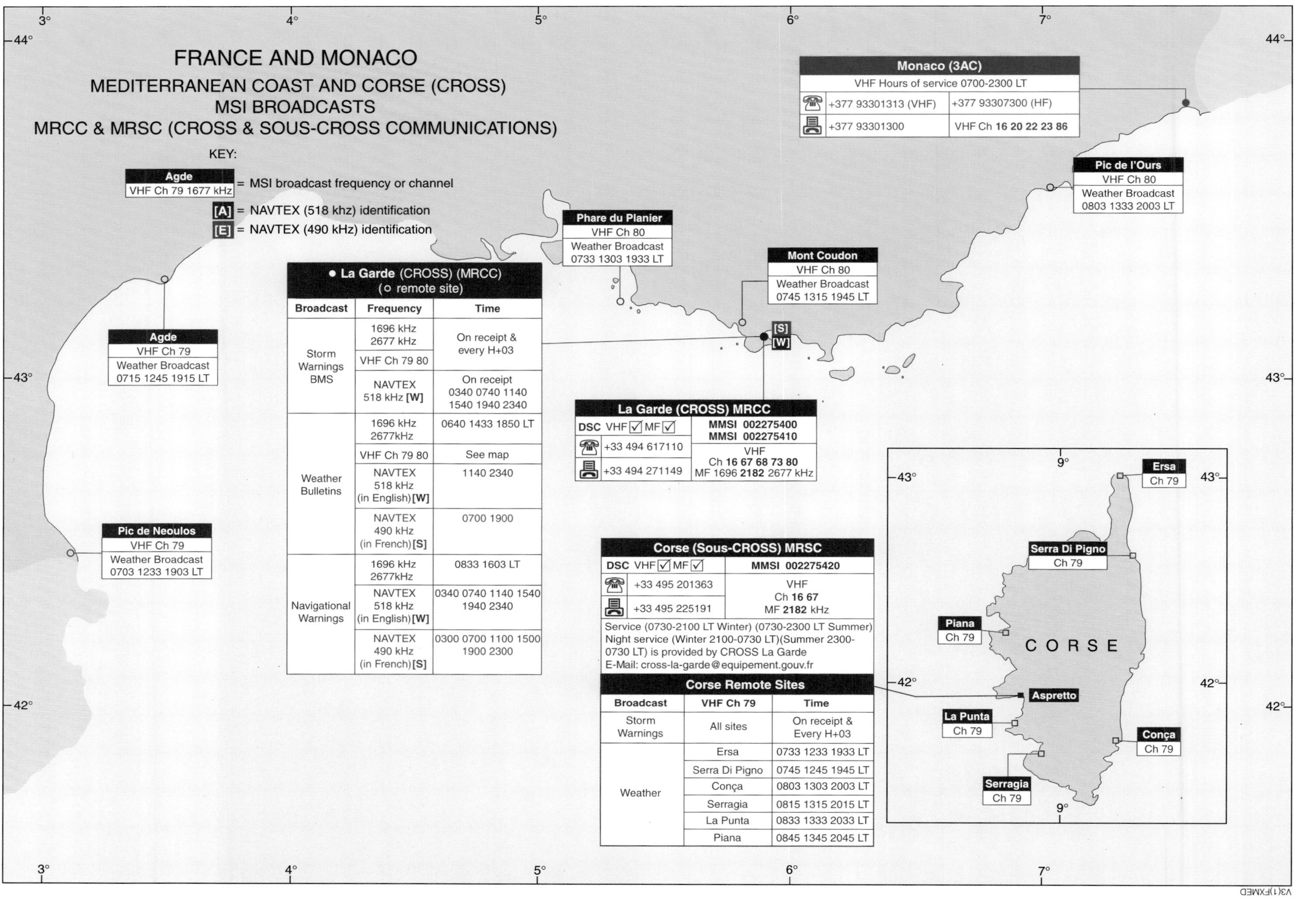

• La Garde (CROSS) (MRCC) (○ remote site)

Broadcast	Frequency	Time
Storm Warnings BMS	1696 kHz 2677 kHz	On receipt & every H+03
	VHF Ch 79 80	
	NAVTEX 518 kHz [W]	On receipt 0340 0740 1140 1540 1940 2340
Weather Bulletins	1696 kHz 2677kHz	0640 1433 1850 LT
	VHF Ch 79 80	See map
	NAVTEX 518 kHz (in English) [W]	1140 2340
	NAVTEX 490 kHz (in French) [S]	0700 1900
Navigational Warnings	1696 kHz 2677kHz	0833 1603 LT
	NAVTEX 518 kHz (in English) [W]	0340 0740 1140 1540 1940 2340
	NAVTEX 490 kHz (in French) [S]	0300 0700 1100 1500 1900 2300

Corse Remote Sites

Broadcast	VHF Ch 79	Time
Storm Warnings	All sites	On receipt & Every H+03
Weather	Ersa	0733 1233 1933 LT
	Serra Di Pigno	0745 1245 1945 LT
	Conça	0803 1303 2003 LT
	Serragia	0815 1315 2015 LT
	La Punta	0833 1333 2033 LT
	Piana	0845 1345 2045 LT

FIRING PRACTICE AREA (Centre d'Essais de la Méditerranée) (D9) (Île du Levant Firing Range)				
	Ch 16	VHF	Île du Levant	43°02′N 6°28′E
Mon-Fri: 0800-1800 LT	**Gunfire Warnings:** Call 'Delta Neuf' on approach and when within 20 n miles of Île du Levant			

CAPELLANS PORT

ARGELÈS SUR MER	**Marina** 779 Berths 30 Visitor Berths	42°32′·7N 3°03′·4E
☎ +33(0)4 68816327	Depth: 2·5 - 4 m, Maximum LOA: 24 m	Fax +33(0)4 68816914 www.argeles-sur-mer.com
FREQUENCY: Ch 09 (0830-1200 & 1400-2000 LT)		

ARGELÈS SUR MER VIEW TO THE W

BAIE-DES-ANGES	**Marina** 474 Berths 53 Visitor Berths 6 - 18 m in Public Port	43°38′N 7°08′·5E
☎ Hr Mr: +33(0)4 92133222 info@portmarinabaiedesanges.com	Depth: 2 - 5 m, Maximum LOA: 30 m	Fax +33(0)4 93204539 www.portmarinabaiedesanges.com
FREQUENCY: Ch 09		HOURS: 0900-1230 1430-1830 LT (Sat: 0900-1200 LT)

BAIE-DES-ANGES

BANDOL	Marina 1600 Berths 120 Visitor Beths	43°08′N 5°45′E
☎ Hr Mr: +33(0)4 94294264	Depth: 1·5 - 3·2 m, Maximum LOA: 30 m	Fax Hr Mr: +33(0)4 94299320
FREQUENCY: Ch 09 16		HOURS: Season: 0800-1900 LT Out of season: 0900-1700 LT

BANYULS-SUR-MER	Marina 380 Berths 50 Visitor Berths	42°31′·9N 3°07′·2E
☎ +33(0)4 68883032	Depth: 1 - 4 m, Maximum LOA: 13 m	Fax +33(0)4 68881746
FREQUENCY: Ch 09		HOURS: Season: 0800-1300 1400-2000 LT Out of season: 0800-1200 1400-1800 LT

BARCARÈS PORT ST-ANGE (GRAU ST-ANGE)	Marina 600 Berths 80 Visitor Berths	42°47′·9N 3°02′·4E
☎ Hr Mr: +33(0)4 68860735	Depth: 2 - 3 m, Maximum LOA: 15 m	Fax Hr Mr: +33(0)4 68864103 (Indicate: for Captainerie)
FREQUENCY: Ch 09		HOURS: Season: 0700-1230 1330-2000 LT Out of season: 0700-1230 1400-1930 LT

BEAULIEU-SUR-MER	Marina 776 Berths 152 Visitor Berths	43°42′N 7°20′E
☎ +33(0)4 93011049	Depth: Outer harbour 4·5m, Basins 1·6 - 4·5 m, Maximum LOA: 30 m	Fax +33(0)4 93011412
FREQUENCY: Ch 09		HOURS: H24

BORMES-LES-MIMOSAS	Marina	1010 Berths 100 Visitor Berths	43°07'·5N 6°22'E
Hr Mr: +33(0)4 94015581 (H24) port.de.bormes@wanadoo.fr	Depth: 2 - 7 m, Maximum LOA: 20 m		Hr Mr: +33(0)4 94015590 www.portdebormes.com
FREQUENCY: Ch 09 16			HOURS: H24

BARCARES-SAINT-ANGE PORT TO THE W

CALANQUE DE PORT-MIOU	Port	550 Berths	43°12'·3N 5°31'·0E
Club Nautico: +33(0)4 429042246	Speed limited to 3 knots		
FREQUENCY: Ch 09			HOURS: H24

BANYULS-SUR-MAR

CANET-EN-ROUSSILON (CANET-PLAGE)	Marina 977 Berths 50 Visitor Berths	42°42′·2N 3°02′·6E
Hr Mr: +33(0)4 68735873 & 68803507	Depth: 2·5 - 4·5 m, Maximum LOA: 24 m	Fax Hr Mr: +33(0)4 68738078
FREQUENCY: Ch 09 Summer 0800-2000 LT, Winter 0800-1230 & 1330-1830 LT		HOURS: H24

CANET-EN-ROUSSILON (CANET-PLAGE)

CANNES (PUBLIC MARINA)	**Marina:** CALL: Cannes Port 840 Berths Maximum of 246 Visitor Berths	43°32′·7N 7°01′·1E
Hr Mr: +33(0)4 92987000 port-cannes@cote-azure.cci.fr	Depth: 1 - 8 m, Maximum LOA: 140 m	Fax Hr Mr: +33(0)4 92987001 www.riviera-ports.com
FREQUENCY: Ch 12 16		HOURS: Season: 0700-2000 LT Out of season: 0800-1800 LT

RADE DE CANNES AND POINTE DE LA CROISETTE

CANNES-MARINA	1730 Berths Rental Berths Only No Visitors	
Hr Mr: +33(0)4 93495127	Depth: 1·5 - 2 m, Maximum LOA: 12 m	Fax Hr Mr: +33(0)4 93491650
FREQUENCY: Ch 09	LOCATION: 43°32′·0N 6°56′·3E	HOURS: 0800-1200 1400-1800 LT

CANNES (PUBLIC MARINA) (Continued)	Marina: CALL: Cannes Port 840 Berths Maximum of 246 Visitor Berths	43°32′·7N 7°01′·1E
PORT-CANTO	650 Berths 100 Visitor Berths	43°32′·5N 7°02′·0E
Tel: Hr Mr: +33(0)4 92188484 port.pierre-canto@wanadoo.fr	Depth: 2 - 7 m, Maximum LOA: 70 m	Fax: Hr Mr: +33(0)4 93431703 www.perso.wanadoo.fr/port.pierre.canto
FREQUENCY: Ch 09		HOURS: H24

CAP D'AGDE	Marina 2450 Berths 40 Visitor Berths	43°16′·1N 3°30′·3E
Tel: Hr Mr: +33(0)4 67260020 port@capdagde.com	Depth: 2·5 - 3 m, Maximum LOA: 25 m	Fax: Hr Mr: +33(0)4 67266620 www.capdagde.com
FREQUENCY: Ch 09		HOURS: Season: 0800-2100 LT Out of season: 0800-1200 1400-1800 LT

CAP D'AIL	Marina 253 Berths 200 Berths in Private Port and 53 in Public Port Limited Visitor Availability	43°43′·4N 7°24′·9E
Tel: Hr Mr: +33(0)4 93782846	Depth: 5 - 15 m, Maximum LOA: 60 m	Fax: Hr Mr: +33(0)4 93419829
FREQUENCY: Ch 09		HOURS: H24

CARNON-PLAGE	Marina 700 Berths 50 Visitor Berths	43°32′·4N 3°58′·6E
Tel: Hr Mr: +33(0)4 67681078 port.carnon@wanadoo.fr	Depth: 2 - 2·5 m	Fax: Hr Mr: +33(0)4 67681413 (Indicate: for Capitainerie Carnon)
FREQUENCY: Ch **09** 16		HOURS: H24

CARQUEIRANNE/SALETTES	Marina 360 Berths 90 Visitor Berths	43°05′N 6°05′E
Tel: Hr Mr: +33(0)4 94585625	Depth: 1 - 1·5 m, Maximum LOA: 10 m	Fax: Hr Mr: +33(0)4 94585976
FREQUENCY: Ch 09 (0900-1200 1400-1700 LT)		HOURS: Season: 0800-1200 1500-1800 LT Out of season: 0830-1200 1400-1730 LT

CARRY-LE-ROUET	Marina 558 Berths 20 Visitor Berths	43°19′·7N 5°09′·2E
Tel: Hr Mr: +33(0)4 42452513	Depth: 1 - 2·5 m, Maximum LOA: 15 m	Fax: Hr Mr: +33(0)4 42451908
FREQUENCY: Ch 09		HOURS: Season: 0600-1200 & 1400-1930 LT Out of season: 0800-1200 1400-1800 LT

CASSIS	Marina 500 Berths 30 Visitor Berths	43°13′·8N 5°32′·1E
Tel: Hr Mr: +33(0)4 42010373 +33(0)4 42017904	Depth: maximum 3·5 m, Maximum LOA: 18 m	Fax: +33(0)4 42010596
FREQUENCY: Ch 09		HOURS: Season: 0800-1200 1400-2030 LT Out of season: 0900-1200 1430-1800 LT

CAVALAIRE	Marina 570 Berths 40 Visitor Berths	43°10′·4N 6°32′·3E
Tel: Hr Mr: +33(0)4 94641781	Depth: 1·5 - 3·5 m, Maximum LOA: 21 m (One Berth of 40 m)	Fax: +33(0)4 94646706
FREQUENCY: Ch 09		HOURS: Season: 0600-2200 LT Out of season: 0800-1200 1300-1700 LT
	Marina 579 Berths	
Tel: Hr Mr: +33(0)4 94641601 & 94641274 info@port-cavalaire.com		Fax: +33(0)4 94643606 www.port.cavalaire.com
FREQUENCY: Ch 09		HOURS: H24

COGOLIN	Port 150 Berths Limited Visitor Availability	43°16′·4N 6°34′·2E
Tel: Hr Mr: +33(0)4 94563039	Maximum LOA: 15 m	Fax: Hr Mr: +33(0)4 94563039
FREQUENCY: Ch 09		HOURS: Season: 0900-1200 1400-1830 LT Out of season: 0800-2000 LT

CAVALAIRE FROM THE N

COGOLIN MARINA	**Marina** 1566 Berths 300 Visitor Berths	43°16'·4N 6°34'·2E
Hr Mr: +33(0)4 94560731 marines.de.cogolin@wanadoo.fr	Depth: Outer Jetties 10 - 15 m, Outer Port 6 - 8 m, Basins 4 - 5 m, Maximum LOA: 35 m	Fax Hr Mr: +33(0)4 94562675 www.marines.de.cogolin.com
FREQUENCY: Ch 09		HOURS: H24 Out of season: 0800-2000 LT

LES MARINA DE COGOLIN

FOS	**Port:** CALL: Fos Port Control	43°25'N 4°51'E
Hr Mr (Port-de-Bouc): +33(0)4 42406005		Fax Hr Mr (Port-de-Bouc): +33(0)4 42406040
FREQUENCY: Hr Mr (Port-de-Bouc): Ch 12 16		HOURS: H24

FRÉJUS	**Marina** 706 Berths 40 Visitor Berths	43°25'·2N 6°45'·1E
Hr Mr: +33(0)4 94826300	Depth: 2 - 3·5 m, Maximum LOA: 30 m	Fax Hr Mr: +33(0)4 94514852
FREQUENCY: Ch 09		HOURS: H24

FRONTIGNAN	**Marina** 600 Berths 60 Visitor Berths	43°25'·8N 3°46'·6E
Hr Mr: +33(0)4 67487521	Depth: 2 - 3 m, Maximum LOA: 16 m	Fax Hr Mr: +33(0)4 67297463 (Indicate: for Capitainerie Frontignan)
FREQUENCY: Ch 09		HOURS: H24

GOLFE-JUAN	Marina 860 Berths 258 Visitor Berths	43°33′·8N 7°04′·7E
Hr Mr: +33(0)4 93639625 port.golfe-juan@cote-azur.cci.fr	Depth: 1 - 3·5 m, Maximum LOA: 22 m	Fax Hr Mr: +33(0)4 93636641 www.riviera-ports.com
FREQUENCY: Ch 12		HOURS: Season: 0700-2000 LT Out of season: 0800-1800 LT
Port Camille Rayon	**Marina** 844 Berths 80 Visitor Berths	
Hr Mr: +33(0)4 93633030 port.c.rayon@wanadoo.fr	Depth: 2 - 5 m, Maximum LOA: 75 m	Fax Hr Mr: +33(0)4 93635507
FREQUENCY: Ch 09		HOURS: H24

GRUISSAN	Marina 900 Berths 80 Visitor Berths	43°06′·7N 3°07′·9E
Hr Mr: +33(0)4 68490820	Depth: 2·5 - 3 m, Maximum LOA: 30 m	Fax Hr Mr: +33(0)4 68491105
FREQUENCY: Ch 09		HOURS: Season: H24 Out of season: H24 (except 1200-1400 LT)

GRUISSAN MARINA

HYÈRES-PORT	Marina 1350 Berths 120 vistior berths	43°04′·8N 6°09′·5E
Hr Mr: +33(0)4 94125440	Depth: 1·5 - 3 m, Maximum LOA: 16 m	Fax Hr Mr: +33(0)4 94125450
FREQUENCY: Ch 09		HOURS: Season (1 July-31 Aug): 0600-2300 LT Out of season: 0800-1200 1400-1700 LT

HYÈRES- PORT TO THE N

LA CIOTAT	Marina and Port (Vieux-Port) Marina: 640 Berths 25 Visitor Berths Port: 700 Berths 40 Visitor Berths	43°10′·5N 5°36′·8E
☎ Marina: +33(0)4 42086290 Port Office: +33(0)4 42716360	Port: Depth: 2 - 4 m, Maximum LOA: 18 m Marina: Depth: maximum 3·5 m, Maximum LOA: 18 m	Fax Marina: +33(0)4 42714601 Port Office: +33(0)4 42838024
FREQUENCY: Ch 09		HOURS: Marina: Season: 0800-1200 1400-2030 LT Out of season: 0900-1200 1430-1800 LT

LA FIGUEIRETTE (MIRAMAR)	Port: CALL: Miramar 250 Berths 20 Visitor Berths	43°29′N 6°56′E
☎ +33(0)4 93750800	Depth: 1·5 - 2 m, Maximum LOA: 17 m	Fax +33(0)4 93750802
FREQUENCY: Ch 09		HOURS: Season: 0800-1200 1400-1900 LT Out of season: 0830-1200 1430-1800 LT

LA GRANDE-MOTTE	Marina 1374 Berths 130 Visitor Berths	43°33′·1N 4°04′·9E
☎ Hr Mr: +33(0)4 67565006 (H24) portlgm@free.fr	Depth: 2·7 m, Maximum LOA: 30 m	Fax Hr Mr: +33(0)4 67297463 (Indicate: for Capitainerie de la Grande-Motte)
FREQUENCY: Ch 09 16		HOURS: H24

LA GRANDE-MOTTE VIEW TO THE NNE

LA NAPOULE	Marina 980 Berths 80 Visitor Beths (Public Port) 780 Berths in Private Port	43°31′·3N 6°56′·7E
☎ Hr Mr: +33(0)4 93392839 Yacht Club: +33(0)4 92977777 portlanapoule@aws.fr	Depth: 1·5 - 7 m, Maximum LOA: 35 m	Fax Yacht Club: +33(0)4 92977878 www.port/la/napoule.com
FREQUENCY: Ch 09		HOURS: Summer 0800-2200 LT Winter 0800-2000 LT

LA RAGUE	Marina 520 Berths 128 Visitor Berths (Public Port)	43°31′·8N 6°56′·4E
☎ Hr Mr: +33(0)4 93498155	Depth: 2 - 4·5 m, Maximum LOA: 30 m	Fax Hr Mr: +33(0)4 93498399
FREQUENCY: Ch 09		HOURS: H24

LA SEYNE-SUR-MER	Port & Marina 300 Berths 7 Visitor Berths	43°06′N 5°53′E
☎ Port Office: +33(0)4 94879534		Fax Port Office: +33(0)4 94060428
FREQUENCY: Ch 09		HOURS: 0800-1200 1400-1800 LT Winter: closed Sat & Sun, Summer: closed Sun
SAINT-MANDRIER	**Marina** 605 Berths 100 Visitor Berths	43°05′N 5°56′E
☎ +33(0)4 94639739		Fax +33(0)4 94228081 (Indicate: for Bureau du Port Saint-Mandrier)
FREQUENCY: Ch 09		HOURS: Season: 0730-2000 LT Out of season: 0800-1200 1400-1800 LT Sat: 0800-1200 LT Sun: Closed

LA SEYNE-SUR-MER

L'AYGUARDE	Marina 480 Berths 130 Visitor Berths	43°06'N 6°10'E
Hr Mr: +33(0)4 94663398		
FREQUENCY: Ch 09		HOURS: Season: 0800-1200 1400-1730 LT Out of season: Mon-Fri: 0800-1200 1400-1730 LT Sat, Sun & holidays: 0800-1200 LT

S. MANDRIER TO THE SSE

LE GRAU-DU-ROI	Port and Marina 120 Berths 31 Visitor Berths	43°32'·1N 4°07'·3E
Port Office: +33(0)4 66535455	Depth: 2·5 - 4 m, Maximum LOA: 9 m	
FREQUENCY: Ch 73		HOURS: Summer 0830-1200 & 1330-1730 LT Bridge opens Mon to Fri: 0800,1315 & 1500 LT Sat: 0800,1100,1300 & 1700 LT Sun: 0800 & 2000 LT

LE LAVANDOU TO THE N

LE LAVANDOU	Marina — 1050 Berths 100 Visitor Berths	43°08′·2N 6°22′·5E
☎ Hr Mr: +33(0)4 94004110 capitainerie.lavandou@wandoo.fr	Depth: 2 - 7 m, Maximum LOA: 30 m	Fax Hr Mr: +33(0)4 94152451 www.lelavandou.com
FREQUENCY: Ch 09		HOURS: Season: 0730-2030 LT Out of season: 0800-1200 1330-1900 LT

PORT DU FRIOUL TO THE NW

MARSEILLE	Vessel Traffic Service	43°19′N 5°22′E
☎ Marseille Port Control (Hr Mr): +33(0)4 91394141 Berthing Office: +33(0)4 91394841		Fax Berthing Office: +33(0)4 91394041
FREQUENCY: Ch **12** 14 16		
	Marinas	
CLUB SOCIÉTÉ NAUTIQUE DE MOUREPIANE	650 Berths 50 Visitor Berths	
☎ Hr Mr: +33(0)4 91460140	Maximum LOA: 14 m	Fax
FREQUENCY: Ch 09		HOURS: HX
LA POINTE ROUGE	1800 Berths 10 Visitor Berths	43°14′·8N 5°21′·9E
☎ Hr Mr: +33(0)4 91731321	Depth: 2·5 - 7 m, Maximum LOA: 20 m	Fax Hr Mr: +33(0)4 91733309
FREQUENCY: Ch 09		HOURS: H24
LE VIEUX-PORT (THE OLD PORT)	3200 Berths 35 Visitor Berths	43°17′·8N 5°22′·0E
☎ Hr Mr: +33(0)4 91332544	Depth: 5 - 7 m, Maximum LOA: 100 m	Fax Hr Mr: +33(0)4 91556664
FREQUENCY: Ch 09		HOURS: H24

MARSEILLE MARINAS (Continued)	Marinas	
PORT DU FRIOUL	1500 Berths 150 Visitor Berths	43°16′·8N 5°18′·5E
Tel: Hr Mr: +33(0)4 91590182	Depth: 2-10m	Fax: Hr Mr: +33(0)4 91590479 www.chez.com/marseillefrioul/
FREQUENCY: Ch 09 16		HOURS: Season: 0700-2000 LT Out of season: 0700-1800 LT
PORTS DU L'ESTAQUE	Total in basin: 1500 Berths	43°21′·4N 05°18′·8E
Tel: +33(0)4 91460140	Depth: 2 - 3 m, Maximum LOA: 20 m	Fax:
FREQUENCY: Ch 09		HOURS: HX

MARSEILLAN-PLAGE	Marina 165 Berths Limited Number of Visitors Berths	43°19′N 3°33′E
Tel: Hr Mr: +33(0)4 67219930	Depth: 1·5 - 2·5 m (prone to silting), Maximum LOA: 8·5 m	Fax:
FREQUENCY: Ch 09	LOCATION: 2 n miles NE of Port Ambre.	HOURS: Summer: H24 Winter Closed.

MARSEILLAN VILLE	Marina 200 Berths 20 Visitor Berths	43°19′N 3°33′E
Tel: Hr Mr: +33(0)4 67773493	Depth: 1·5 - 2·5 m (prone to silting), Maximum LOA: 15 m	Fax: Hr Mr: +33(0)4 67776026
FREQUENCY: Ch 09		HOURS: Summer: H24 Out of season: 0830-1200 1400-1700 LT Closed Sat. afternoon and Sunday.

MARTIGUES	Port & Marina 540 Berths Bassin de Ferriers: 350 Berths 20 Visitor Berths Port de Jonquiers: 368 Berths 10 Visitor Berths Club Nautique: 220 Berths 50 Visitor Berths	43°24′·3N 5°03′·1E
Tel: Port Office: +33(0)4 42070000 Club de Nautique: +33(0)4 42811746 Semovim: +33(0)4 42421435	Depth: 1-3m, Bassin de Ferriers: Maximum LOA: 12 m Club Nautique: Maximum LOA: 12m	Fax: Port: +33(0)4 42070636 Club de Nautique: +33(0)4 42073344 Semovim: +33(0)4 42070636
FREQUENCY: Port: Ch 12 16 Club de Nautique de Martigues: Ch 09		HOURS: Club de Nautique: Season: 0800-1200 1400-1800 LT

MIRAMAR. LA LONDE-LES-MAURES AND BASSIN MARAVENNE

MENTON	Marina 550 Berths 100 Visitor Berths	43°46′·5N 7°30′·7E
☎ Hr Mr: +33(0)4 93358056	Depth: 1·5 - 5 m, Maximum LOA: 28 m	Fax Hr Mr: +33(0)4 93352840
FREQUENCY: Ch 09	LOCATION: Vieux-Port	HOURS: Season: 0800-1200 1500-1900 LT Out of season: 0800-1200 1400-1730 LT
	Marina 800 Berths 144 Visitor Berths	43°47′N 07°31′·4E
☎ Hr Mr: +33(0)4 93287800	Depth: 2 - 5 m, Maximum LOA: 40 m	Fax Hr Mr: +33(0)4 93354801
FREQUENCY: Ch 09	LOCATION: Garavan	HOURS: H24

MIRAMAR	Marina 1140 Berths 200 Visitor Berths	43°07′·9N 6°14′·8E
☎ Hr Mr: +33(0)4 94015345	Depth: 1 - 1·7 m, Maximum LOA: 17 m	Fax Hr Mr: +33(0)4 94015347 www.ot-lalondelesmaures.fr
FREQUENCY: Ch 09		HOURS: Season: 0800-1800 LT Out of season: 0800-1200 1400-1730 LT (except Sundays)

NARBONNE-PLAGE	Marina 591 Berths Limited Visitor Berths	43°10′N 3°11′E
☎ Hr Mr: +33(0)4 68499143	Depth: 1·2 - 1·5 m in Basin Brossolette, 2 - 3 m in Outer Basin, Maximum LOA: 12 m	Fax Hr Mr: +33(0)4 68495907 (Indicate: for Capitainerie)
FREQUENCY: Ch 09 16		HOURS: Season: (15 June-15 Sept) H24 Out of season: 0900-1200 1400-1800 LT
NARBONNE - PORT LA NAUTIQUE	**Marina** 20 Visitor Berths	43°08′N 3°00′E
☎ Hr Mr: +33(0)4 68322606	Depth: 1·2 - 1·5 m in Basin Brossolette, 2 - 3 m in Outer Basin, Maximum LOA: 7·6 m	Fax
	LOCATION: situated on the Étang de Bages South of Narbonne, access by sea via Port-la-Nouvelle	

NICE	Port and Marina 503 Berths 153 Visitor Berths	43°41′·4N 7°17′·3E
☎ Hr Mr: +33(0)4 93895085 Yacht Harbour Office: +33(0)4 92004214	Depth: 3 - 7 m, Maximum LOA: 140 m	Fax Pilots: +33(0)4 93896387 Hr Mr: +33(0)4 93558943 Yacht Harbour Office: +33(0)4 92004290
FREQUENCY: Hr Mr: Ch 16; 12 Marina: Ch 09		HOURS: Summer: 0600-2000 LT Winter: 0800-1800 LT

PALAVAS-LES-FLOTS	Marina 1033 Berths 50 Visitor Berths	43°32′·5N 3°56′·2E
☎ Hr Mr: +33(0)4 67077350	Depth: 3 - 4 m, Maximum LOA: 20 m	Fax Hr Mr: +33(0)4 67506104
FREQUENCY: Ch **09** 16		HOURS: H24

PORQUEROLLES	Marina 500 Berths 200 Visitor Berths	43°00′·3N 6°12′E
☎ Hr Mr: +33(0)4 94583072	Depth: 1·5 - 3 m, Maximum LOA: 30 m	Fax Hr Mr: +33(0)4 94583548
FREQUENCY: Ch 09		HOURS: Season: 0800-2000 LT (1 April-30 June: 0800-1930 LT) Out of season: 0800-1200 1400-1600 LT

PORT AMBONNE	Marina 268 Berths 27 Visitor Berths	43°17′·5N 3°31′·8E
☎ Hr Mr: +33(0)4 67260023 Port Office: +33(0)4 67944183	Depth: 1 m, Maximum LOA: 20 m	Fax
		HOURS: Season: 0800-1200 1400 - 1900 LT Out of season: 0800-1200 1400-1800 LT

PORT-CAMARGUE	Marina 4347 Berths 2105 Berths in Public Harbour 2242 Berths in Marina 10% of Berths Allocated for Visitors	43°31′·3N 4°07′·3E
☎ Hr Mr: +33(0)4 66511010 capitainerie@portcamargue.com	Depth: 2·7 m	Fax Hr Mr: +33(0)4 66511011 (Indicate: for Capitainerie) www.portcamargue.tm.fr
FREQUENCY: Ch **09** 16		HOURS: H24

PORT-CAMARGE

PORT DE BOUC	Marina 448 Berths 70 Visitor Berths	43°23'·7N 4°59'·1E
Hr Mr: +33(0)4 42063850	Depth: 2 - 3 m, Maximum LOA: 16 m	Fax: +33(0)4 42064211
FREQUENCY: Ch 09		HOURS: Season: 0800-1900 LT Out of season: 0800-1200 1400-1800 LT

PORT DE CARRO	Marina 250 Berths 20 Visitor Berths	43°19'·8N 5°02'·6E
Hr Mr: +33(0)4 42807628	Depth: 1 - 2·5 m, Maximum LOA: 11 m	Fax:
		HOURS: HX

PORT DE S. AYGULF	Marina 239 Berths 2 Visitor Berths	43°23'·6N 6°43'·9E
Hr Mr: +33(0)4 94811565 & 94527452	Depth: 2 - 4 m, Maximum LOA: 15 m	Fax: +33(0)4 94527456
FREQUENCY: Hr Mr: Ch 09		HOURS: Season H24 Out of season: 0800-1200 1400-1900 LT

PORT DE S. MANDRIER	Marina 600 Berths 20 Visitor Berths	43°05'N 5°55'E
Hr Mr: +33(0)4 94639739	Depth: 1 - 3 m, Maximum LOA: 17 m	Fax: +33(0)4 94635974
FREQUENCY: Hr Mr: Ch 09		HOURS: Season 0730-2000 LT Out of season: 0800-1200 1400-1800 LT

PORT-GALLICE (JUAN-LES-PINS)	Marina 530 Berths Visitor Berths Available	43°33'·8N 7°06'·8E
Hr Mr: +33(0)4 92937440	Depth: 2 - 3 m, Maximum LOA: 20 m	Fax: Hr Mr: +33(0)4 92937444
FREQUENCY: Ch 09		HOURS: Season: H24 Out of season: 0800-1200 1400-1800 LT

PORT-GARDIAN (SAINTES-MARIES-DE-LA-MER)	Marina 350 Berths 50 Visitor Berths	43°26'·8N 4°25'·5E
Hr Mr: +33(0)4 90978587	Depth: 3 m approximately, Maximum LOA: 14m	Fax: Hr Mr: +33(0)4 90979782
FREQUENCY: Ch 09		HOURS: Summer: H24 Winter 0800-1200 & 1400-1800 LT

PORT-GRIMAUD	**Marina** 851 Berths 300 Visitor Berths	43°16′·3N 6°35′·3E
☎ A.S.P. Port Grimaud Hr Mr: +33(0)4 94562988 capitainerie@port-grimaud.fr	Depth: 3·5 m, Maximum LOA: 55 m	Fax: Hr Mr: +33(0)4 94565031 (Indicate: for Capitainerie)
FREQUENCY: Ch 09		HOURS: Season: 0800-2100 LT Out of season: 0800-1200 1400-1800 LT
PORT-GRIMAUD (Grimaud Sud)	**Marina** 784 Berths 70 Visitor Berths	
☎ Hr Mr: +33(0)4 94567365 & 686374756 aslpg2@wanadoo.fr	Depth: 3 m, Maximum LOA: 20 m	Fax: Hr Mr: +33(0)4 94567363
FREQUENCY: Ch 09		HOURS: Season: 0800-1930 LT Out of season: 0800-1200 1330-1800 LT
PORT-GRIMAUD (Grimaud SNGPIII)	**Marina** 500 Berths 60 Visitor Berths	
☎ Hr Mr: +33(0)4 94560245 marinapg@infonie.fr	Depth: 3 m, Maximum LOA: 20 m	Fax: Hr Mr: +33(0)4 94565672
FREQUENCY: Ch 09		HOURS: Season: 0800-2100 LT Out of season: 0800-1200 1400-1900 LT

PORT LA GALERE	**Port:** CALL: Miramar 185 Berths 18 Visitor Berths	43°29′N 6°56′E
☎ Hr Mr: +33(0)4 93754174	Depth: 1·5 - 2 m, Maximum LOA: 12 m	Fax: Hr Mr: +33(0)4 93750874
FREQUENCY: Ch 09		HOURS: Season: July-August H24 Out of season: 0830-1230 1400-1800 LT

PORT-LA-NOUVELLE	**Port** 130 Berths Visitor Berths Sometimes Available	43°00′·8N 3°04′·2E
☎ Hr Mr: +33(0)4 68481764	Depth: 2 - 4 m, Maximum LOA: 9 m	Fax: Hr Mr: +33(0)4 68403142
FREQUENCY: Hr Mr: Ch 12 16		HOURS: HX

PORT LEUCATE	**Marina** 1100 Berths 100 Visitor Berths	42°52′·4N 3°03′·3E
☎ Hr Mr: +33(0)4 68409124	Depth: 2 - 3 m, Maximum LOA: 20 m	Fax: Hr Mr: +33(0)4 68407227
FREQUENCY: Ch 09 (summer 0800-2200 LT winter 0800-2000 LT)		HOURS: Season: 0800-0400 LT Out of season: 0800-1200 1400-0400 LT

PORT NAPOLEON	**Marina** 290 Berths 20 Visitor Berths	43°22′·64N 4°49′·88E
☎ Hr Mr: +33(0)4 42484121 sales@port-napoleon.com	Depth: 4m	Fax: Hr Mr: +33(0)4 42860663 www.port-napoleon.com
FREQUENCY: Ch 74		

PORT SAINT LOUIS DU RHONE	**Port:** 314 Berths 25 Visitor Berths	43°23′N 4°49′E
☎ Hr Mr (Port-de-Bouc): +33(0)4 42406005 Port de Plaisance: +33(0)4 42863911	Maximum LOA: 12 m	Fax: Hr Mr (Port-de-Bouc): +33(0)4 42406040 Port de Plaisance: +33(0)4 42863921
FREQUENCY: Ch 16		HOURS: H24

PORT-VAUBAN (ANTIBES)	**Marina** 1800 Berths 250 Vistor Berths	43°35′·4N 7°08′·0E
☎ Hr Mr: +33(0)4 92916000	Depth: 2 - 7 m, Maximum LOA: 50 m	Fax: Hr Mr: +33(0)4 93347404
FREQUENCY: Ch 09		HOURS: H24

PORT-VENDRES	**Port**	42°31′·4N 3°07′·1E
☎ Hr Mr: +33(0)4 68321200 Port Services: +33(0)4 68820025		Fax: Hr Mr: +33(0)4 68824840 Port Services: +33(0)4 68825418
FREQUENCY: Ch 12 16		HOURS: 0800-1700 LT
	Marina 253 Berths 30 Visitor Berths	
☎ Port Office: +33(0)4 68820884	Depth: 6 - 8 m, Maximum LOA: 40 m	Fax: +33(0)4 68825418
FREQUENCY: Ch 09		HOURS: Season: 0700-2100 LT Out of season: 0800-1200 1400-1800 LT

PORT LEUCATE

RIVIÈRE AUDE	Marinas Chichoulet: 95 Berths 4 Visitor Berths Cabanes Fleury: 240 Berths	43°12′·7N 3°14′·6E
☎ Chichoulet: +33(0)4 67282849 Cabanes Fleury: +33(0)4 68339332	Chichoulet: Depth: 1·8 m, Maximum LOA: 13 m Cabanes Fleury: Depth: 1·8 m, Maximum LOA: 12 m	Fax Chichoulet:+33(0)4 67266620
FREQUENCY: Ch 09		HOURS: Season: 0700-1700 LT Out of season: 0800-1200 1400-1700 LT

SAINT-CYPRIEN	Marina 2200 Berths 440 Visitor Berths	42°37′·2N 3°02′·4E
☎ Hr Mr: +33(0)4 68210798 & 68212428 contact@port-saint-cyprien.com	Depth: 3 - 4 m, Maximum LOA: 20 m	Fax Hr Mr: +33(0)4 68219011 & 68370318 www.port-saint-cyprien.com
FREQUENCY: Ch 09 Summer: 0700-2100 LT Winter 0800-1200 1400-1800 LT		HOURS: Season: 0700-2100 LT Out of season: 0800-1200 1330-1800 LT

SAINT-CYR-SUR-MER	Marina 420 Berths 30 Visitor Berths	43°10′·0N 5°41′·7E
☎ Hr Mr: +33(0)4 94263981		Fax
FREQUENCY: Ch 09	LOCATION: La Madrague	HOURS: 0830-1200 1400-1730 LT
LES LECQUES (ST-CYR-LECOUES)	**Marina** 431 Berths 30 Visitor Berths	
☎ Hr Mr: +33(0)4 94262198 nport-lesquecques@wanadoo.fr	Depth: 2 - 4 m, Maximum LOA: 15 m	Fax Hr Mr: +33(0)4 94 887192
FREQUENCY: Ch 09 16 0900-1700 LT	LOCATION: Les Lecques/Nouveau Port (43°10′·8N 5°41′·0E)	HOURS: H24

SAINT- CYPRIEN

SAINT-CYR-SUR-MER (Continued)	Marina 420 Berths 30 Visitor Berths	43°10′·0N 5°41′·7E
VIEUX PORT ST CYR SUR MER	Marina 192 Berths	
Hr Mr: +33(0)4 94264449	Depth: 8m	

SAINTE- MARIE LA MER	Marina 510 Berths	42°43′·6N 3°02′·5E
Hr Mr: +33(0)4 68805102	Depth: 2 - 2·5 m (1·5 m in entrance channel), Maximum LOA: 12 m	

SAINTE-MAXIME	Marina 389 Berths 30 Visitor Berths	43°18′·3N 6°38′·3E
Hr Mr: +33(0)4 94967425	Depth: 2 - 5 m, Maximum LOA: 15 m	Hr Mr: +33(0)4 94438203
FREQUENCY: Ch 09		HOURS: Season: 0800-2000 LT Out of season: 0830-1230 1400-1800 LT
	Marina 375 Berths	
Hr Mr: +33(0)4 94960512 & 94960627	Depth: 5 m, Maximum LOA: 26 m	Hr Mr: +33(0)4 94438856
FREQUENCY: Ch 09		HOURS: Season: 0800-2000 LT Out of season: 0830-1200 1400-1800 LT

SAINT-GERVAIS	Marina 840 Berths 35 Visitor Berths	43°25′·6N 4°56′·4E
Hr Mr: +33(0)4 42477057 (H24)	Depth: 2·5 - 3·5 m, Maximum LOA: 13 m	Hr Mr: +33(0)4 42055215 (Indicate: for Capitainerie)
FREQUENCY: Ch 09		HOURS: H24

SAINT-JEAN- CAP-FERRAT	Marina 560 Berths Limited Visitor Berth Availability	43°41′·5N 7°20′·2E
Hr Mr: +33(0)4 93764545	Depth: 1·5 - 4 m, Maximum LOA: 30 m	Hr Mr: +33(0)4 93764546
FREQUENCY: Ch 09		HOURS: 0600-2200 LT

SAINT-LAURENT-DU-VAR	Marina 1096 Berths Visitor Berths Available	43°39′·3N 7°11′·8E
Hr Mr: +33(0)4 93071270	Depth: 2 - 4 m, Maximum LOA: 23 m	Hr Mr: +33(0)4 93073555
FREQUENCY: Ch 09		HOURS: H24

SAINT-PIERRE-DES-EMBIEZ	Marina 700 Berths 20 Visitor Berths	43°04′·9N 5°47′·1E
Hr Mr: +33(0)4 94340751	Depth: 1 - 3·5 m, Maximum LOA: 35 m	Hr Mr: +33(0)4 94749296
FREQUENCY: Ch 09		HOURS: H24

SAINT-RAPHAËL	Port: CALL: Vieux-Port Saint-Raphaël 250 Berths 15 Visitor Berths	43°25′·4N 6°46′·9E
Hr Mr: +33(0)4 94951119	Depth: 1 - 5 m, Maximum LOA: 60 m	Hr Mr: +33(0)4 94822534 (Indicate: for Capitainerie du Vieux-Port)
FREQUENCY: Ch 12		HOURS: Mon-Fri: 0800-1200 1400-1800 LT (1400-1700 LT in Winter)
PORT DE PLAISANCE DE SANTA LUCIA	**Marina** 1542 Berths 359 Visitor Berths	43°25′N 6°46′·5E
Hr Mr: +33(0)4 94953430	Depth: 2 - 10 m	Hr Mr: +33(0)4 94958046
FREQUENCY: Ch 09		HOURS: H24

SAINT-RAPHAËL. PORT DE SANTA LUCIA. BASSIN SUD TO THE NW

SAINT-TROPEZ	Marina 800 Berths 100 Visitor Berths	43°16′·3N 6°38′E
Hr Mr: +33(0)4 94566870	Depth: 2 - 6 m, Maximum LOA: 50 - 65 m	Hr Mr: +33(0)4 94973102
FREQUENCY: Ch 09 16		HOURS: H24

SANARY SUR MER	Marina 1500 Berths 80 Visitor Berths	43°06′·9N 5°48′·1E
Hr Mr: +33(0)4 94329700 & 94742095	Depth: 1 - 4 m, Maximum LOA: 20 m	Hr Mr: +33(0)4 94881204
FREQUENCY: Ch 09		HOURS: Season: 0800-1200 1400-1900 LT Out of season: Mon-Thurs: 0800-1200 1400-1800 LT Fri: 0800-1200 1400-1700 LT

SAN PEÏRE (LES ISSAMBRES)	Marina 443 Berths 110 Visitor Berths	43°20′·4N 6°41′·2E
Hr Mr: +33(0)4 94494029 & 94494032 gepsodeports@aol.com	Depth: 2 - 3 m, Maximum LOA: 15 m	Hr Mr: +33(0)4 94969058
FREQUENCY: Ch 09		HOURS: H24

SAUSSET-LES-PINS	**Marina** 494 Berths 16 Visitor Berths	43°19′·7N 5°06′·5E
Hr Mr: +33(0)4 42445501	Depth: 1 - 4 m, Maximum LOA: 12 m	Hr Mr: +33(0)4 42452707 (Indicate: for Capitainerie)
FREQUENCY: Ch 09 16		HOURS: Season: 0800-1200 1400-1900 LT Out of season: 0800-1200 1400-1730 LT (except Sun & holidays)

SAUSSET-LES-PINS FROM SE

SÈTE	**Port:** CALL: Sémaphore Sète	43°23′·6N 3°42′·1E
Hr Mr: +33(0)4 67463497		Hr Mr: +33(0)4 67463500
FREQUENCY: Hr Mr: Ch 12 Sémaphore de Sète: Ch 16		HOURS: H24
	Marina 220 Berths 22 visitors berths	
Hr Mr: +33(0)4 67749897	Depth: 2 - 7 m, Maximum LOA: 30 m	Hr Mr: +33(0)4 67741557
FREQUENCY: Port de Plaisance: Ch 09		HOURS: Season: 0700-2100 LT Out of season: Mon-Fri: 0800-1800 LT

TOULON	**Port:** CALL: Le Sémaphore de Cépet	43°07′N 5°55′E
Hr Mr: +33(0)4 94032760		Hr Mr: +33(0)4 94033869
FREQUENCY: Hr Mr: Ch 06 12 16		HOURS: Hr Mr: HJ
DARSE VIELLE AND DARSE DU MOURILLON	**Marina** 650 Berths 60 Visitor Berths	
Hr Mr: +33(0)4 94422765	Depth: 6 - 8 m, Maximum LOA: 40 m	Hr Mr: +33(0)4 94422768 www.var.cci.fr
FREQUENCY: Ch 09	LOCATION: Darse Vielle (43°07′·2N 5°55′·9E)	HOURS: Season: 0800-1900 LT Out of season: 0800-1200 1400-1800 LT
PORT DE PLAISANCE DARSE NORD DU ROUSILLION	**Marina** 352 Berths 30 Visitor Berths	
+33(0)4 94412339	Depth: 2 - 8 m	+33(0)4 94412339
FREQUENCY: Ch 09		HOURS: HX

VALRAS-PLAGE	**Marina** 283 Berths Visitor Berths Limited	43°14′·7N 3°18′·1E
Hr Mr: +33(0)4 67323364	Depth: 1·5 - 3 m, Maximum LOA: 13 m	Hr Mr: +33(0)4 67323364
FREQUENCY: Ch 09 16	LOCATION: Harbour lies inside the mouth of the Riviére de L'Orb	HOURS: H24

VILLEFRANCHE-SUR-MER	**Marina** 420 Berths 226 Visitor Berths	43°42′N 7°19′·7E
Hr Mr: +33(0)4 93017070 port-villefranche@cote-azure.cci.fr	Depth: 1·5 - 6 m, Maximum LOA: 30 m	Hr Mr: +33(0)4 93769233
FREQUENCY: Ch 09		HOURS: Season: 0700-2000 LT Out of season: 0730-1200 1400-1800 LT

FRANCE
MEDITERRANEAN COAST, MONACO AND CORSE MARINAS

MARSEILLE
VESSEL TRAFFIC SERVICES

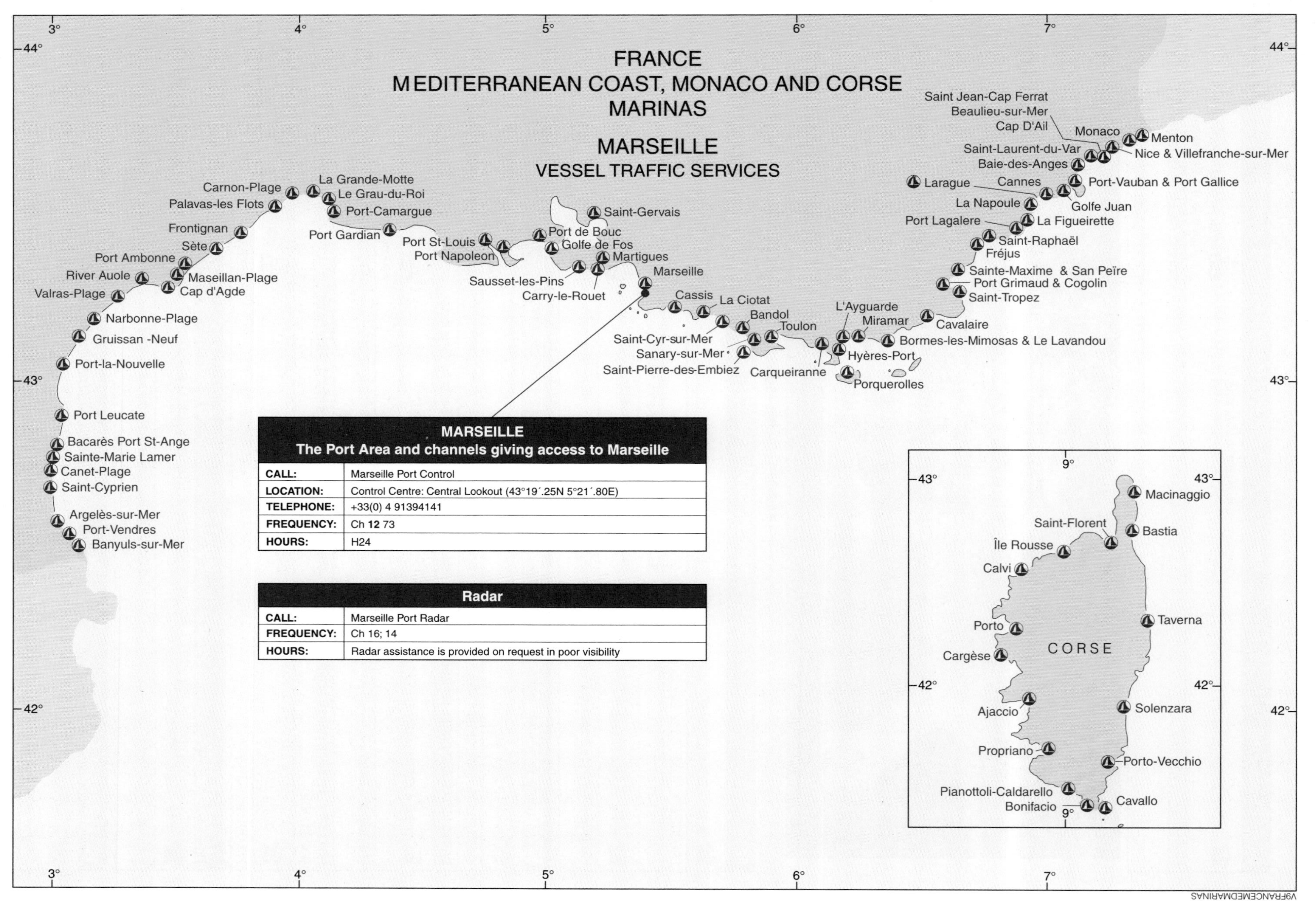

MARSEILLE The Port Area and channels giving access to Marseille	
CALL:	Marseille Port Control
LOCATION:	Control Centre: Central Lookout (43°19´.25N 5°21´.80E)
TELEPHONE:	+33(0) 4 91394141
FREQUENCY:	Ch **12** 73
HOURS:	H24

Radar	
CALL:	Marseille Port Radar
FREQUENCY:	Ch 16; 14
HOURS:	Radar assistance is provided on request in poor visibility

V9FRANCEMEDMARINAS

GREECE

GENERAL NOTES - Basic entry and exit requirements: All tourist pleasure craft under foreign flag arriving at or departing from Greece must do so at one of the fifty two (52) PORTS OF ENTRY. In these ports, apart from the relevant Port Authorities, there are services of Customs, Health Authorities, Passport and currency control.

PORTS OF ENTRY

1. Githio, Lakonia 2. Siros, Kyklades 3. Igoumenitsa, Thesprotia 4. Stilida, Fthiotida 5. Ag. Nikolaos, Lasithi, Kriti 6. Rethymno, Kriti 7. Lefkada 8. Samos 9. Volos, Magnissia 10. Kos 11. Dafni, Agios Oros 12. Ivira, Agios Oros 13. Gerakini, Halkidiki 14. Glifada, Attiki 15. Preveza, Ipiros 16. Patra, Achaia 17. Corfu (Kerkyra) 18. Sitia, Kriti 19. Chios 20. Argostoli, Kefallonia 21. Thessaloniki 22. Korinthos, 23. Kalamata 24. Kavala 25. Ithaki 26. Pilos, Messinia 27. Pithagorio, Samos 28. Lavrio Attiki 29. Iraklio, Kriti 30. Sami, Kefallinia 31. Peiraiás 32. Milos 33. Katakolo, Ilia 34. Souda, Hania, Kriti 35. Itea, Fokida 36 Elefsina, Attiki 37. Mykonos 38. Nafplio, Argolida 39. Halkida, Evia 40. Ródos 41. Zakinthos 42. Thira (Santorini) 43. Kali Limenes, Iraklio 44. Myrina, Limnos 45. Paxi 46. Skiathos 47. Alexandroupoli, Evros 48. Eghio, Achaia 49. Patmos 50. Simi 51. Mytilini, Lesvos 52. Hania, Kriti

National SAR Agency: Safety of Navigation Division, Ministry of Mercantile Marine, Hellenic Coast Guard **Tel:** 21 0419 1183 **Fax:** 21 0412 8150 **E-mail** dan@yen.gr
JRCC Peiraiás is responsible for co-ordinating Search and Rescue operations.
The area for Search and Rescue responsibility is divided into five sub areas: RSC Thessaloniki (N Aegean Sea), RSC Mitilini (central Aegean Sea), RSC Ródos (SE Aegean Sea), RSC Khania (SW Aegean Sea) and RSC Patrai (Ionian Sea). Additionally, all Greek Port Authorities operate as maritime Search and Rescue units and are served by Coast Guard personnel.
A network of Coast Radio Stations maintains a continuous listening watch on international distress frequencies. Contact may also be established with JRCC Peiraiás through Inmarsat and COSPAS-SARSAT.

	Telephone +30	**Fax** +30	**Others**
JRCC PEIRAIÁS	21 0411 2500 21 0422 0772 21 0419 1369	21 0411 5798 21 0419 1561 21 0422 0466	**Telex** +601 211588 RCC GR **Inmarsat A** (IOR) 1133207 RCCG (Tlx) (AOR-E) 1133207 RCCG (Tlx) **Inmarsat C** (IOR) 423767310 RCCG (Tlx) (AOR-E) 423767310 RCCG (Tlx)
RSC KHANIÁ (Chania) (SW Aegean Sea)	2821 098888 2821 028388	2821 028387	**Telex** +601 291101 LIHA GR
RSC MYTILÍNI (Central Aegean Sea)	2251 040827 2251 020320	2251 047888	**Telex** +601 297142 LXM GR
RSC PÁTRAI (Patra) (Ionian Sea)	2610 341002 2610 316400	261 0327136	**Telex** +601 312184 LIPA GR
RSC RÓDOS (SW Aegean Sea)	2241 022220 2241 027365	2241 029294	**Telex** +601 292232 LORD GR
RSC THESSALONIKI (North Aegean Sea)	2310 531504 2310 513675	231 0531506	**Telex** +601 412256 KLTS GR

Vessel Traffic Services (VTS):
Details of VTS control centres and their broadcast frequencies have been included for information only - VTS compliance is **not** mandatory for leisure craft. Certain Ports with VTS areas request **all** vessels to monitor a certain VHF broadcast channel for navigational information and hazard warnings.

NAVTEX [H] [K] [L]

H	Irákleio (Iráklion)	518 kHz	35°20′N 25°07′E
K	Kérkira		39°37′N 19°55′E
L	Límnos		39°52′N 25°04′E

Weather Bulletins

H: 0510 0910 1710 2110	Gale warnings, synopsis, 24 hour forecast and outlook for a further 12 hours for Areas Saronikós, SE Aegean, SW Aegean, SW Kritiko and SE Kritiko
K: 0540 0940 1740 2140	Gale warnings, synopsis, 24 hour forecast and outlook for a further 12 hours for Areas South Adriatic Sea, North / South Ionian Sea, Patraïkós, Korinthiakós and Kithira Sea
L: 0550 0950 1750 2150	Gale warnings, synopsis, 24 hour forecast and outlook for a further 12 hours for Areas North / South Aegean Ikario, Samos Sea, Saronikós, South Evvoikos, Kafireas Strait, Central / North Aegean, Thrakiko and Thermaïkós

Navigational Warnings

H: 0110 0510 0910 1310 1710 2110	Local warnings for the Aegean Sea 34°N-41°N, 22°30′E-30°E
K: 0140 0540 0940 1340 1740 2140	Local warnings for the Ionian Sea east to 22°30′E including Patraïkós Kólpos and Korinthiakós Kólpos
L: 0150 0550 0950 1350 1750 2150	For the Aegean Sea 34°N-41°N, 22°30′E-30°E

OLYMPIA

A	2624	RT (MF)	Ródos	36°27′N 28°15′E
B	2730		Límnos	39°52′N 25°04′E
C	2799		Irákleio	35°20′N 25°07′E
D	2830		Kérkira	39°45′N 19°52′E
E	8424 *(816)* (SVU4)	RADIO-TELEX	Olympia	37°36′N 21°29′E
F VHF	Ch 16	Ándros		37°56′N 24°46′E
		Astipálaia		36°36′N 26°26′E
		Broychas		35°19′N 25°45′E
		Festos		34°59′N 25°12′E
		Kárpathos		35°28′N 27°10′E
	Ch 16 27	Kefallinía		38°08′N 20°39′E
	Ch 16 02	Kérkira		39°45′N 19°52′E
	Ch 16 85	Kíthira		36°16′N 23°03′E
	Ch 16 85	Khíos		38°22′N 26°03′E
	Ch 16 83	Knossós		35°17′N 24°56′E
	Ch 16	Lichada		38°52′N 22°53′E
	Ch 16 82	Límnos		39°54′N 25°04′E
	Ch 16	Mílos		36°40′N 24°23′E
	Ch 16 01	Mítilini		39°04′N 26°21′E
	Ch 16 04	Moystakos		35°18′N 23°36′E
	Ch 16 25	Párnis		38°10′N 23°43′E
	Ch 16	Pátmos		37°18′N 26°32′E
		Pátrai		38°14′N 21°46′E
		Pérama		37°58′N 23°34′E
	Ch 16 83	Petalídhion (Petalidi)		36°55′N 21°51′E
	Ch 16 60	Pilio		39°24′N 23°03′E
	Ch 16	Pírgos		37°45′N 21°26′E
		Póros		37°28′N 23°26′E
	Ch 16 63	Ródos		36°16′N 27°56′E
	Ch 16 23	Sfendami		40°25′N 22°31′E
	Ch 16 04	Síros		37°27′N 24°55′E
	Ch 16 85	Siteía		35°04′N 26°11′E
	Ch 16	Skíros		38°53′N 24°33′E
		Thásos		40°44′N 24°40′E
		Thíra		36°22′N 25°28′E
		Tsoukalas		40°22′N 23°28′E
		Yeránia		38°01′N 23°08′E

DIAGRAM: page 257

Weather Bulletins	
A - D, F: On receipt	**Storm Warnings:** Gale warnings, in Greek and English for Areas 18-53
A - D: 0633 0903 1533 2133 **E:** 0930 1230 **F:** 0600 1000 1600 2200 On request (Ch 16)	Gale warnings, synopsis, 24 hour forecast and outlook for a further 12 hours in Greek and English for Areas 18-53

Navigational Warnings	
A: 0703 1133 1733 2333	In Greek and English for the South Aegean Sea 34°N-38°N, 22°30′E-30°E
B: 0033 0703 1033 1633 **C:** 0703 1133 1733 2333	In Greek and English for the Aegean Sea 34°N-41°N, 22°30′E-30°E
D: 0033 0703 1033 1633	Local warnings in Greek and English for the Ionian Sea east to 22°30′E including Patraïkós Kólpos and Korinthiakós Kólpos
F: On receipt 0500 1100 1730 2330 On request	In Greek and English

ELLINIKI RADIOPHONIA

FM		AM
91·6 & 105·8 MHz	ERA 1 (Athínai)	729
104·0 MHz	Chaniá	1512
96·6 MHz	Florina	1278
102·1 MHz	Ioannina	765
97·5 & 103·6 MHz	Irákleio (Iráklion)	954
105·4 MHz	Kalamáta	
96·3 MHz	Kavála	1602
99·3 MHz	Kérkira	1008
98·1 & 98·4 MHz	Komotini	1404
100·2 & 100·6 MHz	Kozani	1602
98·3 MHz	Laríssa	945
102·1, 103·0 & 104·4 MHz	Mytilíni	
103·5 MHz	Orestiada	
92·5 MHz	Pátrai	1485
102·4 MHz	Pírgos	1350
92·7 & 93·1 MHz	Ródos	1494
101·5 MHz	Serres	1584
95·2 MHz	Tripoli	1314
100·7 & 101·2 MHz	Vólos	1485
95·2 MHz	Zákinthos	927

DIAGRAM: page 257

Weather Bulletins	
0430	Gale warnings, synopsis, 24 hour forecast and outlook for a further 12 hours, in Greek for 18-53 Areas
Navigational Warnings	
On receipt 1330	In English for Greek waters and Mediterranean Sea

NOTE: Broadcasts given 1 hour earlier when DST is in force

ADHAMAS, ÓRMOS MILOU, NÍSOS MÍLOS — Port — 36°43'N 24°27'E

Tel: Port: +30 287 022100 — Fax: Port: +30 287 022100

FREQUENCY: Hr Control: Ch 12 19 — HOURS: H24

AÍYINA (AEGINA), NÍSOS AÍYINA — Port — 37°45'N 22°26'E

Tel: Port: +30 2297 022328 & 025734 — Fax: Port: +30 2297 025145

FREQUENCY: Ch 12 19 — LOCATION: Port Radio: 37°44'·9N 23°25'·6E (approx) — HOURS: H24

AÍYION (EGIO), PELOPÓNNISOS — Port — 38°15'N 22°05'E

Tel: Port: +30 2691 028888 — Fax: Port: +30 2691 061540

FREQUENCY: Port: Ch 12 21 — LOCATION: Port Radio: 38°15'·2N 22°04'·7E — HOURS: H24

ALEXANDROÚPOLIS — Port — 40°50'·60N 25°52'·47E

Tel: Hr Mr: +30 2551 028734 — Fax: Port Auth: +30 2551 021430

FREQUENCY: Ch 12 19 — HOURS: H24

ÁSPRA SPÍTIA (ANDÍKIRA OR ANTIKYRA) — Port — 38°23'N 22°38'E

Tel: Port: +30 2267 041205 — Fax: Port: +30 2267 041205

FREQUENCY: Ch 12 — HOURS: HJ

AGIOS NIKÓLAOS MARINA

ÁYIOS NIKÓLAOS (AGIOS NIKÓLAOS), KRÍTI (CRETE)	**Port**	35°11′N 25°43′E
☎ Port Radio & Hr Office: +30 2841 022312 & 022612		Fax: Port Radio & Hr Office: +30 2841 082733
FREQUENCY: Port: Ch 07 12 19	LOCATION: Port Radio: 35°11′·55N 25°43′·15E	HOURS: H24

AGIOS NIKÓLAOS MARINA	**Marina** **255 Berths** 60 Berths up to 40 m Remainder 4 - 10 m 100 Visitor Berths	35°11′·25N 25°43′·11E
☎ +30 2841 082384 & 082385 reception@marinaofagiosnikolaos.gr	Depth: 3·5 - 5·5 m	Fax: +30 2841 082386
FREQUENCY: Ch 12		HOURS: HX

AGIOS NIKÓLAOS MARINA

DHIÓRIX KORÍNTHOU (CORINTH CANAL)	**Pilot Station:** CALL: Isthmia Pilot	37°56′N 22°59′E
☎ Canal Auth: +30 2741 037700	The canal is closed on Tuesdays (0600-1800 LT) for maintenance	Fax: Canal Auth: +30 2741 037177
FREQUENCY: Ch 11		

ELEVSÍS	Port	38°02′N 23°33′E
☎ +30 21 05543504		Fax: +30 21 05547980
FREQUENCY: Ch 12 19	LOCATION: Port Radio (Port Offices): 38°02′·2N 23°32′·6E	HOURS: H24

ERMOÚPOLIS (SÍROS OR SYROS), NÍSOS SÍROS	Port: CALL: Pilots: Síros Limenarchian Syros	37°27′N 24°57′E
☎ Hr Mr: +30 2281 082690 & 082633		Fax: Port: +30 2281 082633
FREQUENCY: Port: Ch 07 12		HOURS: H24

GAIOS	Marina	39°11′·36N 20°11′·80E
☎ +30 2662 32259		Fax: +30 26620 32259

GAIOS FROM S

GOUVIA (KÉKIRA) (CORFU)	Marina 960 Berths Visitor Berths Available	39°39′·1N 19°51′·1E
☎ +30 2661 091900, 091990 & 091376 ikghm@otenet.gr	Depth: 2 - 6 m, Maximum LOA: 80 m	Fax: +30 2221 091829 www.gouviamarina.gr
FREQUENCY: Ch 16 69		HOURS: H24

IGOUMENÍTSA	Port	39°32′N 20°13′E
☎ Hr Radio: +30 2665 022235 & 022240		Fax: +30 2665 026122
FREQUENCY: Traffic Control (Hr Mr): Ch 07 12 Hr Radio: Ch 12 18		HOURS: Traffic Control: HX Hr Radio: H24

IRÁKLEIO (HERAKLION), KRÍTI (CRETE)	Port Marina Under construction	35°21′N 25°08′E
☎ Hr Office: +30 281 0226110 & 0226024 Sailing Club: +30 281 0228118 lstio@aol.com	Sailing club welcomes visitors	Fax: Hr Office: +30 281 0226176 Sailing Club: +30 281 0242120
FREQUENCY: Ch 12 19		HOURS: H24

ISTHMÍA, PELOPÓNNISOS	Port	37°55′N 23°00′E
☎ Hr Mr & Port Radio: +30 2741 037555		Fax: +30 2741 037777
FREQUENCY: Hr Mr: Ch 19 Port Radio: Ch 12 21		HOURS: H24

ITÉA	Port	38°26′N 22°25′E
☎ Port: +30 2265 032319		Fax: +30 2265 032100
FREQUENCY: Ch 12		HOURS: H24

GOUVIA MARINA

KALAMÁTA (KALÁMI), PELOPÓNNISOS	**Marina** Call: Kalamata Marina 255 Berths Visitor Berths	37°01′·45N 22°06′·30E
☎ Hr Radio: +30 2721 022218 Marina: +30 2721 021054 & 021037 kalamatamarina@yahoo.com	Depth: 2 - 3·5 m, Maximum LOA: 30 m	Fax Hr Radio: +30 2721 096220 Marina: +30 2721 021054 & 021037 www.geocities.com/kalamatamarina/marina.htm
FREQUENCY: Hr Radio: Ch 12 18 Marina: Ch 69	LOCATION: Pilot & Hr Radio: 37°01′·65N 22°06′·69E	HOURS: H24

KALI LIMENES, KRÍTI (CRETE)	**Port:** CALL: Bunkering Station: Seka	34°56′N 24°48′E
☎ Hr Mr: +30 2892 022202 Port Radio & Port Auth: +30 2892 042188		Fax
FREQUENCY: Port: Ch 12		HOURS: HX

KATAKÓLON, PELOPÓNNISOS	**Port**	37°39′N 21°20′E
☎ Hr Office: +30 2621 034008 Hr Radio: +30 2621 041206		Fax Port: +30 2621 041109
FREQUENCY: Port: Ch 12 18	LOCATION: Hr Radio: 37°38′·75N 21°19′·20E (approx)	HOURS: Port: H24

KAVÁLA (CAVALA)	**Port**	40°56′N 24°24′E
☎ Hr Mr: +30 251 0224967		Fax
FREQUENCY: Hr Mr: Ch 12 19	LOCATION: Radio: 40°56′·15N 24°24′·67E	HOURS: H24

KÉRKIRA (KERKYRA) (CORFU)	**Port**	39°38′N 19°55′E
☎ Port: +30 2661 032655, 039513 & 030481		Fax +30 2661 039918
FREQUENCY: Port: Ch 12 18	LOCATION: Port Radio: 39°37′·67N 19°55′·33E	HOURS: H24

KHALKÍS (CHALKIS)	**Port and Swingbridge**	38°28′N 23°35′E
☎ +30 2221 028888 & 077333		Fax Port: +30 2221 088888
FREQUENCY: Ch 12		HOURS: H24

KHANIÁ, (HANIA), KRÍTI (CRETE)	Port	35°31′N 24°01′E
Hr Radio: +30 2821 098888		Hr Radio: +30 2821 028388
FREQUENCY: 2182 kHz (MF) Ch 12 19		HOURS: H24

KHÍOS (CHIOS), NÍSOS KHÍOS	Port and Marina 275 Berths	35°11′·25N 25°43′·11E
Hr Mr: +30 2271 044433 & 044434	Depth: 2 - 3 m, Maximum LOA: 30 m	Port: +30 2271 044432
FREQUENCY: Port: Ch 12 16 19 Marina: Ch 09		HOURS: Port: H24

KOS MARINA	Marina: CAll Kosmarina 250 Berths 100 Visitor Berths	35°53′·84N 27°17′·97E
Marina: +30 2242 057500 Hr Mr: +30 2242 028059 Port Radio: +30 2242 026594, 026595 & 026596		+30 2242 020877
info@kosmarina.gr	Depth: 5 m, Maximum LOA: 50 m	www.kosmarina.gr
FREQUENCY: Marina: Ch 77 Port: Ch 12	LOCATION: Port Radio: 36°53′·7N 27°17′·4E (approx)	HOURS: HX

KOS MARINA

LÁGOS, VISTÓNIKOS ÓRMOS	Port	40°57′·85N 25°07′·55E
Port Radio: +30 2541 096666		
FREQUENCY: Ch 12 19	LOCATION: Port Office: On the N Quay	HOURS: H24

LAKKÍ (PORT LAKKÍ MARINA)	Marina 50 Berths Some Visitor Berths	37°07′·7N 26°51′·0E
+30 2247 026010	Depth: 3 - 5 m, Maximum LOA: 24 m	+30 2247 026009
		HOURS: HX

LAVRÍON (LAURIUM)	Port and Marina 685 Visitor Berths Visitor Berths Available	37°43′N 24°03′E
Hr Mr: +30 2292 025249 Olympic Marina: +30 2292 027701	Depth 4 m	Port: +30 2292 022188 Marina: +30 2292 022569
olympicmarine@internet.gr		www.olympicmarine.com
FREQUENCY: Port: Ch 07 Marina: Ch 12		HOURS: H24

LEROS ISLAND (LAKKI MARINA)	Marina 40 Berths	37°07′·80N 26°50′·90E
+30 2247 025240 & 022120		+30 2247 023921
FREQUENCY: Ch 11		HOURS: HX

LEVKAS	Marina 350 Berths Some Visitor Berths	38°57′·4N 20°45′·3E
+30 2645 026645	Depth: 3·5 - 4 m, Maximum LOA: 60 m	+30 2645 026642
FREQUENCY: Ch 69		HOURS: HX

LEVKAS HARBOUR AND CANAL FROM SSW

LIMÍN ALIVÉRIOU	Port	38°23′N 24°03′E
☎ +30 2223 022318	Port Radio is operated by the Hellenic Coast Guard	Fax +30 2223 023633
FREQUENCY: Port: Ch 12		HOURS: Port H24

LIMÍN KALIMNOS MARINA	Marina 80 Berths Some Visitor Berths	36°56′·84N 26°59′·69E
☎ Kalymna Yachting: +30 2243 024083	Depth: 2 - 3 m, Maximum LOA: 20 m	Fax Kalymna Yacthing: +30 2243 029125
		HOURS: HX

MANDRAKI (RÓDOS)	Marina 115 Berths 15 Visitor Berths	36°27′N 28°24′E
☎ Hr Mr: +30 2241 027634 Marina: +30 2241 037927 & 027242	Depth: 3 m	Fax Marina: +30 2241 034778 & 034949
FREQUENCY: Ch 12		HOURS: HX

METHANA	Marina 70 Berths Visitor Berths Available	37°35′N 23°23′E
☎ Hr Mr: +30 2298 092279 Marina: +30 2298 092822 & 092324	Depth: 3 m	Fax Marina: +30 2298 092822 & 092324
		HOURS: HX

MITILÍNI, NÍSOS LÉSVOS	Port	39°06′N 26°33′E
☎ Hr Auth: +30 2251 040827, 047088 & 024115		Fax Hr Auth: +30 2251 047888
FREQUENCY: Ch 12 19	LOCATION: Hr Radio: 39°06′·35N 26°33′·30E	HOURS: H24

PÁTRAI, PELOPÓNNISOS	Pilots Port and Marina 450 Berths	38°15′·6N 21°44′·0E
☎ Hr Mr's Office & Port: +30 261 0341002 Marina: +30 261 0429130 Nautilus Yachting: +30 261 0622676		Fax Port: +30 261 0327136 Marina: +30 261 022569
FREQUENCY: Port: Ch 12 18 Marina: Ch 12	LOCATION: Hr Mr Office: Harbour Service Building	HOURS: H24

PEIRAIÁS (PIRAEUS)	Port	37°56′N 23°38′E
☎ Hr Radio: +30 21 04511311 & 04511319		Fax Hr Radio: +30 21 04511121 & 04516704
FREQUENCY: Hr Radio: Ch 19 Peiraiás Traffic (Signal Station): Ch 13		HOURS: H24

ALIMOS ((KALMÁKI))	Marina 1100 Berths 378 Visitor Berths	37°54′·8N 23°42′·1E
☎ +30 21 09821850 & 09828642	Depth: 2 - 5 m, Maximum LOA: m	Fax +30 21 09821850 & 09828642
FREQUENCY: Ch 71		HOURS: HX

FLISVOS (FALIRON)	Marina 195 Berths	37°56'·1N 23°40'·8E
☎ +30 21 09829218 & 09887422	Depth: 1·5 - 16 m	Fax: +30 21 09829218 & 09887422
FREQUENCY: Ch 09		HOURS: HX

GLYPHADA MARINA 4	Marina 780 Berths Visitor Berths Available	37°52'·3N 23°44'E
☎ Hr Mr: +30 21 88946327 Marina: +30 21 08947353 & 08947374	Depth: 2·5 m	Fax: Marina: +30 21 08947353 & 08947374
FREQUENCY: Ch 07 19		HOURS: HX

VOULIAGMENI	Marina 115 Beths Visitor Berths Available	37°48'N 23°46'E
☎ Hr Mr: +30 21 08963686 Marina: +30 21 08960012 & 08961148	Depth: 3 - 8 m	Fax: Marina: +30 21 08960012 & 08961148
FREQUENCY: Ch 09		HOURS: HX

ZEA	Marina 650 Berths Visitor Berths Available	37°56'·0N 23°39'·2E
☎ Hr Mr: +30 21 04138231 Marina: +30 21 04284100	Depth: 1·5 - 12 m, Maximum LOA: 45 m	Fax: Marina: +30 21 04287533
FREQUENCY: Ch 09		HOURS: Office: 0800 - 2100 LT daily

PÍLOS (PYLOS), PELOPÓNNISOS	Port and Marina 250 Berths Visitor Berths	36°55'·2N 21°42'·1E
☎ Port: +30 2723 022255	Depth: 2·5 - 3·5 m, Maximum LOA: 20 m	Fax: Port: +30 2723 022007
FREQUENCY: Port: Ch 12 18 Port Radio: Ch 16 68	LOCATION: Port Radio: 36°54'·95N 21°41'·75E	HOURS: H24

PORTO KARRA (PORTO CARRAS MARINA)	Marina 240 Berths Visitor Berths Available	40°06'N 23°48'E
☎ Hr Mr: +30 2374 071381 & 071221	Depth: 5 m, Maximum LOA: 45 m	Fax:
FREQUENCY: Ch 09		HOURS: HX

PORTO SANI	Marina 150 Berths Visitor Berths Available	40°05'·90N 25°18'·52E
☎ +30 2374 031551	Depth: 1·8 m	Fax: +30 2374 031551
FREQUENCY: Ch 09		HOURS: HX

PRÉVEZA	Port and Marina 136 Berths	38°57'·4N 20°45'·3E
☎ Hr Mr: +30 2682 022226 Preveza Marine: +30 2682 024305 Cleopatra Marina: +30 2682 023015 prevmar@otenet.gr	Depth: 2 - 3 m	Fax: Hr Mr: +30 2682 028854 Preveza Marine: +30 2682 029805 Cleopatra Marina: +30 2682 021414
FREQUENCY: Port (Hr Mr): Ch 12 18 Cleopatra Marina: Ch 67	LOCATION: Port Radio: 38°57'·8N 20°45'·3E	HOURS: Port: H24 Marina: HX

RÓDOS, NÍSOS RÓDOS	Pilots and Port	36°27'N 28°14'E
☎ Hr & Pilot Radio: +30 2241 028888, 022220, 028666 & 028689 Hr Mr: +30 2241 027365		Fax:
FREQUENCY: Pilots & Port: Ch 12	LOCATION: Hr & Pilot Radio: 36°27'·0N 28°13'·5E	HOURS: H24

SÁMOS, NÍSOS SÁMOS	Port	37°45'N 26°58'E
☎ +30 2273 027318		Fax: +30 2273 080888
FREQUENCY: Ch 12	LOCATION: Port Radio: 37°45'·55N 26°58'·30E	HOURS: H24

SKÍATHOS, NÍSOS SKÍATHOS	Port	39°10'N 23°29'E
☎ Port Radio: +30 2427 022017		Fax: +30 2427 023720
FREQUENCY: Ch 07 12	LOCATION: Port Radio: 39°09'·75N 23°29'·35E (PA)	HOURS: H24

PRÉVAZA MARINA FROM N

SOÚDHA, KRÍTI (CRETE)	Port: CALL: Soúdha Bay Port Control or Limenarchian Sauda Hanion.	35°30′N 24°05′E
FREQUENCY: Port: Ch 08 12 16	LOCATION: Port Radio: 35°29′·4N 24°04′·5E Port Radio is operated by the Hellenic Coast Guard	HOURS: Ch 16: H24
INFORMATION BROADCASTS: VHF Ch16 is used to broadcast warnings about local Naval exercises		

THESSALONÍKI (SALONICA)	Pilots and Port	40°38′N 22°56′E
☎ Hr Radio & Hr Mr: +30 231 0531504, 0531505 & 0531507		Fax: Hr Mr: +30 231 0593911
FREQUENCY: Hr Radio & Port Control: Ch 07 12	LOCATION: Pilot/Hr Office, East Mole	HOURS: H24

THESSALONIKI MARINA (ARETSOU)	Marina 300 Berths Visitor Berths Available Nautical Club of Thessaloniki: Private Club, Yacht Repairs, Some Visitor Berths Available	40°34′·6N 22°56′·5E
☎ Hr Mr: +30 231 0444541 Marina: +30 231 0444594, 0444595 & 0444598 Nautical Club of Thessaloniki: +30 231 0429945 Mikró Émvolon yacht harbour: +30 231 0414493	Depth: 3 - 4 m, Maximum LOA: 30 m Depth: 1 - 2·5 m (Nautical Club)	Fax: +30 231 0444594, 0444595 & 0444598
FREQUENCY: Ch 09		HOURS: HX

VATHY	Marina	38°25′N 20°43′E
☎ +30 26740 32909 & 32629		Fax: +30 26740 32909

VÓLOS	Port	39°22′N 22°56′E
☎ Hr Mr: +30 2421 032116 Port Radio: +30 2421 038888 Safety Navigation Office: +30 2421 024758		Fax: +30 2421 020115
FREQUENCY: Port: Ch 12	LOCATION: Port Radio: 39°21′·55N 22°56′·70E	HOURS: H24

VOUNAKI (Sunsail Vounaki Marina)	Marina 120 Berths 6 Visitor Berths	38°46′N 20°52′·8E
☎ +30 2643 041944	Depth: 2 - 6 m, Maximum LOA: 18 m	Fax: +30 2643 041944
FREQUENCY: Ch 10		HOURS: H24

XYLOKASTRO	Marina 220 Berths Visitor Berths Available	38°05′N 22°30′E
☎ +30 2743 025620 & 022229		Fax: +30 2743 023404
FREQUENCY: Ch 72		HOURS: HX

PORT VATHY FROM NNW

ZÁKINTHOS (ZAKYNTHOS OR ZANTE), NÍSOS ZÁKINTHOS	Port	37°47′N 20°54′E
☎ Port: +30 2695 028117 & 028118		Fax: Port: +30 2695 048370
FREQUENCY: Port: Ch 12 18	LOCATION: Port Radio: 37°46′·95N 20°54′·23E	HOURS: H24

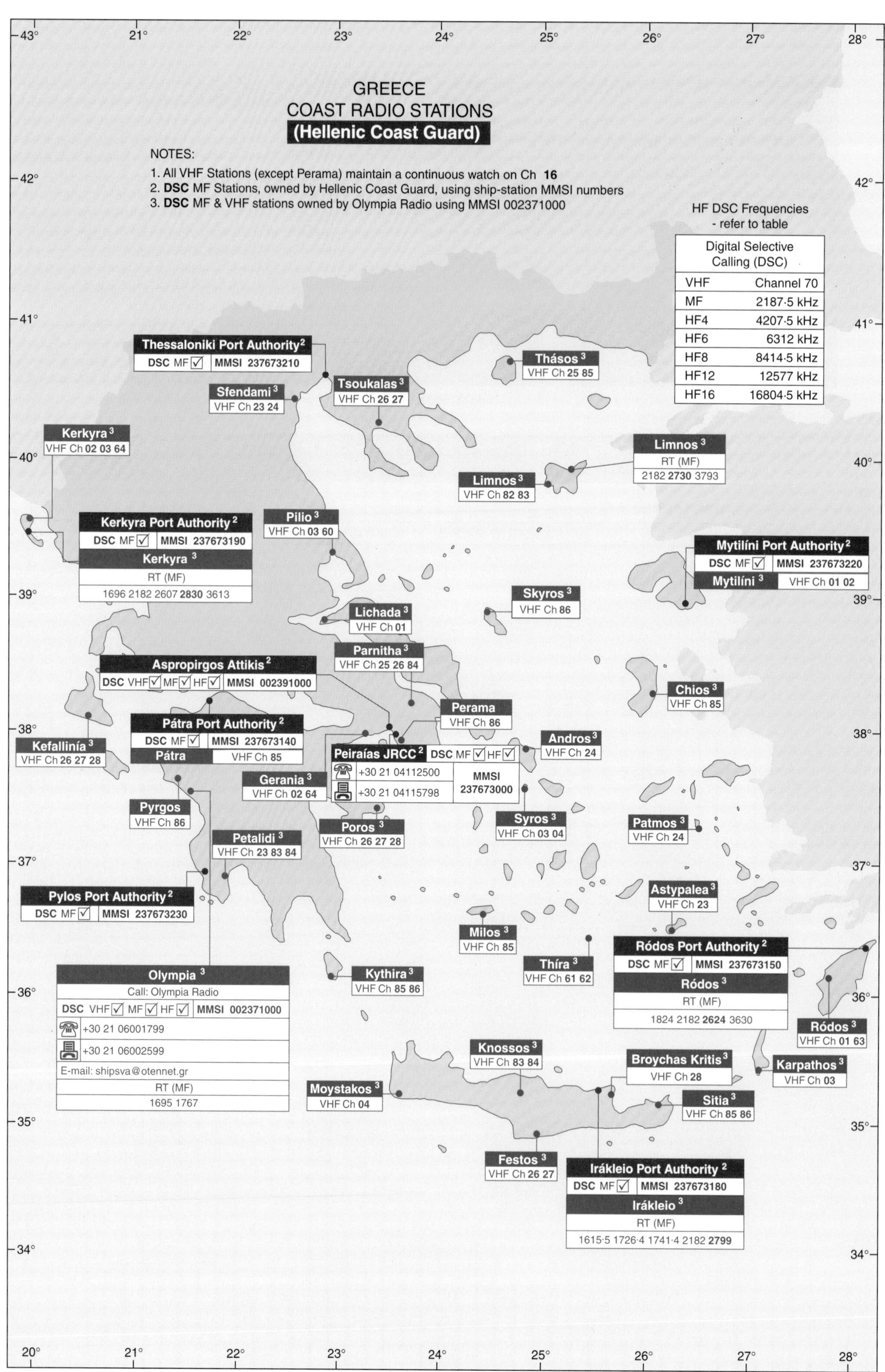

GREECE
COAST RADIO STATIONS
(Hellenic Coast Guard)
NOTES:
1. All VHF Stations (except Perama) maintain a continuous watch on Ch 16
2. DSC MF Stations, owned by Hellenic Coast Guard, using ship-station MMSI numbers
3. DSC MF & VHF stations owned by Olympia Radio using MMSI 002371000
HF DSC Frequencies - refer to table
Digital Selective Calling (DSC)
VHF Channel 70
MF 2187·5 kHz
HF4 4207·5 kHz
HF6 6312 kHz
HF8 8414·5 kHz
HF12 12577 kHz
HF16 16804·5 kHz
Thessaloniki Port Authority [2]
DSC MF ✓ MMSI 237673210
Sfendami [3]
VHF Ch 23 24
Tsoukalas [3]
VHF Ch 26 27
Thásos [3]
VHF Ch 25 85
Kerkyra [3]
VHF Ch 02 03 64
Limnos [3]
RT (MF)
2182 2730 3793
Limnos [3]
VHF Ch 82 83
Pilio [3]
VHF Ch 03 60
Kerkyra Port Authority [2]
DSC MF ✓ MMSI 237673190
Kerkyra [3]
RT (MF)
1696 2182 2607 2830 3613
Mytilíni Port Authority [2]
DSC MF ✓ MMSI 237673220
Mytilíni [3] VHF Ch 01 02
Skyros [3]
VHF Ch 86
Lichada [3]
VHF Ch 01
Parnitha [3]
VHF Ch 25 26 84
Aspropirgos Attikis [2]
DSC VHF ✓ MF ✓ HF ✓ MMSI 002391000
Chios [3]
VHF Ch 85
Perama
VHF Ch 86
Pátra Port Authority [2]
DSC MF ✓ MMSI 237673140
Pátra VHF Ch 85
Kefallinía [3]
VHF Ch 26 27 28
Andros [3]
VHF Ch 24
Peiraías JRCC [2] DSC MF ✓ HF ✓
+30 21 04112500
+30 21 04115798
MMSI 237673000
Gerania [3]
VHF Ch 02 64
Pyrgos
VHF Ch 86
Poros [3]
VHF Ch 26 27 28
Syros [3]
VHF Ch 03 04
Patmos [3]
VHF Ch 24
Petalidi [3]
VHF Ch 23 83 84
Astypalea [3]
VHF Ch 23
Pylos Port Authority [2]
DSC MF ✓ MMSI 237673230
Milos [3]
VHF Ch 85
Ródos Port Authority [2]
DSC MF ✓ MMSI 237673150
Ródos [3]
RT (MF)
1824 2182 2624 3630
Olympia [3]
Call: Olympia Radio
DSC VHF ✓ MF ✓ HF ✓ MMSI 002371000
+30 21 06001799
+30 21 06002599
E-mail: shipsva@otenet.gr
RT (MF)
1695 1767
Kythira [3]
VHF Ch 85 86
Thíra [3]
VHF Ch 61 62
Ródos [3]
VHF Ch 01 63
Knossos [3]
VHF Ch 83 84
Broychas Kritis [3]
VHF Ch 28
Karpathos [3]
VHF Ch 03
Moystakos [3]
VHF Ch 04
Sitia [3]
VHF Ch 85 86
Festos [3]
VHF Ch 26 27
Irákleio Port Authority [2]
DSC MF ✓ MMSI 237673180
Irákleio [3]
RT (MF)
1615·5 1726·4 1741·4 2182 2799
20° 21° 22° 23° 24° 25° 26° 27° 28°
43° 42° 41° 40° 39° 38° 37° 36° 35° 34°
V9GRCCRS

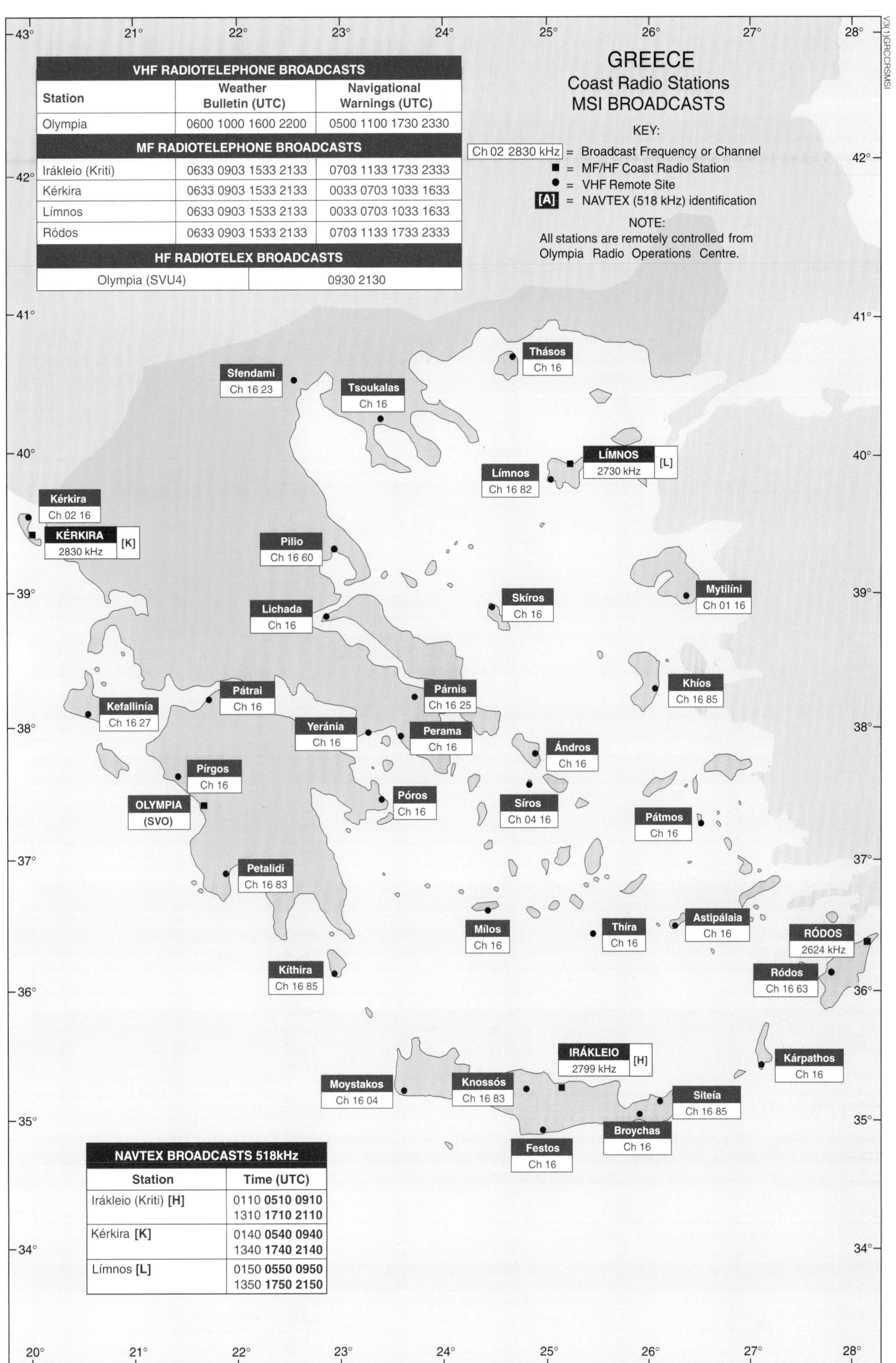

VHF RADIOTELEPHONE BROADCASTS		
Station	**Weather Bulletin (UTC)**	**Navigational Warnings (UTC)**
Olympia	0600 1000 1600 2200	0500 1100 1730 2330
MF RADIOTELEPHONE BROADCASTS		
Irákleio (Kriti)	0633 0903 1533 2133	0703 1133 1733 2333
Kérkira	0633 0903 1533 2133	0033 0703 1033 1633
Límnos	0633 0903 1533 2133	0033 0703 1033 1633
Ródos	0633 0903 1533 2133	0703 1133 1733 2333
HF RADIOTELEX BROADCASTS		
Olympia (SVU4)	0930 2130	

NAVTEX BROADCASTS 518kHz	
Station	**Time (UTC)**
Irákleio (Kriti) **[H]**	0110 **0510 0910** 1310 **1710 2110**
Kérkira **[K]**	0140 **0540 0940** 1340 **1740 2140**
Límnos **[L]**	0150 **0550 0950** 1350 **1750 2150**

ISRAEL

NAVTEX [P]

P	Hefa (Haifa)	518 kHz	32°49′N 35°00′E
DIAGRAM: page 257			
Weather Bulletins			
P: 0020 0420 0820 1220 1620 2020	Gale warnings, synopsis, 12 hour forecast and outlook for a further 12 hours, in English for Areas 32, 33 & 34		
Navigational Warnings			
P: On receipt 0020 0420 0820 1220 1620 2020	Urgent navigational warnings in English. Broadcasts include firing practice warnings as necessary		

HEFA (HAIFA)

	2649	RT (MF)		
	Ch 25	VHF		
DIAGRAM: page 257				
Weather Bulletins				
On receipt 0303 0703 1103 1503 1903 2303	Storm Warnings: Gale warnings in English for Areas Delta, Taurus & Crusade			
0703 1903	Gale warnings, synopsis, 12 hour forecast and outlook for a further 12 hours, in English for Areas 32, 33 & 34			
Navigational Warnings				
On receipt 0303 0703 1103 1503 1903 2303	Broadcasts include firing practice warnings as necessary			
0730 1103 1503 1903	Urgent navigational warnings in English			

AKKO (ACRE)

AKKO (ACRE)	**Marina:** CALL: Marina Akko 80 Berths 5 Visitor Berths	32°55′N 35°04′E
☎ +972(0)4 9919287	Depth: 1 - 3 m, Maximum LOA: 12 m	Fax +972(0)4 89258382
FREQUENCY: Ch 11 16		HOURS: HX

ASHDOD

ASHDOD	**Marina:** CALL: Blue Marina 550 Berths	31°47′·52N 34°37′·3E
☎ +972(0)8 8557246 bmarina@netvision.net.il	Depth: 4 m, Maximum LOA: 35 m	Fax +972(0)8 8556810 www.setur.com.tr
FREQUENCY: Ch 09 16		HOURS: 0830-1530 LT

ASHKELON

ASHKELON	**Marina** 600 Berths	31°41′·19N 34°33′·26E
☎ +972(0)7 6733780 marina@ashkelon.muni.il	Depth: 4 - 6 m, Maximum LOA: 30 m	Fax +972(0)7 6733823 www.ashkelon.muni.il
FREQUENCY: Ch 11 16		

HEFA (HAIFA)

HEFA (HAIFA)	**Port:** CALL: Tatzpit Haifa	32°50′N 35°00′E
☎ +972(0)4 8518111 Hr Co-ordinator: +972(0)4 8460323		Fax +972(0)4 8674853 Hr Co-ordinator: +972(0)4 8410572
FREQUENCY: Ch 12 14 16		HOURS: H24

HERZLIYA

HERZLIYA	**Marina** 800 Berths 30 Visitor Berths	32°09′·56N 34°47′·34E
☎ +927(0)9 9565591 info@herzliya-marina.co.il	Depth: 2·5 m, Maximum LOA: 24 m	Fax +972(0)9 9565594
FREQUENCY: Ch 11 16 Office hours only, Fri 0800 - 1400 LT		HOURS: Marina H24

JAFFA

JAFFA	**Marina:** CALL: Jaffa Marina 100 Berths	32°03′N 34°45′E
☎ +972(0)3 6832255	Depth: 1·5 m, Maximum LOA: 16 m Daylight approach is recommended	Fax +972(0)3 6831337
FREQUENCY: Ch 11 16		HOURS: H24

QUISHON	Port and Marina: 100 Berths	32°49′N 35°00′E
☎ +972(0)4 8422106	Depth: 3 m	Fax +972(0)4 8412730
FREQUENCY: Ch 12 14 16		HOURS: HX

TEL AVIV	Marina: CALL: Tel Aviv Marina	32°05′N 34°46′E
☎ +972(0)3 5272596	Depth: 1·5 - 2·5 m, Maximum LOA: 20 m	Fax +972(0)3 5272466
FREQUENCY: Ch 11 16	Crowded. Very difficult marina entry. Pilot provided free of charge if requested on VHF	HOURS: H24

ITALY, ADRIATIC COAST

PORTO SAN ROCCO MARINA

NAVTEX [V] [T] [R] [U]

V	Augusta	518 kHz	37°14′N 15°14′E
T	Cagliari		39°14′N 9°14′E
R	Roma		41°48′N 12°31′E
U	Trieste		45°41′N 13°46′E

DIAGRAMS: pages 325 and 338

Weather Bulletins	
V: 0330 0730 1130 1530 1930 2330 On receipt	Storm Warnings
V: 0730 1930	Weather forecasts
T: 0310 0710 1110 1510 1910 2310 On receipt	Storm Warnings
T: 0710 1910	Weather forecasts
R: 0250 0650 1050 1450 1850 2250 On receipt	Storm Warnings
R: 0650 1850	Weather forecasts
U: 0320 0720 1120 1520 1920 2320 On receipt	Storm Warnings
U: 0720 1920	Weather forecasts

Navigational Warnings	
V: 0330 0730 1130 1530 1930 2330 On receipt	Navigational warnings
T: 0310 0710 1110 1510 1910 2310 On receipt	Navigational warnings
R: 0250 0650 1050 1450 1850 2250 On receipt	Navigational warnings
U: 0320 0720 1120 1520 1920 2320 On receipt	Navigational warnings

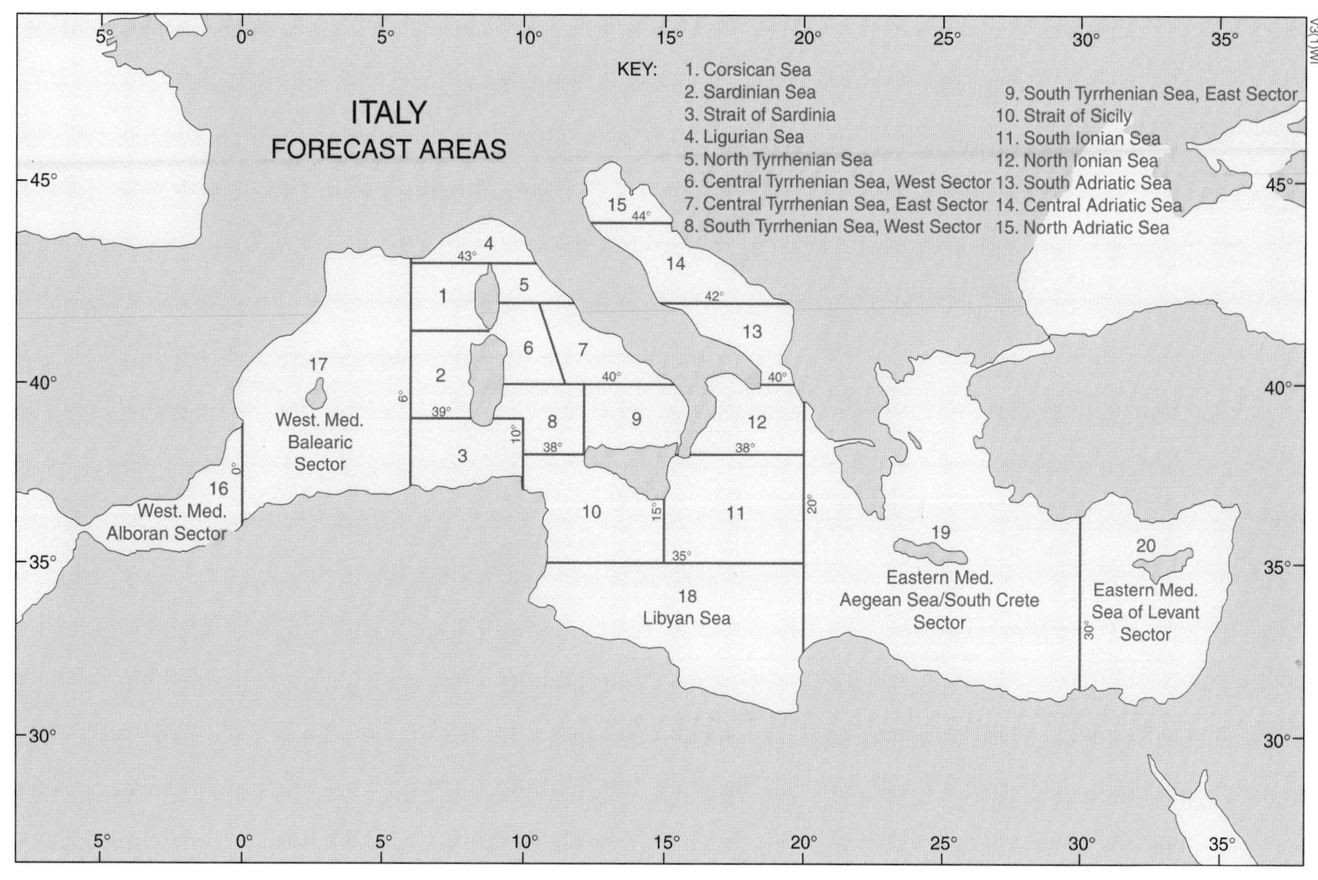

National SAR Agency: Comando Generale delle Capitanerie di Porto
Tel: 06 5923569 & 06 5924145 **Fax:** 06 5922737 & 06 59084793 **E-mail:** cogecap3@flashnet.it **Website:** www.guardiacostiera.it
MRCC Roma is responsible for co-ordinating Search and Rescue operations within Italian waters and liaising with RCCs of other nations. A network of Coast Radio Stations maintains a continuous listening watch on international distress frequencies.
Maritime Safety Information broadcasts are announced on 2182 kHz or VHF Ch 16, before being broadcast on the scheduled frequency or channel number.
Storm and / or Gale Warnings, given the special needs of safety and urgency of Storm Warnings, as soon as warnings are received by the Italian CRS they will proceed with an immediate broadcast.
Weather Bulletins, compiled four times per day (at 0000 0600 1200 1800 UT) by the Italian Air Force Meteorological Service. Italian CRS provide an extract of the bulletin at scheduled broadcast times. (See also SARDEGNA & SICILY, and WEST COAST sections.)

	Telephone +39	**Fax** +39	**Others**
MRSC ANCONA	071 227581 071 53657	071 55393	compmare_ancona@hotmail.com
MRSC BARI	080 5216860 080 520511	080 5211726	compba.amm@interbussines.it
MRSC RAVENNA	0544 453900 0544 453226	0544 455045	cpp.ravenna@tranportinavigazione.it
MRSC TRIESTE	040 676611 040 676612	040 676627	cportots@spin.it
MRSC VENEZIA	041 2405711 041 2405850	041 2405730 041 2405854	capve@portofvenice.net

ANCONA RT (MF) 2656 kHz

DIAGRAMS: pages 325 and 338	
Weather Bulletins	
On receipt, 0433 0933 1333 1733 2133	Storm Warnings: Near gale warnings in Italian and English for Areas 14 & 15
0135 0735 1335 1935	Near gale warnings, synopsis, 12 or 18 hour forecast and outlook for a further 12 hours in Italian and English for Areas 14 & 15
Navigational Warnings	
On receipt, 0433 0933 1333 1733 2133	In Italian and English

BARI RT (MF) 2579 kHz	
DIAGRAMS: pages 325 and 338	
Weather Bulletins	
On receipt 0333 0833 1233 1633 2033	Storm warnings: Near gale warnings in Italian and English on **A** for Areas 10-13 and on **B** for Areas 12 & 13
0135 0735 1335 1935	Near gale warnings, synopsis, 12 or 18 hour forecast and outlook for a further 12 hours in Italian and English for Areas 12 & 13
Navigational Warnings	
On receipt 0333 0833 1233 1633 2033	In Italian and English

CROTONE RT (MF) 2663 kHz	
DIAGRAMS: pages 325 and 338	
Weather Bulletins	
On receipt 0333 0833 1233 1633 2033	Storm warnings: Near gale warnings in Italian and English for Areas 11 & 12
0135 0735 1335 1935	Near gale warnings, synopsis, 12 or 18 hour forecast and outlook for a further 12 hours in Italian and English for Areas 11 & 12
Navigational Warnings	
On receipt 0333 0833 1233 1633 2033	In Italian and English

PALERMO				
Adriatic Coast				
A	1852	RT (MF)		
J	Ch 05	VHF	Abate Argento	40°52′N 17°17′E
	Ch 27		Bari	41°06′N 17°00′E
K	Ch 81		Casa D'orso	41°42′N 15°57′E
	Ch 01		Monte Calvario	42°05′N 14°40′E
DIAGRAMS: pages 325 and 338				
Weather Bulletins				
A: On receipt 0333 0833 1233 1633 2033	Storm warnings: Near gale warnings in Italian and English for Areas 8-10			
J & K: On receipt	Storm warnings: Near gale warnings in Italian and English on: **J** for Areas 12 & 13; **K** for Areas 13 & 14			
A-K: 0135 0735 1335 1935	Near gale warnings, synopsis, 12 or 18 hour forecast and outlook for a further 12 hours in Italian and English on: **J** for Areas 12 & 13; **K** for Areas 13 & 14			
Navigational Warnings				
A-K: On receipt 0333 0833 1233 1633 2033	In Italian and English			

ROMA VHF				
Adriatic Coast				
J	Ch 65	VHF	Silvi	42°34′N 14°06′E
K	Ch 87		Monte Secco	42°58′N 13°53′E
	Ch 02		Monte Conero	43°33′N 13°36′E
	Ch 25		Forte Garibaldi	43°36′N 13°32′E
	Ch 27		Ravenna	44°25′N 12°12′E
	Ch 26		Monte Cero	45°15′N 11°40′E
	Ch 01		Piancavallo	46°05′N 12°32′E
L	Ch 83		Conconello	45°40′N 13°48′E
DIAGRAMS: pages 325 and 338				
Weather Bulletins				
J-L: On receipt	Storm warnings: Near gale warnings in Italian and English on: **J** for Areas 13 & 14; **K & L** for Areas 14 & 15			
J-L: 0135 0735 1335 1935	Near gale warnings, synopsis, 12 or 18 hour forecast and outlook for a further 12 hours in Italian and English on: **J** for Areas 13 & 14; **K & L** for Areas 14 & 15			

ROMA VHF (Continued)

Navigational Warnings	
J-L: On receipt L: 0333 0833 1233 1633 2033 J, K: 0433 0933 1333 1733 2133	In Italian and English

SAN BENEDETTO DEL TRONTO RT (MF) 1855 kHz
TRIESTE RT (MF) 2624 kHz

DIAGRAMS: pages 325 and 338

Weather Bulletins	
On receipt 0433 0933 1333 1733 2133	Storm warnings: Near gale warnings in Italian and English for Areas 14 & 15
0135 0735 1335 1935	Near gale warnings, synopsis, 12 or 18 hour forecast and outlook for a further 12 hours in Italian and English for Areas 14 & 15
Navigational Warnings	
On receipt 0433 0933 1333 1733 2133	In Italian and English

ANCONA	Port and Marina : CALL: Ancona Port Captain	43°37′·0N 13°31′·5E
☎ Port: +39 071 2074697 Yacht Club: +39 071 204497 info@porucuale.ancona.it	Depth: 1 - 6 m, Maximum LOA: 12 m	Fax: +39 071 51697 & 2074697 www.autoritaportuale.ancona.it
FREQUENCY: Ch 11 16		HOURS: Port: H24

APRILA MARITTIMA CENTRALE	Marina 682 Berths	45°41′·8N 13°04′·3E
☎ +39 0431 53123 circolo-nautico@apriliamarittma.it	Depth: 3 m, Maximum LOA: 20 m	Fax: +39 0431 53458
FREQUENCY: Ch 09		HOURS: 0900-1200 1430-1900 LT
MARINA CAPO NORD	**Marina 650 Berths 60 Visitor Berths**	**45°41′·7N 13°04′·0E**
☎ +39 0431 527000 & 53123 circolo-nautico@apriliamarittma.it	Depth: 3 - 3·5 m, Maximum LOA: 20 m 3 mile canal leads from sea to harbour	Fax: +39 0431 527950 www.netanday.it/aprilia
FREQUENCY: Ch 09		HOURS: H24
MARINA PUNTA GABBIANI	**Marina 300 Berths**	**45°41′·7N 13°04′·4E**
☎ +39 0431 528000 info@puntagabbiani.it	Depth: 3 m, Maximum LOA: 25 m	Fax: +39 0431 528300
FREQUENCY: Ch 09 16		HOURS: H24

BARI & MOLA DI BARI	Port & Marina 350 Berths	41°03′·7N 17°06′·1E
☎ Port: +39 080 5216860 & 4741573 Mola di Bari: +39 080 4742121 apbari@Porto.bari.it nauticapeter@libero.it	Depth: 1 - 4 m, Maximum LOA: 15 m	Fax: Port: +39 080 5211726
FREQUENCY: Port Ch 11 16		HOURS: 0800-2000 LT

BARLETTA	Port	41°19′N 16°17′E
☎ +39 0883 531020	Depth: 1 - 7 m	Fax: +39 0883 533400
FREQUENCY: Ch 11 16		HOURS: 0700-2000 LT

BISCEGLIE	Marina 90 Berths	41°14′·8N 16°30′·5E
☎ +39 080 3957895	Depth: 1 - 5 m, Maximum LOA: 20 m	Fax:
FREQUENCY: Ch 16		HOURS: HX

MARINA PUNTA GABBIANI　　APRILIA MARITTIMA MARINA　　MARINA CAPO NORD

APRILIA MARITTIMA MARINAS FROM NE

BRINDISI	Port and Marina 300 Berths	40°39′·7N 17°59′·8E
Port: +39 0831 521022 & 521023 Lega Navale: +39 0831 418824	Depth: 2 - 7 m, Maximum LOA: 18 m	Fax: +39 0831 568113
FREQUENCY: Port: Ch 11 16		HOURS: Port: 0700-1900 LT

CHIOGGIA	Port and Marinas Berths: 300 - Sporting Club 150 Darsena Mosella 10 Visitor Berths	45°13′N 12°17′·9E
Port: +39 041 400242 Sporting Club Marina: +39 041 400530 Darsena Mosella: +39 041 404993	Depth: Darsena Mosella 2 - 2·5 m Maximum LOA: 16m Sporting Club Marina 2 - 2·5 m Maximum LOA: 21m	Fax: +39 041 5506812
FREQUENCY: Ch 15 16		HOURS: Port: 0700-1900 LT Marinas: HX

CIVITANOVA	Marina 600 Berths	43°18′·9N 13°44′·1E
+39 0733 810395 circomarecivitanova@tiscali.it	Depth: 0·5 - 4 m, Maximum LOA: 18m	Fax: +39 0733 815497
FREQUENCY: Ch 16		HOURS: 0800-2400 LT

DARSENA DELL'OROLOGIO	Marina 450 Berths 40 Visitor Berths	45°35′·8N 12°52′·3E
+39 0421 84207	Depth: 3 - 3·5 m, Maximum LOA: 20 m	Fax: +39 0421 210158
FREQUENCY: Ch 09 16		HOURS: HX

DARSENA NAUTEC	Marina 200 Berths 10 Visitor Berths	45°47′·7N 13°33′·5E
+39 048 1790416	Depth: 3 - 6 m, Maximum LOA: 25 m	Fax:
		HOURS: HX

ERACLEA (MARICLEA CLUB)	**Marina** 187 Berths	45°32'·4N 12°45'·5E
Tel: +39 0421 66261	Depth: 2 - 3 m, Maximum LOA: 12 m	Fax: +39 0421 66438
FREQUENCY: Ch 09 16		HOURS: HX

FIUME TAGLIAMENTO MARINA UNO	**Marina** 435 Berths 50 Visitor Berths	45°39'N 13°05'·7E
Tel: +39 0431 428677 info@lignanopineta.com	Depth: 3 m, Maximum LOA: 17 m	Fax: +39 0431 428677 & 428701
FREQUENCY: Ch 10		HOURS: HX

GIULIANOVA	**Port & Marina** 350 Berths	42°45'·3N 13°58'·7E
Tel: +39 085 8004918 & 8000731 circomare.giulianova@libero.it	Depth: 2 - 4·5m	Fax: +39 085 8004918 & 8000731
FREQUENCY: Ch 14 16		HOURS: H24

GRADO	**Port and Marina** 1730 Berths	45°41'·2N 15°23'·2E
Tel: +39 0431 80050 & 82119	Depth: 1 - 4 m, Maximum LOA: 25 m	Fax: +39 0431 80050
FREQUENCY: Ch 15 16		HOURS: 0700-2100 LT

LIGNANO DARSENA MARINA	**Marina** 380 Berths	45°41'·81N 13°08'·60E
Tel: Hr Mr: +33(0)2 98049162 darsensabbiador@marinasnordadria.com	Depth: 3·5 m (max vessel draft 2 m), Maximum LOA: in transit berths 15 m	Fax: www.aptlignano.it
FREQUENCY: Ch 09 16		HOURS: HX

LIGNANO SABBIADORO	**Marina** 1200 Berths	45°42'N 13°08'E
Tel: +39 0431 70315 & 70573 info@marinapuntafaro.it	Maximum LOA: 25 m	Fax: +39 0431 70573 www.marinapuntafaro.it
FREQUENCY: Ch 09		HOURS: HX

MANFREDONIA (PORTO VECCHIO)	**Port & Marina** 365 Berths	41°37'·2N 15°55'·5E
Tel: +39 0884 23871 & 221519	Depth: 1 - 5 m, Maximum LOA: 20 m	Fax: +39 0884 27388
FREQUENCY: Port: Ch 14 16		HOURS: 1 Oct-31 May: 0700-1900 LT 1 June-30 Sept: H24

MARINA DE BRONDOLO	**Marina** 150 Berths Visitor Berths	45°10'·95N 12°16'·40E
Tel: +39 041 490950	Depth: 3·5 m, Maximum LOA: 16 m.	Fax:
FREQUENCY: Ch 09 16		HOURS: HX

MARINA DI CAMPALTO	**Marina** 200 Berths 10 Visitor Berths	45°28'·6N 12°18'·2E
Tel: +39 041 5310161	Depth: 2 - 5 m, Maximum LOA: 25 m	Fax: +39 041 5312219
		HOURS: HX

MARINA DI CARRARA	**Port and Marina** 190 Berths 10 Visitor Berths	44°01'·6N 10°02'·5E
Tel: Port: +39 0585 787822 Yacht Club: +39 0585 785150 capitaneria_carrara@tin.it	Depth: 2 - 8 m, Maximum LOA: 30 m	Fax: Port: +39 0585 787880 Yacht Club: +39 0585 785364
FREQUENCY: Port: Ch 15 16 Yacht Club: Ch 06		HOURS: 16 June-15 Sept: H24 16 Sept-15 June: 0700-1900 LT

MARINA DI LIO GRANDO	**Marina** 200 Berths 10 Visitor Berths	45°25'·2N 12°26'·2E
Tel: +39 041 966044	Depth: 2 - 5 m, Maximum LOA: 25 m	Fax: +39 041 5300872
		HOURS: HX

LIGNANO SABBIADORO MARINAS FROM N

MARINA DI PORTO LEVANTE	Marina 530 Berths Visitor Berths	45°02′·98N 12°21′·98E
☎ +39 0426 666047 portolevanti@infinito.it	Depth: 3·5 m, Maximum LOA: 18 m	Fax www.marinaportolevante.it
FREQUENCY: Ch 09		HOURS: HX

MARINA DI VALLUGOLA	Marina 150 Berths	43°55′·5N 12°54′·6E
☎ +39 0541 967918 & 958134	Depth: 1·5 - 2·5 m, Max LOA	Fax
FREQUENCY: Ch 09		HOURS: 0800-2000 LT

MARINA NUOVA DI PORTO LEVANTE	Marina 200 Berths 10 Visitor Berths	45°02′·7N 12°19′·2E
☎ +39 0426 330289	Depth: 3·5 m, Maximum LOA: 10 m	Fax
FREQUENCY: Ch 09		HOURS: HX

MARINA PUNTA VERDE	Marina 270 Berths	45°38′·92N 13°04′·99E
☎ +39 0431 427131	Depth: 3 m, Maximum LOA: 18 m	Fax +39 0431 427290
FREQUENCY: Ch 09 16		HOURS: H24

ORTONA	Port	42°21′N 14°24′E
☎ +39 085 9063290		Fax +39 085 9063290
FREQUENCY: Ch 15 16		HOURS: 0700-1900 LT

OTRANTO	Port 80 Berths	40°09′N 18°29′E
☎ +39 0836 801073	Depth: 1 - 7 m, Maximum LOA: 12 m	Fax
FREQUENCY: Ch 11 16		HOURS: 0700-1900 LT

PUNTA VERDE MARINA FROM SW

PESARO	Port 400 Berths	43°55'N 12°54'E
☎ Hr Mr: +39 0721 400016 & 400017 compamarepesareosicnac@intfree.it	Leisure craft are accommodated on W Quay at Banchina di Ponete and Darsena Nuova at the port entrance.	Fax Hr Mr: +39 0721 21711 & 400016
FREQUENCY: Ch 15 16		HOURS: 16 June-15 Sept: 0700-2300 LT 16 Sept-15 June: 0700-1900 LT

PESCARA	Port and Marina	42°28'N 14°13'E
☎ +39 085 694040		Fax Port: +39 085 4510117
FREQUENCY: Port: Ch 11 16		HOURS: 0700-1900 LT
	Marina 860 Berths 80 Visitor berths	42°27' 9N 14°14' 2E
☎ +39 085 4510180 & 4510173	Depth: 2 - 3·5 m, Maximum LOA: 30 m	Fax
FREQUENCY: Ch 06 16		HOURS: HX
PROCEDURE: The Approach Channel to the marina is usable by vessels of a maximum draught of 3·3 m		

PORTO BASELEGHE	Marina 500 Berths 20 Visitor Berths	45°36'·7N 12°54'·7E
☎ +39 0431 43686	Depth: 1 - 3·5 m, Maximum LOA: 20 m	Fax +39 0431 439192
FREQUENCY: Ch 09 16		HOURS: HX

PORTO DI PIAVE VECCHIA PORTO TURISTICO DI JESOLO	Marina 487 Berths 40 Visitor Berths	45°28'·6N 12°35'·1E
☎ +39 041 971488 touristport@marconinet.it	Depth: 3·5 m, Maximum LOA: 40 m	Fax +39 0421 972568 www.marconinet.it/jesolo/porto/index.htm
		HOURS: Hx
MARINA DEL FARO	**Marina** 98 Berths 5 Visitor Berths	45°28'·92N 12°35'·15E
☎ +39 041 968076	Depth: 2 - 2·5 m, Maximum LOA: 15 m	Fax +39 041 5370404
MARINA DEL CAVALLINO	**Marina** 320 Berths 30 Visitor Berths	45°28'·92N 12°35'·19E
☎ +39 041 968045, 968361 & 5370083 info@marinadelcavallino.it	Depth: 3 m, Maximum LOA: 30 m	Fax +39 041 5370365 www.marinadelcavallino.com
DARSENA FARO	**Marina** 100 Berths	45°28'·85N 12°35'·12E
☎ +39 0421 971787	Depth: 1·5 - 2·5 m, Maximum LOA: 10 m	Fax

PIAVE VECCHIA MARINAS

PORTO DI PIAVE VECCHIA PORTO TURISTICO DI JESOLO (Continued)	Marina 487 Berths 40 Visitor Berths	45°28′·6N 12°35′·1E
NAUTICA DAL Vi	Marina 300 Berths	45°29′·07N 12°35′·23E
Tel: +39 0421 971486, 377315 & 971134 dalvi@marconinet.it	Depth: 2 - 4 m, Maximum LOA: 16 m	Fax: +39 0421 971676 www.dalvi.it
MARINA DI CORTELLAZZO	Marina 150 Berths 15 Visitor Berths	45°32′·25N 12°43′·56E
Tel: +39 0421 980356 & 980357	Depth: 1·4 - 5 m	Fax:

PORTO GARIBALDI (MARINA DEGLI ESTENI)	Marina & Port 300 Berths 30 Visitor Berths	44°40′·6N 12°15′·0E
Tel: Marina: +39 0533 328428 Port: +39 0544 327141	Depth: 2·5 - 4 m, Maximum LOA: 25 m	Fax: Marina: +39 0533 328429 Port: +39 0533 325672
FREQUENCY: Ch 11 16		HOURS: 0700-1900 LT

PORTO SAN GIORGIO	Marina 861 Berths 86 Visitor Berths	43°09′·8N 15°23′·8E
Tel: +39 0734 675263 marina.psg@libero.it	Depth: 3·8 - 4 m, Maximum LOA: 30 m	Fax: +39 0734 675263
FREQUENCY: Ch 14 16		HOURS: H24

PORTO SAN ROCCO	Marina 520 Berths 50 Visitors Berths	45°36′·62N 13°45′·16E
Tel: +39 040 273090 infoport@portosanrocco.it	Maximum LOA: 60 m	Fax: +39 040 9279203 www.portosanrocco.it
FREQUENCY: Ch 16 74		HOURS: HX

PORTO SANTA MARGHERITA (MARINA 4)	Marina 420 Berths 40 Visitor Berths	45°35′·42N 12°51′·82E
Tel: +39 0421 260469	Depth: 2 - 3·5 m, Maximum LOA: 20 m	Fax: +39 0421 261254
FREQUENCY: Ch 09		HOURS: HX

NAUTICA DAL VI

MARINA DEL CAVALLINO

PORTO SAN ROCCO

PORTO SAN VITO	**Marina** 165 Berths	45°40′·0N 13°22′·8E
☎ +39 0431 83600	Depth: 3·5 m, Maximum LOA: 20 m	Fax +39 0431 85926
FREQUENCY: Ch 71		HOURS: HX
LEGA NAVALE	**Marina** 70 Berths 12 Visitor Berths	45°41′·0N 13°22′·8E
☎ +39 0431 81706	Depth: 2 - 4 m, Maximum LOA: 20 m	Fax
MARINA SAN MARCO	**Marina** 60 Berths 5 Visitor Berths	45°41′·7N 13°23′·1E
☎ +39 0431 81548	Depth: 1 - 3 m, Maximum LOA: 12 m	Fax
MARINA LE COVE	**Marina** 150 Berths 10 Visitor Berths	45°40′·2N 15°23′·2E
☎ +39 0431 82596	Depth: 3 m, Maximum LOA: 7 m	Fax
FREQUENCY: Ch 15 16		HOURS: 0700-1900 LT

PORTO VERDE	Marina 350 Berths 20 Visitor Berths	43°58′·30N 12°43′·11E
☎ +39 0541 615023	Depth: 2 - 3 m, but under 2 m in entrance, Maximum LOA: 20 m	Fax +39 0541 615023
		HOURS: 0800-2000 LT

RAVENNA	Port and Marinas	44°25′N 12°13′E
☎ +39 0544 590222 info@port.ravenna.it		Fax +39 0544 421945 www.port.ravenna.it
FREQUENCY: Hr Mr: Ch 11 16		HOURS: 16 June-15 Sept: 0700-2300 LT 16 Sept-15 June: 0700-1900 LT
NOTE: Vessels which must transit the floating swing bridge are obliged to call on VHF Ch 12 to request the bridge to be opened		
MARINARA	Berths 1000 Visitor Berths	44°29′·6N 12°17′·5E
☎ Lega Navale:+39 0544 530513	Depth: 2 - 5 m, Maximum LOA: 40 m	Fax
MARINA DI RAVENNA	Berths 685	44°29′·6N 12°17′·5E
☎ Lega Navale:+39 0544 530513	Depth: 0·5 - 3·5 m, Maximum LOA: 15 m	Fax
FREQUENCY: Capitaneria Ch 11 16		HOURS: 0700-1900 LT

RIMINI	Port 400 Berths Some Visitor Berths	44°04′·9N 12°34′·6E
☎ +39 0541 50121 cprimini@libero.it	Depth: 2 - 4 m, Maximum LOA: 16 m	Fax +39 0541 54373
FREQUENCY: Ch 11 16		HOURS: 16 June-15 Sept: 0700-2300 LT 16 Sept-15 June: 0700-1900 LT

MARINA DI RIMINI

SAN BENEDETTO DEL TRONTO	Marina 380 Berths	42°57′·5N 13°53′·7E
☎ Port: +39 0735 2744 Marina: +39 0735 584255	Depth: 2 - 4·5 m, Maximum LOA: 25 m	Fax Port: +39 0735 69094 Marina: +39 0735 594675
FREQUENCY: Ch 11 16		HOURS: 0700-1900 LT

SENIGALLIA	Port & Marina 300 Berths	43°43′N 13°13′E
☎ Port: +39 071 62980 Marina: +39 071 64780	Depth: 2·5 - 3 m, Maximum LOA: 15 m	Fax
FREQUENCY: Ch 11 16		HOURS: 16 June-15 Sept: 0700-2300 LT 16 Sept-15 June: 0700-1900 LT

S. FOCA DI MELENDUGNO	Marina 400 Berths	40°18′·1N 18°24′·3E
☎ +39 0832 881010	Depth: 1 - 1·5 m, Max LOA: 12 m	Fax
FREQUENCY: Ch 16		HOURS: HX

SISTIANA	Marina 600 Berths 10 Visitor Berths	45°46′·1N 13°37′·7E
☎ +39 040 6766111	Depth: 3 - 5 m, Maximum LOA: 10 m	Fax
FREQUENCY: Ch 16		HOURS: HX

TRIESTE	Marina 225 Berths	45°39′N 13°45′E
☎ Marina San Giusto: +39 040 303036 Port: +39 040 366666	Maximum LOA: 22 m	Fax Marina: +39 040 303036 Port: +39 040 368707
FREQUENCY: Ch 11 16		HOURS: 0700-1900 LT

VENEZIA (DARSENA DEC)	Marina 400 Berths	45°29′·01N 12°15′·24E
☎ +39 041 5310161	Depth: 2·5 - 3·5 m, Maximum LOA: 15 m	Fax +39 041 5312219
FREQUENCY: Ch 09	LOCATION: Marina is 5 km from Venezia	HOURS: HX

VENEZIA MARINAS		45°26′N 12°20′E
PORTO TURISTICO VENEZIANO	**Marina** 60 Berths 20 Visitor berths	45°26′·4N 12°18′·5E
☎ Port: +39 041 5203044 Marina: +39 041 5207555	Depth:1 - 6 m, Maximum LOA: 20 m	Fax
VENEZIA SANTELENA	**Marina** 230 Berths	45°25′·8N 12°21′·9E
☎ +39 041 5231927	Depth:1·5 - 4 m, Maximum LOA: 15 m	Fax
VENEZIA S.GIORGIO	**Marina** 70 Berths	45°25′·95N 12°20′·80E
☎ +39 041 710723	Depth:2 - 2·5 m, Maximum LOA:15 m	Fax
VENEZIA TRONCHETTO	**Marina** 60 Berths 20 Visitor Berths	45°26′·2N 12°18′·4E
☎ +39 041 5207555	Depth:1·5 - 5 m, Maximum LOA: 20 m	Fax
FREQUENCY: Marinas: Ch 11 16		H24

VIESTE	Marina 200 Berths	41°53′·9N 16°10′·8E
☎ +39 0884 78791	Depth: 1 - 3 m, Maximum LOA: 25 m	Fax
FREQUENCY: Ch 14 16		HOURS: 0700-1900 LT

VILLAGIO DEL PESCATORE S. MARCO	Marina 1050 Berths	45°46′·7N 13°35′·1E
☎ +39 040 209855	Depth: 1·5 - 3 m, Maximum LOA: 12 - 15 m	Fax
		HOURS: HX

VILLANOVA	Marina 250 Berths	40°47′·4N 17°35′·2E
☎ Lega Navale: +39 0831 359277	Depth: 1 - 2·5 m, Maximum LOA: 18 m	Fax
FREQUENCY: Ch 73		HOURS: HX

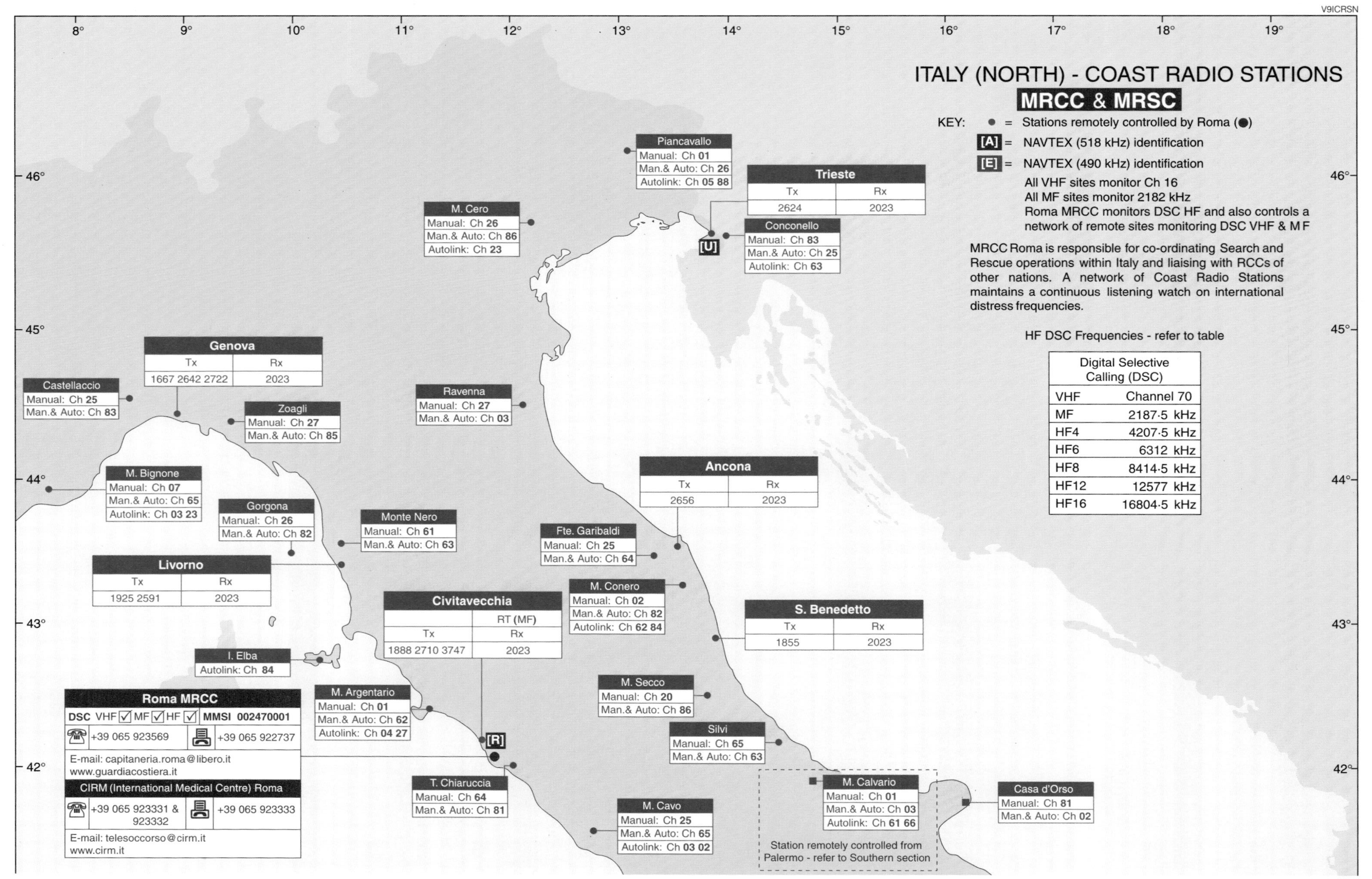

Digital Selective Calling (DSC)	
VHF	Channel 70
MF	2187·5 kHz
HF4	4207·5 kHz
HF6	6312 kHz
HF8	8414·5 kHz
HF12	12577 kHz
HF16	16804·5 kHz

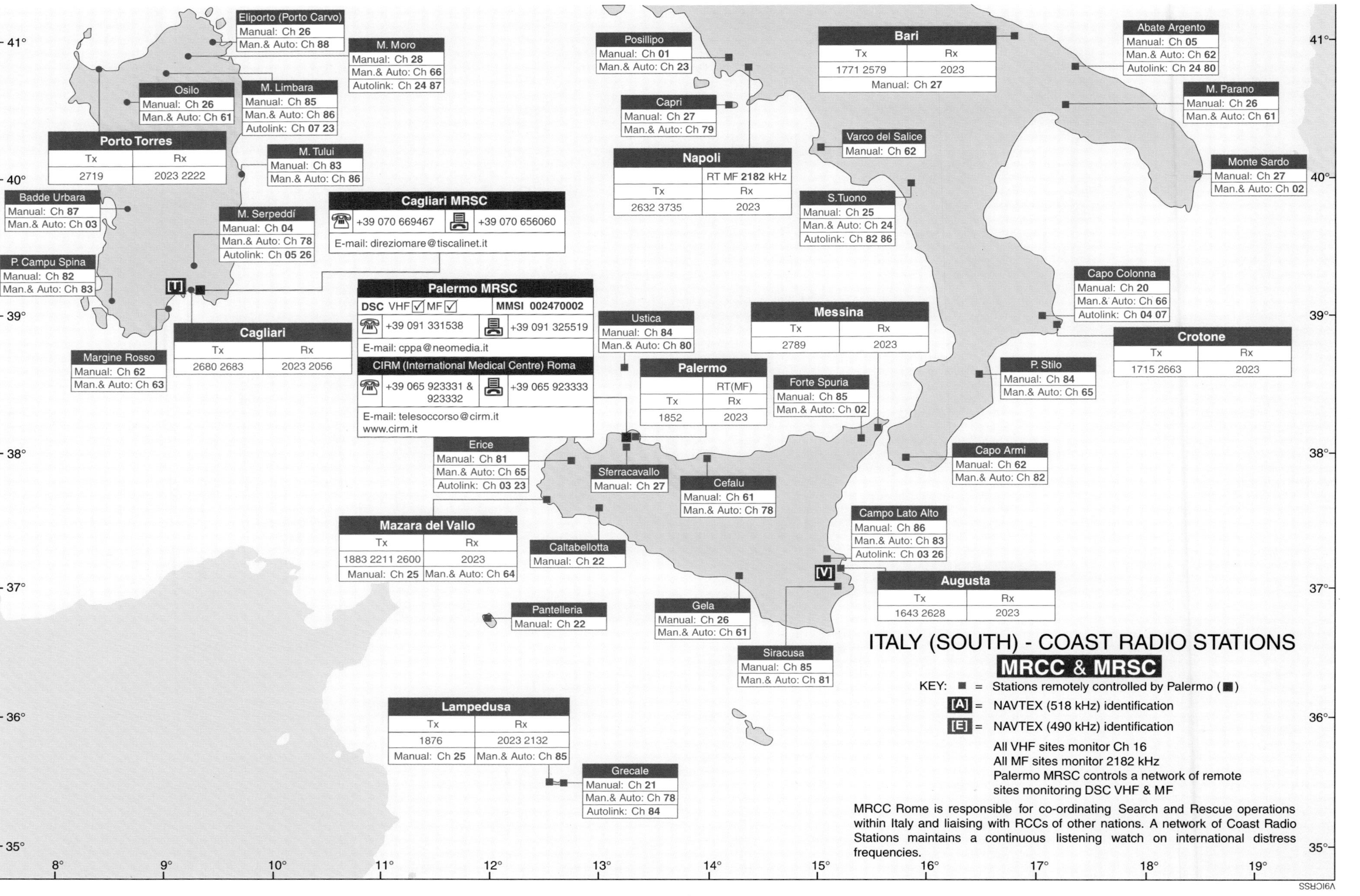
ITALY (SOUTH) - COAST RADIO STATIONS
MRCC & MRSC
KEY: ■ = Stations remotely controlled by Palermo (■)
[A] = NAVTEX (518 kHz) identification
[E] = NAVTEX (490 kHz) identification
All VHF sites monitor Ch 16
All MF sites monitor 2182 kHz
Palermo MRSC controls a network of remote sites monitoring DSC VHF & MF
MRCC Rome is responsible for co-ordinating Search and Rescue operations within Italy and liaising with RCCs of other nations. A network of Coast Radio Stations maintains a continuous listening watch on international distress frequencies.
Eliporto (Porto Carvo) Manual: Ch 26 Man.& Auto: Ch 88
M. Moro Manual: Ch 28 Man.& Auto: Ch 66 Autolink: Ch 24 87
Osilo Manual: Ch 26 Man.& Auto: Ch 61
M. Limbara Manual: Ch 85 Man.& Auto: Ch 86 Autolink: Ch 07 23
Porto Torres Tx 2719 Rx 2023 2222
M. Tului Manual: Ch 83 Man.& Auto: Ch 86
Badde Urbara Manual: Ch 87 Man.& Auto: Ch 03
M. Serpeddí Manual: Ch 04 Man.& Auto: Ch 78 Autolink: Ch 05 26
Cagliari MRSC +39 070 669467 +39 070 656060 E-mail: direziomare@tiscalinet.it
P. Campu Spina Manual: Ch 82 Man.& Auto: Ch 83
[T]
Cagliari Tx 2680 2683 Rx 2023 2056
Margine Rosso Manual: Ch 62 Man.& Auto: Ch 63
Palermo MRSC DSC VHF ☑ MF ☑ MMSI 002470002
+39 091 331538 +39 091 325519
E-mail: cppa@neomedia.it
CIRM (International Medical Centre) Roma
+39 065 923331 & 923332 +39 065 923333
E-mail: telesoccorso@cirm.it
www.cirm.it
Posillipo Manual: Ch 01 Man.& Auto: Ch 23
Capri Manual: Ch 27 Man.& Auto: Ch 79
Napoli RT MF 2182 kHz Tx 2632 3735 Rx 2023
Bari Tx 1771 2579 Rx 2023 Manual: Ch 27
Varco del Salice Manual: Ch 62
S.Tuono Manual: Ch 25 Man.& Auto: Ch 24 Autolink: Ch 82 86
Abate Argento Manual: Ch 05 Man.& Auto: Ch 62 Autolink: Ch 24 80
M. Parano Manual: Ch 26 Man.& Auto: Ch 61
Monte Sardo Manual: Ch 27 Man.& Auto: Ch 02
Capo Colonna Manual: Ch 20 Man.& Auto: Ch 66 Autolink: Ch 04 07
Crotone Tx 1715 2663 Rx 2023
Ustica Manual: Ch 84 Man.& Auto: Ch 80
Messina Tx 2789 Rx 2023
Palermo RT(MF) Tx 1852 Rx 2023
Forte Spuria Manual: Ch 85 Man.& Auto: Ch 02
P. Stilo Manual: Ch 84 Man.& Auto: Ch 65
Erice Manual: Ch 81 Man.& Auto: Ch 65 Autolink: Ch 03 23
Sferracavallo Manual: Ch 27
Cefalu Manual: Ch 61 Man.& Auto: Ch 78
Capo Armi Manual: Ch 62 Man.& Auto: Ch 82
Mazara del Vallo Tx 1883 2211 2600 Rx 2023 Manual: Ch 25 Man.& Auto: Ch 64
Caltabellotta Manual: Ch 22
Campo Lato Alto Manual: Ch 86 Man.& Auto: Ch 83 Autolink: Ch 03 26
[V]
Augusta Tx 1643 2628 Rx 2023
Pantelleria Manual: Ch 22
Gela Manual: Ch 26 Man.& Auto: Ch 61
Siracusa Manual: Ch 85 Man.& Auto: Ch 81
Lampedusa Tx 1876 Rx 2023 2132 Manual: Ch 25 Man.& Auto: Ch 85
Grecale Manual: Ch 21 Man.& Auto: Ch 78 Autolink: Ch 84
41° 40° 39° 38° 37° 36° 35°
8° 9° 10° 11° 12° 13° 14° 15° 16° 17° 18° 19°
V9ICRSS

ITALY - COAST RADIO STATIONS
MSI BROADCASTS

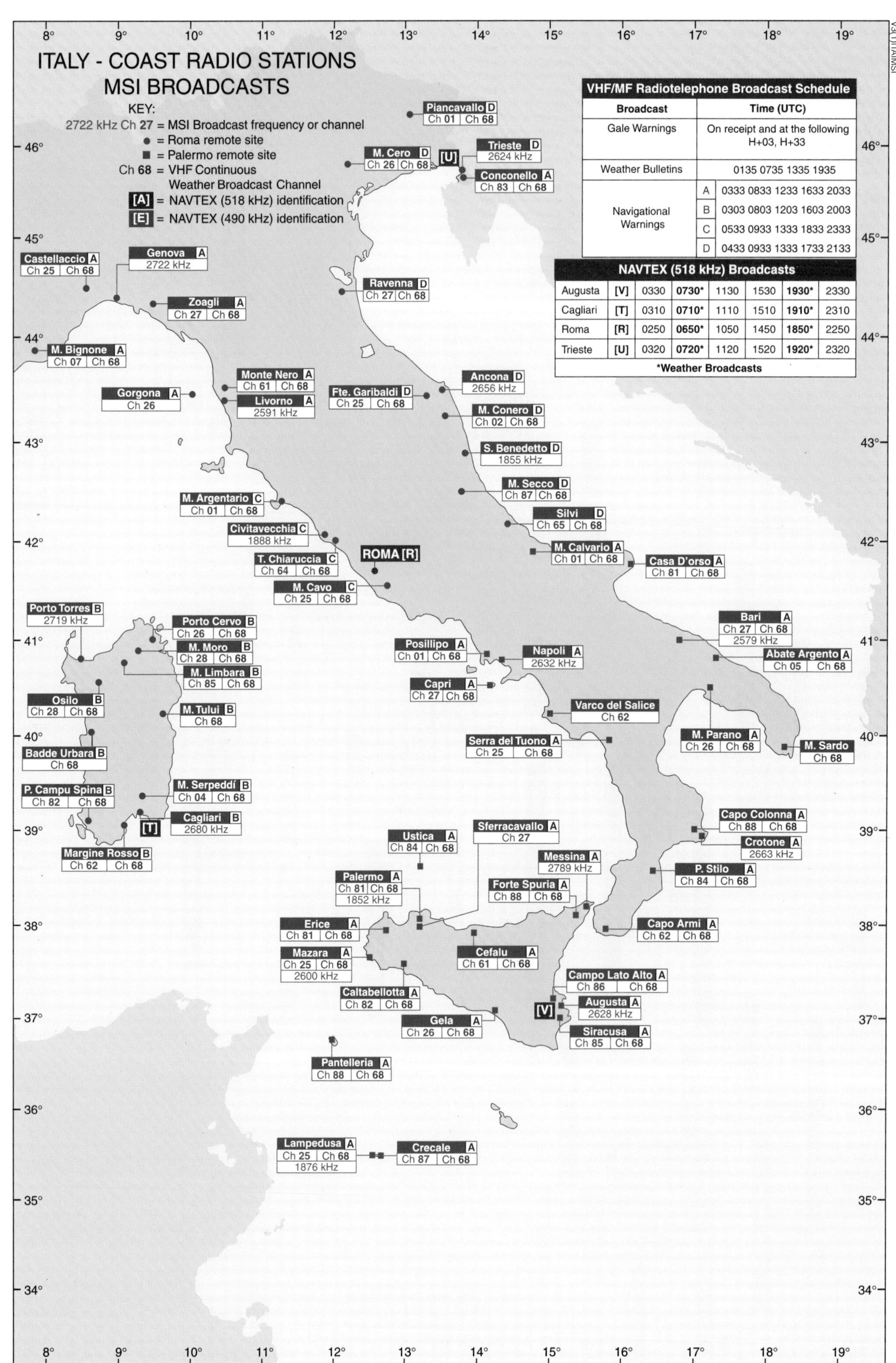

VHF/MF Radiotelephone Broadcast Schedule

Broadcast		Time (UTC)
Gale Warnings		On receipt and at the following H+03, H+33
Weather Bulletins		0135 0735 1335 1935
Navigational Warnings	A	0333 0833 1233 1633 2033
	B	0303 0803 1203 1603 2003
	C	0533 0933 1333 1833 2333
	D	0433 0933 1333 1733 2133

NAVTEX (518 kHz) Broadcasts

Augusta	[V]	0330	**0730***	1130	1530	**1930***	2330
Cagliari	[T]	0310	**0710***	1110	1510	**1910***	2310
Roma	[R]	0250	**0650***	1050	1450	**1850***	2250
Trieste	[U]	0320	**0720***	1120	1520	**1920***	2320

***Weather Broadcasts**

V3(1)ITAIMSI

ITALY, SARDEGNA & SICILIA

	Telephone +39	Fax +39	Others
MRSC CAGLIARI	070 605171 070 658225	070 60517218	direziomare@tiscalinet.it
MRSC CATANIA	095 7474111 095 538888 095 7474319	095 533962 095 532022	compa@ctonline.it
MRSC PALERMO	091 331538 091 604311 091 327213	091 325519	cppa@neomedia.it

AUGUSTA RT (MF) 2628 kHz

DIAGRAMS: pages 325 and 338	
Weather Bulletins	
On receipt 0333 0833 1233 1633 2033	Storm warnings: Near gale warnings in Italian and English for Areas 10 & 11
0135 0735 1335 1935	Near gale warnings, synopsis, 12 or 18 hour forecast and outlook for a further 12 hours in Italian and English for Areas 10 & 11
Navigational Warnings	
On receipt 0333 0833 1233 1633 2033	In Italian and English

CAGLIARI RT (MF) 2680 kHz

DIAGRAMS: pages 325 and 338	
Weather Bulletins	
On receipt 0303 0803 1200 1603 2003	Storm warnings: Near gale warnings in Italian and English for Areas 2, 3 & 6-9
0135 0735 1335 1935	Near gale warnings, synopsis, 12 or 18 hour forecast and outlook for a further 12 hours in Italian and English for Areas 2, 3 & 6-9
Navigational Warnings	
On receipt 0303 0803 1203 1603 2003	In Italian and English

LAMPEDUSA RT (MF) 1876 kHz
MAZARA DEL VALLO RT (MF) 2600 kHz

DIAGRAMS: pages 325 and 338	
Weather Bulletins	
On receipt 0333 0833 1233 1633 2033	Storm warnings: Near gale warnings in Italian and English for Area 10
0135 0735 1335 1935	Near gale warnings, synopsis, 12 or 18 hour forecast and outlook for a further 12 hours in Italian and English for Area 10
Navigational Warnings	
On receipt 0333 0833 1233 1633 2033	In Italian and English

MESSINA RT (MF) 2789 kHz

DIAGRAMS: pages 325 and 338	
Weather Bulletins	
On receipt 0333 0833 1233 1633 2033	Storm warnings: Near gale warnings in Italian and English for Areas 8, 9, 11 & 12
0135 0735 1335 1935	Near gale warnings, synopsis, 12 or 18 hour forecast and outlook for a further 12 hours in Italian and English for Areas 8, 9, 11 & 12
Navigational Warnings	
On receipt 0333 0833 1233 1633 2033	In Italian and English

PALERMO

A	1852	RT (MF)		
West Coast				
B	Ch 27	VHF	Capri	40°33′N 14°15′E
	Ch 01		Posillipo	40°41′N 14°10′E
	Ch 25		Serra del Tuono	39°55′N 15°50′E
	Ch 62		Varco del Salice	40°19′N 15°04′E
Sicilia				
D	Ch 61	VHF	Cefalu	38°01′N 13°58′E
E	Ch 81		Erice	38°05′N 12°35′E
C	Ch 85		Forte Spuria	38°16′N 15°37′E
D	Ch 27		Sferracavallo	38°08′N 13°23′E
	Ch 84		Ustica	38°42′N 13°11′E
Sicilian Channel				
E	Ch 22	VHF	Pantelleria	36°45′N 12°00′E
Sicilia				
F	Ch 82	VHF	Caltabellotta	37°35′N 13°13′E
G	Ch 86		Campo Lato Alto	37°17′N 15°12′E
F	Ch 26		Gela	37°04′N 14°15′E
	Ch 25		Mazara del Vallo	37°41′N 12°37′E
G	Ch 85		Siracusa	37°06′N 15°13′E
Isole Pelagie				
H	Ch 21	VHF	Grecale	35°31′N 12°38′E
	Ch 25		Lampedusa	35°30′N 12°36′E
South Coast				
I	Ch 62	VHF	Capo Armi	35°57′N 15°41′E
	Ch 20		Capo Colonna	39°02′N 17°10′E
	Ch 26		Monte Parano	40°27′N 17°26′E
	Ch 84		Ponta Stilo	38°26′N 16°34′E

DIAGRAMS: pages 325 and 338

Weather Bulletins

A: On receipt 0333 0833 1233 1633 2033	Storm warnings: Near gale warnings in Italian and English for Areas 8-10
B-I: On receipt	Storm warnings: Near gale warnings in Italian and English on: **B** for Areas 6-9; **C** for Areas 8, 9, 11 & 12; **D** & **E** for Areas 8-10; **F** & **H** for Area 10; **G** for Areas 10 & 11; **I** for Areas 11 & 12
A-I: 0135 0735 1335 1935	Near gale warnings, synopsis, 12 or 18 hour forecast and outlook for a further 12 hours in Italian and English on: **A, D** & **E** for Areas 8-10, **B** for Areas 6-9; **C** for Areas 8, 9, 11 & 12; **F** & **H** for Area 10; **G** for Areas 10 & 11; **I** for Areas 11 & 12

Navigational Warnings

A-I: On receipt 0333 0833 1233 1633 2033	In Italian and English

PORTO TORRES RT (MF) 2719 kHz

DIAGRAMS: pages 325 and 338

Weather Bulletins

On receipt 0303 0803 1203 1603 2003	Storm Warnings: Near gale warnings in Italian and English for Areas 1, 2, 6 & 7
0135 0735 1335 1935	Near gale warnings, synopsis, 12 or 18 hour forecast and outlook for a further 12 hours in Italian and English for Areas 1, 2, 6 & 7

Navigational Warnings

On receipt 0303 0803 1203 1603 2003	In Italian and English

ALGHERO

ALGHERO	Port and Marina 850 Berths 150 Visitor Berths	40°34′N 8°19′E
☎ +39 079 953174 & 986811	Depth: 1 - 4 m, Maximum LOA: 15 m	Fax +39 079 984606
FREQUENCY: Ch 11 16		HOURS: 0700-1900 LT

ARBATAX	Port and Marina 80 Berths in Port 350 in Marina	39°56′·60N 9°42′·07E
☎ Port and Marina: +39 0782 667093 & 627878	Depth: 4 - 10 m, Maximum LOA: 30 m	Fax Port: +39 0782 667093

AUGUSTA, SICILIA	Marinas	37°13′·87N 15°13′·06E
☎ +39 0931 978695, 978922 & 521881 harbour@augol.it	Cala Del Molo: Depth: 8 m, Maximum LOA: 25 m Darsena Servizi: Depth: 7 m, Maximum LOA: 40 m Terravecchia: Depth: 2·5 - 6·6 m	Fax +39 0931 978009 www.augol.it/porto
FREQUENCY: Port Operations: Ch 09 11 16	LOCATION: Cala del Molo	HOURS: 0700-1900 LT

BOSA	Marina 270 Berths	40°17′N 8°28′E
☎ Porto Fluviale: +39 0785 375550 Porto Commerciale: +39 0785 373554 Bosa Marina: +39 0785 373419	Depth: 2 - 4·5 m in River Temo, 1 - 12 m in the Bay	Fax
FREQUENCY: Ch 14 16		HOURS: 0700-1900 LT

CAGLIARI	Port and Marina 500 Berths 30 Visitor Berths	39°12′N 9°06′E
☎ Port: +39 070 669467 & 669468 Marina: +39 070 6051901 Yacht Club: +39 070 300240	Maximum LOA: No Limit	Fax Port: +39 070 669467 & 669468 Marina: +39 070 653501
FREQUENCY: Port & Y.C.: Ch 11 16 Marina: Ch 09 16		HOURS: Port: 0700-1900 LT

CANNETO DI LIPARI, ISOLE EOLIE	Port	38°29′N 14°58′E
☎ Port: +39 090 9811320 Emergency: +39 090 9813222		Fax +39 090 9811320
FREQUENCY: Ch 11 16		HOURS: H24

CANNIGIONE	Marina 400 Berths	41°01′·7N 9°32′·6E
☎ +39 0789 88422	Depth: maximum 3·5 m, Maximum LOA: 25 m	Fax +39 0789 99580
FREQUENCY: Ch 11 16		HOURS: 0700-1900 LT

CARLOFORTE, ISOLA DI SAN PIETRO	Marina and Port 325 Berths	39°09′N 8°19′E
☎ Port: +39 0781 854023 Jetty Legal Navale: +39 0781 855658 Jetty Siddi-Bakika: +39 0781 854437 Jetty Mirinatur: +39 0330 430095	Depth: 1 - 5 m, Maximum LOA: 30 m	Fax Port: +39 0781 854023
FREQUENCY: Port: Ch 11 16 Siddi-Bakika Jetty: Ch 72		HOURS: H24

CASTELSARDO	Marina 500 Berths	40°54′·8N 8°42′·1E
☎ +39 079 470916	Depth: 1 - 5 m, Maximum LOA: 28 m	Fax
FREQUENCY: Ch 09		HOURS: HX

CATANIA, SICILIA	Port	37°30′N 15°06′E
☎ +39 095 531667		Fax +39 095 533962
FREQUENCY: Ch 12 16		HOURS: H24
CATANIA	**Yacht Clubs (YC)**	**37°29′·16N 15°05′·90E**
☎ YC1: +39 095 531443 YC2: +39 095 531347 YC3: +39 095 531178 YC4: +39 095 531139	Depth: YC1: 4 - 8 m, 25 Berths YC2: 4 - 10 m, Maximum LOA: 25 m. 100 Berths YC3: 3 - 12 m, Maximum LOA: 15 m 160 Berths YC4: 3 - 10 m, Maximum LOA: 20 m 65 Berths	Fax YC4: +39 095 531167
FREQUENCY: YC1: Ch 77 YC2: Ch 06 YC3: Ch 09 16 YC4: Ch 12 16		HOURS: Port: 0700-1900 LT

GELA, SICILIA	Port	37°03′·7N 14°13′·8E
Tel: +39 0933 922024		Fax: +39 0933 917755
FREQUENCY: Ch 15 16		HOURS: 0700-1900 LT

ISOLA MADDALENA	Port — Very Few Visitor Berths	41°12′·57N 9°24′·57E
Tel: Port: +39 0789 790600 Marina: +39 0789 728133		Fax: Port: +39 0789 737361
FREQUENCY: Ch 9 11 16		HOURS: 0700-1900 LT

LICATA, SICILIA	Port	37°06′N 13°56′E
Tel: +39 0922 774113	Depth: 2 m (Leisure craft)	Fax: +39 0922 776655 & 774113
FREQUENCY: Ch 14 16		HOURS: H24

MARINA DELL'ORSO	Marina — 450 Berths 50 Visitor Berths	41°08′·5N 9°29′·7E
Tel: Port: +39 0789 99477	Depth: 2·4 - 3·4 m, Maximum LOA: 35 m	Fax: Port: +39 0789 99468
FREQUENCY: Ch 09 16		HOURS: HX

MARINA DI CAPITANA	Marina — 445 Berths 90 Visitor Berths	39°12′·28N 9°17′·90E
Tel: +39 0703 71385	Depth: 3 m, Maximum LOA: 27 m	Fax: +39 0703 73077
FREQUENCY: Ch 09 16		HOURS: HX

MARINA DI PORTISCO	Marina — 600 Berths 65 Visitor Berths 18 Dedicated Berths for 50 m + Vessels	41°02′N 9°31′·4E
Tel: +39 0789 33520	Depth: 3 - 12 m, Maximum LOA: 100 m	Fax: +39 0789 33560
FREQUENCY: Ch 09		HOURS: HX

MARZAMENI	Marina — 100 Berths	36°44′·0N 15°07′·5E
Tel: +39 0931 841505	Depth: 1 - 7 m, Maximum LOA: 20 m	Fax:
FREQUENCY: Ch 06 16		HOURS: HX

MAZARA DEL VALLO, SICILIA	Port	37°39′N 12°35′E
Tel: Port: +39 0923 946388		Fax: +39 0923 941020
FREQUENCY: Port: Ch 16		HOURS: H24

MESSINA, SICILIA	Port	38°12′N 15°34′E
Tel: +39 090 45830 & 41896		Fax: +39 090 59350
FREQUENCY: Port: Ch 14 16 25		HOURS: Port Operations: H24
All vessels should maintain a continuous listening watch on VHF Ch 16 while passing through the Stretto di Messina		

MESSINA MARINA DEL NETTUNO	Marina — 160 Berths Visitor Berths Available	38°11′·8N 15°33′·6E
Tel: +39 090 344139 danilobl@tin.it	Maximum LOA: 20 m	Fax:
FREQUENCY: Ch 09		HOURS: HX

MOLFETTA	Marina — 80 Berths	41°12′·9N 16°35′·4E
Tel: +39 080 9971727	Depth: 1 - 6 m, Maximum LOA: 30 m	Fax: +39 080 9971727
FREQUENCY: Ch 14 16		HOURS: 0700-1900 LT

MONFALCONE	Port	45°48′N 13°32′E
☎ +39 0481 712111, 712112, 712108 & 485049 cpmflamm@libero.it		Fax: +39 0481 483408 www.porto.monfalcone.gorizia.it
FREQUENCY: Ch 11 16 and MF 2182 kHz		HOURS: 0600-2000 LT
HANNIBAL MARINA	**Marina** 300 Berths	45°46′·95N 13°32′·25E
☎ +39 0481 411541	Depth:3 - 13 m, Maximum LOA: 12 m	Fax: +39 0481 40446
FREQUENCY: Ch 09 16		

MONOPOLI	Port and Marina	40°57′·4N 17°18′·4E
☎ Port: +39 080 742855, 79502 & 802017 Marina: +39 080 9303105 circomare.monopoli@tiscalinet.it	Depth: Close to the head of Molo Margherita 4·5 m, at the centre of the basin 4 m, Maximum LOA: 100 m	Fax: Marina: +39 080 937509
FREQUENCY: Ch 16 22		HOURS: Port: 0700-1900 LT Marina: HX

NUMANA	Marina 700 Berths	43°30′·5N 13°37′·7E
☎ +39 071 7360377	Depth: 2 - 3·5 m, Maximum LOA: 25 m	Fax:
FREQUENCY: Ch 09		HOURS: HX

OLBIA	Port & Marina 200 Berths	40°55′N 9°34′E
☎ Port: +39 0789 21243 Circolo Nautico: +39 0789 26187	Depth: 2·5 - 7 m, Maximum LOA: 25 m	Fax: +39 0789 27737
FREQUENCY: Port: Ch 11 16 Circolo Nautico: Ch 12		HOURS: H24

PALERMO, SICILIA	Port and Marina	38°07′N 13°22′E
☎ Port: +39 091 334051		Fax: Port: +39 091 325519
FREQUENCY: Ch 11 12 16	LOCATION: Molo Trapezoidale	HOURS: Port: 0800-2000 LT
	Marina 475 Berths	38°08′·66N 13°22′·46E
☎ +39 091 364123	Depth: 2 - 12 m, Maximum LOA: 60 m	Fax: +39 091 364225
FREQUENCY: Ch 16 74	LOCATION: Marina Villa Igiea, Porto Acquasanta	HOURS: HX

PANTELLERIA, ISOLA DI PANTELLERIA	Port	36°50′N 11°57′E
☎ +39 0923 911027 circomarepantelleria@interfree.it		Fax: +39 0923 911027
FREQUENCY: Ch 14 16		HOURS: H24

PERD'E' SALI	Marina 200 Berths 20 Visitor Berths	39°01′·7N 9°02′E
☎ +39 0709 253145	Depth: 2 - 3 m, Maximum LOA: 18 m	Fax: +39 0709 253145
FREQUENCY: Ch 16 74		HOURS: HX

PORTO CERVO	Marina 720 Berths 80 Visitor Berths	41°08′·2N 9°32′·5E
☎ Capitainerie: +39 0789 737095 Marina: +39 0789 905111	Maximum LOA: 100 m	Fax: Marina: +39 0789 91153
FREQUENCY: Ch 09 11 16		HOURS: 0700-1900 LT

PORTO CONTO MARINA	Marina 250 Berths	40°35′N 8°12′E
☎ +39 0799 42013	Maximum LOA: 25 m	Fax: +39 0799 42013
FREQUENCY: Ch 09		HOURS: HX

PORTO DI SANT' ANTIOCO (PONTE ROMANO)	Port: CALL: Sant' Antioco Capitaneria	39°03'N 8°28'E
Tel: +39 0781 83071		Fax: +39 0781 83071
FREQUENCY: Ch 14 16		HOURS: 0700-1900 LT

PORTO EMPEDOCLE, SICILIA	Port	37°17'N 13°32'E
Tel: Port: +39 0922 636640		Fax: Hr Mr: +39 0922 535747
FREQUENCY: Port: Ch 14 16		HOURS: Port: 0700-1900 LT

PORTO ROTONDO	Marina 633 Berths 63 Visitor Berths	41°01·7N 9°32'·6E
Tel: Port: +39 0789 34203	Depth: 1·5 - 4·8 m, Maximum LOA: 35 m	Fax: Port: +39 0789 34368
FREQUENCY: Ch 09 H24		HOURS: Office: 0900-1300 1500-1900 LT

PORTO TORRES	Port and Marina 150 Berths	40°50'N 8°24'E
Tel: Port: +39 079 502258 & 502259 Cormoranoc Marina: +39 079 512290 cormarano@rentec.net	Depth: 1 - 4 m, Maximum LOA: 35 m	Fax: Port: +39 079 502090 Cormoranoc Marina: +39 079 512250
FREQUENCY: Port: Ch 09 12 14 16 Marina: Ch 16 74		HOURS: Port: 0800-2100 LT

PORTO OTTIOLU	Marina 405 Berths 100 Visitor Berths	40°44'·2N 9°42'·6E
Tel: +39 0784 846205 portottioulu@isitalia.it	Depth: 2·7 - 3 m, Maximum LOA: 30 m	Fax: +39 0784 846209
FREQUENCY: Ch 09		HOURS: HX

PORT PALAU	Marina 500 Berths	41°10'N 9°23'E
Tel: Port: +39 0789 709501 Marina: +39 0789 708435	Depth: 2 - 4 m, Maximum LOA: 25 m	Fax: Marina: +39 0789 708435
FREQUENCY: Ch 09 16		HOURS: HX

PORT RAPHAEL YACHT CLUB	Marina 50 Berths	41°11'N 9°22'E
Tel: +39 0789 700151	Depth: maximum 4·5 m, Maximum LOA: 40 m	Fax:
FREQUENCY: Ch 09		HOURS: HX

PUNTA MARANA	Marina 300 Berths	41°00'·3N 9°33'·7E
Tel: Port: +39 0789 32088	Depth: 2 - 2·5m, Maximum LOA: 12 m	Fax: Port: +39 0789 32089
FREQUENCY: Ch 09 16		HOURS: HX

RIPOSTO SICILIA	Port & Marina 335 Berths	37°44'·0N 15°12'·6E
Tel: Port: +39 095 931862 Marina: +39 095 937825	Depth: 1 - 12 m, Maximum LOA: 50 m	Fax: Port: +39 095 931862
FREQUENCY: Ch 14 16		HOURS: 0700-1900 LT

SAN NICOLO L'ARENA, SICILIA	Marina 450 Berths 45 Visitor Berths	38°0'·9N 13°37'·0E
Tel: +39 091 8125946	Depth: 1 - 5 m, Max LOA: 15 m	Fax:
FREQUENCY: Ch 14 16		HOURS:

SAN NICOLA L'ARENA, SICILIA	Marina 800 Berths 80 Visitor Berths	38°01'·70N 13°37'·19E
Tel: +39 0941 874560 maresud@gestelnet.it	Depth: 0·5 - 4 m, Maximum LOA: 35 m	Fax: +39 0941 874655
FREQUENCY: Ch 14 16		HOURS: Summer H24 Winter 0800-2000 LT

SANTA TERESA DI GALLURA	Marina 1000 Berths	41°14′·6N 9°12′·0E
☎ +39 0789 754602	Depth: 2 - 5 m, Maximum LOA: 30 m	Fax
FREQUENCY: Ch 06 09 16 73		HOURS: HX

SCIACCA, SICILIA	Port: CALL: Circomare Sciacca 150 Berths	37°29′·9N 13°04′·7E
☎ +39 0925 22219 & 905166 circomaresciacca@ibero.it	Depth: 2 - 5 m, Maximum LOA: 15 m	Fax +39 0925 22219
FREQUENCY: Ch 16		HOURS: 0700-1900 LT

SIBARI MARINA, SICILIA	Marina 500 Berths 20 Visitor Berths	39°44′·8N 16°29′·5E
☎ +39 0981 79027 cantnaut@tiscalinet.it	Depth: 3 m	Fax +39 0981 79147 www.marina-sibari.it
FREQUENCY: Ch 09 16		HOURS: Summer H24 Winter 0730-1700 LT

SIRACUSA, SICILIA	Port	37°03′·2N 15°17′·7E
☎ Port Operations: +39 0931 66616 & 759077	Grand Harbour: Depth: 4 - 8 m, Maximum LOA: 50 m Port Piccolo: Depth: 1 - 3 m, Maximum LOA: 10 m	Fax Port Operations: +39 0931 69260 & 759077
FREQUENCY: Ch 09 16		HOURS: H24

STINTINO (PORTO MANNU)	Marina 125 Berths 30 Visitor Berths	40°56′·12N 8°13′·97E
☎ +39 079 523381	Depth: 2 - 2·5 m, Maximum LOA: 13 m	Fax
FREQUENCY: Ch 09		HOURS: HX

TERMINI IMERESE, SICILIA	Port 30 Visitor Berths	37°59′N 13°42′E
☎ Port: +39 091 8141007 Club Punto a Sud +39 091 8111912 circomare-termini@libero.it	Depth: 2 - 10 m, Maximum LOA: 15 m	Fax +39 091 911027
FREQUENCY: Port: Ch 14 16		HOURS: 0700-1900 LT

TORRE GRANDE	Port & Marina 400 Berths	39°54′·1N 8°29′·6E
☎ Port: +39 0783 72262 Marina: +39 0783 22189	Depth: 1·5 - 3 m, Maximum LOA: 25 m	Fax Marina: +39 0783 28800
FREQUENCY: Ch 09 16		HOURS: HX

ITALY, WEST COAST

	Telephone +39	**Fax** +39	**Others**
MRCC ROMA	06 5923569 06 5924145 06 59084527 06 59084697	06 5922737 06 59084793	**Telex** +43 614103 COGECAP, **Inmarsat A** (AOR-E) 1151233 (Tel) (AOR-E) 1151234 (Fax) capitaneria.roma@libero.it
MRSC GENOVA	010 2412222 010 2777388	010 261064	mrsc@mrsc.porto.genova.it
MRSC LIVORNO	0586 894493 0586 893362	0586 826090	compliop@portnet.it
MRSC NAPOLI	081 5536017 081 2445111	081 2450347 081 2510412	cp_napoli@libero.it
MRSC REGGIO CALABRIA	0965 6561 0965 650092	0965 656333	comprc@netonline.it

CIVITAVECCHIA RT (MF) 1888 kHz

DIAGRAMS: pages 325 and 338	
Weather Bulletins	
On receipt 0533 0933 1333 1833 2333	Storm warnings: Near gale warnings in Italian and English for Areas 5-9
0135 0735 1335 1935	Near gale warnings, synopsis, 12 or 18 hour forecast and outlook for a further 12 hours in Italian and English for Areas 5-9
Navigational Warnings	
On receipt 0533 0933 1333 1833 2333	In Italian and English

GENOVA RT (MF) 2722 kHz

DIAGRAMS: pages 325 and 338	
Weather Bulletins	
On receipt 0333 0833 1233 1633 2033	Storm warnings: Near gale warnings in Italian and English for Areas 1, 4 & 5
0135 0735 1335 1935	Near gale warnings, synopsis, 12 or 18 hour forecast and outlook for a further 12 hours in Italian and English for Areas 1, 4 & 5
Navigational Warnings	
On receipt 0333 0833 1233 1633 2033	In Italian and English

LIVORNO RT (MF) 2591 kHz

DIAGRAMS: pages 325 and 338	
Weather Bulletins	
On receipt 0333 0833 1233 1633 2033	Storm warnings: Near gale warnings in Italian and English for Areas 4-7
0135 0735 1335 1935	Near gale warnings, synopsis, 12 or 18 hour forecast and outlook for a further 12 hours in Italian and English for Areas 4-7
Navigational Warnings	
On receipt 0333 0833 1233 1633 2033	In Italian and English

NAPOLI RT (MF) 2632 kHz

DIAGRAMS: pages 325 and 338	
Weather Bulletins	
On receipt 0333 0833 1233 1633 2033	Storm warnings: Near gale warnings in Italian and English for Areas 6-9
0135 0735 1335 1935	Near gale warnings, synopsis, 12 or 18 hour forecast and outlook for a further 12 hours in Italian and English for Areas 6-9
Navigational Warnings	
On receipt 0333 0833 1233 1633 2033	In Italian and English

ROMA VHF

Sardegna				
A	Ch 82	VHF	P. Campu Spina	39°23′N 8°34′E
	Ch 62		Margine Rosso	39°14′N 9°14′E
	Ch 04		Monte Serpeddi	39°22′N 9°18′E
B	Ch 26		Porto Cervo	41°08′N 9°32′E
	Ch 28		Monte Moro	41°06′N 9°31′E
	Ch 85		Monte Limbara	40°51′N 9°10′E
	Ch 26		Osilo	40°44′N 8°40′E
West Coast				
C	Ch 07	VHF	Monte Bignone	43°52′N 7°44′E
	Ch 25		Castellaccio	44°26′N 8°56′E
	Ch 27		Zoagli	44°19′N 9°19′E
D	Ch 26		Gorgona	43°26′N 9°54′E
	Ch 61		Monte Nero	43°29′N 10°21′E
E	Ch 01		Monte Argentario	42°23′N 11°10′E
	Ch 64		Torre Chiaruccia	42°02′N 11°50′E
F	Ch 25		Monte Cavo	41°45′N 12°43′E

DIAGRAMS: pages 325 and 338

Weather Bulletins	
A-F: On receipt	Storm warnings: Near gale warnings in Italian and English on: **A** for Areas 2, 3 & 6-9; **B** for Areas 1, 2, 6 & 7; **C** for Areas 1, 4 & 5; **D** for Areas 4-7; **E** for Areas 5-9; **F** for Areas 5-7
A-F: 0135 0735 1335 1935	Near gale warnings, synopsis, 12 or 18 hour forecast and outlook for a further 12 hours in Italian and English on: **A** for Areas 2, 3 & 6-9; **B** for Areas 1, 2, 6 & 7; **C** for Areas 1, 4 & 5; **D** for Areas 4-7; **E** for Areas 5-9; **F** for Areas 5-7
Navigational Warnings	
A-F: On receipt	In Italian and English - refer to diagram MSI Broadcasts

ACCIAROLI

ACCIAROLI	Marina 100 Berths	40°10′·5N 15°02′·7E
Tel: +39 0974 904477	Depth: 2 - 4 m, Maximum, LOA: 20 m	Fax:
		HOURS: HX

AGROPOLI

AGROPOLI	Marina 1100 Berths	40°21′·3N 14°58′·9E
Tel: +39 0974 824545 euromar@oneonline.it	Depth: 1 - 6 m, Maximum LOA: 50 m	Fax: +39 0974 824710 www.oneonline.it/euromar
FREQUENCY: Ch 16		HOURS: HX

ALASSIO

ALASSIO	Port and Marina 400 Berths Visitor Berths Available	44°01′·1N 08°11′·7E
Tel: Port: +39 0182 642586 Marina: +39 0182 645012 cnamalassio@triscalinet.it	Depth: 2 - 5 m, Maximum LOA: 30 m	Fax: Port: +39 0182 640840 Marina: +39 0182 648655
FREQUENCY: Ch 09 16		HOURS: Marina: 0900-1200 1500-1800 LT

ALBARELLA

ALBARELLA	Marina 453 Berths 45 Visitor Berths	45°03′·7N 12°21′·5E
Tel: +39 0426 332262	Depth: 2·5 - 4 m, Maximum LOA: 25 m	Fax: +39 0426 332263
FREQUENCY: Ch 09		HOURS: HX

AMALFI

AMALFI	Port 300 Berths	40°37′·79N 14°36′·05E
Tel: +39 089 871366		Fax: +39 089 871366
FREQUENCY: Ch 14 16		HOURS: 0800-2000 LT

ANDORA MARINA	Port 750 Berths	43°56'·9N 08°09'·5E
☎ +39 0182 88313 porto@andora.it	Depth: 1 - 4 m, Maximum LOA: 20 m	Fax +39 0182 681707
FREQUENCY: Ch 16		HOURS: 0800-1900 LT

ANZIO	Port	41°27'N 12°38'E
☎ Port: +39 0698 46235		Fax +39 0698 46235
FREQUENCY: Port: Ch 11 16		HOURS: H24
NETTUNO	**Marina 850 Berths 80 Visitor Berths**	**41°27'·1N 12°39'·6E**
☎ +39 0698 05404 info@marina-di-nettuno.it	Depth: 3 - 5 m, Maximum LOA: 20 m	Fax +39 06 9881780 www.marina.di.nettuno.it
FREQUENCY: Ch 09 16		HOURS: H24

ARENZANO	Marina 186 Berths	44°24'·1N 08°41'·1E
☎ +39 010 91234537	Depth: 1·5 - 4 m, Maximum LOA: 18 m	Fax
FREQUENCY: Ch 09		HOURS:

BAGNARA CALABRIA	Port	38°17'N 15°48'E
☎ +39 0966 371303		Fax
FREQUENCY: Ch 11 16		HOURS: 0700-1300 LT

BORDIGHERA	Port and Marina 250 Berths	43°47'N 7°39'·2E
☎ +39 0184 265656 & 266688	Depth: 2 - 5 m, Maximum LOA: 20 m	Fax
FREQUENCY: Ch 16 25		HOURS: 0700-1900 LT

CAMOGLI	Harbour 40 Berths	44°21'·1N 9°09'·0E
☎ Harbour Office +39 0185 770032 Nautica Star (Berths): +39 0185 773673	Max LOA: 9 m	Fax
FREQUENCY: Ch 16		HOURS: HX

CAPRI (MARINA GRANDE)	Marina 300 Berths	40°33'·5N 14°14'·6E
☎ Luise Int. & Co.: +39 081 5528670 Porto Turistico di Capri: +39 081 8377602	Depth: 3 - 10 m, Maximum LOA: 50 m	Fax Luise Int. & Co.: +39 081 5527368 Porto Turistico di Capri: +39 081 8375318
FREQUENCY: Port: Ch 14 16		HOURS: Port Authorities: 0700-1900 LT

CASAMICCIOLA	Marina 90 Berths	40°45'·1N 13°54'·6E
☎ +39 081 980686	Depth: 1 - 7 m, Maximum LOA: 20 m	Fax +39 081 995666
FREQUENCY: Ch 09 16		HOURS: HX

CASTELLAMMARE DEL GOLFO	Marina 400 Berths	38°02'·0N 12°52'·9E
☎ +39 0924 31261		Fax
FREQUENCY: Ch 16		HOURS: 0800-1400 LT

CASTELLAMARE DI STABIA	Port and Marina	40°41'N 14°29'E
☎ +39 081 8711077 & 8711086 compcs@tin.it		Fax +39 081 8710078
FREQUENCY: Ch 09 11 16		HOURS: 0700-1900 LT

CATANZARO	Marina: CALL: Catanzaro Lido	38°49'N 16°37'E
☎ +39 0961 31642		Fax:
FREQUENCY: Ch 14 16		HOURS: 0700-1900 LT

CAVO	Marina 300 Berths	42°51'·6N 10°25'·6E
☎ +39 0565 949910 cavo@capitaneriaisolad'elba.it	Depth: 1 - 2·5 m, Maximum LOA: 15 m	Fax: +39 0565 949910
FREQUENCY: Ch 16		HOURS: HX

CERVIA	Port 300 Berths	44°16'·1N 12°21'·6E
☎ +39 0544 72355	Depth: 2 - 3 m, Maximum LOA: 22 m	Fax:
FREQUENCY: Ch 14 16		HOURS: 0700-1900 LT

CHIAIOLELLA	Marina 230 Berths	40°44'·7N 14°00'·5E
☎ +39 330 811949 & 335 833414 info@nauticacostamer.it	Depth: 1 - 5 m, Maximum LOA: 18 m	Fax: +39 081 8969029 www.nauticacostamare.it
FREQUENCY: Ch 11 16		HOURS: 0700-1900 LT

CHIAVARI	Marina 469 Berths	44°18'·7N 09°19'·1E
☎ +39 0185 364081	Depth: 2·5 - 5 m, Maximum LOA: 25 m	Fax: +39 0185 376007
FREQUENCY: Ch 09 16		HOURS: 0700-1900 LT

CIVITAVECCHIA	Port	42°05'·97N 11°46'·32E
☎ +39 0766 35993 & 501717	Depth: 4 - 8 m, Maximum LOA: 50 m	Fax: +39 0766 20250
FREQUENCY: Ch 06 15 16		HOURS: 0700-1900 LT

COPPOLA PINETAMARE	Marina 500 Berths	40°59'·0N 13°58'·3E
☎ +39 081 5097373	Depth: 1·5 - 3 m, Maximum LOA: 20 m	Fax:
FREQUENCY: Ch 12		HOURS: HX

CROTONE	Port & Marina 150 Berths Visitor Berths Available	39°05'N 17°08'E
☎ Port: +39 0962 20721 Ciro' Marina: +39(0)962 36328	Depth: 5 - 6·5 m, Maximum LOA:15 m	Fax: +39 0962 902094
FREQUENCY: Port: Ch 11 16	LOCATION: New Marina 2 miles south of Punta Alice	HOURS: Port: 0700-1900 LT

DIANO MARINA	Marina 270 Berths 13 Visitor Berths	43°54'·44N 8°05'·19E
☎ +39 0183 494793	Depth: 1 - 2 m, Maximum LOA:14 m	Fax:
FREQUENCY: Ch 16		HOURS: 0100-1900 LT

FINALE LIGURE	Port and Marina 550 Berths	44°10'N 8°21'E
☎ +39 019 691985	Depth: 2 - 4·5 m, Maximum LOA: 18 m	Fax:
FREQUENCY: Ch 16 69		HOURS: 0600-1900 LT

FIUMICINO	Marina 200 Berths	41°46'·2N 12°13'·3E
☎ Capitaneria: +39 06 6581911 & 6451911	Maximum LOA: 15 m	Fax:
FREQUENCY: Port: Ch 16 Operations: Ch 13		HOURS: H24

FORMIA (PORTO NUOVO)	Harbour 500 Berths	41°15'·1N 13°37'·0E
☎ +39 0771 21552	Depth: 0·5 - 6 m, Maximum LOA: 30 m	Fax:
FREQUENCY: Ch 16		HOURS: 0800-2000 LT

GAETA	Port	41°13′N 13°35′E
☎ +39 0771 460100		Fax +39 0771 464724
FREQUENCY: Port: Ch 11 16		HOURS: 0700-1900 LT

GALLIPOLI	Port	40°03′·6N 17°58′·8E
☎ Port: +39 0833 476862	Depth: 5 - 12 m in Port, Depths in Senno del Canneto: 1 - 4 m, Maximum LOA: 20m	Fax Port: +39 0833 264023
FREQUENCY: Port: Ch 11 16		HOURS: Port: 0700-1900 LT

GENOVA	Port and Marinas	44°23′·3N 8°55′·3E
☎ Hr Mr: +39 010 2412226		Fax Hr Mr: +39 010 2412385
FREQUENCY: Signal Station: Ch 10 16 Port: Ch 11 16		HOURS: Port: 0700-1900 LT
SESTRI PONENTE	**Marina** 1200 Berths	
☎ +39 010 6512476	Depth: 2·5 - 8 m, Maximum LOA: 40 m	Fax +39 010 6512282
		HOURS: HX
FIERA DI GENOVA	**Marina** 280 Berths	
☎ +39 010 580760	Depth: 4 - 7 m, Maximum LOA: 25 m	Fax +39 010 532423
FREQUENCY: Ch 74		HOURS: 0830-1830 LT
ABRUZZI YACHT CLUB	**Marina**	
☎ +39 010 2461206	Depth: 6 - 7 m	Fax
FREQUENCY: Ch 11 16		HOURS: HX
MARINA PORTO ANTICO	**Marina** 280 Berths 25 Visitor Berths	44°24′·60N 08°55′·55E
☎ +39 010 2470039	Depth: 4·5 - 6 m, Maximum LOA: 35 m	Fax +39 010 252097 www.marinaportoantico.it
FREQUENCY: Ch 74		HOURS: HX
MARINA MOLO VECHIO	**Marina** 160 Berths	
☎ +39 010 27011 mmv@mmv.it or pesto@pesto.it	Depth: 9 - 11 m, Maximum LOA: 150 m	Fax +39 010 2701200 www.marinamolvechio.com
FREQUENCY: Ch 71		HOURS: HX

IMPERIA	Port & Marina 645 Berths 50 Visitor Berths	43°53′N 8°01′E
☎ Port: +39 0183 666333	Depth: 2 - 8 m, Maximum LOA: 30 m	Fax Port: +39 0183 652224
FREQUENCY: Ch 11 12 16 Porto Maurizio: Ch 09 16		HOURS: H24

ISCHIA, ISOLA D'ISCHIA	Port	40°44′N 13°56′E
☎ +39 081 991417		Fax +39 081 983853
FREQUENCY: Ch 13 15 16		HOURS: 1 June-30 Sept: H24 1 Oct-31 May: 0700-1900 LT

ISOLA DEL GIGLIO GIGLIO MARINA	Marina 190 Berths Limited Visitor Availability in Season	42°21′·5N 10°55′·4E
☎ +39 0564 809480	Depth: 1·5 - 5 m, Maximum LOA: 15 m	Fax
FREQUENCY: Ch 14 16		HOURS: 0700-1300 LT

LAMPEDUSA, ISOLA DI LAMPEDUSA	Port	35°29′N 12°36′E
☎ +39 0922 970141		Fax
FREQUENCY: Ch 14 16		HOURS: 0700-1900 LT

LA SPEZIA	Port 470 Berths	44°06′·2N 9°50′·3E
☎ +39 0187 28580	Depth: 2 - 4 m, Maximum LOA: 12 m	Fax +39 0187 770510
FREQUENCY: Port: Ch 09 11 12 14 16		HOURS: Port: 16 June-15 Sept: 0700-2300 LT 16 Sept-15 June: 0700-1900 LT

LAVAGNA	Marina 1600 Berths 140 Visitor Berths	44°18′·25N 09°20′·52E
☎ +39 0185 364192 portolavagna@tin.it	Depth: 2 - 5 m, Maximum LOA: 50 m	Fax +39 0185 376308
FREQUENCY: Ch 09 16		HOURS: H24

LIVORNO	Port and Marina 120 Berths	43°33′·4N 10°17′·2E
☎ Port: +39 0586 893362 Yacht Club: +39 0586 894123	Depth: 3 - 6 m, Maximum LOA: 30 m	Fax Port: +39 00586 8845578 Yacht Club: +39 0586 895355
FREQUENCY: Capitaneria: Ch 16 Yacht Club: Ch 09		HOURS: H24

LOANO	Port 475 Berth	44°08′·2N 08°16′·2E
☎ +39 019 675519 & 675445	Depth: 1·5 - 3 m, Maximum LOA: 30 m	Fax +39 019 669264
FREQUENCY: Ch 09 16		HOURS: H24

MARATEA	Marina 600 Berths	39°59′·2N 15°42′·6E
☎ +39 0973 877307	Depth: 2 - 7 m, Maximum, LOA: 35 m	Fax
FREQUENCY: Ch 16		HOURS: HX

MARCIANA MARINA	Marina 150 Berths	42°48′·4N 10°11′·9E
☎ Hr Mr: +39 0565 99169 Marina: +39 0565 99027	Depth: 2 - 7 m, Maximum LOA: 35 m	Fax Hr Mr: +39 0565 99169 Marina: +39 0565 904325
FREQUENCY: Hr Mr Ch 14 16. Marina: Ch 09		HOURS: HX

MARINA DI CALA GALERA	Marina 750 Berths 80 Visitor Berths	42°24′·2N 11°12′·6E
☎ +39 0564 833010	Depth: 2·5 - 5 m, Maximum LOA: 50 m	Fax +39 0564 832385
FREQUENCY: Ch 09 16		HOURS: HX

MARINA DI CAMEROTA	Marina 250 Berths	40°00′N 15°23′E
☎ +39 0974 920211	Depth: 1 - 4 m, Maximum LOA: 15 m	Fax
		HOURS: HX

MARINA DI CAMPO	Marina	42°44′·4N 10°14′·3E
☎ +39 0565 977980	Depth: 1·5 - 8 m	Fax
FREQUENCY: Ch 16		HOURS: 0800-1400 LT

MARINA VIGLIENA	Marina 180 Berths	40°50′·00N 14°18′·15E
☎ +39 081 7529017	Depth: 2 - 4·5 m, Maximum LOA: 22 m	Fax +39 081 7524570
FREQUENCY: Ch 16 72		HOURS: HX

MARSALA	Marina 100 Berths	40°00′N 15°23′E
☎ +39 0923 951184	Depth: 2 - 6 m, Maximum LOA: 20 m	Fax +39 0923 951030
FREQUENCY: Ch 14 16		HOURS: 0700-1900 LT

NAPOLI	Port and Marina	40°50'N 14°16'E
Port: +39 081 206118 Marina Vigliena: +39 081 7529017 & 7527632 Marina Molosiglio: +39 081 5511806, 5512331 & 5514057 Marina Santa Lucia: +39 081 7645517		Fax: Port:: +39 081 206149 Marina Vigliena: +39 081 7524570
FREQUENCY: Port: Ch 14 16 Marina: Ch 72		HOURS: H24
NOTES: 1. Vessels bound for the Anchorage Zones must report to the Operations Centre at the Napoli Harbour Master's Office on VHF Ch 14 at least 1h before ETA 2. All vessels leaving the port must report to the Operations Centre at the Napoli Harbour Master's Office on VHF Ch 14		

NISIDA	Marina 400 Berths	40°47'·9N 14°09'·9E
Sena: +39 081 7622194 Onda Azzura: +39 081 5708000	Depth: 1 - 6 m, Maximum LOA: 26 m	Fax:
		HOURS: HX

PONZA, ISOLA DI PONZA	Port	40°54'N 12°58'E
+39 0771 80027		Fax:
FREQUENCY: Ch 14 16		HOURS: 0700-1900 LT

PORTICI	Marina	40°48'N 14°20'E
+39 081 7767827		Fax:
FREQUENCY: Ch 11 16		HOURS: 0700-1900 LT

PORTO ERCOLE	Marina 1700 Berths 80 Visitor Beerths	42°23'·6N 11°12'·7E
+39 0564 833923 & 833010	Depth: 1 - 5 m, Maximum LOA: 50 m	Fax: +39 0564 813325
FREQUENCY: Ch 16		HOURS: HX

PORTOFERRAIO	Port & Marina 300 Berths	42°48'·7N 10°19'·8E
+39 0565 914041	Depth: 3 - 10 m, Maximum LOA: 40 m	Fax: +39 0565 918598
FREQUENCY: Capitaneria: Ch 11 16		HOURS: Summer 0700-2300 LT Winter 0700-1900 LT

PORTOFINO	Marina 270 Berths	44°18'·2N 09°12'·9E
+39 0185 269040	Depth: 1 - 4 m, Maximum LOA: 80 m	Fax:
FREQUENCY: Ch 12		HOURS: 0100-1900 LT

PORTO LOTTI	Marina 550 Berths	42°48'·5N 10°11'·9E
+39 0187 5321 portolotti@pn.itnet.it	Depth: 2·8 - 7·5 m, Maximum LOA: 50 - 60 m	Fax: +39 0187 53245 www.nautica.it/portolotti/home.htm
FREQUENCY: Ch 09		HOURS: HX

PORTO MAURIZIO	Port 610 Berths 35 Visitor Berths	43°52'·4N 08°01'·8E
+39 0183 666705 impmare@tin.it	Depth: 2 - 8 m, Maximum LOA: 30 m	Fax: +39 0183 650246
FREQUENCY: Ch 09 16		HOURS: HX

PORTO SANT ANTONIO	Marina 150 Berths 15 Visitor Berths	41°13'·0N 13°34'·8E
+39 0771 311013	Depth: 2 - 4 m, Maximum LOA: 50 m	Fax: +39 0771 464580
FREQUENCY: Ch 09		HOURS: H24

PORTO SANTO STEFANO	Port and Marina 130 Berths 20 Visitor Berths	42°26'·3N 11°07'·4E
☎ +39 0564 810395 circomarecivitanova@tiscali.it	Depth: 4 - 8 m, Maximum LOA: 30 m	Fax +39 0564 813325
FREQUENCY: Port: Ch 14 16		HOURS: Port: 16 June-15 Sept: 0700-2300 LT 16 Sept-15 June: 0700-1900 LT

PORTO VENERE	Marina 32 Berths Visitor Berths	44°03'N 09°50'·2E
☎ +39 0187 793040	Depth: 1 - 4 m, Maximum LOA: 20 m	Fax +39 0187 793041
FREQUENCY: Ch 09 11		HOURS: HX

POZZUOLI	Marina 150 Berths	40°49'·2N 14°06'·9E
☎ +39 081 5261140	Depth: 1 - 6 m, Maximum LOA: 35 m	Fax +39 081 5261140
FREQUENCY: Ch 14 16		HOURS: 0700-1900 LT

PROCIDA	Marina	40°46'N 14°02'E
☎ +39 081 8967381		Fax +39 081 8967381
FREQUENCY: Ch 11 16		HOURS: 0700-1900 LT

PUNTA ALA MARINA	Marina 895 Berths 90 Visitor Berths	42°48'·5N 10°44'·0E
☎ +39 0564 922217 Torre di Controllo: +39 0564 922 784	Depth: 1·8 - 4 m, Maximum LOA: 32 m	Fax +39 0564 921086
FREQUENCY: Ch 09 16		HOURS: HX

RAPALLO	Marina 400 Berths	44°20'·6N 09°14'·1E
☎ +39 0185 6891 & 50583	Depth: 3 - 7 m, Maximum LOA: 40 m	Fax +39 0185 63619
FREQUENCY: Ch 09 25		HOURS: 1000-1900 LT

REGGIO CALABRIA	Marina Visitor Berths (Stretto di Messina)	38°07'·55N 15°39'·10E
☎ Capitaneria: +39 0965 21139 & 0966 371303	Depth: 4 - 7 m, Maximum LOA: 12 m	Fax
FREQUENCY: Ch 11 16		HOURS: H24

RIO MARINA	Marina 100 Berths Visitor Berths	42°48'·9N 10°26'·0E
☎ +39 0565 962109	Depth: 1 - 4 m, Maximum LOA: m	Fax
FREQUENCY: Ch 16		HOURS: HX

RIVA DI TRAIANO	Marina 1054 Berths 113 Visitor Berths	42°03'N 11°49'E
☎ +39 0766 580193 rivaditraiano@eturia.net	Depth 2·4 m, Maximum LOA: 42 m	Fax +39 0766 500696
FREQUENCY: Ch 09 16	LOCATION: Near Torre Marangone	HOURS: H24

ROMA - PORTO TURISTICO DI ROMA	Marina 808 Berths 160 Visitor Berths	41°44·15N 12°14'·72E
☎ +39 06 56188242 agenzia.commerciale@portodiroma.com	Depth: 3·5 - 4·5 m, Maximum LOA: 60 m	Fax +39 06 56188243 www.portodiroma.it
FREQUENCY: Ch 74	LOCATION: 9 km from "Leonardi Da Vinci" airport	HOURS: 0700 - 2300 LT

RIVIERE TEVERE	Marina Berths 10 Visitor Berths	41°44'·3N 12°14'·1E
Marina Porto di Roma	**Marina**	
☎ +33 06 561881	Depth: 1 - 2·5 m, Maximum LOA: 15 m	Fax +33 06 56188276
		HOURS: HX

RIVIERE TEVERE (Continued)	Marina Berths 10 Visitor Berths	41°44′·3N 12°14′·1E
Darsena Netter	**Marina** 70 Berths 10 Visitor Berths	
☎ +33 06 65029308	Depth: 3 - 4·5 m, Maximum LOA: 30 m	Fax: +33 06 6581615
		HOURS: HX

SALERNO	Port	40°39′·8N 14°44′·6E
☎ Port: +39 089 224544 & 255000 Yacht Berths: +39 089 241201 cpsalerno@libero.it	Depth: 0·5 - 6 m, Maximum LOA: 15 m	Fax: +39 089 258089
FREQUENCY: Port: Ch 11 16		HOURS: Port Authorities: 0700-1900 LT

SAN FELICE CIRCEO	Marina 380 Berths	42°33′·3N 11°08′·1E
☎ +39 0773 527336	Depth: 0·5 - 4 m, Maximum LOA: 20 m	Fax: +39 0773 546184
FREQUENCY: Ch 09 16		HOURS: HX

SANNAZZARO (MERGELLINA)	Marina	40°49′·5N 14°13′·5E
☎ +39 081 7611633 luise@luise.it	Depth: 1 - 8 m, Maximum LOA: 75 m	Fax: +39 081 5523450 www.luise.it
FREQUENCY: Ch 09		HOURS: HX

SAN REMO	Port	43°49′N 7°47′E
☎ +39 0184 505531 & 504603 cpsanremo@web.it		Fax: +39 0184 509968
FREQUENCY: Ch 14 16		HOURS: 1 June-30 Sept: H24 1 Oct-31 May: 0700-1900 LT
PORTO SOLE	**Marina** 903 Beths 80 Visitor Berths	42°41′·7N 9°27′·2E
☎ +39 0184 15371	Depth: 2·5 - 7·5 m, Maximum LOA: 90 m	Fax: +39 0184 504251
FREQUENCY: Ch 09 16		HOURS: HX
PORTO COMMUNALE	**Marina** 15 Visitor Berths	42°42′·5N 9°27′·4E
☎ Hr Mr: +39 0184 505531	Depth: 1 - 7 m, Maximum LOA: 30 m	Fax:
FREQUENCY: Ch 09		HOURS: Summer H24 winter 0700-1900 LT

SANTA MARGHERITA LIGURE	Marina 350 Berths 50 Visitor Berths	44°19′·1N 09°13′·1E
☎ +39 0185 287029	Depth: 2 - 12 m, Maximum LOA: 60 m	Fax:
FREQUENCY: Ch 11 16		HOURS: Summer H24 winter 0800-1900 LT

SANTA MARINELLA	Marina 285 Berths	42°02′·60N 11°52′·57E
☎ +39 0766 710484	Depth: 1 - 5 m, Maximum LOA: 15 m	Fax:
FREQUENCY: Ch 09 16	LOCATION: 7 miles from Civitavecchia	HOURS: 0800 - 1630 LT

SAVONA	Port	44°19′N 8°29′E
☎ Port: +39 019 856666 & 851530 Information Service: +39 019 821452 capitaneria@portosavona.net circomaresciacca@libero.it		Fax: Port: +39 019 856498 Information Service: +39 019 821113
FREQUENCY: Port: Ch 13 16 Information Service: Ch 13 16		HOURS: H24
DARSENA VECCHIA	**Marina** 310 Berths 12 Visitor Berths	
☎	Depth: 5 - 10 m, Maximum LOA: 25 m	Fax: +39 019 821451
		HOURS: HX

TALAMONE	Marina	42°33′·3N 11°08′·1E
☎ Hr Mr: +39 0564 887003	Depth: 1 - 4 m, Maximum LOA:13 m	Fax: +39 0564 887003
FREQUENCY: Ch 09		HOURS: HX

TARANTO	Port & Marinas 200 Berths	40°28′·49N 17°13′·36E
☎ Port: +39 099 4707527 & 4713601 Taranto Yacht Marina: +39 099 4716666 info@tarantoyacht.it	Depth: 8 m, Maximum LOA: 35 m	Fax: Port: +39 099 4718288 Taranto Yacht Marina: +39 099 4716095 www.tarantoyacht.it
FREQUENCY: Port: Ch 12 16 Marina: Ch 12; Castello Signal Station: Ch 67		HOURS: H24
(1) All vessels anchored in the roads should maintain a listening watch on VHF Ch 12 from H+15 to H+20 every hour so that instructions and information can be relayed (2) It is obligatory for Italian and foreign vessels passing through the Canale Navigable (entering or departing) to maintain a listening watch on VHF Ch 67 in order to make direct contact with the Castello Signal Station		

TERMOLI	Port & Marina 80 Berths	42°00′·2N 15°00′·5E
☎ Port: +39 0875 706484 Marina: +39 0875 702238	Depth: 1·5 - 5 m, Maximum LOA: 20 m (Tremiti Islands)	Fax: Port: +39 0875 703096
FREQUENCY: Ch 14 16		HOURS: 0700-1900 LT
NOTE: Before entering the port, and at least 1 n mile from the entrance, vessels should contact the Harbour Master on VHF Ch 16 to obtain entry permission		

TERRACINA	Port and Yacht Harbour 300 Berths Fishing and Pleasure Craft Occupy Available Berths	41°17′N 13°13′E
☎ Port: +39 0773 720060 & 720061 circte@libero.it	Depth in Molo Gregoriano 2·7 m (used for motor craft) Depth in Darsena Vecchia: 1·5 m Depth in Darsena di Levante: 1·3 m Depths in small craft harbour are subject to continuous change	Fax: + 39 0773 720060
FREQUENCY: Ch 14 16		HOURS: 0700-1900 LT

TERRAMARE MARINA PUNTA FARO	Marina 1200 Berths 50 Visitor Berths	40°00′·7N 15°23′·7E
☎ +39 0431 70315 & 70573 marinapuntaverde@libero.it	Depth: 3·5 m, Maximum LOA: 25 m	Fax: +39 0431 70573
FREQUENCY: Ch 09		HOURS: H24

TORRE ANNUNZIATA	Port and Marina	40°45′N 14°27′E
☎ Port: +39 081 8611855 & 8622978 Marina: +39 081 5261160		Fax: Port: +39 081 8717196
FREQUENCY: Port: Ch 09 15 16 Marina: Ch 06 13		HOURS: 0700-1900 LT

TORRE DEL GRECO	Port & Marina 450-500 Berths	40°47′N 14°22′E
☎ +39 081 8812200 & 8819150 guardiacostieratg@tiscalinet.it	Depth: 2 - 8 m, Maximum LOA: 15 m	Fax: +39 081 8815480
FREQUENCY: Hr Mr Ch 16 Port Operations Ch 14		HOURS: 0700-1900 LT

TRANI	Port & Marina 250 Berths	41°17′·2N 16°25′·9E
☎ Port: +39 0883 583783 Marina: +39 0883 42028	Depth: 1 - 4·5 m, Maximum LOA: 25 m	Fax:
FREQUENCY: Ch 14 16		HOURS: Port: 0700-1900 LT Marina: HX

TROPEA	Marina 60 Berths	38°40′·81N 15°54′·31E
☎ +39 0963 603192 & 61781	Depth: 2·5 - 5 m, Maximum LOA: 25 m	Fax:
FREQUENCY: Ch 16		HOURS: 0800 - 1630 LT

VARAZZE	Marina 300 Berths	44°21′·1N 08°34′·1E
☎ +39 019 95919	Depth: 1·5 - 4 m, Maximum LOA: 25 m	Fax:
FREQUENCY: Ch 16 25		HOURS: 1000-1900 LT

VIAREGGIO	Port and Marina 1000 Berths	43°51′·7N 10°14′·1E
Tel: Port: +39 0584 49500 & 44444 Marina Madonnia: +39 0584 32033 Lusben Craft: +39 0584 384111	Maximum LOA: 12.5 m	Fax: Port: +39 0584 388388 Lusben Craft: +39 0584 396458
FREQUENCY: Port: Ch 11 16 Marina: Ch 12		HOURS: H24

VIBO VALENTIA	Marina 400 Berths Visitor Berths	38°43′·26N 16°07′·8E
Tel: Marina Stella del Sud: +39 0963 573202 Marina Carmelo: +39 0963 572630 +39 0963 573202 stellsud@tin.it	Depth: 1 - 7 m, Maximum LOA: 30 m	Fax: www.tecnosys.com/stellasud
FREQUENCY: Captianeria: Ch 11 16 Carmello: Ch 16 12 Stella del Sud: Ch 16		HOURS: Capitaneria: 0700-1900 LT

LEBANON

BEIRUT (BEYROUTH)	Port	33°54′N 35°30′E
☎ Port: +961(0)1 580211 580216	TWO MARINAS BEING BUILT IN BEIRUT, TO OPEN 2003	Fax:
FREQUENCY: Port: Ch 13 16		

MARINA JOSEPH KOURY	Marina 800 Berths	33°56′·09N 35°35′·00E
☎ +961(0)1 418826, 3 744676 & 3 262629 info@lamarinajk.com	Depth: 2·5 m, Maximum LOA: 100 m	Fax: +961(0)4 415590 & 1892805 www.lamarinajk.com
FREQUENCY: Ch 11 16	LOCATION: Dbaye, North Metn	

PORT DE JOUNIEH	Port and Marina 500 Berths Visitor Berths Available With First Three Days Mooring Free	33°59′N 35°37′E
☎ +961(0)9 640979 Marina ATCL: +961(0)9 932020	Depth: 3 - 5 m, Maximum LOA: 23 m	Fax: +961(0)9 640220 Marina: +96(0)9 640579 & 934662
FREQUENCY: Ch 11 16	To request entry, call “OC” on Ch 11 when 20 n miles offshore and a bearing of 270° from port. Entry should only be made during daylight	

LIBYA

GENERAL NOTES

All vessels (arriving, departing or on passage between Libyan ports) within Libyan territorial waters must make regular contact every 4h with a Libyan CRS on VHF Ch 16 or a Port Radio on VHF Ch 11 or 16. Vessels must maintain a continuous listening watch on VHF Ch 16

TARĀBULUS (TRIPOLI)

A	2182	RT (MF)		
B	2197			
Weather Bulletins				
B: 0833 1733	For area between 10°E to 25°E and Libyan coast to 34°N			
Navigational Warnings				
A: 0903 1903	For area between 10°E to 25°E and Libyan coast to 34°N			

ABU KAMMĀSH, SIDI SAID

Port — 33°05'N 11°49'E

FREQUENCY: Port: Ch 10 16

BANGHĀZI (BENGĀSI)

Port — 32°07'N 20°03'E

FREQUENCY: 2182; 2816 Khz (MF)
Ch 12 16

HOURS: 0800-1800 LT

DARNAH (DERNA)

Pilots and Port — 32°46'N 22°40'E

Tel: Port: +218(0)81 22074 & 23141

Fax:

FREQUENCY: Port Control: Ch 16

MIŞURĀTAH (QAŞR AḨMED)

Pilots and Port: CALL: Mişurātah Port Control — 32°22'N 15°13'E

Tel: +218(0)51 742750, 742751 & 742796

Fax: +218(0)51 742444

FREQUENCY: Ch 12 16

ŢARĀBULUS (TRIPOLI)

Port: — 32°54'N 13°12'E

Tel: +218(0)21 3331532, 3332536 & 3347011

Fax:

FREQUENCY: 2182 kHz (MF)
Ch 08 12 16
Emergency: Ch 14

HOURS: H24

ZUWĀRAH (ZUARA)

Port — 32°55'N 12°07'E

Tel: +218(0)25 025305

Fax:

FREQUENCY: Ch 16

MALTA

National SAR Agency: Armed Forces of Malta **Tel:** +356 809279 **Fax:** +356 809860 **Telex:** +406 1489 MW
The Operations Centre of the Armed Forces of Malta (AFM) doubles as Malta RCC and is responsible for co-ordinating SAR Operations within the Malta SRR. Malta Radio, Malta Maritime Authority and Malta International Airport plc assist RCC Malta in the conduct of such operations. Distress information originating from COSPAS-SARSAT and Inmarsat is transmitted to Malta RCC either directly or through Malta Radio or the Malta International Airport plc Air Traffic Control Tower. Malta Radio maintains a continuous listening watch on international distress frequencies.

	Telephone +356	**Fax** +356	**Others**
RCC MALTA	21 809279 21 824212	21 809860 21 241001 (HJ)	**Telex** +406 1489 +406 1305
MALTA RADIO	21 456767 21 447929	21 452935	**Telex** +406 1317 MALRDO MW

NAVTEX [O]

O	Malta	518 kHz	35°49′N 14°32′E
	Weather Bulletins		
O: 0620 1820	Gale warnings, synopsis, 12 hour forecast for coastal waters of Malta up to 50 n miles offshore		
	Navigational Warnings		
O: 0220 0620 1020 1420 1820 2220	Local and NAVAREA III warnings for central Mediterranean up to 10 days old are broadcast Monday - Saturday. All warnings still in force are broadcast on Sunday		

MALTA

	2625	RT (MF)		
	Ch 04	VHF		
	Weather Bulletins			
On receipt	Storm warnings: Gale warnings for coastal waters of Malta up to 50 n miles offshore			
0603 1003 1603 2103	Gale warnings, synopsis, 12 hour forecast for coastal waters of Malta up to 50 n miles offshore			
	Navigational Warnings			
1003 1603 2103	Local and NAVAREA III warnings for central Mediterranean up to 10 days old are broadcast Monday - Saturday. All warnings still in force are broadcast on Sunday			

MARSAMXATT

MARSAMXATT	**Harbour**	**35°54′·5N 14°30′·9E**
☎ Yachting Centre Ta'Xbiex: +356 21 332800 Manoel Island Yacht Yard: +356 21 334453 & 334454 info@yachtyard-malta.com	Maximum LOA: 60 m	Fax: Yachting Centre, Xatt Ta'Xbiex: +356 21 332141 Manoel Island Yacht Yard: +356 21 319301
FREQUENCY: Ch 12 16		HOURS: HX
MANOEL ISLAND MARINA	**Marina** 60 Berths 120 by 2003	**35°53′·8N 14°30′·1E**
☎ Hr Mr: +356 21 800900	Maximum LOA: 10 - 40 M	Fax
TA' XBIEX QUAY	57 Berths	**35°53′·8N 14°30′·1E**
☎ Hr Mr: +356 21 330975 & 235711	Maximum LOA: 30 m	Fax
FREQUENCY: Ch 08 09 M		HOURS: HX

MGARR, GOZO

MGARR, GOZO	**Marina** 110 Berths	**36°01′·60N 14°18′·20E**
☎ +356 21 558856	Port of Entry - June to September only	Fax +356 21 562672
		HOURS: HX

MSIDA CREEK MARINA

MSIDA CREEK MARINA	**Marina** 750 Berths Berths 6 Visitor Berths	**35°53′·8N 14°30′·1E**
☎ +356 21 330975 & 235711	Depth: 5 m minimum, Maximum LOA: 18 m	Fax
FREQUENCY: Ch 08 09 M		HOURS: HX

PORTOMASO MARINA	Marina CALL: Portomaso Marina 130 Berths 10 Visitor Berths Stern to Moorings	35°55′·26N 14°29′·69E
Marina: +356 21 387803 Mobile: +356 994 95768	Depth: 4 m, Maximum LOA: 17 m	+356 21 389655
FREQUENCY: Ch 13	Part of the Hilton hotel complex	HOURS: 0700-2400 LT

VALLETTA	Port: CALL: Valletta Port Control	35°54′N 14°31′E
Port Control: +356 21 241363 & 241364 Hr Mr: +356 21 239010		Port Auth: +356 21 222208 & 226309
FREQUENCY: Port: Ch 11 **12** 14 16 Leisure Craft: Ch 09	LOCATION: Palace Tower Signal Station	HOURS: H24
GRAND HARBOUR MARINA (VITTORIOSA QUAY)	**Marina** **350 Berths** 227 Berths of 10 m - 25 m 30 Superyacht Berths up to 75 m LOA	
Hr Mr: +356 21 800700	Maximum LOA: 75 m Superyachts stern to, other berths on pontoons	
		HOURS: HX
S & D YACHTS LIMITED	**Yacht Service Centre**	
+356 320577, 21 339908 & 331515 info@sdyachts.com		+356 21 332259 www.sdyachts.com
	LOCATION: Grand Harbour	
LEISURE CRAFT INFORMATION:		

Port of Entry Requirements:
Yachts and leisure craft wishing to visit Malta are requested to contact Valletta Port Control on VHF Ch 12. Vessels arriving from a foreign port should display the Q flag. During office hours clearance will be obtained from the Yachting Centre at the entrance to Msida Creek Marina, a section of the quay behind the marina wall is reserved for clearing yachts. Craft arriving after 1730LT are to proceed to Valletta Customs House, Grand Harbour. Yachts should note that there are no mooring facilities in the Grand Harbour and are advised to clear during office hours. During the period 16th June to 30th September, clearance may also be made at Mgarr on Gozo.

Bezzina Ship Repair Yard +356 21 826283 & 829901
Kalkara Boat Yard Valletta +356 21 661306 Fax: +356 21 690420

MONACO

National SAR Agency: Monaco Maritime Police **Tel:** +377 93153016 **Fax:** +377 93302245

The Monaco Maritime Police Headquarters is equipped with terrestrial maritime radio communication facilities and is the location of the foreign alerting post for MRCC La Garde. An agreement for co-operation in SAR operations has been established with France.

	Telephone +377	**Fax** +377	**Others**
MONACO RADIO	93307300	93301300	**Telex** +42 369300 MCORAD MC

MONACO

A	4363 *(403)*	RT (HF)		0600-2200 (Winter) 0500-2100 (Summer)
B	8728 *(804)*			
C	8806 *(830)*			
D	13152 *(1226)*			
E	17323 *(1628)*			
F	22768 *(2225)*			
G	Ch 20 22	VHF		
H	Ch 25			
I	Ch 23 (Navimet)			
J	Ch 24			

DIAGRAMS: pages 180 and 181

Weather Bulletins

G: Every H+03 (during hours of service)	Storm warnings: For Areas 514-516, 521-523 and 531-534, in French and English
A, G: 0903 1403 1915 LT	Forecast for Areas 514-516, 521-523, 531-534, in French and English
C-F: 0930	Forecast for METAREA II, in French and English
B-C: 0715 1830	Forecast for Areas 511-516, 521-525 and 531-537, in French and English
H: Continuous Broadcast	Forecast for coastal waters from Port Camargue to Saint Raphaël. Bulletins updated 3 times a day, in French and English
I: Continuous Broadcast	Forecast for coastal waters up to 20 n miles offshore from Saint Raphaël to Menton. Bulletins updated 3 times a day, in French and English
J: Continuous Broadcast	Forecast for coastal waters of Corse. Bulletins updated 3 times a day, in French and English

Navigational Warnings

A, G: 0803 LT	Urgent navigational warnings in French; also available in English on request

RADIO RIVIERA

	106·3 MHz	FM	Monaco	
	106·5 MHz		San Remo & S. Tropez	

Weather Bulletins

Mon-Fri: 0715 0815 1240 1710 1915 LT	Forecast in English for the coastal waters between Saint Tropez and the Italian border and Corse

FONTVIEILLE

Marina 140 Berths — 43°44′N 7°25′E

Hr Mr: +377 93158569

Depth: 1·5 - 5 m, Maximum LOA: 30 m

Fax Hr Mr: +377 93153712

FREQUENCY: Ch 09

HOURS: 1 May-30 Sept: 0800-2200 LT
1 Oct-30 April: 0800-2000 LT

MONACO

Port: CALL: Monaco Port — 700 Berths 60 Visitor Berths — 43°44′·2N 7°25′·7E

Hr Mr: +377 93158678
Customs: +377 97970230
Maritime Police: +377 93153016

Depth: 2 - 25 m, Maximum LOA: 130 m

Fax Hr Mr: +377 93153715

FREQUENCY: Ch 12 (Pilot)
6 12 16 (Port Authority)

HOURS: Mon-Fri: 0830-1830 LT
Sat & Sun: Call Pilots

Arrival: Within 24 hours of berthing, vessels representative must report to the Direction des Ports producing the Admittance form, duly completed together with ship's papers and pay all necessary harbour fees
Departure: Notify the Pilot Office on Ch12, if departure is between 2300 and 0800 LT. Please advise the Pilot Office or Port Authority the day before departure

MOROCCO

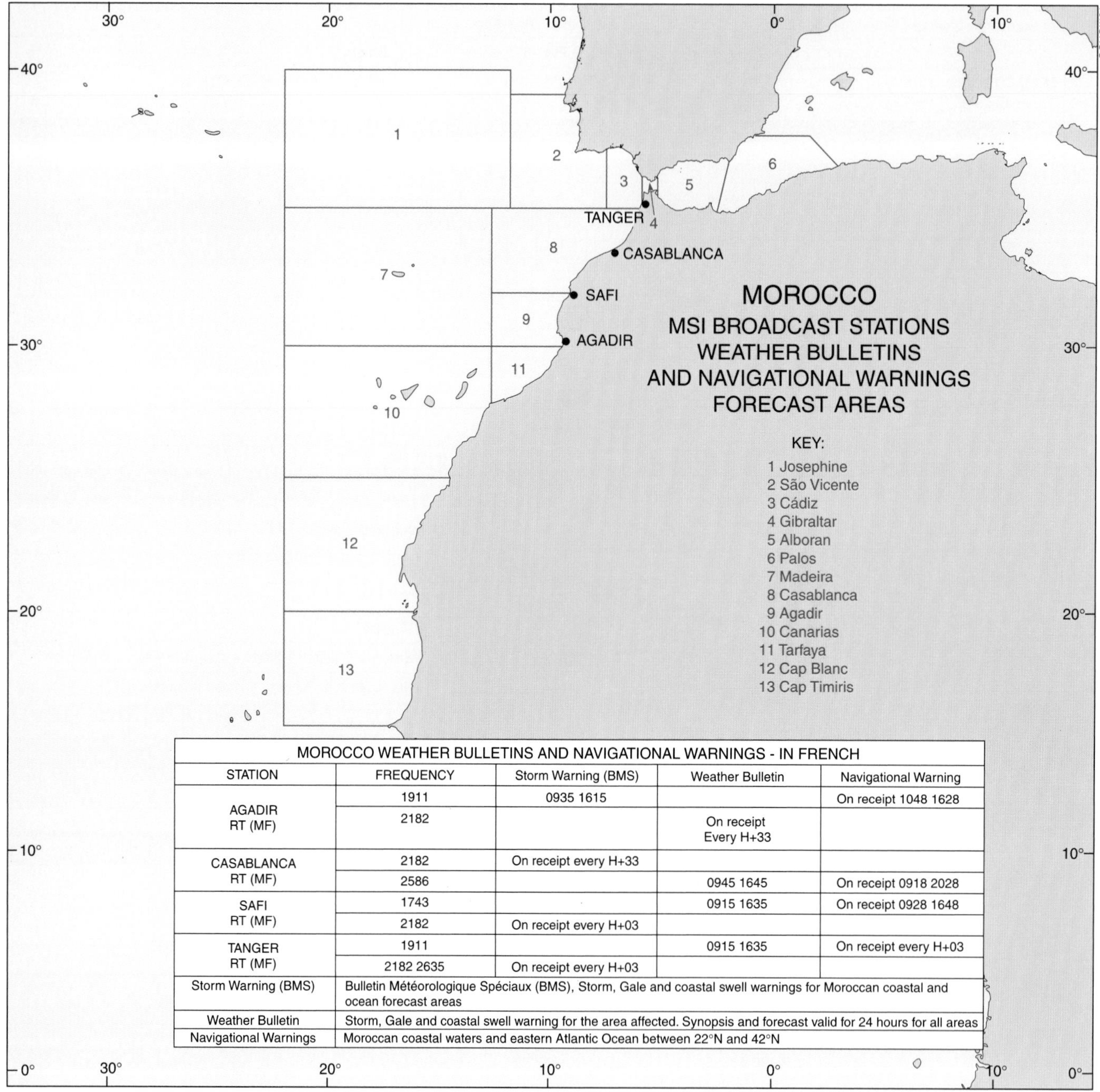

MOROCCO WEATHER BULLETINS AND NAVIGATIONAL WARNINGS - IN FRENCH				
STATION	FREQUENCY	Storm Warning (BMS)	Weather Bulletin	Navigational Warning
AGADIR RT (MF)	1911	0935 1615		On receipt 1048 1628
	2182		On receipt Every H+33	
CASABLANCA RT (MF)	2182	On receipt every H+33		
	2586		0945 1645	On receipt 0918 2028
SAFI RT (MF)	1743		0915 1635	On receipt 0928 1648
	2182	On receipt every H+03		
TANGER RT (MF)	1911		0915 1635	On receipt every H+03
	2182 2635	On receipt every H+03		
Storm Warning (BMS)	Bulletin Météorologique Spéciaux (BMS), Storm, Gale and coastal swell warnings for Moroccan coastal and ocean forecast areas			
Weather Bulletin	Storm, Gale and coastal swell warning for the area affected. Synopsis and forecast valid for 24 hours for all areas			
Navigational Warnings	Moroccan coastal waters and eastern Atlantic Ocean between 22°N and 42°N			

National SAR Agency: Directorate of the Merchant Marine, Casablanca, Morocco
Tel: +212 2 227 8092, 2 221 931 & 2 227 6010 **Fax:** +212 2 227 3340 **Telex:** 24613 M **E-mail:** marine@maroconline.com
A network of Coast Radio Stations maintains a continuous listening watch on international distress frequencies.

Atlantic	**Telephone** +212	**Fax** +212	**Others**
MRSC TANGER	3 993 2090	3 993 2093	**Telex** +407 336 85
TANGER RADIO	9 935 059		**Telex** +407 33319
MRSC NADOR **Mediterranean**	5 660 8706	5 634 9117	**Telex** +407 65633

RADIODIFFUSION-TÉLÉVISION MAROCAINE				
	701 1048 1187 1332 7225	AM	90·0 92·1 MHz	FM
	Weather Bulletins			
1228	Storm warnings, forecast in English			
0758, 1315, 2015	Storm warnings, forecast in French			

AL HOCEÏMA	Pilots and Port 10 Yacht Berths Available	35°15′N 3°55′W
FREQUENCY: Hr Mr & Naval Base: Ch 16		HOURS: H24
PROCEDURE: Pilotage is compulsory. Pilot requires 1h notice and will board at the junction of the leading lines in position 35°14′·78N 3°54′·92W		

CEUTA (SPAIN)	Port and Marina 277 Berths	35°53′N 5°19′W
Tel: Marina: +34(0)956 513753		Fax: Marina: +34(0)956 513753
FREQUENCY: Ch 09 (Port control) **16**		HOURS: H24

KABILA MARINA	Marina 150 Berths Visitors Berths Available	35°43′·3N 5°20′·1W
Tel: +212(0)3 9975005 & 9975264	Depths: 1·5 - 2·5 m, Maximum LOA: 16 m	Fax:
FREQUENCY: Ch 09 16		

MARINA SMIR	Marina 450 Berths 100 Visitors Berths	35°45′·2N 5°20′·2W
Tel: +212(0)3 9977333 & 997335 +212(0)9 977250 & 977252	Depths: 2·5 - 4·5 m, Maximum LOA: 80 m	Fax: +212(0)3 9977265
FREQUENCY: Ch 09		

MELILLA (SPAIN)	Port and Marina	35°17′·4N 2°55′·5W
Tel: Marina: +34(0)952 683559	Depths: 2 - 3 m	Fax: Marina: +34(0)952 683559
FREQUENCY: Ch 11 12 **14** 16		HOURS: HX

TANGER (TANGIER)	Port	35°47′N 5°49′W
Tel: Port Captain: +212(0)3 9931882 Port: +212(0)3 9936040 & 9936045		Fax: Port: +212(0)3 9931505
FREQUENCY: Port: Ch 06 14		HOURS: Port: HJ

SERBIA AND MONTENEGRO

BAR

	1720·4	RT (MF)	
	Ch 24	VHF	
Weather Bulletins			
0850 1420 2050	Storm warnings, synopsis, 24 hour forecast in Serbo-Croat and English for the Adriatic Sea		
Navigational Warnings			
0850 1420 2050	In Serbo-Croat and English for coastal waters of Montenegro		

BAR	Port & Marina	900 Berths	42°05′N 19°05′E
Hr Mr Office: +381(0)85 27382 Marina: +381(0)85 317786			Fax:
FREQUENCY: Port: Ch 14 16			HOURS: 0500-0900 1300-1500 LT

BUDVA	Marina	300 Berths	42°27′N 18°46′E
Marina: +381(0)86 451227			Hr Mr: +381(0)82 13053
FREQUENCY: Port: Ch 14 16			HOURS: H24

BUDVA FROM SE

KOTOR	Port & Marina	87 Berths	42°27′N 18°46′E
Hr Mr: +381(0)82 14950 Marina: +381(0)82 3525578 & 325581			Hr Mr: +381(0)82 13053
FREQUENCY: Port: Ch 16			HOURS: H24

SLOVENIA

KOPER (HARBOUR MASTER'S OFFICE)	MMSI 002780200 (DSC): Ch 70	45°32'N 13°59'E
☎ +386(0) 5 66272290	Port of Entry	Fax +386(0) 5 66271447
FREQUENCY: VHF Ch 16 This station does not accept public correspondence; accepting distress, urgent and safety traffic only		HOURS: H24

KOPER	Marina 85 Berths	45°32'·9N 13°43'·6E
☎ +386(0)5 6272120 info@marina-koper.si	Maximum LOA: 18 m	Fax +386(0)5 6272370 www.marina-koper.si
FREQUENCY: Ch 16 17		HOURS: HX

KOPER FROM SW

MARINA IZOLA	Marina 650 Berths Visitor Berths Available	45°32'·2N 13°39'·2E
☎ Marina: +386(0)5 6400250 & 6415169 Yacht Centre: +386(0)5 6630990 Marina: info@marinaizola.com Yacht Centre: lad.izola.prodaja@siol.net	Depth: 1·5 - 3·5 m, Maximum LOA: 30 m	Fax Marina: +386(0)5 6418346 Yacht Centre: +386(0)5 6630952 www.marinaizola.com
FREQUENCY: Ch 17	Port of Entry, tourist season only.	HOURS: HX

MARINA IZOLA FROM SW

PIRAN	Port	Limited Visitor Availability	45°31′·5N 13°34′·0E
☎ +386(0)5 6710192			Fax +386(0)5 6710193
FREQUENCY: Ch 16			HOURS: H24

PORTOROŽ MARINA FROM W

PORTOROŽ	Marina	640 Berths 50 Visitor Berths	45°30′·3N 13°36′·1E
☎ +386(0)5 6761100 marina.portoroz@marinap.si	Depth: 1 - 4·5 m, Maximum LOA: 24 m		Fax +386(0)5 6761210 www.marinap.si
FREQUENCY: Ch 17			HOURS: H24

SPAIN, MEDITERRANEAN COAST

NAVTEX [G] [X]

G	Tarifa	518 kHz	36°01′N 5°34′W
X	Valencia (Cabo La Nao)		38°43′N 0°09′E
Weather Bulletins			
G: 0900	Storm warnings, synoptic situation and development, forecast valid for the following 18 hours for N Atlantic and West Mediterranean Sea within 450 n miles from coast. In English.		
G: 2100	Storm warnings, synoptic situation and development, forecast valid for the following 36 hours for N Atlantic and West Mediterranean Sea within 450 n miles from coast. In English.		
X: 0750	Storm warnings, synoptic situation and development, forecast valid for the following 18 hours for West Mediterranean Sea within 450 n miles from coast. In English.		
X: 1950	Storm warnings, synoptic situation and development, forecast valid for the following 36 hours for West Mediterranean Sea within 450 n miles from coast. In English.		
Navigational Warnings			
G: 0100 0500 1300 1700	NAVAREA II warnings; coastal warnings from Portuguese border to Europa Point (Gibraltar) in English		
X: 0350 0750 1150 1550 1950 2350	NAVAREA III warnings, coastal warnings for the Mediterranean coast of Spain and Islas Baleares in English		

ALGECIRAS (MRSC)

	Ch 74	VHF	36°07′N 5°26′W
DIAGRAMS: pages 139 and 147			
Weather Bulletins			
0315 0515 0715 1115 1515 1915 2315	In Spanish and English		

ALMERÍA (MRCC)

	Ch 74	VHF	36°50′N 2°29′W
DIAGRAMS: pages 139 and 147			
Weather Bulletins			
Every odd H+15	Gale warnings and forecast for Alborán and Palos in Spanish and English. Gale warnings and forecast for coasts of Murcia, Almería, Granada, Melilla and Isla de Alborán, in Spanish		
Navigational Warnings			
On receipt Every odd H+15	In Spanish and English		

BARCELONA (MRCC)

A	Ch 10	VHF	41°20′N 2°09′E
B	Ch 16		
DIAGRAMS: pages 139 and 147			
Weather Bulletins			
A: 0700 1100 1600 2100 LT	In Spanish and English		
Navigational Warnings			
B: 0700 1100 1600 2100 LT	In Spanish and English		

CASTELLÓN (MRSC)

	Ch 74	VHF	39°58′N 0°01′E
DIAGRAM: page 139			
Weather Bulletins			
0900 1400 1900 LT	In Spanish and English		
Navigational Warnings			
On receipt	In Spanish and English		

PORTO COLOM ENTRANCE VIEW FROM MARINA

MÁLAGA (CCR GROUP II)				
A	1656	RT (MF)	Chipiona	36°42′N 6°25′W
	1704		Tarifa	36°03′N 5°33′W
B	Ch 27	VHF	Cabo Gata	36°43′N 2°12′W
	Ch 26		Cádiz	36°21′N 6°17′W
	Ch 26		Málaga	36°36′N 4°36′W
	Ch 81		Tarifa	36°03′N 5°33′W
DIAGRAMS: pages 139 and 147				
Weather Bulletins				
A: 0733 1933	Forecast for Mediterranean and Atlantic areas in Spanish			
A: 1233	48 hours forecast for Mediterranean and Atlantic areas in Spanish			
B: 0833 2003	Forecast for coastal areas in Spanish			
B: 1133	48 hours forecast for coastal areas in Spanish			
Navigational Warnings				
A: 0733 1933	General warnings			
B: 0833 2003	Coastal warnings			

PALMA (MRCC)			
	Ch 10	VHF	39°33′N 2°38′E
DIAGRAM: page 139			
Weather Bulletins			
0635 0935 1435 2035 (Summer) LT 0735 1035 1535 2035 (Winter) LT	In Spanish and English		

TARRAGONA (MRSC)				
	Ch 13	VHF		36°01′N 5°34′W
DIAGRAMS: pages 139 and 147				
Weather Bulletins				
0630 1030 1630 2130 LT	In Spanish and English			
Navigational Warnings				
0630 1030 1630 2130 LT	In Spanish and English			

VALENCIA (CCR GROUP I)				
A	1755	RT (MF)	Palma	39°21′N 2°58′E
	1767		Cabo Gata	36°43′N 2°12′W
B	Ch 85	VHF	Alicante	38°20′N 0°42′W
	Ch 23		Bagur	42°17′N 3°15′E
	Ch 60		Barcelona	41°25′N 2°07′E
	Ch 01		Cabo La Nao	38°43′N 0°10′W
	Ch 04		Cartagena	37°35′N 0°58′W
	Ch 25		Castellón	39°52′N 0°19′W
	Ch 03		Ibiza	38°55′N 1°16′E
	Ch 85		Menorca	39°59′N 4°07′E
	Ch 20		Palma	39°44′N 2°43′E
	Ch 23		Tarragona	41°21′N 1°32′E
DIAGRAMS: pages 139 and 147				
Weather Bulletins				
A: 0750 1950	Forecast for Mediterranean areas in Spanish			
A: 1303	48 hours forecast for Mediterranean areas in Spanish			
B: 0910 2110	Forecast for coastal areas in Spanish			
B: 1410	48 hours forecast for coastal areas in Spanish			

VALENCIA (CCR GROUP I) **(Continued)**	
Navigational Warnings	
A: 0750 1950	General warnings
B: 0910 2110	Coastal warnings

VALENCIA (MRCC)			
	Ch 10	VHF	39°27′N 0°20′E
DIAGRAMS: pages 139 and 147			
Weather Bulletins			
Every even H+15	Gale warnings and forecast for coasts of Alicante, Valencia, Castellón, Cabo de Palos, Argelia and Islas Baleares In Spanish and English		
Navigational Warnings			
Every even H+15	Coasts of Alicante, Valencia, Castellón, Cabo de Palos, Argelia and Islas Baleares In Spanish and English		

ADRA	**Marina** 261 Berths	36°44′·6N 3°01′·1W
Tel: +34 950 401417	Depth: 1 - 5 m, Maximum LOA: 20 m	Fax: +34 950 400712
FREQUENCY: Ch 09 16		HOURS: HX

AGUADULCE	**Marina** 764 Berths	36°49′·1N 2°33′·6W
Tel: +34 950 343115 & 341502	Depth: 2·5 m	Fax: +34 950 343164
FREQUENCY: Ch 09 16		HOURS: HX

AIGUADOLÇ	**Marina** 742 Berths	41°14′·2N 1°49′·5E
Tel: Marina: +34 938 942600	Depth: 2·5 m, Maximum LOA: 26 m	Fax: Marina: +34 938 942750
FREQUENCY: Ch 09		HOURS: HX

ALGECIRAS	**Marina and Port:** CALL: Algeciras Prácticos 900 Berths Phone Marina for Visitor Availability	36°08′N 5°26′W
Tel: Marina: +34 956 585425 Port: +34 956 572620 apba@apba.es		Fax: +34 956 585444 www.apba.es/bahianet
FREQUENCY: Ch 09 16	LOCATION: Muelle Pesquero	HOURS: HX

ALICANTE AREA		Use International dialing code +34	Marina Frequency: Ch 09
Marina		**Telephone and Facsimile numbers**	**Additional information**
C.N. Les Basetes	38°39′·0N 00°05′·2W	Tel: 965 831213 & Fax: 965 831213	
Marina Deportiva De Alicante	38°19′·8N 00°29′·3W	Tel: 965 213600 & Fax: 965 213177	810 Berths Maximum LOA: 50 m Depth: 4 - 10 m
Puerto Costa Blanca	38°21′·0N 00°26′·3W	Tel: 965 265986 & Fax 965 265986	
Puerto De Benidorm	38°30′·0N 00°07·8′W	Tel: 965 413574 & Fax: 965 866563	
Puerto De Campello	38°25·6′N 00°23′·0W	Tel: 965 631748 & Fax: 965 631964	421 Berths 250 Visitors Max LOA: 15 m
Puerto De La Lisla De Tabarca	38°09′·0N 00°28·7′W	Tel: 965 413574	
Real Club Regatas De Alicante	38°19′·8N 00°29′·3W	Tel: 965 218600 & Fax: 965 219234	400 Berths
Villajoyosa	38°30′·0N 00°13′·1W	Tel: 965 893606 & Fax: 966 851504	325 Berths Maximum LOA: 20 m Depth: 1 - 7 m

ALMERÍA	**Port and Marina** 277 Berths	36°48′·9N 2°27′·8W
Tel: Club de Mar: +34 950 230780 & 242659 cma@clubdemaralmeria.com	Depth: 2·5 - 3 m, Maximum LOA: 15 m	Fax: Club de Mar: +34 950 230599 Marina: +34 950 621147 www.clubdemaralmeria.com
FREQUENCY: Ch 09 16		HOURS: HX

ALMERIMAR	**Marina:** CALL: Almerimar 1997 Berths 200 Visitor Beths	36°41′·8N 2°47′·8W
Tel: +34 950 497350 & 951 497353	Depth: 4 m, Maximum LOA: 60 m	Fax: Marina: +34 950 497353 www.marina-almeria.com
FREQUENCY: Ch 04 09 16		HOURS: HX

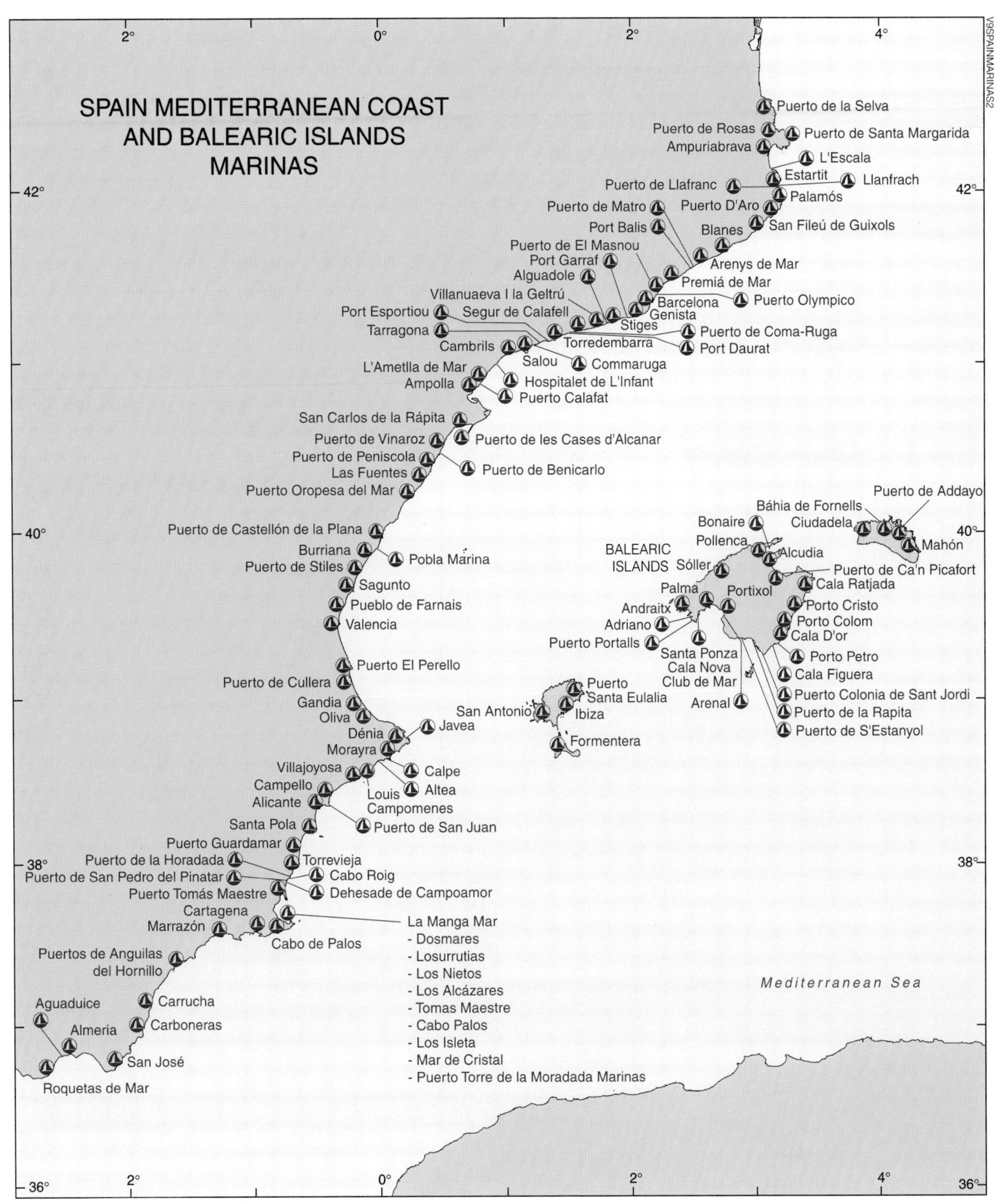

SPAIN MEDITERRANEAN COAST AND BALEARIC ISLANDS MARINAS
V9SPAINMARINAS2
Puerto de la Selva
Puerto de Rosas
Puerto de Santa Margarida
Ampuriabrava
L'Escala
Estartit
Llanfrach
Puerto de Llafranc
Palamós
Puerto de Matro
Puerto D'Aro
San Fileú de Guixols
Port Balis
Blanes
Puerto de El Masnou
Port Garraf
Arenys de Mar
Alguadole
Premiá de Mar
Villanuaeva I la Geltrú
Barcelona
Puerto Olympico
Port Esportiou
Segur de Calafell
Genista
Stiges
Tarragona
Puerto de Coma-Ruga
Cambrils
Torredembarra
Port Daurat
Salou
Commaruga
L'Ametlla de Mar
Ampolla
Hospitalet de L'Infant
Puerto Calafat
San Carlos de la Rápita
Puerto de Vinaroz
Puerto de les Cases d'Alcanar
Puerto de Peniscola
Puerto de Benicarlo
Las Fuentes
Puerto Oropesa del Mar
Puerto de Addayo
Báhia de Fornells
Bonaire
Ciudadela
Puerto de Castellón de la Plana
Pollenca
Mahón
BALEARIC ISLANDS
Alcudia
Burriana
Pobla Marina
Puerto de Stiles
Sóller
Puerto de Ca'n Picafort
Sagunto
Cala Ratjada
Palma
Portixol
Pueblo de Farnais
Andraitx
Porto Cristo
Valencia
Adriano
Porto Colom
Cala D'or
Puerto Portalls
Santa Ponza
Porto Petro
Cala Nova
Puerto El Perello
Cala Figuera
Puerto de Cullera
Club de Mar
Puerto
Santa Eulalia
Arenal
Puerto Colonia de Sant Jordi
Gandia
Oliva
San Antonio
Ibiza
Puerto de la Rapita
Puerto de S'Estanyol
Dénia
Javea
Formentera
Morayra
Villajoyosa
Calpe
Campello
Altea
Louis
Alicante
Campomenes
Santa Pola
Puerto de San Juan
Puerto Guardamar
Puerto de la Horadada
Torrevieja
Puerto de San Pedro del Pinatar
Cabo Roig
Puerto Tomás Maestre
Dehesade de Campoamor
Cartagena
Marrazón
La Manga Mar
Cabo de Palos
- Dosmares
- Losurrutias
Puertos de Anguilas del Hornillo
- Los Nietos
- Los Alcázares
Mediterranean Sea
Aguaduice
Carrucha
- Tomas Maestre
- Cabo Palos
Almeria
Carboneras
- Los Isleta
- Mar de Cristal
San José
- Puerto Torre de la Moradada Marinas
Roquetas de Mar
2°
0°
2°
4°
42°
40°
38°
36°

ALTEA (CLUB NÁUTICO DE ALTEA)	Marina 370 Berths	38°35′·1N 0°03′·0E
Tel: Marina: +34 965 841591	Depth: 1 - 3 m, Maximum LOA: 25 m	Fax: Marina: +34 965 841579
FREQUENCY: Ch 09		HOURS: HX
ALTEA (CLUB NÁUTICO MASCARAT)	**Marina** 542 Berths	38°38′·2N 0°04′·1E
Tel: Marina: +34 965 842200	Depth: 7 m	Fax: Marina: +34 965 842307
FREQUENCY: Ch 09		HOURS: HX

AMPOLLA	Marina 432 Berths	40°48′N 0°43′E
Tel: Marina: +34 977 460211	Depth: 2 - 4 m, Maximum LOA: 15 m	Fax: Marina: +34 977 593007
FREQUENCY: Ch 09		HOURS: HX

AMPURIABRAVA	Marina 700 Berths	42°14′·6N 3°08′·8E
Tel: Marina: +34 972 451239	Depth: 1·7 - 2·4 m, Maximum LOA: 25 m	Fax: Marina: +34 972 452291
FREQUENCY: Ch 09		HOURS: HX

ARENYS DE MAR	Marina: 415 Berths 100 Visitor Berths	41°34′·5N 2°33′·18E
Tel: +34 937 920980 & 921600	Depth: 2 - 6 m, Maximum LOA: 23 m	Fax: +34 937 920744
FREQUENCY: Ch 09		HOURS: HX

PORT VELL, BARCELONA

BARCELONA - PORT OLIMPIC	Marina: 743 Berths	41°23′·12N 2°12′·60E
Tel: +34 932 259220	Depth: 3 - 5 m, Maximum LOA: 30 m	Fax: +34 932 259221
FREQUENCY: Ch 09		HOURS: HX
BARCELONA MARINAS		
PORT VELL	**Marina** 410 Berths 300 Visitor Berths	41°20′·1N 2°10′·2E
Tel: +34 934 842300 info@marinaportvell.com	Depth: 7 - 10 m, Maximum LOA: 60 m	Fax: +34 934 842333 www.marinaportvell.net
FREQUENCY: Ch 09		HOURS: Summer 0800-1900 LT Winter HX
REAL CLUB MARÍTIMO	**Marina:** CALL: Club Marítimo 200 Berths 30 Visitor Berths	41°22′N 2°11′E
Tel: +34 932 214959	Depth: 7 - 10 m, Maximum LOA: 60 m	Fax: +34 932 216253

BARCELONA MARINAS (Continued)		
REAL CLUB NÁTICO	**Marina:** CALL: Club Marítimo 115 Berths	41°20'·1N 2°10'·2E
Tel: +34 932 216521	Maximum LOA: 35 m	Fax: +34 932 216253

BENALMADENA	Marina 1050 Berths	36°35'·7N 4°30'·7W
Tel: +34 952 577022 info@puertobenelmadena.org	Depth: 3 m, Maximum LOA: 35 m	Fax: +34 952 441344 www.costadelsol.spa.es/puerto_benelmadena
FREQUENCY: Ch 09 16		HOURS: HX

BLANES, CLUB VELA de BLANES	Marina 326 Berths 33 visitor berths	41°40'·3N 2°47'·8E
Tel: Marina: +34 972 330552	Depth: 2 - 3 m, Maximum LOA: 15 m	Fax: Marina: +34 972 331498
FREQUENCY: Ch 09		HOURS: HX

BURRIANA (CLUB NÁUTICO)	Marina 200 Berths	39°51'·5N 0°04'W
Tel: Marina: +34 964 586073 Port: +34 964 585265	Depth: 3 m, Maximum LOA: 20 m	Fax: Port: +34 964 585922
FREQUENCY: Marina: Ch 09 Port: Ch 16		HOURS: HX

CABO PINO	Marina 169 Berths Limited Number of Visitor Berths	36°29'N 4°44'W
Tel: +34 952 831975	Depth: 2·5 m, Maximum LOA: 16 m	Fax: +34 952 830237
FREQUENCY: Ch 09 16		HOURS: HX

CABO ROIG	Marina 200 Berths 60 Visitors Berths	37°54'·4N 0°43'·5W
Tel: Marina: +34 966 760167	Depth: 1 - 3 m, Maximum LOA: 13 m	Fax: Marina: +34 966 760038
FREQUENCY: Ch 09		HOURS: HX

CALPE (CLUB NÁUTICO)	Marina 289 Berths	38°38'·1N 0°04'·2E
Tel: Marina: +34 965 831809	Depth: 1 - 3 m, Maximum LOA: 30 m	Fax: Marina: +34 965 834931
FREQUENCY: Ch 09		HOURS: HX

CAMBRILS	**Marina:** CALL: Cambrils Náutico 480 Berths 50 Visitor Berths	41°03'·6N 1°03'·6E
Tel: +34 977 360531	Depth: 2 - 3 m, Maximum LOA: 20 m	Fax: +34 977 362654
FREQUENCY: Ch 09		HOURS: HX

CAMPELLO	Marina 474 Berths Limited Number of Visitor Berths	38°26'·5N 0°23'·5W
Tel: Marina: +34 965 631748	Depth: 2·5 - 4 m, Maximum LOA: 15 m	Fax:
FREQUENCY: Ch 09		HOURS: HX

CARTAGENA	Port & Marina 395 Berths 90 Visitor Berths	37°35'·1N 0°59'·0W
Tel: Port: +34 968 325800 Marina: +34 968 503100 cartagena@apc.es	Maximum LOA: 20 m	Fax: Port: +34 968 325815 Marina: +34 968 523622 www.apc.es
FREQUENCY: Ch 09		HOURS: HX

CASTELLÓN (CLUB NÁUTICO)	Marina **250 Berths**	39°58'N 0°01'6E
Tel: Marina: +34 964 282520	Depth: 7 - 8 m, Maximum LOA: 25 m	Fax: Marina: +34 964 283905
FREQUENCY: Ch 09		HOURS: HX

COMARRUGA	Marina **265 Berths**	41°10'·50N 1°30'·75E
Tel: Marina: +34 977 680120	Depth: 3 - 5 m, Maximum LOA: 15 m	Fax: Marina: +34 977 681753
FREQUENCY: Ch 09		HOURS: HX

COSTA BLANCA (CLUB NÁUTICO)	Marina 230 Berths	38°21′N 0°26′W
Marina: +34 965 154491	Depth: 1·7 - 3 m, Maximum LOA: 9 m	Fax Marina: +34 965 265848
FREQUENCY: Ch 09		HOURS: HX

DEHESA DE CAMPOAMOR	Marina 364 Berths 30 Visitors Berths	37°54′N 0°45′W
Marina: +34 965 320386	Maximum LOA: 14 m	Fax Marina: +34 965 320388
FREQUENCY: Ch 09		HOURS: HX

DÉNIA	Port and Marinas	38°50′·8N 0°07′·6E
Port: +34 967 800650	Depth: 1·5 - 3 m	Fax Marina: +34 966 424387
FREQUENCY: Ch 09 16	A Yacht Harbour lies close SE of Muelle de Atraque. 500 small public berths, up to 8 m are located in the NW sector of the port	
CLUB NAUTICO DE DÉNIA	601 Berths 292 Visitor Berths	38°50′N 0°07′E
+34 965 780989 cndenia@ctv.es		Fax +34 965 780850
MARINA DE DÉNIA	409 Berths 205 Visitor Berths	38°50′N 0°07′E
+34 966 424307 marinadedenia@teleline.es	Maximum LOA: 50 m	Fax +34 966 424387
FREQUENCY: Ch 16		

DOS MARES	Marina 150 Berths 75 Visitors Berths	37°39′·5N 0°14′·0W
Marina: +34 968 140342	Maximum LOA: 15 m	Fax Marina: +34 968 140117
FREQUENCY: Ch 09		HOURS: HX

DUQUESA	Marina 328 Berths	36°21′·5N 5°13′·6W
Marina: +34 952 890100 mdoquesa@ncs.es	Depth: 3 m, Maximum LOA: 20 m	Fax +34 952 890101 www.eppa.es
FREQUENCY: Ch 09 10 16		HOURS: HX

EL CANDALO	Marina 250 Berths	36°42′·9N 4°20′·7W
+34 952 296097 & 290547	Depth: 2·3 m, Maximum LOA: 10 m	Fax +34 952 295804
FREQUENCY: Ch 09 16		HOURS: HX

EL MASNOU	Marina 1081 Berths 270 Visitors Berths	41°28′·5N 2°18′·6E
+34 935 403000	Depth: 2 - 6 m, Maximum LOA: 23 m	Fax +34 935 403004
FREQUENCY: Ch 09 16		HOURS: HX

EMPURIABRAVA	Marina 5000 Berths 700 Berths for Vessels up to 26 m	41°28′·5N 2°18′·6E
+34 972 451239 info@empuriabrava.com	Depth: 5 m, Maximum LOA: 60 m	Fax +34 972 456161 www.empuriaport.com
FREQUENCY: Ch 09 16		HOURS: HX

ESTARTIT (CLUB NÁUTICO)	Marina 738 Berths 380 Visitor Berths	42°3′·1N 3°12′·4E
Marina: +34 972 751402	Depth: 2 - 2·5 m, Maximum LOA: 25 m	Fax Marina: +34 972 751717
FREQUENCY: Ch 09 16		HOURS: HX

ESTEPONA	Marina 446 Berths	36°24′·8N 5°09′·4W
+34 952 801800 & 801096 marinamediterraneo@arrakis.es	Depth: 1 - 6 m, Maximum LOA: 35 m	Fax +34 952 802497
FREQUENCY: Ch 09 16		HOURS: HX

FUENGIROLA	Marina 275 Berths	36°32′·6N 4°36′·8W
Tel: +34 952 468000	Depth 3·75 m, Maximum LOA: 20 m	Fax: +34 952 469989
FREQUENCY: Ch 09 16		HOURS: HX

GANDÍA	Port and Marina 479 Berts	38°59′·6N 0°09′·0W
Tel: Marina: +34 962 481050 Port: +34 962 842901 & 842902	Depth: 2·5 - 7 m, Maximum LOA: 20 m	Fax: Marina: +34 962 481050
FREQUENCY: Ch 09 16	Gandía Yacht Harbour lies at the root of Dique Norte.	

GARRUCHA	Port & Marina 249 Berths 55 Visitor Berths	37°10′·8N 1°48′·9W
Tel: Port: +34 950 460048 Marina: +34 950 132410 pdgarruch@distrito.com	Depth: 2·7 m, Maximum LOA: 14 m	Fax: Port: +34 950 133026 Marina: +34 950 132315
FREQUENCY: Ch 09 16		HOURS: HX

GINESTA (CASTELLDEFELS)	Marina 1065 Berths 223 Visitor Berths	41°15′·75N 1°57′·50E
Tel: Torre de Control: +34 936 643661 Club Náutico de Castelldefels (CNC): +34 933 652446	Depth: 3 - 6 m, Maximum LOA 25 m	Fax: +34 936 650166
FREQUENCY: Ch 27		
PROCEDURE: Vessels should report to the Torre de Control for documentation and berth allocation.		

HOSPITALET DE L'INFANT	Marina 575 Berths	40°59′·11N 0°55′·60E
Tel: Marina: +34 977 823004 & 8231878	Depth: 1·5 - 2·6 m, Maximum LOA: 18·5 m	Fax: Marina: +34 977 820534
FREQUENCY: Ch 09 16		HOURS: HX

JÁVEA	Marina 352 Berths	38°48′·0N 0°11′·2E
Tel: Marina: +34 965 791025	Depth: 3 m, Maximum LOA: 18 m	Fax: Marina: +34 965 791025
FREQUENCY: Ch 09	Limited space for visiting yachts	HOURS: HX

JOSÉ BANUS	Port & Marina 915 Berths 568 Visitor Berths	36°29′·0N 4°57′·3W
Tel: Port: +34 952 814750 & 814752 Marina: +34 952 909800	Depth: 3 m, Maximum LOA: 50 m	Fax: Port: +34 952 810899
FREQUENCY: Ch 09 16		HOURS: HX

LA CALETA DE VÉLEZ	Marina 227 Berths	36°44′·9N 4°04′·2W
Tel: +34 952 511390 caleta@eppa.es	Depth: 4 m, Maximum LOA: 20 m	Fax: +34 952 550526 www.eppa.es
FREQUENCY: Ch 10		HOURS: HX

L'AMETLLA DE MAR	Marina 257 Berths	40°52′·8N 0°48′·2E
Tel: Marina: +34 977 457240	Depth: 1 - 5 m, Maximum LOA: 25 m	Fax: Marina: +34 977 457240
FREQUENCY: Ch 09 16		HOURS: HX

LA MANGA MARINA TOMÁS MAESTRE	Marina 773 Berths	37°44′·0N 0°43′·3W
Tel: Marina: +34 968 140725	Depth: 2·5 - 4 m, Maximum LOA: 25 m	Fax: Marina: +34 968 140675
FREQUENCY: Ch 09		HOURS: HX

LA MANGA MAR MENOR AND PUERTO TORRE DE LA HORADADA MARINAS		Marina Frequency: Ch 09
Marina	**Telephone and Facsimile** Use International dialing code +34	**Additional information**
Cabo Palos 37°37′·57N 00°42′·00W	Tel: 968 563515	160 Berths 40 for Visitors Maximum LOA: 10 m
Dos Mares 37°39′·50N 00°44′·00W	Tel: 968 140117	150 Berths 75 Visitors
La Isleta 37°39′·00N 00°43′·15W	Tel: 968 145339	
Los Alcazares 37°44′·15N 00°50′·60W	Tel: 968 57529	280 Berths Maximum LOA: 14 m
Los Nietos 37°39′·20N 00°47′·10W	Tel: 968 133300	450 Berths Depth: 1·5 - 3 m
Los Urrutias 37°40′·73N 00°49′·40W	Tel: 968 134438 & Fax: 968 134367	253 Berths 80 Visitors
Mar De Cristal 37°38′·45N 00°45′·35W	Tel: 968 569107	
Puerto Tomas Maestre 37°45′·00N 00°45′·00W	Tel: 968 140725 & Fax: 968 140672	773 Berths Maximum LOA: 25 m
Puerto Torre De La Horadada 37°52′·0N 00°45′·30W torrehoradada@xpress.es	Tel: 966 769087 & Fax: 966 769669	506 Berths Depth: 1 - 2 m

LAS FUENTES	Marina 274 Berths	40°15′·0N 0°17′·30E
Marina: +34 964 412084	Depth: 2 m, Maximum LOA: 20 m	Marina: +34 964 414657
FREQUENCY: Ch 09		HOURS: HX

L' ESCALA	Marina 825 Berths	42°07′·0N 3°8′·6E
Marina: +34 972 770016	Depth: 1·5 - 3 m, Maximum LOA: 14 m	Marina: +34 972 770158
FREQUENCY: Ch 09		HOURS: HX

LOS ALCÁZARES C.N. MAR MENOR	Marina 282 Berths	37°44′·12N 0°51′·60W
Marina: +34 968 575129	Depth: 1 - 2 m, Maximum LOA: 12 m	Marina: +34 968 575129
FREQUENCY: Ch 09		HOURS: HX

LOS NIETOS (CLUB NÁUTICO)	Marina 437 Berths	37°39′·6N 0°47′W
Marina: +34 968 133300	Depth: 1·5 - 3 m, Maximum LOA: 12 m	Marina: +34 968 133640
FREQUENCY: Ch 09		HOURS: HX

LOS URRUTIAS	Marina 253 Berths 80 Visitors Berths	37°40′·67N 0°49′·49W
Marina: +34 968 134438	Maximum LOA: 12 m	Marina: +34 968 134438
FREQUENCY: Ch 09		HOURS: HX

LUIS CAMPOMANES MARINA GREENWICH	Marina 542 Berths 100 Berths for Public Use	38°38′·1N 0°04′·2E
Marina: +34 965 842200	Depth: 2·5 - 5 m, Maximum LOA: 30 m	Marina: +34 965 842307
FREQUENCY: Ch 09		HOURS: HX

MÁLAGA, REAL CLUB MEDITERRANEO DE MÁLAGA	Marina 83 Berths	36°42′·5N 4°29′·9W
Marina: +34 952 226300 & 226203 cbotes@realclubmediterraneo.com	Depth: 2 m, Maximum LOA: 12 m	+34 952 216311
FREQUENCY: Ch 09 16		HOURS: HX

MARBELLA	Marina 377 Berths 100 Visitor Berths	36°30′·4N 4°53′·4W
+34 952 825869	Depth: 2 m, Maximum LOA: 20 m	Port: +34 952 824462
FREQUENCY: Ch 09 16		HOURS: 0900 - 1900 LT

MARINA DE BAJADILLA	Marina 266 Berths	36°31′·0N 5°52′·5W
Capitanía +34 952 858404	Maximum LOA: 15 m	+34 952 858426
FREQUENCY: Ch 09		HOURS: HX

MAZARRON	Marina 207 Berths	37°33′·5N 1°16′·4W
☎ Marina: +34 968 594011 Club de Regatas de Mazarron (Yacht Club): +34 968 594520		Fax Yacht Club: +34 968 595253
FREQUENCY: Ch 09 16	Depth: 3 - 5 m, Maximum LOA: 15 m	Yacht Club and office situated in the NE corner of the harbour
PROCEDURE: Vessels should report to the Club de Regatas Office on arrival for berth allocation. Some visitors berths available.		

MORAYRA	Marina 593 Berths	38°41′·0N 0°08′·3E
☎ +34 965 744319	Depth: 3 - 7 m, Maximum LOA: 30 m	Fax +34 965 744750
FREQUENCY: Ch 09 27		HOURS: H24

MOTRIL	Port and Marina 125 Berths	36°43′·1N 3°31′·3W
☎ Marina: +34 958 600037 cnauticomotril@radiovision.es	Depth: 0·5 - 8 m, Maximum LOA: 20 m	Fax Marina: +34 958 601247 www.motril.org/clubnautico.es
FREQUENCY: Ch 09 16		HOURS: HX

OLIVA	Marina 300 Berths	38°56′·9N 0°05′·0W
☎ Club Náutico de Oliva: +34 962 850596	Depth: 2-4m	Fax +34 962 839000
FREQUENCY: Ch 09 16	LOCATION: Capitain de Puerto's Office: NW side of Club Náutico de Oliva	

OROPESA DEL MAR	Marina: CALL: Club Nautico Oropesa del Mar 668 Berths	40°04′·57N 0°08′·40E
☎ +34 964 313055		Fax +34 964 310000
FREQUENCY: Ch 09 16		HOURS: H24

PALAMÓS	Port 250 Berths. 30 for Visitors Marina: CALL: Palamós Club 869 Berths. 225 for Visitors	41°50′N 3°08′E
☎ Port: +34 972 314070 Marina: +34 972 601000 nautica@intercom.es	Maximum LOA: 18 m	Fax Marina: +34 972 602266 www.palamos.org
FREQUENCY: Port: Ch 16 Marina: Ch 09		HOURS: HX

PORT BALIS	Marina 775 Berths 140 Visitor Berths	41°35′·5N 2°30′·5E
☎ Marina: +34 937 929900	Depth: 3 - 5 m, Maximum LOA: 25 m	Fax Marina: +34 937 927261
FREQUENCY: Ch 09 16		HOURS: HX

PORT D'ARO, CLUB NÁUTICO	Marina 838 Berths 40 Visitor Berths	41°48′·2N 3°3′·8E
☎ Marina: +34 972 818929	Depth: 3 m, Maximum, LOA: 15 m	Fax Marina: +34 972 825909
FREQUENCY: Ch 09 16		HOURS: HX

PORT DAURAT	Marina 550 Berths Visitor Berths Available	41°10′N 1°28′E
☎ +34 977 138024 info@portdauratmatmarinadebra.com	Depth: 5 m, Maximum, LOA: 60 m	Fax Marina: +34 977 138066 www.portdauratmatmarinadebra.com
FREQUENCY: Ch 09		HOURS: HX

PORT DE LA SELVA	Marina	42°20′N 3°12′E
☎ Capitanía: +34 972 387000		Fax Capitanía: +34 972 387001
FREQUENCY: Ch 09		HOURS: HX

PORT GARRAF	Marina 593 Berths	41°14′·9N 1°54′·0E
☎ Marina: +34 936 320126	Depth: 3 m, Maximum, LOA: 18 m	Fax Marina: +34 936 320126
FREQUENCY: Ch 09		HOURS: HX

PORT MATARO
Marina: 1080 Berths 200 Visitor Berths | 41°31'·5N 2°26'·5E

Tel: +34 937 550961 & 550901
info@portmataro.com
Depth: 5 m
Fax: +34 937 902942
www.portmataro.com
FREQUENCY: Ch 09
HOURS: HX

PORT ROSAS
Marina: 457 Berths 106 Visitor Berths | 42°15'·25N 3°10'·59E

Tel: +34 972 154412
Depth Mouth: 9 m, Basin: 3 - 6 m, Maximum LOA: 35 m
Fax: +34 972 153768
FREQUENCY: Ch 09
Opening summer 2003
HOURS: HX

PREMIÁ DE MAR (SAN CRISTOBAL DE PREMIÁ)
Marina 250 Berths | 41°29'·1N 2°20'·9E

Tel: Torre de Control & Club Náutico de Premiá (CNP): +34 937 514111
FREQUENCY: Ch 27
PROCEDURE: Vessels should report to the Torre de Control for documentation and berth allocation

PUEBLA DE FARNALS
Marina 825 Berths | 39°34'N 0°17'W

Tel: Capitain del Puerto's Office: +34 961 441928 & 442411
Pobla Marina: +34 961 463223
Depth: 2 m, Maximum LOA: 25 m
Fax: Marina: +34 961 462587
FREQUENCY: Ch 04 **09** 27
LOCATION: Capitain del Puerto's office: NW corner of harbour close by berth pontoon No 1

PUERTO CALAFAT
Marina 404 Berths | 40°55'·6N 0°51'·0E

Tel: Marina: +34 977 486023
Depth: 2·5 - 3 m, Maximum LOA: 20 m
Fax: Marina: +34 977 486023
FREQUENCY: Ch 09
HOURS: HX

PUERTO DE CASTELLÓN DE LA PLANA
Port & Marina | 39°58'N 0°01'E

Tel: Hr Mr: +34 964 282352
Club Náutico: +34 964 282520
Maximum LOA: 20 m
Fax: Club Náutico: +34 964 283905
FREQUENCY: Port: Ch 12 13 16 Marina: Ch 09
Floating pontoons at the Club Náutico
HOURS: HX

PUERTO DE LA HORADADA
Marina 500 Berths | 37°52'·0N 0°45'·3W

Tel: Marina: +34 966 769087
Depth: 1 - 2 m
Fax: Marina: +34 966 769669
FREQUENCY: Ch 09
HOURS: HX

PUERTO DE LES CASES D'ALCANAR
Marina | 40°33'N 0°32'W

Tel: +34 977 735014
Depth: 1 - 2 m
FREQUENCY: Ch 09
HOURS: HX

PUERTO DE LIAFRANC
Marina 147 Berths | 41°53'·5N 3°11'·6E

Tel: Marina: +34 972 300754
Depth: 1 - 3 m, Maximum LOA: 15 m
Fax: Marina: +34 972 300754
FREQUENCY: Ch 09
In season visiting yachts berth at the fuel quay
HOURS: HX

PUERTO DE SILES
Marina 564 Berths | 39°40'·8N 0°12'·0W

Tel: Marina: +34 962 609223
Depth: 2·5 m, Maximum LOA: 12 m
Fax: Marina: +34 962 609223
FREQUENCY: Ch 09
HOURS: HX

PUERTO EL PERELLO
Marina | 39°17'N 0°16'E

Tel: Club Náutico: +34 961 770386
Maximum LOA: 12 m
Fax: Club Náutico: +34 961 770412
FREQUENCY: Ch 09
HOURS: HX

PUERTO GUADAMAR - MARINA DE LAS DUNAS
Marina 490 Berths | 38°6'·8N 0°38'·5W

Tel: Marina: +34 965 971938
Depth: 2 - 3 m, Maximum LOA: 15 m
Fax: Marina: +34 965 971938
FREQUENCY: Ch 09
HOURS: HX

PUERTO OROPESA DEL MAR	Marina 668 Berths	40°04'·30N 0°08'·8E
Marina: +34 964 313055	Depth: 3 m, Maximum LOA: 15 m	Fax Marina: +34 964 310000
FREQUENCY: Ch 09		HOURS: HX

PUERTO SANTA MARGARIDA	Marina 500 Berths	42°14'·5N 3°07'·5E
+34 972 257700	Depth: 1·8 - 2 m, Maximum LOA: 22 m	Fax +34 972 151178
		HOURS: HX

PUERTOS DE AGUILAS Y DEL HORNILLO	Marina	37°24'N 1°34'W
+34 968 411951		Fax +34 968 411951
FREQUENCY: Ch 09	Fishing nets often laid at entrance to harbour	HOURS: HX

PUNTA DE LA MONA (MARINA DEL ESTE)	Marina 227 Berths	36°43'·8N 3°43'·4W
+34 958 827018 & 827078	Depth: 4 m, Maximum LOA: 30 m	Fax +34 958 827240
FREQUENCY: Ch 09 16		HOURS: HX

ROQUETAS DE MAR	Marina 243 Berths	36°45'·5N 2°36'·1W
Marina: +34 950 320789	Depth: 4·5 m, Maximum LOA: 15 m	Fax +34 950 320144
FREQUENCY: Ch 09 16		HOURS: HX

SALOU	Marina 230 Berths	41°04'·4N 1°07'·8E
Marina: +34 977 382166 & 382167	Depth: 3 m, Max LOA: 24 m	Fax Marina: +34 977 384454
FREQUENCY: Ch 09 16		HOURS: HX

SANT CARLES DE LA RÁPITA	Marina 480 Berths	40°36'·5N 0°36'·1E
Marina: +34 977 471103 Port: +34 977 740059	Depth: 3 m, Maximum LOA: 15 m	Fax Marina: +34 977 741103
FREQUENCY: Ch 09 16		HOURS: HX

SAN FELIÚ DE GUIXOLS	**Port & Marina:** CALL: San Feliú Náutico 300 Berths 25 Visitor Berths	41°46'N 3°01'E
Hr Mr: +34 972 320967 Marina: +34 972 321300 & 971 321700	Depth: 3·5 - 4 m, Maximum LOA: 14 m	Fax Marina: +34 972 321300
FREQUENCY: Port: Ch 16 Marina: Ch 09		HOURS: HX

SAN JOSÉ	Marina 244 Berths Very Limited Availability	36°45'·8N 2°06'·1W
Port: +34 950 380041	Depth: 1·5 - 2·5 m, Maximum LOA: 15 m	Fax +34 950 380041
FREQUENCY: Ch 09 16		HOURS: HX

SANTA POLA, PUERTO DEPORTIVO	Marina 400 Berths Approximately 80 Visitor Berths	38°10'·09N 0°33'·80W
Marina: +34 956 412403	Maximum LOA: 8 m	Fax
FREQUENCY: Ch 09		HOURS: HX

SANTA POLA (CLUB NÁUTICO)	Marina 550 Berths Approximately 30 Visitor Berths	38°11'·35N 0°33'·70W
Marina: +34 965 412403	Depth: 2·5 - 4 m, Maximum LOA: 28 m	Fax Marina: +34 966 690261
FREQUENCY: Ch 09		HOURS: HX

SEGUR DE CALAFELL	Marina 225 Berths	41°11'·2N 1°34'·8E
+34 977 692323	Depth: 1 - 1·5 m, Maximum LOA: 10 m	Fax
FREQUENCY: Ch 27	Torre de Control: situated at the head of the breakwater	

SITGES	Port: CALL: Aiguadolo Puerto 740 Berths 130 Visitor Berths	41°14′N 1°48′E
Tel: +34 938 942600	Depth: 2 - 5 m, Maximum LOA: 25 m	Fax:
FREQUENCY: Ch 09 16	LOCATION: Aiguadolo	HOURS: HX

SOTOGRANDE	Port & Marina 683 Berths	36°17′·3N 5°16′·1W
Tel: Port: +34 956 790000 Marina: +34 956 762284 puertosotogrande@nexo.es	Depth: 3 - 4·5 m, Maximum LOA: 50 m	Fax: Marina: +34 956 790109 www.puertosotogrande.com
FREQUENCY: Ch 09 16		HOURS: HX

TARRAGONA	Port: and Marina 441 Berths 50 Visitor Berths	41°05′·1N 1°13′·3E
Tel: Port Office: +34 977 226611 & 226709 Marina: +34 977 213100	Depth: 5 - 8 m, Maximum LOA: 20 m	Fax: Port Office: +34 977 225499 & 219638 Marina: +34 977 212702
FREQUENCY: Port: Ch 12 14 16 Marina Ch 09 16		

TORREDEMBARRA	Marina 820 Berths 200 Visitors Berths	41°08′·30N 1°24′·15E
Tel: Marina: +34 977 643234	Depth: 3 - 5 m, Maximum LOA: 20 m	Fax: Marina: +34 977 643236
FREQUENCY: Ch 09 16		HOURS: HX

TORREVIEJA	Marinas	
Marina International	860 Berths 215 Visitor Berths	37°57′·9N 0°41′·2W
Tel: Port: +34 965 710234 Mobile: +34 908 000736 +34 965 713650	Depth: 1·5 - 4 m, Maximum LOA: 40 m	Fax: +34 965 714 266
Real Club Nautico	600 Berths 50 Visitor Berths	
Tel: +34 965 710108 & 710112 info@rcnt.com (General Information) desk@rcnt.com (Reservations etc)	Maximum LOA: 50 m	Fax: +34 965 710882 www.rcnt.com
FREQUENCY: Ch 09		HOURS: HX

VALENCIA	Marina: CALL: Real Club Nautico Yacht Harbour 1252 Berths	39°27′N 0°20′W
Real Club Nautico		
Tel: Marina: +34 963 679011 Port-Saplaya: +34 963 550033 Port: +34 963 230991 & 3674391	Max LOA: 60m	Fax: Marina: +34 963 677737 Port: +34 963 233272 & 3672752 www.valenciaport.com
FREQUENCY: Ch 09 16	LOCATION: 1 n mile SW of the head of Dique del Sur	HOURS: H24

VALENCIA MARINAS	Use International dialing code +34	Marina Frequency: Ch 09
Marina	**Telephone and Facsimile numbers**	**Additional information.**
Canet d'en Berenguer Marina 39°40′·0N 00°12′·0W	Tel: 962 608132	564 Berths, Maximum LOA: 12 m
Dearsena Deportiva El Perelló 39°16′·5N 00°17′·0W	Tel: 961 770386 & Fax: 961 770412	
Nautico De Las Fuentes 40°15′·0N 00°17′·3E	Tel: 964 412084 & Fax: 964 414657	274 Berths
Puerto De Benicarló 40°24′·7N 00°26′·0E	Tel: 964 474209 & Fax 964 473461	
Puerto De Castellón 39°58′·0N 00°01′·6E	Tel: 964 282520	250 Berths
Puerto De Cullera 39°10′·0N 00°14′·0W	Tel: 961 721154	
Puerto De Peñíscola 40°21′·2N 00°24′·1E	Tel: 964 489436	
Puerto De Vinaroz 40°28′·2N 00°28′·5E	Tel: 964 451705 & Fax: 964 400258	

VILLAJOYSA (CLUB NÁUTICO)	Marina 330 Berths 160 Visitors Berths	38°30′N 0°14′W
Tel: Marina: +34 965 893606	Maximum LOA: 20 m	Fax: Marina: +34 966 851504
FREQUENCY: Ch 09		HOURS: HX

VILLANUEVA I LA GELTRÚ	Port & Marina: CALL: Villanueva I La Geltrú Nautico Radio 810 Berths 230 Visitor Berths	41°13'N 1°44'E
☎ Port: +34 938 155219 Marina: +34 938 150267 cnv@deinfo.es	Depth: 1 - 3 m, Maximum LOA: 22 m	Fax Marina: +34 938 156469
FREQUENCY: Ch 09 16		HOURS: HX

ISLAS BALEARES		

FORMENTERA	Marina	38°44'N 1°25'E

FORMENTERA MAR	Marina 90 Berths 20 Visitor Berths	38°44'·0N 1°25'·1E
☎ +34 971 323235 & 322693 formentera@mundivia.es		Fax +34 971 322222 www.formenteramar.com
FREQUENCY: Ch 09		HOURS: HX
MARINA DE FORMENTERA	**Marina** 108 Private Berths 42 Public Berths	38°44'·1N 1°25'·1E
☎ +34 971 322346 info@marinadeformentera.com	Depth: 2·5 - 3 m, Maximum LOA: 30 m	Fax +34 971 323252 www.marinadeformentera.com
FREQUENCY: Ch 09		HOURS: HX

IBIZA		

IBIZA MARINAS	Marinas	
Ibeza Nueva	CALL: Ibeza Nueva 536 Berths	38°54'N 1°26'E
☎ +34 971 312062	Depth: 4 - 6 m, Maximum LOA: 55 m	Fax +34 971 313523
FREQUENCY: Ch 09		HOURS: HX
Marina Botafoch	428 Berths 107 Visitor Berths	38°55'N 1°26'E
☎ +34 971 312231 & 331711	Depth: 3·5 - 4 m, Maximum LOA: 30 m	Fax +34 971 311557
FREQUENCY: Ch 09		HOURS: HX
Port D'Eivissa	146 Berths	38°27'N 1°55'E
☎ +34 971 228487		Fax +34 971 726948
FREQUENCY: Ch 09 VHF Ch 14		HOURS: HX
Club Nautico Ibiza	340 Berths	38°27'N 1°55'E
☎ +34 971 313363	Depth: 0·5 - 3 m, Maximum LOA: 20 m	Fax +34 971 194335
FREQUENCY: Ch 09		HOURS: HX
Puerto Deportivo Santa Eulalia	755 Berths	38°59'N 1°32'E
☎ +34 971 336161 & 339754 ptostaeulalia@interbook.net	Depth: 1·5 - 3 m, Maximum LOA: 22 m	Fax +34 971 332810
FREQUENCY: Ch 09		HOURS: HX
Club Nautic Sant Antoni de Pormany	300 Berths 150 Visitor Berths	38°27'N 1°55'E
☎ +34 971 340645 Mobile: 626477153	Depth: 2 - 4·5 m, Maximum LOA: 18 m	Fax +34 971 345607
FREQUENCY: Ch 09		HOURS: HX

SAN ANTONIO	Port CALL: San Antonio Náutico 350 Berths	38°58·6'N 1°17'·9E
☎ Port: +34 971 340503	Maximum LOA: 17 m	Fax
FREQUENCY: Ch 09 16		HOURS: HX

MALLORCA

ALCUDIA	Port: CALL: Alcudia Prácticos	39°50′N 3°08′E
Tel: Port:+34 971 545076		Fax: +34 971 549167
FREQUENCY: Ch 11 13 14 16		HOURS: 0600-2400 LT

CALA D'OR MARINA

MALLORCA MARINAS	Marina Frequency: Ch 09	
Alcudimar S.A.	753 Berths 300 - 350 Visitor Berths	39°49′N 3°08′E
Tel: +34 971 546000 alcudiamar@bitel.es	Depth: 2 - 4 m, Maximum LOA: 30 m	Fax: +34 971 548920 www.alcudiiamar.es
Cala d'Or	570 Berths	39°22′N 3°14′E
Tel: +34 971 657070	Depth: 3 m, Maximum LOA: 26 m	Fax: +34 971 657068
Cala Nova	214 Berths	39°33′N 2°26′E
Tel: +34 971 402512	Depth: 1·5 - 7 m, Maximum LOA: 16 m	Fax: +34 971 403911
Club Maritimo de San Antonio	396 Berths 99 Visitor Berths	39°32′N 2°43′E
Tel: +34 971 745076 cmsap@cmsap.com	Depth: 2 - 3 m, Maximum LOA: 16 m	Fax: +34 971 0261638
Club Nautico de Arenal	152 Berths	39°30′N 2°45′E
Tel: +34 971 440142 administracion@cnarenal.com	Depth: 2 - 5 m, Maximum LOA: 30 m	Fax: +34 971 440568 www.cnarenal.com
Club Nautico de Santa Ponsa	522 Berths	39°31′N 2°28′E
Tel: +34 971 694950	Depth: 2·5 - 5 m, Maximum LOA: 20 m	Fax: +34 971 694488
FREQUENCY: VHF Ch 16		

MALLORCA MARINAS (Continued)	Marina Frequency: Ch 09	
Club Nautico La Rapita	460 Berths	39°21′N 2°57′E
☎ +34 971 640001	Depth: 1 - 4 m, Maximum LOA: 20 m	Fax +34 971 640821
Club Nautico S'Estanyol	285 Berths	39°22′N 2°55′E
☎ +34 971 640085	Maximum LOA: 12 m	Fax +34 971 640682
Port Adriano	404 Berths	39°29′N 2°28′E
☎ +34 971 232494 ortadriano@sp-editores.es	Depth: 2 - 5 m, Maximum LOA: 20 m	Fax +34 971 232566 www.portadriano.com
Porto Colom	252 Berths	39°24′·7N 3°16′·1E
☎ +34 971 824658	Depth: 1 - 4 m, Maximum LOA: 20 m	Fax +34 971 825399
Club Nautico de Porto Cristo	206 Berths 61 Visitor Berths	39°32′N 3°20′E
☎ +34 971 821253 cnpc@maptel.es	Depth: 3 m, Maximum LOA: 16 m	Fax +34 971 820650
FREQUENCY: VHF not monitored		HOURS: H24 all year
Porto de Porto Cristo		39°32′·2N 3°20′·4E
☎ +34 971 820419		Fax +34 971 820419
Porto Petro	201 Berths	39°01′N 3°13′E
☎ +34 971 657657 reialcluibnauticoportopetro@bt.link	Depth: 1 - 2·4 m, Maximum LOA: 15 m	Fax +34 971 659216
Puerto de Bonaire	324 Berths	39°52′N 3°08′E
☎ +34 971 546955	Depth: 1·5 - 7 m, Maximum LOA: 20 m	Fax +34 971 546564
Puerto de Cala Ratjada	90 Berths	39°43′N 3°28′E
☎ +34 971 565067	Depth: 1·5 - 4 m, Maximum LOA: 60 m	Fax +34 971 565067
FREQUENCY: VHF Ch 16		HOURS: H24 all year
Puerto de Ca'n Picafort	470 Berths	39°45′N 3°10′E
☎ +34 971 850010	Depth: 1·5 - 2·5 m, Maximum LOA: 15 m	Fax +34 971 850010
FREQUENCY: VHF Ch 16		
Puerto de Pollensa	375 Berths 75 Visitor Berths	39°54′N 3°05′E
☎ +34 971 864635 rcnpp@sertebal.com	Depth: 0·5 - 2·7 m, Maximum LOA: 25 m	Fax +34 971 864636 www.rcnpp.net
Puerto Portals	664 Berths 165 Visitor Berths	39°32′N 2°35′E
☎ +34 971 171100 puertoportals@oninet.com	Depth: 3 - 7 m, Maximum LOA: 80 m	Fax +34 971 171117
FREQUENCY: VHF Ch 16		HOURS: H24 all year
Puerto de Soller	226 Berths	39°47′N 2°41′E
☎ +34 971 633316	Depth: 4 - 5 m, Maximum LOA: 30 m	Fax +34 971 633316
FREQUENCY: VHF Ch 16		
Santa Ponza	500 Berths	39°31′N 2°28′E
☎ +34 971 694950	Depth: 2 - 3 m, Maximum LOA: 20 m	Fax +34 971 694488
Port de Cala Bona	194 Berths	39°31′N 2°28′E
☎ +34 971 586256	Depth: 0·5 - 3 m, Maximum LOA: 12 m	Fax +34 971 586256
FREQUENCY: VHF Ch 16		

PORTO PETRO BREAKWATER FROM SSE

PALMA	Port and Marina: CALL: Palma Prácticos	39°33′N 2°38′E
☎ Port & Marina: +34 971 715100 baleares@baleares.portel.es		Fax Port & Marina: +34 971 726948
FREQUENCY: Ch 06 14 16		HOURS: H24
INFORMATION BROADCASTS: Gale warnings for Mallorca are broadcast by Palma on VHF Ch 20		

PALMA MARINAS	Marina Frequency: Ch 09	39°33′N 2°38′E
Club de Mar	625 Berths Limited Visitor Availability	
☎ +34 971 403611 secretaria@clubdemar-mallorca.com	Depths: 4 - 12 m, Maximum LOA: 120 m	Fax +34 971 403618 www.clubdemar-mallorca.com
Escuela Nacional de Vela Cala Nova	214 Berths	
☎ +34 971 402512	Depth: 1·6 - 7 m, Maximum LOA:16 m	Fax +34 971 403911
Club Nautico Portitxol	240 Berths	
☎ +34 971 242424	Depth: 1·4 - 2 m, Maximum LOA:12 m	Fax +34 971 242424
Club Maritimo Molinar de Levante		
☎ +34 971 249460		Fax +34 971 249460
Club Nautico Cala Gamba		
☎ +34 971 261849		Fax +34 971 491900
Club Maritimo San Antonio de la Playa	396 Berths	
☎ +34 971 745076 cmsap@cmsap.com	Depth: 1 - 3·5 m, Maximum LOA: 20 m	Fax +34 971 261638 www.cmsap.com
Marina Port de Mallorca	CALL: Club de Mar 152 Berths	
☎ +34 971 739030 comercial@portdemallorca.com	Depth: 3·5 - 5 m, Maximum LOA: 30 m	Fax +34 971 221621 www.portdemallorca.com
Real Club Náutico	996 Berths 300 Visitor Berths	
☎ +34 971 726848 rcnp@pmi.servicom.es	Depth: 1·3 - 6 m, Maximum LOA: 30 - 40 m	Fax +34 971 718636 www.club-nautico-palma.com
FREQUENCY: Ch 09 16		HOURS:0800-2000 LT (Office)

PUERTO DE ANDRAITX	Port and Marina: CALL: Andraitx Vela 475 Berths 118 Visitor Berths	39°33′·5N 2°23′·5E
☎ Port: +34 971 674216 Marina "Club de Vela": +34 971 671721	Depth: 2 - 2·5 m, Maximum LOA: 36 m	Fax Port: +34 971 633316 Marina "Club de Vela": +34 971 674271
FREQUENCY: Ch 09 11		HOURS: HX

PORTO PETRO (MARINA AND REAL CLUB NÄUTIC)

MENORCA

MAHÓN, MENORCA	Marina	1100 Berths	39°63′N 4°18′E
Marina: +34 971 363066 Port: +34 971 362666 & 367254			Fax
Puerto Deportivo de Mahón			
FREQUENCY: Marina: Ch 09			HOURS: HX

MENORCA MARINAS	Marina Frequency: Ch 09		
Puerto de Ciutadella		100 Berths	39°59′N 3°49′E
Tel: +34 971 381193	Depth: 2·5 - 5 m, Maximum LOA: 20 m		Fax: +34 971 381193
FREQUENCY: VHF Ch 16			
Club Nautic Ciutadella		120 Berths	39°59′N 3°49′E
Tel: +34 971 383918	Depth: 2·5 - 5 m, Maximum LOA: 20 m		Fax: +34 971 385871
Port Deportiu de Cala'n Bosch		256 Berths	39°59′N 3°49′E
Tel: +34 971 387171	Depth: 1·5 - 2·5 m, Maximum LOA: 15 m		Fax: +34 971 387170
Port de Mao		158 Berths	39°52′N 4°18′E
Tel: +34 971 363066	Depth: 2 - 23 m		Fax: +34 971 363010
FREQUENCY: VHF Ch 16			
Porto D'Hivernada de Mao		230 Berths 50 Visitor Berths	39°52′N 4°18′E
Tel: +34 971 359821	Depth: 2 - 10 m, Maximum LOA: 18 m		Fax: +34 971 386966
hivernadamaho@pormao.com			www.portmao.com
Club Maritimo de Mahon		158 Berths 12 Visitor Berths	39°52′N 4°18′E
Tel: +34 971 365022	Depth: 2 - 10 m, Maximum LOA: 40 m		Fax: +34 971 360762
cmmahon@infotelecom.es			
FREQUENCY: VHF Ch 16			
Ribera del Puerto		240 Berths	39°52′N 4°18′E
Tel: +34 971 354844	Depth: 2 - 10 m, Maximum LOA: 27 m		Fax: +34 971 354327
Port d'Addaia		150 Berths Some Visitor Availability	40°01′N 4°10′E
Tel: +34 971 188871	Depth: 1·5 - 3 m, Maximum LOA: 25 m		Fax: +34 971 188871

MENORCA MARINAS (Continued)	Marina Frequency: Ch 09	
Port de Fornells	Visitor Berths Available	40°03′N 4°08′E
☎ +34 971 376604	Depth: 3 m	Fax +34 971 376358

SYRIA

National SAR Agency: General Directorate of Ports **Tel:** 41 233333, 41 233876 & 41 235 890 **Fax:** 41 235805 **Telex:** 451216 MWANI SY
The General Director of Ports in Al Lādhiqīyah (Lattakia) is responsible for co-ordinating Search and Rescue operations. A network of Coast Radio Stations maintains a continuous listening watch on international distress frequencies.

	Telephone +963	**Fax** +963	**Others**
MRCC SYRIA	41 233333	41 235805	**Telex** +492 451216 MWANI SY

AL LĀDHIQĪYAH (LATAKIA) — Pilots — 35°31′N 35°46′E

☎ +963 12155

FREQUENCY: Pilot Station: Ch 12 14 16 — HOURS: H16

ŢARŢŪS — Port — 35°54′N 35°52′E

☎ Government Agency: +963 43 20940 & 21541
Hr Mr: +963 43 20562

FREQUENCY: Port: Ch 08 10 16
Government Agency: Ch 16
HOURS: H24

TUNISIA

LA GOULETTE PORT

A	1743	RT (MF)		
B	2182			
Weather Bulletins				
B: On receipt Repeated at H+03	Storm warnings: In French for coasts of Tunisia			
A: 0405 1905	Weather summary, 12 hour forecast and outlook for further 12 hours in French for Tunisian coast			
Navigational Warnings				
B: On receipt 0003 0403 0603 1003 1303 1803 1903 2103	In French for Tunisian coast, Western Mediterranean south of 40°N, east of a line from Tunisian-Algerian frontier to C. Spartivento (38°52′N 8°52′E)			

TUNIS

	1820 2670	RT (MF)		
Weather Bulletins				
0805 1705	Weather summary, 12 hour forecast and outlook for further 12 hours, in French, for Tunisian coast			
Navigational Warnings				
On receipt 0803 1203 2003	In French for Tunisian coast, Western Mediterranean south of 40°N, east of a line from Tunisian-Algerian frontier to C. Spartivento (38°52′N 8°52′E)			

RADIO TUNIS

629	AM	11970	AM
962		15225	
7225			
Weather Bulletins			
1200 1215 1230 1300 1830 1900	Storm warnings: Special meteorological bulletins and storm warnings		
0630 1830 0600 (15 June - 15 Sept)	General situation, 12 hour forecast, in French, for coastal waters of Tunisia		

BIZERTE

BIZERTE	Port: and Marina 178 Berths 110 Visitor Berths	37°16′N 9°53′E
☎ Port: +216 72 31139 & 31412 Yacht Club : +216 72 36610 bizerte.sailing@gnet.tn	Depth: 1 - 3·5 m, Maximum LOA: 40 m	Fax Yacht Club: +216 72 35681 www.portplaisance.bizerte1.com
FREQUENCY: Port: 2182 kHz Ch 10 12 14 16 67 68	LOCATION: Pilot Station: NW side of Canal entrance	HOURS: Port: 0500-0900 1500-1900 LT

EL KANTAOUI

EL KANTAOUI	Marina 345 Berths 150 Visitor Berths Available	35°53′N 10°36′E
☎ Capirainaire:+216 73 348799	Depth: 2 - 4 m, Maximum LOA: 40 m	Fax +216 73 348961
FREQUENCY: Ch 09 16		HOURS: HJ

GHANNOUCHE (GABÈS)

GHANNOUCHE (GABÈS)	Port: 400 Berths 10 Visitor Berths	33°55′N 10°06′E
☎ Port: +216 75 20373 Hr Mr: +216 75 22922	Depth: 2 - 4·5 m, Maximum LOA: 19 m	Fax
FREQUENCY: 2182 kHz (MF) Ch 12 15 16 17		HOURS: 0800-1000 LT 1400-1600 LT

LA GOULETTE/TUNIS (INCLUDING RADES)

LA GOULETTE/TUNIS (INCLUDING RADES)	Port: 150 Berths 30 Visitor Berths	36°48′N 10°18′E
☎ Hr Mr: +216 71 275 007 Yacht Club: +216 71 276 284	Depth: 2 - 5 m, Maximum LOA: 12 m	Fax
FREQUENCY: 2182kHz; 1743 kHz Ch 10 12 14 16		HOURS: H24

PROCEDURE:
1. Vessels should send ETA 12h in advance.
2. Vessels in Canal de Tunis should maintain a continuous listening watch on VHF Ch 10.

MAHARÈS	Harbour 124 Berths 7 Visitor Berths	35°30′·8N 10°29′·9E
☎ +216 74 90543	Depth: 1·8 m in Channel 1·2 m in basin, Maximum LOA: 12 m	Fax
FREQUENCY: Ch 16		HOURS: 0830-1330 LT for Port Office

MAHDIA	Harbour 610 Berths 15 Visitor Berths	35°29′·8N 11°04′·1E
☎ +216 74 81595	Depth: 2 - 5 m, Maximum LOA: 30 m	Fax
FREQUENCY: Ch 16		HOURS: 0730-1330 1500-1700 LT

MARINA CAP MONASTIR	Marina 440 Berths 200 Visitor Berths	35°46′·7N 10°50′·1E
☎ +216 73 462305, 460953 & 460951	Depth: 3 - 5·5 m, Maximum LOA: 45 m	Fax +216 73 462066 www.caesum.fr/capmonastir
FREQUENCY: Ch 16		HOURS: 0700 - 1730 LT

SFAX	Port:	34°44′N 10°46′E
☎ Port Captain: +216 74 225040		Fax Port Auth: +216 74 225107
FREQUENCY: 2182; 1743 kHz (MF) Ch 12 14 16		HOURS: H24

SIDI BOU SAÏD	Marina 360 Berths 60 Visitor Berths	36°52′N 10°21′E
☎ +216 71 741645	Depth: 2 - 4·5 m, Maximum LOA: 15 m	Fax +216 71 744217
FREQUENCY: Ch 09 16		

SOUSSE	Port:	35°49′N 10°38′E
☎ +216 73 20401		Fax
FREQUENCY: 2182; 1743 kHz (MF) Ch 10 12 16 67		HOURS: 0500-0900 1500-1900 LT

TABARKA	Port and Marina 50 Berths Visitor Berths Available	36°57′·5N 8°45′·9E
☎ +216 78 44599 & 44595	Depth: 2 - 4·5 m, Maximum LOA: 40 m	Fax +216 78 44595
FREQUENCY: Ch 16 17 69		HOURS: 0830-1330 LT for Port Office
PORT DE PLAISANCE	Marina 100 Berths 70 Visitor Berths	36°57′·2N 8°45′·3E
☎ Marina: +216 78 670599	Maximum LOA: 40 m	Fax +216 78 673595
FREQUENCY: Marina: Ch 14 16 72 Tabarka Radio: Ch 10 16		HOURS: H24
INFORMATION: Keep to starboard of channel when approaching marina, call Tabarka radio on Ch 10 or 16 and await instructions		

YASMINE HAMMAMET	Marina 740 Berths 100 Visitor Berths	36°22′·25N 10°32′·84E
☎ Capirainaire: +216 2 241111 Marina: +216 71 840655 marina.yasmine@planet.tn	Depth: 0·6 - 2·3 m, Maximum LOA: 110 m	Fax Capirainaire: +216 2 241212 Marina: +216 71 842417 www.yasmine.com
FREQUENCY: Ch 16		HOURS: HX

TURKEY

AYVALIK MARINA

National SAR Agency: General Directorate of Maritime Transport, Undersecretariat for Maritime Affairs **Tel:** +90 312 2319105 & 312 2324783 **Fax:** +90 312 2320823 **Telex:** 44144 DZMS **E-mail:** cpt.durmaz@mynet.com			
Undersecretariat for Maritime Affairs, Prime Ministry at Ankara, in conjunction with regional Turkish Coast Guard centres, are responsible for the co-ordination of all maritime distress and safety incidents within the Maritime Search and Rescue Region of Turkey. A network of Coast Radio Stations maintains a continuous listening watch on international distress frequencies, including VHF, MF and HF DSC.			
	Telephone +90	**Fax** +90	**Others**
RSC İSTANBUL (Marmara Denizi Region) (Turkish Coast Guard)	212 2429710	212 2423093	**Telex** +607 26905
MRSC MERSİN (Mediterranean Sea Region) (Turkish Coast Guard)	324 2371919 324 2372222	324 2374602	**Telex** +607 67302 +607 67300

NAVTEX [F] [D] [I]

F	Antalya (Mediterranean Coast)	518 kHz	36°53′N 30°42′E
D	İstanbul (Marmara Denizi)		41°04′N 28°57′E
I	İzmır (Aegean Coast)		38°21′N 26°35′E
Weather Bulletins			
D: 0030 0430 0830 1230 1630 2030	SW part of Black Sea		
Navigational Warnings			
F: On receipt 0050 0450 0850 1250 1650 2050	In English		
D: On receipt 0030 0430 0830 1230 1630 2030	In English for SW part of Black Sea		
I: On receipt 0120 0520 0920 1320 1720 2120	In English		

BANDIRMA (YMB20) RADIO-TELEX 4560 kHz

Weather Bulletins	
Every H+10 H+30	Gale Warnings and forecast for Black Sea, Marmara Denizi, Aegean Sea and 15°E of Eastern part of Mediterranean. In Turkish, repeated in English

İSTANBUL (TAH)

A	2670	RT (MF)		
B	4405 *(417)*	RT (HF)		
	8812 *(832)*			
	13128 *(1218)*			
C	4560	RADIO-TELEX		
	8431 *(830)*			
	12654 *(12151)*			
D	Ch 67	VHF	Keltepe	40°38′N 30°05′E
			Şarköy	40°41′N 27°01′E
			Çamlıca	41°02′N 29°04′E
			Kayalıdağ	39°58′N 26°38′E
			Akdağ	38°33′N 26°30′E

DIAGRAM: page 257

Weather Bulletins	
D: 0700 1900	Forecast for local Turkish coastal areas. In English and Turkish
D: 0730 0930 1130 1330 1530 1730	Sea observations. In Turkish
C: 0800 2000 **B:** 1000 1800	Gale warnings, synopsis and forecast for Mediterranean Areas 12-27. In English and Turkish
D: 0900 1930	3 day outlook. In Turkish

Navigational Warnings	
A: 0033 0433 0833 1233 1633 2033	In English and Turkish

İZMIR RT (MF) 1850 2760 kHz

Navigational Warnings	
0333 0733 1133 1533 1933 2333	In Turkish

MERSIN RT (MF) 2820 kHz

Navigational Warnings	
0133 0533 0933 1333 1733 2133	In Turkish

VHF CHANNEL 67 WEATHER BROADCASTS

Gale warnings and forecasts for coastal waters of Turkey are broadcast on VHF Ch 67 by most CRSs. Broadcasts are announced through VHF Ch 16, before transferring to VHF Ch 67. Each station voice call sign is "METEOR" followed by the station name, e.g. "METEOR IZMIR". Broadcasts are repeated 3 times at 5 minute intervals at 0900 1200 1500 1800 2100 LT from the stations shown in the following table:

Station	Position	Broadcast language	Forecast Area
İstanbul	40°58′N 28°49′E	Turkish	W Black Sea Coast & Marmara Denizi
Tekirdağ	40°59′N 27°29′E		
Çanakkale	40°08′N 26°24′E		
İzmır	38°30′N 27°01′E	English & Turkish	Aegean Coast & W Mediterranean Coast
Gökçeada	40°11′N 25°54′E	Turkish	
Ayvalık	39°19′N 26°42′E		
Dikili	39°03′N 26°52′E		
Kuşadası	37°52′N 27°15′E		
Bodrum	37°02′N 27°26′E		
Marmaris	36°51′N 28°16′E		
Antalya	36°52′N 30°44′E	English & Turkish	Mediterranean Coast
Finike	36°18′N 30°09′E	Turkish	
Anamur (1 June - 31 Oct)	36°05′N 32°50′E		
Alanya (1 June - 31 Oct)	36°33′N 32°00′E		

TURKISH RADIO — TELEVISION CORPORATION			
	200	AM	Ankara
	245		Erzurum
	630		Tarsus
	891		Antalya
	927		İzmır
	1017		İstanbul
	1062		Diyarbakir
	1467		Dededoruk
Navigational Warnings			
On receipt, 0430 1000 1600 2000	In Turkish		

ALTIN YUNIS SETUR	Marina 125 Berths	38°19′·30N 26°20′·42E
☎ +90(0)232 7231631 & 7231434 seturcesme@superonline.com		Fax +90(0)232 7234620
FREQUENCY: Ch 16 73		

ANTALYA	Port and Marinas	36°50′N 30°37′E
☎ Hr Directorate: +90(0)242 2591212		Fax Port Auth: +90(0)242 2591350
FREQUENCY: Ch 12 16		HOURS: H24
	Marina	
(1) **Setur Antalya Marina (Antalya Commercial Harbour) Boatyard**	CALL: Setur Marina 250 Berths Visitor Berths Available	36°50′·06N 36°37′·02E
☎ +90(0)242 2591290 (6 lines) antalya@seturmarinas.com	Depth: 3·5 - 4 m, Maximum LOA: 60 m	Fax +90(0)242 2591182 www.setur.com.tr
FREQUENCY: Ch 09 16		HOURS: 0830 - 2300 LT
(2) **Kaleici Turban Marina**	CALL: Antalya Marina 65 Berths Limited Visitor Berths	36°53′·00N 30°42′·06E
☎ +90(0)242 2423676	Depth: 1 - 4 m, Maximum LOA: 20 m	Fax +90(0)242 2423675
FREQUENCY: Ch 12 16		

AYVALIK (SETUR AYVALIK MARINA)	Marina CALL: Setur Marina 200 Berths Visitor Berths Available	39°19′N 26°41′E
☎ +90(0)266 3122696 ayvalik@seturmarinas.com	Depth: 3 - 4·7 m, Maximum LOA: 30 m	Fax +90(0)266 3122316
FREQUENCY: Ch 16 73		HOURS: 0800 - 2000 LT (1800 LT Winter)

BANDIRMA	Port	40°21′N 27°58′E
☎ Port Auth: +90(0)266 7134966 & 7187530		Fax Port Auth: +90(0)266 736011
FREQUENCY: Ch 09 16		HOURS: H24

BAY MARINA		36°46′·10N 28°07′·55E
☎ +90(0)252 4868203		Fax +90(0)252 4868206
FREQUENCY: Ch 16 72		

BODRUM KARADA MARINA	Marina 400 Berths 20 - 25 Visitor Berths	37°01′·52N 27°27′·35E
☎ +90(0)252 3161860 & 3161865 karada@karadamarinabodrum.com.tr	Depth: 2 - 5 m, Maximum LOA: 35 m	Fax +90(0)252 3161406 www.karadamarinabodrum.com.tr
FREQUENCY: Ch 73		

DOĞUŞ TURGUTREIS MARINA	Marina: CALL: Turgutreis Marina 550 Berths Call For Visitor Availabilty	36°59′·57N 27°15′·19E
☎ +90(0)252 3829065, 3829066, & 3829067 dmarin@dogusinsaat.com.tr	Depth: 3 - 8 m, Maximum LOA: 50 m	Fax +90(0)252 3829068
FREQUENCY: Ch 16	LOCATION: Turgutreis, Bodrum-Mugla Opens May 2003	

DOĞUŞ TURGUTREIS MARINA

ÇANAKKALE BOĞAZI (THE DARDANELLES)	
Vessels should maintain a listening watch on VHF Ch 16 when passing through Çanakkale Boğazı:	
Control Centres	
Çanakkale Traffic Control	40°09′·07N 26°24′·15E
☎ +90(0)286 2124540	Fax +90(0)286 2124876
Gelibolu Control Station (Dardanelles North)	40°24′·62N 26°40′·93E
☎ +90(0)286 5665473	Fax +90(0)286 5665474
Mehmetcik Control	40°02′·57N 26°11′·42E
☎ +90(0)286 8620162	Fax +90(0)286 8620163

ÇANAKKALE MARINA	Marina	40°08′·48N 26°23′·54E
☎ +90(0)216 2128453		Fax +90(0)286 2132851 +90(0)286 2170848 www.canakkale-bld.gov.tr
FREQUENCY: Ch 09		HOURS: H24

ÇEŞME	Port and Marina	38°19′N 26°18′E
☎ Port Auth: +90(0)232 7126005		Fax Port Auth: +90(0)232 7126005
FREQUENCY: Ch 16		
Setur Çeşme Marina	**Marina** 180 Berths Limited Visitor Availability	38°19′N 26°20′E
☎ +90(0)232 7231434 cesme@seturmarinas.com	Depth: 2 - 5 m, Maximum LOA: 30 m	Fax +90(0)232 7234620
FREQUENCY: Ch 16 73		HOURS: H24

CLUB MARINA (FETHİYE)		36°45′·5N 28°55′·8E
☎ +90(0)252 6451800 clubmarina@superonline.com		Fax +90(0)252 6451804
FREQUENCY: Ch 16 **72**		HOURS: H24

DARICA	Port	40°45′N 29°23′E
☎ Atabay Drydock: +90(0)262 6555854		Fax Atabay Drydock: +90(0)262 6555616
FREQUENCY: Ch 16 14		

DİKİLİ	Port	39°04′N 26°53′E
☎ Port Auth: +90(0)232 6714400 & 6712029		Fax Port Auth: +90(0)232 6712029
FREQUENCY: Pilots: Ch 16		
PROCEDURE: Pilotage is compulsory for foreign vessels. Vessels should send request for pilots 24h in advance		

FETHİYE	**Port and Marina**	36°38′N 29°06′E
☎ +90(0)252 6144235		Fax +90(0)252 6141187
FREQUENCY: Ch 16 25 28		
	Marina 100 Berths Visitor Berths Available	36°38′·9N 29°05′·9E
☎ +90(0)252 6143539	Depth: 2 - 5 m	Fax +90(0)252 6146792
FREQUENCY: Ch 16		HOURS: H24

FİNİKE	**Port**	36°18′N 30°09′E
☎ +90(0)242 8553787		Fax +90(0)242 8552643
FREQUENCY: Ch 16		HOURS: HX
SETUR FİNİKE MARINA	**Marina** 350 Berths Visitor Berths Available	36°17′N 30°09′E
☎ +90(0)242 8555030 finike@seturmarinas.com	Depth: 3 - 5 m, Maximum LOA: 70 m	Fax +90(0)252 8555031 www.setur.com.tr
FREQUENCY: Ch 16 **73**		HOURS: Ch 16 0830 - 1900 Ch 73 H24

GEMLIK, GEMPORT	**Port:** CALL: Gemlik Pilots	40°26′N 29°09′E
☎ Hr Mr: +90(0)224 5241133		Fax Port Auth: +90(0)224 5248830
FREQUENCY: Pilots: Ch 16 71		HOURS: H24

GÖCEK PORT, GÖCEK MARINA	**Marina** 380 Berths 56+ Visitor Berths	36°44′·9N 28°56′·6E
☎ +90(0)252 6451520, 6451736 & 6451934 Yacht Services Boatyard: +90(0)252 6451730 enquiries@portgocek.com.tr	Depth: 1·5 - 20 m, Maximum LOA: 45 m	Fax +90(0)252 6451897
FREQUENCY: Ch 16 **73**	Operated by Camper & Nicholsons	HOURS: H24
GÖCEK MUNICIPAL MARINA	**Marina**	36°46′·3N 28°56′·3E
☎ +90(0)252 6451794		Fax +90(0)252 6451793
FREQUENCY: Ch 16	LOCATION: Middle of town	HOURS: Open H24
GÖCEK SKOPEA MARINA	**Marina** 50 Berths Visitor Berths Available	36°46′·5N 28°56′·3E
☎ +90(0)252 6451794 eggyacht@unimedya.net.tr	Depth: 2 - 5 m, Maximum LOA: 35 m	Fax +90(0)252 6451793
FREQUENCY: Ch 72		HOURS: Open H24
GÖCEK CLUB MARINA	**Marina** CALL: **Club Marina** 200 Berths 10 - 15 Visitor Berths Available	36°45′N 28°55′E
☎ +90(0)252 6451800 clubmarina@superonline.com	Depth: 2 - 7 m, Maximum LOA: 25 m	Fax +90(0)252 6451804 www.turkeyclubmarina.net
FREQUENCY: Ch 72	LOCATION: SE corner of Bay	HOURS: Open H24

GOLDEN DOLPHIN MARINA	**Marina**	38°19′N 26°21′E
☎ +90(0)232 7231434 & 7231631		Fax +90(0)232 7234620
FREQUENCY: Ch 16	LOCATION: Altin Yumus	

GÜLLÜK	**Port**	37°14′N 27°36′E
☎ Port Auth: +90(0)252 5522220		Fax
FREQUENCY: Ch 06		

İSKENDERUN	**Port**	36°36′N 36°11′E
☎ Hr Mr: +90(0)326 6132740 Port Auth: +90(0)326 6140044		Fax Hr Mr: +90(0)326 6140226 Port Auth: +90(0)326 6142424
FREQUENCY: Ch 13 16		HOURS: Port: H24

İSTANBUL	**Port:** CALL: Kavak or Harem	41°01′N 28°59′E
☎ Port Auth: +90(0)212 2522100		Fax Port Auth: +90(0)212 2497415
FREQUENCY: Ch 12 14 16		HOURS: H24

ATAKÖY	**Marina:** CALL: Ataköy Marina 700 Berths Visitor Berths Available	40°58′·22N 28°52′·55E
☎ +90(0)212 5604270 marina@atakoymarina.com.tr	Depth: 5 m, Maximum LOA: 40 m	Fax +90(0)212 5607270 www.atakoymarina.com.tr
FREQUENCY: Ch 16 73		

KALAMIŞ AND FENERBAHÇE	**Marina:** CALL: Setur Kalamiş Marina KALAMIŞ (Amiral Fahri Koruturk) 540 berths FENERBAHÇE 300 berths Boat yard 200 berths Visitor Berths Available	40°58′·30N 29°02′·10E
☎ +90(0)216 3462346 kalamis@seturmarinas.com	Depth: 2 - 5 m, Maximum LOA: 70 m	Fax +90(0)216 3461656 www.setur.com.tr
FREQUENCY: Ch 16 72		HOURS: H24

İZMİR	**Port**	38°26′N 27°08′E
☎ Hr Mr: +90(0)232 4220643 Port Auth: +90(0)232 4631600		Fax Port Auth: +90(0)232 4632248
FREQUENCY: Hr Mr: Ch 11 12 16		

İZMİT	**Port**	40°46′N 29°55′E
☎ +90(0)262 3213110		Fax +90(0)262 3213645
FREQUENCY: Ch 16	LOCATION: Seka/İzmit Paper and Pulp Factory Jetty	HOURS: HX

KALEICI MARINA	**Marina**	36°53′·00N 30°42′·06E
☎ +90(0)242 2423676		Fax +90(0)242 2423675
FREQUENCY: Ch 16 72		

KALKAN	**Harbour and Marina** 50 Berths	36°15′·1N 29°24′·9E
☎ +90(0)242 8441131 & 8441020		Fax
FREQUENCY: Ch 16		HOURS: HX

KARACASÖGÜT JETTY (SETUR)	**Marina**	36°57′N 28°10′E
☎ Jetty Berths: +90(0)252 4665345 & 4665346 Bareboat Charter: +90(0)252 4126530 edoruk@mail.koc.net	Moorings situated in preservation area 25 km from Marmaris	Fax Jetty Berths: +90(0)252 4665347 Bareboat Charter: +90(0)252 4124608 www.setur.com.tr
FREQUENCY: Ch 16 72	LOCATION: Cove on southern shore of Gökova Harbour	HOURS: H24 (April to 15th November)

KAŞ	**Port and Marina** 180 Berths	36°11′·9N 29°38′·5E
☎ +90(0)242 8361099 & 8361020	New marina under construction, NE side of Bucak Deniz. When complete will contain 650 berths	Fax
FREQUENCY: Ch 16		HOURS: HX

KUŞADASI	**Port Boatyard and Marina**	37°52′N 27°16′E
☎ Hr Mr: +90(0)256 6141581 Port Auth: +90(0)256 6141025 & 6141310 Boatyard: +90(0)256 6141752		Fax Port Auth: +90(0)256 6141310
FREQUENCY: Ch 12 16		HOURS: HX
Kuşadasi Setur	**Marina:** 474 Berths Visitor Berths Available	37°52′·20N 27°15·′46E
☎ +90(0)256 6181460 kusadasi@seturmarinas.com	Depth: 2 - 7 m, Maximum LOA: 70 m	Fax +90(0) 256 6181464 www.setur.com.tr
FREQUENCY: Ch 16 73		HOURS: H24

LEVENT MARINA	Marina 110 Berths Visitor Berths Available	38°24′N 27°04′E
Tel: +90(0)232 2771111 & 2597794	Depth: 2 - 6 m, Maximum LOA: 20 m	Fax: +90(0)232 2599049
FREQUENCY: Ch 16 **73**	LOCATION: Near Guzelyali.	HOURS: H24

MARMARİS	Port and Marinas	36°51′N 28°16′E
Tel: Hr Mr: +90(0)252 4121013		Fax: Hr Mr: +90(0)252 2627797
FREQUENCY: Ch 16		
Marmaris Netsel Marina	**Marina:** 750 Berths Visitor Berths Available	36°51′·2N 28°16′·6E
Tel: Marina Manager: +90(0)252 4122708 netselmarina@hotmail.com	Depth: 2 - 15 m, Maximum LOA: 40 m	Fax: Marina Manager: +90(0)252 4125351 www.setur.com.tr
FREQUENCY: Ch 06 16		
Marmaris Albatros Marina and Boatyard	250 Berths 60 Visitor Berths Winter 150 Summer	36°50′·48N 28°17′·12E
Tel: +90(0)252 4122456 & 4128684 albatrosmarina@superonline.com	Depth: 2 - 8 m, Maximum LOA: 30 m	Fax: +90(0)252 4125547 www.setur.com.tr
FREQUENCY: Ch 06 16		
Marmaris Yacht Marine	**Call:** Yacht Marine Visitor Berths Available	36°49′·05N 28°18′·32E
Tel: +90(0)252 4220022 & 4220054	Depth: 2 - 8 m	Fax: +90(0)252 4220049
FREQUENCY: Ch 72 73		
Marmarin Marina	**Call:** Marmarin Marina 80 Berths Visitor Berths Available	
Tel: +90(0)252 4220001 & 4220002 marmarin@escortnet.com	Depth: 1·8 - 3·5 m, Maximum LOA: 18 m	Fax: +90(0)252 4220010
FREQUENCY: Ch 16		
Marmaris Bay Marina	50 Berths	36°46′·10N 28°07′·55E
Tel: +90(0)252 4868203		Fax: +90(0)252 4868206
FREQUENCY: Ch 16 72		
Pupa Yat Hotel	25 Berths Visitor Berths Available	
Tel: +90(0)252 4133566 marmarin@escortnet.com	Depth: 1·8 - 3·5 m	Fax: +90(0)252 4138487
FREQUENCY: Ch 16		
Boatyards	Boatyards with a few Berths, Call For Availability	
Tel: Sunmarina: +90(0)252 2144141 Yat Lift Turizm: +90(0)252 3167842		Fax:
FREQUENCY: Ch 06		

MARTI MARINA	Marina 300 Berths Visitor Berths Available	36°45′·30N 28°08′·30E
Tel: Marina: +90(0)252 4871063, 4871064 & 4871065 martimarina@hotmail.com	Depth: 4 - 20 m, Maximum LOA: 50 m	Fax: Marina: +90(0)252 4871066 www.marti.com.tr
FREQUENCY: Ch 16 **73**	LOCATION: Marina on the east side of entrance to Keci Buku.	HOURS: H24

MERSIN	Port 60 Berths Visitor Berths Available	36°47′N 34°38′E
Tel: Hr Mr: +90(0)324 2333522 Port Auth: +90(0)324 2311267 & 2333272	Depth: 1·5 - 2·5 m	Fax: Port Auth +90(0)324 2311350
FREQUENCY: Port: Ch 16		HOURS: Ch 12: H24

NEMRUT LİMANI	Port	38°46'N 26°55'E
☎ Habaş Jetty: +90(0)232 6251171 Çukurova Jetty: +90(0)232 6251295 Metaş/Limaş Jetty: +90(0)232 6251274 Nemtaş Jetty: +90(0)232 6251313 Ege Gübre Sanayi Jetty: +90(0)232 6251253		Fax: Habaş Jetty: +90(0)232 6251380 Çukurova Jetty: +90(0)232 6251293 Metaş/Limaş Jetty: +90(0)232 6251272 & 4334041 Nemtaş Jetty: +90(0)232 6251319 Ege Gübre Sanayi Jetty: +90(0)232 6251245
FREQUENCY: Ch 16		HOURS: HX

PARK KEMER MARINA	**Marina Call:** Kemer Marina 200 Berths Visitor Berths Available	36°36'·14N 30°34'·28E
☎ +90(0)242 8141490 Kemer Boatyard: +90(0)242 8141490 parkmarina@superonline.com	Depth: 2 - 5 m, Maximum LOA: 20 m	Fax: Marina: +90(0)242 8141552
FREQUENCY: Ch 16 (Hours 0820-2000) Ch 73 (H24)		

PARK KEMER MARINA

SETUR MARINA	Marina	36°50'·06N 30°37'·02E
☎ +90(0)252 2591290 seturmar@antnet.net.tr		Fax: +90(0)252 2591182
FREQUENCY: Ch 9 16		

TEKIRDAĞ	Pilots and Port	40°58'·4N 27°31'·1E
☎ Hr Office: +90(0)282 2612255 Port Auth: +90(0)282 2610800		Fax: Port Auth: +90(0)282 2612025
FREQUENCY: Tekirdağ CRS: Ch 16 23 27		HOURS: Ch 16: H24
PROCEDURE: Pilotage is compulsory for Turkish merchant vessels of 1000 GT or more, foreign vessels of 150 GT or more and yachts entering or leaving the harbour, anchoring and berthing		

BEACONS TRANSMITTING DGPS CORRECTIONS

The **Beacons Transmitting DGPS Corrections** table includes identification numbers for the Reference Stations from which the corrections are derived as well as the Transmitting Stations which broadcast the information. The Reference Station numbers are included in the header of every Type 1 or Type 9 message. The Transmitting Station numbers are included in Type 7 messages.

Integrity Monitoring provides an indication within the header of a Type 1 or Type 9 message that the reference station is healthy, unhealthy or unmonitored.

GPS Message Type Numbers shown in parentheses are either provisional, as in Japan, or a possible addition for the future, as in Poland.

GPS Message Type Number	Title	GLONASS Message Type Number
1	Differential GNSS corrections (full set of satellites)	31
2		
3	Reference stations parameters	32
4	Datum used	–
5	Constellation health	33
6	Null frame (No information)	34
7	Radiobeacon Almanacs	35
9	Sub-set differential GNSS corrections	34
15	Ionospheric corrections	–
16	Special messages	36

Station name	Position	DGPS Corrections		Identification No. of		Range (in n miles)	Integrity Monitoring	Status	Transmitted Message Types
		tx fx (in kHz)	tx rate (in bps)	Reference Station	Transmit Station				
ALGERIA									
Ras Caxine Lt	36°48′·83N 2°57′·37E	162·5						On trial	
BELGIUM									
Oostende	51°14′·36N 2°55′·94E	312	200	640 641	420	38	Yes	On trial	1 3 6 7 16
EGYPT (Mediterranean Coast)									
Great Pass Low Lt, Alexandria	31°09′·28N 29°50′·77E	284		440 441	320	150	Yes	Operational	
Mersa Matrûḩ	31°21′·55N 27°14′·80E	307		448 449	324	150	Yes	Operational	
Port Said (Bûr Sa'îd) Lt	31°16′·34N 32°17′·57E	290		442 443	321	126	Yes	Operational	
FRANCE (Atlantic Coast)									
Cap Ferret Lt	44°38′·77N 1°14′·84W	310	100	466	336	97	Yes	Operational	1 3 5 7 9
La Hague	49°34′·0N 1°46′·0W	299	100	460		97	Yes	Operational	1 3 5 7 9
Les Sables d'Olonne	43°31′·0N 1°48′·0W	307	100	464		108	Yes	Operational	1 3 5 7 9
Pen Men, Île de Groix	47°38′·91N 3°30′·49W	309	100	463		97	Yes	Operational	1 3 5 7 9
Ponte de Buis	48°18′·00N 4°05′·00W	308·5	100	462		108	Yes	Operational	1 3 5 7 9
Pointe S. Mathieu Lt[1]	48°19′·85N 4°46′·17W	310·5	100	462	332	97		On Trial	1 3 5 7 9

(1) This station will continue to broadcast intermittently for an indeterminate period but should not be used for navigation.

Station name	Position	DGPS Corrections		Identification No. of		Range (in n miles)	Integrity Monitoring	Status	Transmitted Message Types
		tx fx (in kHz)	tx rate (in bps)	Reference Station	Transmit Station				
FRANCE (Mediterranean Coast)									
Cap Béar Lt	42°31′·00N 3°08′·27E	304·5	100	468	338	90	Yes	Operational	1 3 5 7 9 16
Porquerolles Lt, Cap d'Armes	42°59′·07N 6°12′·43E	286.5	100	469	339	130	Yes	Operational	1 3 5 7 9
IRELAND, REPUBLIC OF									
Loop Head Lt	52°33′·65N 9°55′·90W	293	100	665	432	100	Yes	Operational	3 7 9 16
Mizen Head	51°27′·05N 9°48′·80W	284	100	660	430	100	Yes	Operational	3 7 9 16
Tory Island Lt	55°16′·35N 8°14′·92W	288·5	100	670	435	150	Yes	Operational	3 7 9 16
See Remarks for the United Kingdom									
NETHERLANDS									
Gilze-Rijen	51°37′N 4°56′E	302	200		426	100		On Trial	
Hoek van Holland	51°58′·90N 4°06′·83E	312·5	200	650 651	425	120	Yes	Operational	2 3 5 7 9 16
Vlieland Lt	53°18′N 5°04′E	294	200	655 656	428	120	Yes	Operational	2 3 5 7 9
PORTUGAL									
Cabo Carvoeiro Lt	39°21′·53N 9°24′·40W	301			62			On trial	
Cabo Espichel Lt	38°24′·83N 9°12′·90W	306			351			On trial	
SPAIN (Islas Baleares)									
Cala Figuera Lt, Punta de Mallorca	39°27′·53N 2°31′·40E	286	100	522 523	361	100		On trial	3 5 6 7 9 16
Mahón Menorca	39°52′N 4°18′E	292·5	100	524 525	362	100		On trial	3 5 6 7 9 16
SPAIN (Islas Canarias)									
Lantailla Lt, Punta Fuerteventura	28°13′·70N 13°56′·80W	292·5	100	530 531	367	100		On trial	3 5 6 7 9 16
SPAIN (Mediterranean Coast)									
Castellón	39°58′N 0°01′E	286	100	526 527	363	100		On trial	3 5 6 7 9 16
Llobregat, Punta	41°19′N 2°39′E	304	100	530 531	365	100		On trial	3 5 6 7 9 16
Palos, Cabo	37°38′N 0°41′W	302	100	517 518	359	100		On trial	

Station name	Position	DGPS Corrections		Identification No. of		Range (in n miles)	Integrity Monitoring	Status	Transmitted Message Types
		tx fx (in kHz)	tx rate (in bps)	Reference Station	Transmit Station				
SPAIN (Mediterranean Coast)									
Rota	36°38′N 6°23′W	303·5	100	509 510	355	100		On trial	
Salou, Cabo	41°03′N 1°10′E	288	100	528 529	364	100		On trial	3 5 6 7 9 16
San Sebastian, Cabo	41°53′N 3°12′E	290·5	100	532 533	366	100		On trial	3 5 6 7 9 16
Tarifa	36°00′N 5°36′W	302·5	100	511 512	356	100		On trial	
SPAIN (North Coast)									
Estaca de Bares Lt, Punta	43°47′·17N 7°41′·07W	293	100	505 506	353	100		Operational	3 5 6 7 9 16
Finisterre, Cabo	42°53′·00N 9°16′·23W	289	100	507 508	354	100		Operational	3 5 6 7 9 16
Machichaco	43°27′N 2°45′W	285	100	500 501	350	100		On trial	
UNITED KINGDOM									
Butt of Lewis Lt	58°30′·93N 6°15′·72W	295.5	100	684	444	150	Yes	Operational	3 7 9 16
Flamborough Head Lt	54°06′·95N 0°04′·87W	290.5	100	687	447	150	Yes	Operational	3 7 9 16
Girdle Ness Lt	57°08′·32N 2°02′·83W	297	100	686	446	150	Yes	Operational	3 7 9 16
Lizard Lt	49°57′·58N 5°12′·07W	306	100	681	441	150	Yes	Operational	3 7 9 16
Nash Point Lt	51°24′·03N 3°33′·06W	309.5	100	689	449	100	Yes	Operational	3 7 9 16
North Foreland	51°22′·49N 1°26′·85E	299.5	100	688	448	100	Yes	Operational	3 7 9 16
Point Lynas Lt	53°24′·97N 4°17′·30W	297.5	100	682	442	150	Yes	Operational	3 7 9 16
S. Catherine's Point Lt	50°34′·52N 1°17′·80W	307.5	100	680	440	100	Yes	Operational	3 7 9 16
Stirling	56°04′·3N 4°03′·6W	285.5	100	693	443	200	Yes	Operational	3 6 7 9 16
Sumburgh Head Lt, Shetland Is.	59°51′·30N 1°16′·37W	291.5	100	685	445	150	Yes	Operational	3 7 9 16
Wormleighton	52°11′·8N 1°21′·9W	291	100	691	439	170	Yes	Operational	3 6 7 9 16

DGPS is referenced to the World Geodetic System 1984 (WGS 84) Datum. Accordingly UKHO Charts of the United Kingdom and the Republic of Ireland are gradually being converted to the current equivalent of WGS 84 Datum for Europe, the European Terrestrial Reference System 1989 Datum. Most DGPS receivers have the facility to convert positions from WGS 84 Datum to the regional datum of charts yet to be converted. However, the resulting accuracy depends on the conversion parameters contained within the software of the receiver used. It is therefore advisable to take the position referenced to WGS 84 Datum from the DGPS receiver and apply the position shift values given on the relevant nautical chart before plotting the position thereon. Position shifts for those charts which do not include a 'Satellite Derived Positions' note are given in Admiralty Annual Notice to Mariners 19.

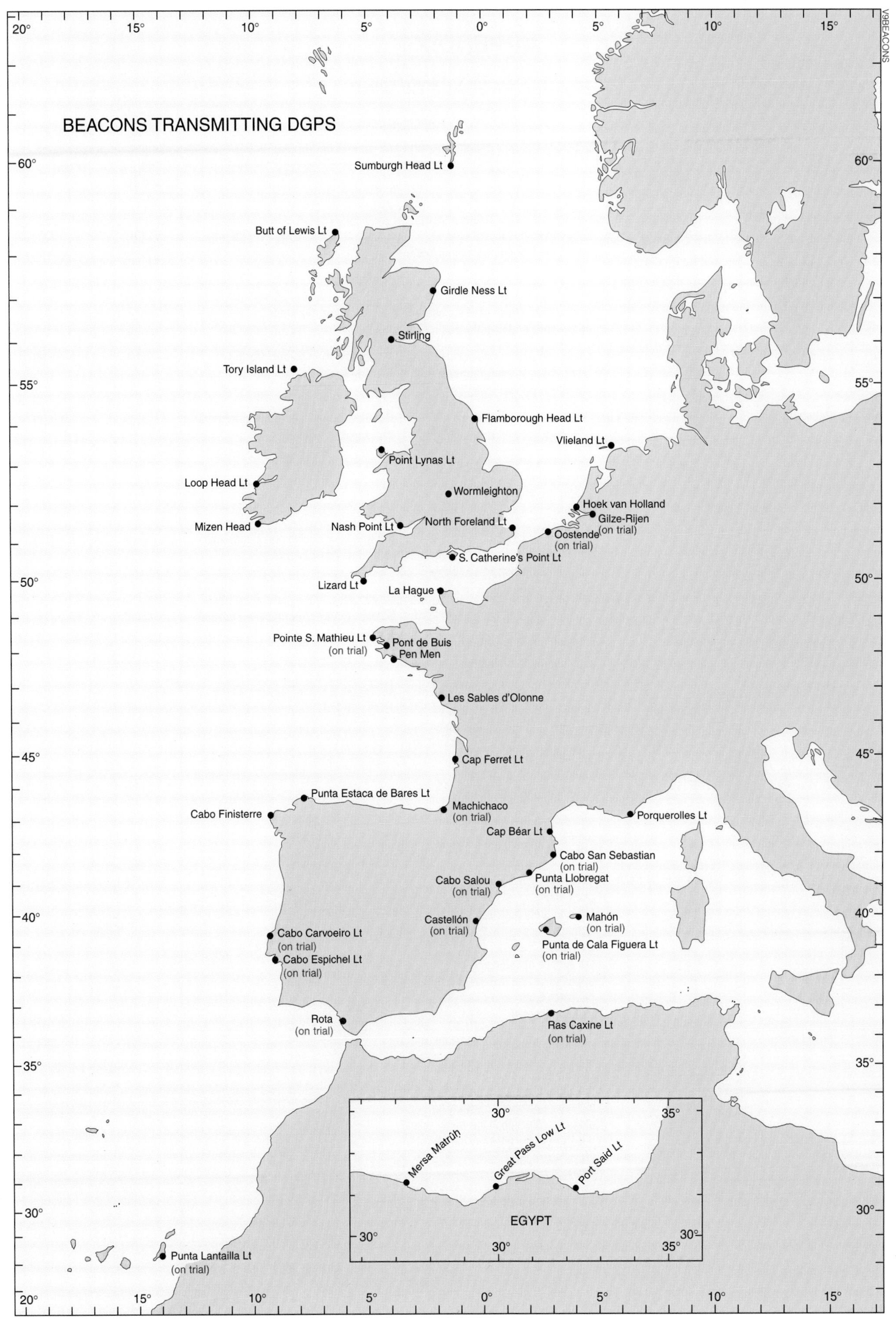
V9BEACONS
BEACONS TRANSMITTING DGPS
20°
15°
10°
5°
0°
5°
10°
15°
60°
55°
50°
45°
40°
35°
30°
Sumburgh Head Lt
Butt of Lewis Lt
Girdle Ness Lt
Stirling
Tory Island Lt
Flamborough Head Lt
Vlieland Lt
Point Lynas Lt
Loop Head Lt
Wormleighton
Hoek van Holland
Gilze-Rijen
(on trial)
Mizen Head
Nash Point Lt
North Foreland Lt
Oostende
(on trial)
S. Catherine's Point Lt
Lizard Lt
La Hague
Pointe S. Mathieu Lt
(on trial)
Pont de Buis
Pen Men
Les Sables d'Olonne
Cap Ferret Lt
Punta Estaca de Bares Lt
Cabo Finisterre
Machichaco
(on trial)
Porquerolles Lt
Cap Béar Lt
Cabo San Sebastian
(on trial)
Punta Llobregat
(on trial)
Cabo Salou
(on trial)
Castellón
(on trial)
Mahón
(on trial)
Punta de Cala Figuera Lt
(on trial)
Cabo Carvoeiro Lt
(on trial)
Cabo Espichel Lt
(on trial)
Rota
(on trial)
Ras Caxine Lt
(on trial)
Mersa Matrûh
Great Pass Low Lt
Port Said Lt
EGYPT
30°
35°
Punta Lantailla Lt
(on trial)

APPENDIX I

BEAUFORT SCALE OF WIND

Beaufort Number	Descriptive Term	Mean velocity		SPECIFICATIONS		Probable wave height* in metres	Probable wave height* in feet
		Knots	m/s	Sea	Coast		
0	Calm	>1	0-0·2	Sea like a mirror	Calm	—	—
1	Light air	1-3	0·3-1·5	Ripples with the appearance of scales are formed, but without foam crests	Fishing smack just has steerage way	0·1 (0·1)	1 (1)
2	Light breeze	4-6	1·6-3·3	Small wavelets, still short but more pronounced; crests have a glassy appearance and do not break	Wind fills the sails of smacks which then travel at about 1-2 knots	0·2 (0·3)	½ (1)
3	Gentle breeze	7-10	3·4-5·4	Large wavelets; crests begin to break; foam of glassy appearance; perhaps scattered white horses	Smacks begin to careen and travel about 3-4 knots	0·6 (1)	2 (3)
4	Moderate breeze	11-16	5·5-7·9	Small waves, becoming longer; fairly frequent white horses	Good working breeze, smacks carry all canvas with good list	1 (1·5)	3½ (5)
5	Fresh breeze	17-21	8·0-10·7	Moderate waves, taking a more pronounced long form; many white horses are formed (chance of some spray)	Smacks shorten sail	2 (2·5)	6 (8½)
6	Strong breeze	22-27	10·8-13·8	Large waves begin to form; the white foam crests are more extensive everywhere (probably some spray)	Smacks have double reef in mainsail; care required when fishing	3 (4)	9½ (13)
7	Near gale	28-33	13·9-17·1	Sea heaps up and white foam from breaking waves begins to be blown in streaks along the direction of the wind	Smacks remain in harbour and those at sea lie-to	4 (5·5)	13½ (19)
8	Gale	34-40	17·2-20·7	Moderately high waves of greater length; edges of crests begin to break into the spindrift; the foam is blown in well-marked streaks along the direction of the wind	All smacks make for harbour, if near	5·5 (7·5)	18 (25)
9	Strong gale	41-47	20·8-24·4	High waves; dense streaks of foam along the direction of the wind; crests of waves begin to topple, tumble and roll over; spray may affect visibility	—	7 (10)	23 (32)
10	Storm	48-55	24·5-28·4	Very high waves with long overhanging crests; the resulting foam, in great patches, is blown in dense white streaks along the direction of the wind; on the whole, the surface of the sea takes a white appearance; the tumbling of the sea becomes heavy and shock-like; visibility affected	—	9 (12·5)	29 (41)
11	Violent storm	56-63	28·5-32·6	Exceptionally high waves (small and medium-sized ships might be for a time lost to view behind the waves); the sea is completely covered with long white patches of foam lying along the direction of the wind; everywhere the edges of the wave crests are blown into froth; visibility affected	—	11·5 (16)	37 (52)
12	Hurricane	64 and over	32·7 and over	The air is filled with foam and spray; sea completely white with driving spray; visibility very seriously affected	—	14 (—)	45 (—)

*This table is only intended as a guide to show roughly what may be expected in the open sea, remote from land. It should never be used in the reverse way; ie. for logging or reporting the state of the sea. In enclosed waters, or when near land, with an off-shore wind, wave heights will be smaller and the waves steeper. Figures in brackets indicate the probable/maximum height of waves.

A

AÇORES

ANGRA DO HERÓISMO, ILHA TERCEIRA 83
HORTA (RADIONAVAL) 82
HORTA, ILHA DO FAIAL 83
MADALENA, ILHA DO PICO 83
NAVTEX [F] [J] 82
PONTA DELGADA (RADIONAVAL) 83
PONTA DELGADA, ILHA DE SÁO MIGUEL 83
SANTA CRUZ, ILHA DAS FLORES 83
VILA DO PORTO, ILHA DE SANTA MARIA 83

ALBANIA

DURRËS 252
SARANDË 252
SHËNGJIN 252
VLORË (VALONA) 252

ALGERIA

ANNABA (BÔNE) 259
ARZEW 259
BEJAIA (BOUGIE) 259
GHAZAOUET 259
MOSTAGANEM 259
ORAN 259
RADIODIFFUSION-TELEVISION ALGERIENNE 259

C

CROATIA

BAKAR 264
BAŠKA, OTOK KRK 264
BIOGRAD 264
  KORNATI 264
  MARINA SANGULIN 264
BOŽAVA, DUGI OTOK 265
CONTINUOUS VHF WEATHER BROADCAST 264
CRES ACI CRES 265
CRIKVENICA 265
DALMACIJA 265
DRVENIK VELI MARINA ZIRONA 265
DUBROVNIK 262, 265
GAŽENICA 265
GENERAL INFORMATION 262
HVAR (PAKLENI OTOCI) ACI PALMIÝANA 266
IST, OTOK IST 266
JABLANAC 266
JELSA, OTOK HVAR 266
  JEZERA (O. ŽUT) ACI ŽUT 266
  JEZERA (PANITULA VELA) ACI PÎŠKERA 267
KARLOBAG 267
KOMIŽA, OTOK VIS 267
KORČULA (O.KORČULA) ACI KORČULA 267
KRALJEVICA 267
KRK, OTOK KRK 267
LUMBARDA (O.KORÄULA) 267
MAKARSKA 267
MALI LOŠINJ, OTOK LOŠINJ 268
MALINSKA, OTOK KRK 268
MARINA BETINA 268
MARINA VELI IŽ 268
METKOVIĆ 268
MILNA, OTOK BRAČ 268
MOŠČENIČKA DRAGA 268
MURTER HRAMINA 268
NAVTEX [Q] 262
NEZERINE LOSINJ 268
NOVALJA, OTOK PAG 268
NOVI VINODOLSKI 269
NOVIGRAD (ISTRIA) 268
OMIŠ 269
OMIŠALJ, OTOK KRK 269
OPATIJA 269
OREBIC MARINA 269
PAG, OTOK PAG 269
PLOČE 269
PODGORA MARINA 270
POREČ 270
POREČ ČERVAR-PORAT 270
PREKO, OTOK UGLJAN 271
PRIMOŠTEN 271
PULA 272
  VERUDA-TEHNOMONT 272
PUNAT 272
RAB, OTOK RAB 272
RABAC 272
RAŠA (INCLUDING TRGET) 273
RIJEKA 264, 274
ROGAČ, OTOK ŠOLTA 274
ROGOZNICA 274
  MARINA FRAPA 274
ROVINJ 274
  MARINA VALALTA 274
  MARINA VRSAR 274
  ROVINJ ACI ROVINJ 274
SALI, OTOK DUGI 274
SENJ 275
ŠIBENIK 275
SILBA, OTOK SILBA 275
ŠILO, OTOK KRK 276
SKRADIN ACI SKRADIN 276
SPLIT 264, 276
STARIGRAD, OTOK HVAR 276
STARIGRAD-PAKLENICA 276
SUČURAJ, OTOK HVAR 276
SUMARTIN, OTOK BRAČ 277
SUPERTAR, OTOK BRAČ 277
SUSAK, OTOK SUNO TAGNO TAGSAK 277
SVETI JURAJ 277
TISNO, OTOK MURTER 277
TRIBUNJ 277
TROGIR 277
TUCEPI MARINA 277
UBLI, OTOK LASTOVO 278
UMAG 278
VELA LUKA, OTOK KORČULA 278
VELI IŽ (O. IÝ) 278
VIS, OTOK VIS 278
VODICE 279
VRBOSKA (O. HVAR) ACI VRBOSKA 279
ZADAR 280

CYPRUS

AKROTIRI 281
BRITISH FORCES BROADCASTING SERVICES ONE (BFBS ONE) 281
FAMAGUSTA 281
KYRENIA 281
LARNACA 281
LIMASSOL 282
NAVTEX [M] 281
PAPHOS 282
VASILIKOS 282

E

EGYPT

EL ISKANDARÎYA (ALEXANDRIA) INCLUDING EL DIKHEILA 283
PORT SAID YACHT CLUB MARINA 283
QUANÂT EL SUWEIS (SUEZ CANAL) 283

F

FRANCE, ATLANTIC COAST

AMBÈS 84
ANGLET 85
ARCACHON 85
ARS-EN-RÉ 85
ARZAL-CAMOËL 85
BAYONNE 86
BÉNODET 88
BLAYE 88
BONNE ANSE - PORT DE LA PALMYRE 88
BORDEAUX 88
BOURGENAY 88
BREST 89
CAMARET-SUR-MER 89
CAPBRETON 89
CONCARNEAU 89
DONGES 89
DOUARNENEZ 90
ÉTEL 84, 90
HENDAYE 90
JARD SUR MER 91
LA GIRONDE 91
LA LOIRE 91
LA ROCHELLE-CHARENTE - VIEUX PORT 92
LES MINIMES 92
LA TRINITÉ-SUR-MER 92
LA TURBALLE 92
LE CONQUET 92
LE CROISIC 92
LE CROUESTY 92
LE DOUHET 93
LE GUILVINEC-LÉCHIAGAT 93
LE PALAIS, BELLE-ÎLE 93
BELLE ÎLE SAUZON 93
LE POULIGUEN 93
LES SABLES-D'OLONNE 93
LE VERDON 93
L' HERBAUDIÈRE, ÎLE DE NOIRMOUTIER 94
LOCTUDY 94
LORIENT 95
KERNÉVEL 95
MORGAT 95
NANTES 95
PAUILLAC 95
PIRIAC-SUR-MER 96
PORNIC 96
PORNICHET 96
PORT DE BOURGENAY 96
PORT DE LA FLOTTE 97
PORT-HALIGUEN 97
PORT-JOINVILLE, ÎLE D'YEU 97
PORT-LA FORÊT 97
PORT TUDY (ÎLE DE GROIX) 97
ROCHEFORT 97
ROYAN 98
SAINT-DENIS-D'OLÉRON 98
SAINT-GILLES-CROIX-DE-VIE (PORT LA VIE) 98
SAINT GUÉNOLE 98
SAINT-JEAN-DE-LUZ (CIBOURE) 98
SAINT-NAZAIRE 98
TONNAY-CHARENTE 98
VANNES 104

FRANCE, CORSE

AJACCIO 284
BASTIA 285
BONIFACIO 285
CALVI 285
CARGÈSE 285
CAVALLO 285
CORSE MMSI 002275420 284
ÎLE-ROUSSE 285
MACINAGGIO 286
PIANOTTOLI-CALDARELLO 286
PORTO 286
PORTO-VECCHIO 286
PROPRIANO 286
SAINT-FLORENT 286
SOLENZARA 286
TAVERNA, PORT DE CAMPOLORO 286

FRANCE, MEDITERRANEAN COAST

ARGELÉS-SUR-MER 290
BAIE-DES-ANGES 290
BANDOL 291
BANYULS-SUR-MER 291
BARCARÈS PORT ST-ANGE (GRAU ST-ANGE) 291
BEAULIEU-SUR-MER 291
BORMES-LES-MIMOSAS 292
CALANQUE DE PORT-MIOU 292
CANET-EN-ROUSSILON (CANET-PLAGE) 293
CANNES (PUBLIC MARINA) 293
CAP D'AGDE 294
CAP D'AIL 294
CARNON-PLAGE 294
CARQUEIRANNE/SALETTES 294
CARRY-LE-ROUET 294
CASSIS 294
CAVALAIRE 294
CENTRES RÉGIONAUX OPÉRATIONNELS DE SURVEILLANCE ET DE SAUVETAGE (CROSS) 287
COGOLIN 294
COGOLIN MARINA 295
FIRING PRACTICE AREA 290
FOS 295
FRÉJUS 295
FRONTIGNAN 295
GOLFE-JUAN 296
GRUISSAN 296
HYÈRES-PORT 296
L'AYGUARDE 298
LA CIOTAT 297
LA FIGUEIRETTE (MIRAMAR) 297
LA GARDE (CROSS) 288
LA GARDE MMSI 002275400 MMSI 002275410 288
LA GRANDE-MOTTE 297
LA NAPOULE 297
LA RAGUE 297
LA SEYNE-SUR-MER 297
LE GRAU-DU-ROI 298
LE LAVANDOU 299
MARSEILLAN-PLAGE 300
MARSEILLAN-VILLE 300
MARSEILLE 299
MARTIGUES 300
MENTON 301
MIRAMAR 301
NARBONNE-PLAGE 301
NARBONNE - PORT LA NAUTIQUE 301
NAVTEX [A] [W] [E] [S] 287
NICE 301
PALAVAS-LES-FLOTS 301
PORQUEROLLES 301
PORT AMBONNE 301
PORT ARGELÈS 290
PORT DE BOUC 302
PORT DE CARRO 302
PORT DE S. AYGULF 302
PORT DE S. MANDRIER 302
PORT LA GALERE 303
PORT LEUCATE 303
PORT NAPOLEON 303
PORT SAINT LOUIS DU RHONE 303
PORT-CAMARGUE 301
PORT-GALLICE (JUAN-LES-PINS) 302
PORT-GARDIAN (SAINTES-MARIES-DE-LA-MER) 302
PORT-GRIMAUD 303

PORT-LA-NOUVELLE 303
PORT-VAUBAN (ANTIBES) 303
PORT-VENDRES 303
RIVIÈRE AUDE 304
SAINT-CYPRIEN 304
SAINT-CYR-SUR-MER 304
SAINT-GERVAIS 305
SAINT-JEAN - CAP-FERRAT 305
SAINT-LAURENT-DU-VAR 305
SAINT-PIERRE-DES-EMBIEZ 305
SAINT-RAPHAËL 306
SAINT-TROPEZ 306
SAINTE-MARIE LA MER 305
SAINTE-MAXIME 305
SAN PEÏRE (LES ISSAMBRES) 306
SANARY-SUR-MER 306
SAUSSET-LES-PINS 307
SÈTE 307
TOULON 307
VALRAS-PLAGE 307
VILLEFRANCHE-SUR-MER 307

FRANCE, NORTH COAST

BARFLEUR 108
BINIC 108
BOULOGNE-SUR-MER 108
CAEN 108
CALAIS 108
CARENTAN 111
CARTERET 111
CENTRES RÉGIONAUX OPÉRATIONNELS DE SURVEILLANCE ET DE SAUVETAGE (CROSS) 105
CHERBOURG 111
CORSEN (CROSS) (MRCC) 106
COURSEULLES-SUR-MER 111
DAHOUËT 111
DEAUVILLE-TROUVILLE 112
DIELETTE 112
DIEPPE 112
DINARD 113
DUNKERQUE 113
ÉTAPLES-SUR-MER 113
FÉCAMP 114
GRANDCAMP-MAISY 114
GRANVILLE 115
GRAVELINES 115
GRIS-NEZ (CROSS) (MRCC) 106, 107
HONFLEUR 115
ISIGNY-SUR-MER 115
JOBOURG (CROSS) (MRCC) 107
JOBOURG MMSI 002275200 107
L'ABERWRACH 115
LE HAVRE (INCLUDING PORT DU HAVRE-ANTIFER) 115
LE LÉGUÉ-SAINT-BRIEUC 116
LE TOUQUET 116
LE TRÉPORT 116
LÉZARDRIEUX 116
MORLAIX 116
NAVTEX [A] [W] [E] [S] 105
OUISTREHAM 117
PAIMPOL 117
PERROS-GUIREC 117
PLOUER-SUR-RANCE 117
PONTRIEUX 117
PORT BAIL 118
PORT DIÉLETTE 118
PORT GUILLAUME, DIVES-SUR-MER 118
PORT-EN-BESSIN 118
RADIO FRANCE (BULLETIN INTER-SERVICE-MER) 108
ROSCOFF-BLOSCON 119
ROUEN 119
ROUEN TO PARIS 119
SAINT CAST 119
SAINT MALO 119
SAINT-QUAY-PORTRIEUX 120
SAINT-VAAST-LA HOUGUE 120
S. VALÉRY-EN-CAUX 120
TANCARVILLE 120
TRÉBEURDEN 120
TRÉGUIER 121

G

GIBRALTAR

BFBS GIBRALTAR 122
GIBRALTAR 122
GIBRALTAR BROADCASTING CORPORATION 122
MARINA BAY 122
QUEEN'S HARBOUR MASTER 122
QUEENSWAY QUAY MARINA 123
SHEPHERDS MARINA 123

GREECE

ADHAMAS, ÓRMOS MILOU, NÍSOS MÍLOS 311
AÍYINA (AEGINA), NÍSOS AÍYINA 311
AÍYION (EGIO), PELOPÓNNISOS 311
ALEXANDROÚPOLIS 311
ÁSPRA SPÍTIA (ANDÍKIRA OR ANTIKYRA) 311
ÁYIOS NIKÓLAOS (AGIOS NIKÓLAOS), KRÍTI (CRETE) 312
  AGIOS NIKÓLAOS MARINA 312
DHIÓRIX KORÍNTHOU (CORINTH CANAL) 312
ELEVSÍS 313
ELLINIKI RADIOPHONIA 311
ERMOÚPOLIS (SÍROS OR SYROS), NÍSOS SÍROS 313
GAIOS 313
GENERAL NOTES 309
GOUVIA (KÉKIRA) (CORFU) 313
IGOUMENÍTSA 313
IRÁKLEIO (HERAKLION), KRÍTI (CRETE) 313
ISTHMÍA, PELOPÓNNISOS 313
ITÉA 313
KALAMÁTA (KALÁMI), PELOPÓNNISOS 314
KALI LIMENES, KRÍTI (CRETE) 314
KATAKÓLON, PELOPÓNNISOS 314
KAVÁLA (CAVALA) 314
KÉRKIRA (KERKYRA) (CORFU) 314
KHALKÍS (CHALKIS) 314
KHANIÁ, (HANIA), KRÍTI (CRETE) 315
KHÍOS (CHIOS), NÍSOS KHÍOS 315
KOS MARINA 315
LÁGOS, VISTÓNIKOS ÓRMOS 315
LAKKÍ (PORT LAKKÍ MARINA) 315
LAVRÍON (LAURIUM) 315
LEROS ISLAND (LAKKI MARINA) 315
LEVKAS 315
LIMÍN ALIVÉRIOU 316
LIMÍN KALIMNOS MARINA 316
MANDRAKI (RÓDOS) 316
METHANA 316
MITILÍNI, NÍSOS LÉSVOS 316
NAVTEX [H] [K] [L] 309
OLYMPIA 310
PÁTRAI, PELOPÓNNISOS 316
PEIRAIÁS (PIRAEUS) 316
  ALIMOS (KALMÁKI) 316
  FLISVOS (FALIRON) 317
  GLYPHADA MARINA 4 317
  VOULIAGMENI 317
  ZEA 317
PÍLOS (PYLOS), PELOPÓNNISOS 317
PORTO KARRA (PORTO CARRAS MARINA) 317
PORTO SANI 317
PRÉVEZA 317
RÓDOS, NÍSOS RÓDOS, 317
SÁMOS, NÍSOS SÁMOS 317
SKÍATHOS, NÍSOS SKÍATHOS 317
SOÚDHA, KRÍTI (CRETE) 318
THESSALONÍKI (SALONICA) 318
  THESSALONIKI MARINA (ARETSOU) 318

VATHY 318
VÓLOS 318
VOUNAKI (SUNSAIL VOUNAKI MARINA) 318
XYLOKASTRO 318
ZÁKINTHOS (ZAKYNTHOS OR ZANTE), NÍSOS ZAKINTHOS 319

I

IRELAND, REPUBLIC OF

ARKLOW 128
BALTIMORE 128
BANTRY 129
BURTONPORT 129
CARLINGFORD MARINA 129
CASTLETOWN BEARHAVEN 129
CORK 129
EAST FERRY MARINA 129
ROYAL CORK YACHT CLUB MARINA 129
COURTMACSHERRY 129
CROSSHAVEN BOATYARD MARINA 129
SALVE MARINE, CROSSHAVEN 130
DINGLE 130
DROGHEDA 130
DUBLIN 130
DUBLIN CITY MOORINGS 130
EAST-LINK LIFTING BRIDGE 130
DUBLIN (COAST GUARD MRCC) 127
DUNDALK 130
DUN LAOGHAIRE 130
FENIT 130
FOYNES HARBOUR 131
GALWAY 131
GREENORE 131
HOWTH MARINA 131
KILLYBEGS 131
KILMORE QUAY MARINA 131
KILRUSH CREEK MARINA, SHANNON ESTUARY 131
KINSALE 131
CASTLE PARK MARINA, KINSALE 131
KINSALE YACHT CLUB MARINA 132
LAWRENCE COVE MARINA 132
MALAHIDE MARINA 132
MALIN HEAD (COAST GUARD MRSC) 127
NAVTEX [Q] [W] 125
RADIO TELEFÍS ÉIREANN - RADIO 1 (RTE - RADIO 1) 128
ROSSLARE 132
SLIGO 132
VALENTIA (COAST GUARD MRSC) 127
WATERFORD 132
WICKLOW 132
YOUGHAL 132

ISRAEL

AKKO (ACRE) 322
ASHDOD 322
ASHKELON 322
ḤEFA (HAIFA) 322
ḤEFA (HAIFA) 322
HERZLIYA 322
JAFFA 322
NAVTEX [P] 322
QUISHON 323
TEL AVIV 323

ITALY, ADRIATIC COAST

ANCONA 325, 327
APRILA MARITTIMA CENTRALE 327
MARINA CAPO NORD 327
MARINA PUNTA GABBIANI 327
BARI 326
BARI & MOLA DI BARI 327
BARLETTA 327
BISCEGLIE 327
BRINDISI 328
CHIOGGIA 328
CIVITANOVA 328
CROTONE 326
DARSENA DELL'OROLOGIO 328
DARSENA NAUTEC 328
ERACLEA (MARICLEA CLUB) 329
FIUME TAGLIAMENTO MARINA UNO 329
GIULIANOVA 329
GRADO 329
LIGNANO DARSENA MARINA 329
LIGNANO SABBIADORO 329
MANFREDONIA (PORTO VECCHIO) 329
MARINA DE BRONDOLO 329
MARINA DI CAMPALTO 329
MARINA DI CARRARA 329
MARINA DI LIO GRANDO 329
MARINA DI PORTO LEVANTE 330
MARINA DI VALLUGOLA 330
MARINA NUOVA DI PORTO LEVANTE 330
MARINA PUNTA VERDE 330
NAVTEX [V] [T] [R] [U] 324
ORTONA 330
OTRANTO 330
PALERMO 326
PESARO 331
PESCARA 331
PORTO BASELEGHE 331
PORTO DI PIAVE VECCHIA PORTO TURISTICO DI JESOLO 331
PORTO GARIBALDI (MARINA DEGLI ESTENI) 332
PORTO SAN GIORGIO 332
PORTO SAN ROCCO 332
PORTO SAN VITO 333
LEGA NAVALE 333
MARINA LE COVE 333
MARINA SAN MARCO 333
PORTO SANTA MARGHERITA (MARINA 4) 332
PORTO VERDE 334
RAVENNA 334
RIMINI 334
ROMA 326
S. FOCA DI MELENDUGNO 335
SAN BENEDETTO DEL TRONTO 327, 334
SENIGALLIA 334
SISTIANA 335
TRIESTE 327, 335
VENEZIA MARINAS 335
VENEZIA (DARSENA DEC) 335
VIESTE 335
VILLAGIO DEL PESCATORE S. MARCO 335
VILLANOVA 335

ITALY, SARDEGNA & SICILIA

ALGHERO 340
ARBATAX 341
AUGUSTA 339, 341
BOSA 341
CAGLIARI 339, 341
CANNETO DI LIPARI, ISOLE EOLIE 341
CANNIGIONE 341
CARLOFORTE, ISOLA DI SAN PIETRO 341
CASTELSARDO 341
CATANIA, SICILIA 341
GELA, SICILIA 342
ISOLA MADDALENA 342
LAMPEDUSA 339
LICATA, SICILIA 342
MARINA DELL'ORSO 342
MARINA DI CAPITANA 342
MARINA DI PORTISCO 342
MARZAMENI 342
MAZARA DEL VALLO 339, 342
MESSINA 339, 342

MESSINA MARINA DEL NETTUNO 342
MOLFETTA 342
MONFALCONE 343
MONOPOLI 343
NUMANA 343
OLBIA 343
PALERMO 340, 343
PANTELLERIA, ISOLA DI PANTELLERIA 343
PERD'E' SALI 343
PORT PALAU 344
PORT RAPHAEL YACHT CLUB 344
PORTO CERVO 343
PORTO CONTO MARINA 343
PORTO DI SANT' ANTIOCO (PONTE ROMANO) 344
PORTO EMPEDOCLE, SICILIA 344
PORTO OTTIOLU 344
PORTO ROTONDO 344
PORTO TORRES 340, 344
PUNTA MARANA 344
RIPOSTO, SICILIA 344
SAN NICOLA L'ARENA, SICILIA 344
SANTA TERESA DI GALLURA 345
SCIACCA, SICILIA 345
SIBARI MARINA, SICILIA 345
SIRACUSA, SICILIA 345
STINTINO (PORTO MANNU) 345
TERMINI IMERESE, SICILIA 345
TORRE GRANDE 345

ITALY, WEST COAST

ACCIAROLI 347
AGROPOLI 347
ALASSIO 347
ALBARELLA 347
AMALFI 347
ANDORA MARINA 348
ANZIO 348
  NETTUNO 348
ARENZANO 348
BAGNARA CALABRIA 348
BORDIGHERA 348
CAMOGLI 348
CAPRI (MARINA GRANDE) 348
CASAMICCIOLA 348
CASTELLAMMARE DEL GOLFO 348
CASTELLAMMARE DI STABIA 348
CATANZARO 349
CAVO 349
CERVIA 349
CHIAIOLELLA 349
CHIAVARI 349
CIVITAVECCHIA 346, 349
COPPOLA PINETAMARE 349
CROTONE 349
DIANO MARINA 349
FINALE LIGURE 349
FIUMICINO 349
FORMIA (PORTO NUOVO) 349
GAETA 350
GALLIPOLI 350
GENOVA 346, 350
IMPERIA 350
ISCHIA, ISOLA D'ISCHIA 350
ISOLA DEL GIGLIO, GIGLIO MARINA 350
LA SPEZIA 351
LAMPEDUSA, ISOLA DI LAMPEDUSA 350
LAVAGNA 351
LIVORNO 346, 351
LOANO 351
MARATEA 351
MARCIANA MARINA 351
MARINA DI CALA GALERA 351
MARINA DI CAMEROTA 351
MARINA DI CAMPO 351
MARINA VIGLIENA 351
MARSALA 351
NAPOLI 346, 352
NISIDA 352
PONZA ISOLA DI PONZA 352
PORTICI 352
PORTO ERCOLE 352
PORTO LOTTI 352
PORTO MAURIZIO 352
PORTO SANT ANTONIO 352
PORTO SANTO STEFANO 353
PORTO VENERE 353
PORTOFERRAIO 352
PORTOFINO 352
POZZUOLI 353
PROCIDA 353
PUNTA ALA MARINA 353
RAPALLO 353
REGGIO CALABRIA 353
RIO MARINA 353
RIVA DI TRAIANO 353
ROMA 347
ROMA - PORTO TURISTICO DI ROMA 353
  RIVIERE TEVERE 353
SALERNO 354
SAN FELICE CIRCEO 354
SAN REMO 354
SANNAZZARO (MERGELLINA) 354
SANTA MARGHERITA LIGURE 354
SANTA MARINELLA 354
SAVONA 354
TALAMONE 355
TARANTO 355
TERMOLI 355
TERRACINA 355
TERRAMARE MARINA PUNTA FARO 355
TORRE ANNUNZIATA 355
TORRE DEL GRECO 355
TRANI 355
TROPEA 355
VARAZZE 355
VIAREGGIO 356
VIBO VALENTIA 356

L

LEBANON

BEIRUT (BEYROUTH) 357
MARINA JOSEPH KOURY 357
PORT DE JOUNIEH 357

LIBYA

ABU KAMMĀSH, SIDI SAID 358
BANGHĀZI (BENGĀSI) 358
DARNAH (DERNA) 358
MIŞURĀTAH (QAŞR AḤMED) 358
ŢARĀBULUS (TRIPOLI) 358
ZUWĀRAH (ZUARA) 358

M

MALTA

MALTA 359
MARSAMXATT 359
  MANOEL ISLAND MARINA 359
  TA' XBIEX QUAY 359
MGARR, GOZO 359
MSIDA CREEK MARINA 359
NAVTEX [O] 359
PORTOMASO MARINA 360
VALLETTA 360
  GRAND HARBOUR MARINA (VITTORIOSA QUAY) 360
  S & D YACHTS LIMITED 360

MONACO

FONTVIEILLE 361
MONACO 361
MONACO 361
RADIO RIVIERA 361

MOROCCO

AL HOCEÏMA 363
CEUTA (SPAIN) 363
KABILA MARINA 363
MARINA SMIR 363
MELILLA (SPAIN) 363
RADIODIFFUSION-TÉLÉVISION MAROCAINE 363
TANGER (TANGIER) 363

P

PORTUGAL

CASCAIS (MARINA DE CASCAIS) 134
FARO 134
FIGUEIRA DA FOZ 134
LAGOS 134
LEIXÕES 134
LISBOA 134
NAVTEX [G] R] 133
NAZARÉ 135
OLHÃO 135
PENICHE 135
PORTIMÃO 136
PÓVOA DE VARZIM 136
RADIONAVAL PORTUGAL 133
SESIMBRA 136
SETÚBAL 136
SEVILLE (RIO GUADALQUIVIR) 144
SINES 136
VIANA DO CASTELO 137
VILA REAL DE SANTO ANTÓNIO 137
VILAMOURA 137

R

RADIO-FACSIMILE & RADIO-TELEX

ATHINÁI (SVJ4) [FACSIMILE] 75
NORTHWOOD [FACSIMILE] 76
OFFENBACH (MAIN) / PINNEBERG [FACSIMILE] 79
OFFENBACH (MAIN) / PINNEBERG 80

S

SERBIA AND MONTENEGRO

BAR 364
BAR 364
BUDVA 364
KOTOR 364

SLOVENIA

KOPER 365
KOPER (HARBOUR MASTERS OFFICE) 365
MARINA IZOLA 365
PIRAN 366
PORTOROŽ 366

SPAIN, ATLANTIC COAST

AYAMONTE 142
BARBATE 142
BILBAO (CCR GROUP IV) 140
BILBAO (MRCC) 140
CÁDIZ, REAL CLUB NAUTICO DE CÁDIZ 142
CENTRO NAUTICO ELCANO 142
CHIPIONA (PUERTO DE CHIPIONA) 142
CORUÑA (CCR GROUP III) 140
CORUÑA (MRSC) 140
EL ROMPIDO 142
FINISTERRE 141
GIJÓN 141
HUELVA 142
PUERTO DEPORTIVO MAZAGON (PALOS DE LA FRONTERA - HUELVA) 143
HUELVA (MRSC) 141
ISLA CRISTINA 143
MARINA ISLA CANELA 143
NAVTEX [D] [G] [X] 139
PUERTO AMERICA 143
PUERTO DE SANTA MARIA (REAL CLUB NAUTICO) 143
PUERTO GELVES MARINA 144
ROTA 144
SANCTI PETRI 145
SANTANDER 141
TARIFA 141
TELEPHONE MARINE WEATHER INFORMATION SERVICE 142
VIGO 141

SPAIN, MEDITERRANEAN COAST

ADRA 370
AGUADULCE 370
AIGUADOLÇ 370
ALGECIRAS 367, 370
ALICANTE AREA 370
ALMERÍA 367, 370
ALMERIMAR 370
ALTEA (CLUB NÁUTICO DE ALTEA) 372
ALTEA (CLUB NÁUTICO MASCARAT) 372
AMPOLLA 372
AMPURIABRAVA 372
ARENYS DE MAR 372
BARCELONA 367
BARCELONA - PORT OLIMPIC 372
BARCELONA MARINAS 372
BENALMADENA 373
BLANES, CLUB VELA DE BLANES 373
BURRIANA (CLUB NÁUTICO) 373
CABO PINO 373
CABO ROIG 373
CALPE (CLUB NÁUTICO) 373
CAMBRILS 373
CAMPELLO 373
CARTAGENA 373
CASTELLÓN (CLUB NÁUTICO) 373
CASTELLÓN (MRSC) 367
COMARRUGA 373
COSTA BLANCA (CLUB NÁUTICO) 374
DEHESA DE CAMPOAMOR 374
DÉNIA 374
CLUB NAUTICO DE DÉNIA 374
MARINA DE DÉNIA 374
DOS MARES 374
DUQUESA 374
EL CANDALO 374
EL MASNOU 374
EMPURIABRAVA 374
ESTARTIT (CLUB NÁUTICO) 374
ESTEPONA 374
FORMENTERA 381
FORMENTERA MAR 381
MARINA DE FORMENTERA 381
FUENGIROLA 375
GANDÍA 375
GARRUCHA 375
GINESTA (CASTELLDEFELS) 375
HOSPITALET DE L'INFANT 375
IBIZA 381
IBIZA MARINAS 381
SAN ANTONIO 381

ISLAS BALEARES 381
JÁVEA 375
JOSÉ BANUS 375
L' ESCALA 376
L'AMETLLA DE MAR 375
LA CALETA DE VÉLEZ 375
LA MANGA MAR MENOR AND PUERTO TORRE DE LA HORADADA MARINAS 376
LA MANGA MARINA TOMÁS MAESTRE 375
LAS FUENTES 376
LOS ALCÁZARES C.N. MAR MENOR 376
LOS NIETOS (CLUB NÁUTICO) 376
LOS URRUTIAS 376
LUIS CAMPOMANES MARINA GREENWICH 376
MÁLAGA (CCR GROUP II) 369
MÁLAGA, REAL CLUB MEDITERRANEO DE MÁLAGA 376
MALLORCA 382
  ALCUDIA, MALLORCA 382
  ANDRAITX, MALLORCA 384
  MALLORCA MARINAS 382
  PALMA 384
MARBELLA 376
MAZARRON 377
MENORCA 385
  MAHÓN, MENORCA 385
  MENORCA MARINAS 385
MORAYRA 377
MOTRIL 377
NAVTEX [G] [X] 367
OLIVA 377
OROPESA DEL MAR 377
PALAMÓS 377
PALMA (MRCC) 369
PORT BALIS 377
PORT D'ARO, CLUB NÁUTICO 377
PORT DAURAT 377
PORT DE LA SELVA 377
PORT GARRAF 377
PORT MATARO 378
PORT ROSAS 378
PREMIÁ DE MAR (SAN CRISTOBAL DE PREMIÁ) 378
PUEBLA DE FARNALS 378
PUERTO CALAFAT 378
PUERTO DE CASTELLÓN DE LA PLANA 378
PUERTO DE LA HORADADA 378
PUERTO DE LES CASES D'ALCANAR 378
PUERTO DE LIAFRANC 378
PUERTO DE SILES 378
PUERTO EL PERELLO 378
PUERTO GUADAMAR - MARINA DE LAS DUNAS 378
PUERTO OROPESA DEL MAR 379
PUERTO SANTA MARGARIDA 379
PUERTOS DE AGUILAS Y DEL HORNILLO 379
PUNTA DE LA MONA (MARINA DEL ESTE) 379
ROQUETAS DE MAR 379
SALOU 379
SAN CARLOS DE LA RÁPITA, SANT CARLES DE LA RÁPITA 379
SAN FELIÚ DE GUIXOLS 379
SAN JOSÉ 379
SANTA POLA, PUERTO DEPORTIVO 379
  SANTA POLA (CLUB NÁUTICO) 379
SEGUR DE CALAFELL 379
SITGES 380
SOTOGRANDE 380
TARRAGONA 369, 380
TORREDEMBARRA 380
TORREVIEJA 380
VALENCIA 369, 370, 380
VALENCIA AREA 380
VILLAJOYSA (CLUB NÁUTICO) 380
VILLANUEVA I LA GELTRÚ 381

SPAIN, NORTH COAST

BAYONA 148
BILBAO 148
CAMARIÑAS 148
CARAMIÑAL 148
GIJÓN 149
GUETARIA 149
HONDARRIBIA 149
LA CORUÑA 150
PASAJES 150
PORTO PEDRAS NEGRAS (SAN VICENTE DO MAR) 150
PORTOSIN 150
RIANJO 150
SADA 150
SANTA EUGENIA DE RIVIERA 150
SANTANDER 150
SAXENXO (SANGENJO) MARINA 150
VIGO 150
VILLAGARCIA DE AROSA 151
ZUMAIA 151

SYRIA

AL LĀDHIQĪYAH (LATAKIA) 387
ṬARTŪS 387

T

TUNISIA

BIZERTE 388
EL KANTAOUI 388
GHANNOUCHE (GABÈS) 388
LA GOULETTE / TUNIS (INCLUDING RADES) 388
LA GOULETTE PORT 388
MAHARÈS 389
MAHDIA 389
MARINA CAP MONASTIR 389
RADIO TUNIS 388
SFAX 389
SIDI BOU SAÏD 389
SOUSSE 389
TABARKA 389
  PORT DE PLAISANCE 389
TUNIS 388
YASMINE HAMMAMET 389

TURKEY

ALTIN YUNIS SETUR 392
ANTALYA 392
AYVALIK (SETUR AYVALIK MARINA) 392
BANDIRMA 392
BANDIRMA (YMB20) RADIO-TELEX 4560 KHZ 390
BAY MARINA 392
BODRUM KARADA MARINA 392
ÇANAKKALE BOĞAZI (THE DARDANELLES) 393
ÇANAKKALE MARINA 393
ÇEŞME 393
CLUB MARINA (FETHİYE) 393
DARICA 393
DİKİLİ 393
DOĞUS TURGUTREIS MARINA 393
FETHİYE 394
FİNİKE 394
  SETUR FINIKE MARINA 394
GEMLIK, GEMPORT 394
GÖCEK PORT GÖCEK MARINA
  GÖCEK CLUB MARINA 394
  GÖCEK MUNICIPAL MARINA 394
  GÖCEK SKOPEA MARINA 394
GOLDEN DOLPHIN MARINA 394
GÜLLÜK 394
ISKENDERUN 394
İSTANBUL 395
  ATAKÖY 395
  KALAMIŞ AND FENERBAHÇE 395

İSTANBUL (TAH) 391
IZMIR 395
İZMıR RT (MF) 1850 2760 KHZ 391
IZMIT 395
KALEICI MARINA 395
KALKAN 395
KARACASÖGÜT JETTY (SETUR) 395
KAŞ 395
KUŞADASI 395
LEVENT MARINA 396
MARMARIS 396
MARTI MARINA 396
MERSIN 396
MERSIN RT (MF) 2820 KHZ 391
NAVTEX [F] [D] [I] 390
NEMRUT LIMANI 397
PARK KEMER MARINA 397
SETUR MARINA 397
TEKIRDAĞ 397
TURKISH RADIO - TELEVISION CORPORATION 392
VHF CHANNEL 67 WEATHER BROADCASTS 391

U

UNITED KINGDOM

NAVTEX AND WEATHER FORECAST AREAS 154
  BRITISH BROADCASTING CORPORATION - RADIO 4 155
  NAVTEX [G] [S] [K] [O] [U] [I] [A] [C] 154

UNITED KINGDOM, ENGLAND - EAST COAST

AMBLE MARINA LTD 163
BERWICK-UPON-TWEED 163
BLACKWATER MARINA, RIVER BLACKWATER 163
BLYTH 163
BOSTON 163
  BOSTON MARINA 163
BRADWELL MARINA, RIVER BLACKWATER 164
BRENTFORD DOCK MARINA, RIVER THAMES 164
BRIDLINGTON 164
BRIGHTLINGSEA 164
BURNHAM YACHT HARBOUR, RIVER CROUCH 164
CADOGAN PIER, RIVER THAMES 164
CHATHAM MARITIME MARINA 164
CHELSEA HARBOUR MARINA, RIVER THAMES 164
CHISWICK QUAY MARINA LTD, RIVER THAMES 164
COLCHESTER, CONYER MARINA 164
CUXTON MARINA, ROCHESTER 164
ELMHAVEN MARINA, ROCHESTER 165
ESSEX MARINA, RIVER CROUCH 165
FELIXSTOWE FERRY 165
FELIXSTOWE FERRY BOAT YARD 165
FOX'S MARINA IPSWICH, RIVER ORWELL 165
  DEBBAGE YACHTING, RIVER ORWELL 165
  IPSWICH HAVEN MARINA 165
GALLIONS POINT MARINA, RIVER THAMES 165
GILLINGHAM MARINA 166
GOOLE 166
GREAT YARMOUTH 166
GREENWICH YACHT CLUB, RIVER THAMES 166
GRIMSBY 166
  GRIMSBY MARINA (MERIDIAN QUAY) 166
HALCON MARINE LTD, CANVEY ISLAND 168
HARTLEPOOL MARINA 168
HARWICH (OPERATIONS MMSI 002320025) 168
HAVENGORE BRIDGE 169
HEYBRIDGE LOCK, RIVER BLACKWATER 169
HOO MARINA, RIVER MEDWAY 169
HULL MARINA 169
HUMBER (COASTGUARD MRSC) MMSI 002320007 162
KING'S LYNN 169
LIMEHOUSE BASIN, RIVER THAMES 171
LONDON AND THE RIVER THAMES 171
  BOW LOCK, RIVER THAMES 173
  KING GEORGE V DOCK LOCK 173
  PORT CONTROL 171
  RADIO AND RADAR: PORT RADIO FREQUENCIES 171
LONDON COASTGUARD MMSI 002320063 162
LOWESTOFT 174
  ROYAL NORFOLK & SUFFOLK YACHT CLUB 174
MALDON, RIVER BLACKWATER 174
MEDWAY PORTS 175
  ALLINGTON MARINA, RIVER MEDWAY 175
  MEDWAY BRIDGE MARINA 175
  MEDWAY PIER MARINE LTD 175
NEPTUNE MARINA, IPSWICH 175
NORTH FAMBRIDGE YACHT CENTRE, RIVER CROUCH 175
POPLAR DOCK MARINA, RIVER THAMES 175
PORT MEDWAY MARINA 175
QUEENBOROUGH, RIVER MEDWAY 175
RICE & COLE, SEA END BOATHOUSE, RIVER CROUCH 175
ROYAL QUAYS (TYNE) 176
S. KATHARINE HAVEN LTD, RIVER THAMES 177
S. PETER'S MARINA, RIVER TYNE 177
SCARBOROUGH 177
SEAHAM 177
SHOTLEY MARINA, HARWICH HARBOUR 177
SOUTH DOCK MARINA, RIVER THAMES 177
SOUTH FERRIBY MARINA, RIVER HUMBER 177
SUFFOLK YACHT HARBOUR LTD, RIVER ORWELL 177
SUNDERLAND 178
SWALE MARINA, CONYER CREEK 178
TEES 178
THAMES (COASTGUARD MRSC) MMSI 002320009 162
THAMES BARRIER CONTROL ZONE 173
  NAVIGATION THROUGH THE BARRIER 174
  THAMES LOCK 173
TIDEMILL YACHT HARBOUR LTD, RIVER DEBEN 178
TITCHMARSH MARINA, WALTON BACKWATERS 179
TOLLESBURY MARINA, RIVER BLACKWATER 179
WELLS-NEXT-THE-SEA 179
WEST MERSEA MARINE, RIVER COLNE 179
WEST WICK MARINA, RIVER CROUCH 179
WHITBY 179
WHITSTABLE 179
WHITTON MARINE, RIVER MEDWAY 179
WISBECH 180
WOOLVERSTONE MARINA, RIVER STOUR 181
YARMOUTH (COASTGUARD MRCC) MMSI 002320008 163

UNITED KINGDOM, ENGLAND - SOUTH COAST INCLUDING THE CHANNEL ISLANDS

BBC RADIO JERSEY 182
BEAUCETTE MARINA (GUERNSEY) 185
BEMBRIDGE MARINA, ISLE OF WIGHT 185
BIRDHAM POOL, CHICHESTER 185
BRAYE (ALDERNEY HARBOUR) 188
BRIDPORT 188
BRIGHTON MARINA 188
BRIXHAM (COASTGUARD MRSC) MMSI 002320013 182
BRIXHAM MARINA 188
BUCKLER'S HARD YACHT HARBOUR 188
CATTEWATER HARBOUR, PLYMOUTH 188
CHARLESTOWN, S. AUSTELL BAY 189
CHICHESTER 189
  CHICHESTER MARINA 189
COBBS QUAY MARINA, POOLE 189
COWES YACHT HAVEN LTD 190
COWES, ISLE OF WIGHT 190
DARTMOUTH 190
  DART MARINA 191
  DARTHAVEN MARINA LTD 191
  DARTSIDE QUAY 191
  DOLPHIN SHIPYARD, RIVER DART 191
  NOSS-ON-DART MARINA 191

DOVER 191
  DOVER MARINA 191
DOVER (COASTGUARD MRCC) MMSI 002320010 183
EAST COWES MARINA, ISLE OF WIGHT 191
EMSWORTH YACHT HARBOUR LTD,
  CHICHESTER HARBOUR 191
EXMOUTH 192
FALMOUTH 192
FALMOUTH (COASTGUARD MRCC) MMSI 002320014 184
FALMOUTH MARINA 192
FAREHAM MARINA 192
FAREHAM YACHT HARBOUR 192
FOLKESTONE 193
FOULKES & SON RIVERSIDE BOATYARD,
  SOUTHAMPTON WATER 193
FOWEY 193
GOREY, JERSEY 193
GOSPORT MARINA (CAMPER & NICHOLSONS) 193
GUERNSEY, S. PETER PORT (COMMUNICATION
  SERVICES) MMSI 002320064 DSC CH70 183
  S. PETER PORT 183
GUNWHARF MARINA, PORTSMOUTH 193
HAMBLE RIVER 193
  HAMBLE POINT MARINA 193
  HAMBLE YACHT SERVICES 194
  PORT HAMBLE MARINA 193
HASLAR MARINA, PORTSMOUTH 194
HYTHE MARINA VILLAGE, SOUTHAMPTON WATER 194
ISLAND HARBOUR MARINA, ISLE OF WIGHT 194
ITCHEN MARINA, SOUTHAMPTON 194
JERSEY 183
  CHANNEL ISLANDS 182
JERSEY (COMMUNICATION SERVICES)
  MMSI 002320060 DSC CH 70 183
  S. HELIER PIERHEADS 183
KEMPS QUAY, SOUTHAMPTON WATER 194
LAKEYARD, POOLE 195
LANGSTONE HARBOUR 195
LITTLEHAMPTON 195
  ARUN YACHT CLUB 195
  LITTLEHAMPTON MARINA 195
LOOE HARBOUR 195
LYME REGIS 195
LYMINGTON MARINA 195
LYMINGTON YACHT HAVEN 195
MALPAS MARINE, TRURO 195
MAYFLOWER INTERNATIONAL MARINA, PLYMOUTH 196
MERCURY YACHT HARBOUR, RIVER HAMBLE 196
MEVAGISSEY 196
MILLBAY MARINA VILLAGE, PLYMOUTH 196
MYLOR YACHT HARBOUR, FALMOUTH BAY 196
NAVTEX AND WEATHER FORECAST AREAS
  NAVTEX [T] [M] 182
  OOSTENDE 184
NEWHAVEN, 196 197
  NEWHAVEN MARINA LTD 197
NEWLYN 197
NEWPORT, ISLE OF WIGHT 197
NEWTON FERRERS HARBOUR, RIVER YEALM
  (NEWTON CREEK) 197
NORTHNEY MARINA, LANGSTONE HARBOUR 198
OCEAN VILLAGE MARINA, SOUTHAMPTON WATER 198
PENZANCE 198
PLYMOUTH (LONG ROOM PORT CONTROL) 198
  PLYMOUTH YACHT HAVEN 198
POOLE HARBOUR 198
  POOLE YACHT CLUB HAVEN 198
PORT PENDENNIS MARINA 200
PORT SOLENT MARINA 200
PORTLAND (COASTGUARD MRSC) MMSI 002320012 185
QUEEN ANNE'S BATTERY MARINA, PLYMOUTH 200
RAMSGATE 200
RETREAT BOATYARD, TOPSHAM 200
RIBS MARINA, LITTLE AVON MARINA,
  CHRISTCHURCH 201
RYDE LEISURE HARBOUR, ISLE OF WIGHT 202
RYE, RIVER ROTHER 202
S. HELIER, JERSEY 203
  ELIZABETH MARINA 203
  LA COLLETTE YACHT BASIN 203
  S. HELIER MARINA 203
S. MARY'S HARBOUR, ISLES OF SCILLY 204
S. MAWES 204
S. PETER PORT, GUERNSEY 206
  VICTORIA MARINA, GUERNSEY 206
SALCOMBE 202
  WINTERS MARINE LTD 202
SALTERNS MARINA, POOLE 202
SHAMROCK QUAY AND SAXON WHARF,
  SOUTHAMPTON WATER 203
SHEPARDS WHARF BOATYARD, COWES 203
SHOREHAM 204
  LADY BEE MARINA 204
SOLENT (COASTGUARD MRSC) MMSI 002320011 185
SOUTHAMPTON, PORTSMOUTH AND THE SOLENT 206
  WARSASH MARINE 206
SOUTHDOWN MARINA, TORPOINT 204
SOUTHSEA MARINA 204
SOVEREIGN HARBOUR MARINA LTD, EASTBOURNE 204
SPARKES YACHT HARBOUR HAYLING ISLAND 204
SUTTON HARBOUR MARINA, PLYMOUTH 206
SWANWICK MARINA, RIVER HAMBLE 207
TEIGNMOUTH 207
THORNHAM MARINA, CHICHESTER HARBOUR 207
TORBAY HARBOUR 207
TORPOINT YACHT HARBOUR 207
TORQUAY MARINA 208
TOWN QUAY MARINA, SOUTHAMPTON WATER 208
TRURO 208
UNIVERSAL SHIPYARDS, SARISBURY GREEN,
  RIVER HAMBLE 208
WEYMOUTH 208
WICOR MARINA, PORTSMOUTH 210
YARMOUTH HARBOUR, ISLE OF WIGHT 210

UNITED KINGDOM, ENGLAND - WEST COAST

APPLEDORE-BIDEFORD 212
AVONMOUTH SIGNAL STATION 212
BRISTOL CITY DOCKS 212
  BRISTOL HARBOUR 212
  BRISTOL MARINA 212
  THE PASSAGE - BRISTOL TO SHARPNESS 214
  THE PASSAGE - SHARPNESS TO BRISTOL 214
BUDE 214
DOUGLAS BOATYARD (RIVER RIBBLE) 214
DOUGLAS, ISLE OF MAN 214
FLEETWOOD HARBOUR VILLAGE MARINA 215
GLASSON BASIN YACHT CO LTD, FLEETWOOD 215
HAYLE HARBOUR 215
ILFRACOMBE 215
ISLE OF MAN PORTS 215
  CASTLETOWN 215
  LAXEY HARBOUR 215
  PEEL 215
  PORT ERIN HARBOUR 215
  PORT S. MARY 215
  RAMSEY 215
LIVERPOOL (COASTGUARD MRSC) MMSI 002320019 212
LIVERPOOL MARINA 217
MARYPORT MARINA 217
MINEHEAD 218
PADSTOW 218
PORTISHEAD MARINA 218
PRESTON MARINA 218
S. IVES 219
SHARPNESS 218
WATCHET 219
WHITEHAVEN 220
WORKINGTON 220

UNITED KINGDOM, NORTHERN IRELAND

ARDGLASS (PHENNICK COVE MARINA) 222
BALLYCASTLE 222
BANGOR 222
BELFAST 222
BELFAST (COASTGUARD MRCC) MMSI 002320021 222
CARRICKFERGUS MARINA 222
COLERAINE 222
COPELANDS MARINA 222
GLENARM HARBOUR 223
KILKEEL 223
KILLYLEAGH 223
LARNE 223
LONDONDERRY 223
PORTAFERRY MARINA 223
PORTRUSH 223
SEATONS MARINA, RIVER BANN 223
STRANGFORD HARBOUR 223
WARRENPOINT 223

UNITED KINGDOM, SCOTLAND

ABERDEEN 227
ABERDEEN (COASTGUARD MRCC) MMSI 002320004 224
ANSTRUTHER HARBOUR 227
ARDFERN YACHT CENTRE LTD 227
ARDORAN MARINE, LERAGS, OBAN 228
  OBAN YACHTS & MARINE SERVICES LTD 228
ARDROSSAN 228
  CLYDE 228
ARINAGOUR PIER, ISLE OF COLL 228
ARISAIG 228
AYR, FIRTH OF CLYDE 228
BALINTORE, MORAY FIRTH 229
BALTASOUND HARBOUR, UNST, SHETLAND 229
BANFF 229
BBC RADIO SCOTLAND 227
BUCKIE 229
BURGHEAD 229
CALEDONIAN CANAL 229
  CALEY MARINA AND YACHT SERVICE CENTRE 229
  CLACKNAHARRY SEA LOCK 229
  CORPACH SEA LOCK 229
  INVERNESS 229
CAMPBELTOWN 229
CLYDE (COASTGUARD MRCC) MMSI 002320022 224
CRAIGNURE PIER, ISLAND OF MULL 230
CRAOBH MARINA 230
CRINAN CANAL 230
  ARDRISHAIG (EASTERN END) 230
  CRINAN (WESTERN END) 230
CROMARTY FIRTH (INCLUDING INVERGORDON) 230
DUNDEE 232
DUNSTAFFNAGE MARINA 232
EYEMOUTH HARBOUR 232
FORTH (COASTGUARD MRSC) MMSI 002320005 226
FORTH AND CLYDE CANAL 232
  BOWLING HARBOUR 232
  CARRON SEA LOCK 232
FORTH PORTS PLC - FORTH NAVIGATION SERVICE 232
FRASERBURGH 232
GAIRLOCH HARBOUR 232
GARLIESTON 234
GIRVAN 234
GOTT BAY PIER, TIREE 234
GRANTON, FIRTH OF FORTH 234
HOLY LOCH MARINA 234
HOPEMAN 234
IRVINE 234
  IRVINE HARBOUR BRIDGE 234
ISLE OF WITHORN 234
KILMELFORD YACHT HAVEN 234
KINLOCHBERVIE 235
KIP MARINA 235
KIPPFORD. SOLWAY YACHT CLUB 235
KIRKCUDBRIGHT 235
KIRKWALL ORKNEY 235
KYLE OF LOCHALSH 235
LARGS YACHT HAVEN 236
LEITH 236
LERWICK, SHETLAND 236
LOCH MADDY 236
LOCHINVER HARBOUR 236
LOSSIEMOUTH 236
MACDUFF 237
MALLAIG 237
MELFORT PIER & HARBOUR 237
METHIL DOCKS 237
MONTROSE 237
NORTH QUEENSFERRY NAVAL SIGNAL STATION 237
OBAN 237
ORKNEY HARBOURS NAVIGATION SERVICE 237
PERTH 237
PETERHEAD MARINA 238
PIEROWALL (WESTRAY PIER), ORKNEY 238
PORT EDGAR MARINA 238
PORTPATRICK 238
PORTREE HARBOUR, ISLAND OF SKYE 238
RHU MARINA 238
ROTHESAY, BUTE 239
S. KILDA 240
SALEN JETTY 239
SANDPOINT MARINA (DUNBARTON) 239
SCALLOWAY, SHETLAND 239
SCRABSTER, THURSO 239
SHETLAND (COASTGUARD MRSC) MMSI 002320001 226
SILVERS MARINE 239
STONEHAVEN 240
STORNOWAY (COASTGUARD MRSC) MMSI 002320024 226
STORNOWAY, LEWIS 240
STRANRAER 240
STROMNESS ORKNEY 240
TARBERT, JURA 240
TOBERMORY, MULL 240
TROON YACHT HAVEN 240
UIG, ISLE OF SKYE 240
ULLAPOOL 241
WHITEHILLS 241
WICK 241

UNITED KINGDOM, WALES

ABERAERON 243
ABERDOVEY 243
ABERYSTWYTH 244
BANGOR AND MENAI STRAIT (PORT PENRHYN) 244
BARMOUTH 244
BARRY DOCKS 244
BBC RADIO CYMRU / WALES 243
CAERNARFON 244
CARDIFF 244
CONWY 245
  CONWY MARINA 245
DINORWIC MARINA 245
FISHGUARD 245
HOLYHEAD 246
  HOLYHEAD MARINA 246
HOLYHEAD (COASTGUARD MRSC) MMSI 002320018 242
LAWRENNY YACHT STATION 246
MILFORD HAVEN (COASTGUARD MRSC) MMSI 002320017 242
MILFORD MARINA 246
MONKSTONE CRUISING & SAILING CLUB 246
NEW QUAY 246
NEWPORT 246
NEYLAND YACHT HAVEN 246
PENARTH MARINA 247
PORTHCAWL 248
PORTHMADOG 248
PWLLHELI MARINA (HAFEN PWLLHELI) 248
  ABERSOCH LAND & SEA LTD 248

SAUNDERSFOOT 248
SWANSEA 249
SWANSEA MARINA 250
SWANSEA (COASTGUARD MRCC) MMSI 002320016 242
TENBY 250

NOTES